Henderson

_ 1965 _

P9-DFL-393

*Dairy*

*Microbiology*

# Dairy

# Microbiology

**EDWIN M. FOSTER, Ph.D.**
*Professor of Bacteriology, University of Wisconsin*

**F. EUGENE NELSON, Ph.D.**
*Professor of Dairy Bacteriology, Iowa State College*

**MARVIN L. SPECK, Ph.D.**
*Professor of Dairy Bacteriology, North Carolina State College*

**RAYMOND N. DOETSCH, Ph.D.**
*Associate Professor of Bacteriology, University of Maryland*

**JOSEPH C. OLSON, Jr., Ph.D.**
*Professor of Dairy Bacteriology, University of Minnesota*

*Prentice - Hall, Inc.*

ENGLEWOOD CLIFFS, NEW JERSEY

© Copyright, 1957, by
PRENTICE-HALL, INC.
Englewood Cliffs, N. J.

ALL RIGHTS RESERVED. NO PART OF THIS BOOK
MAY BE REPRODUCED IN ANY FORM, BY MIMEO-
GRAPH OR ANY OTHER MEANS, WITHOUT PER-
MISSION IN WRITING FROM THE PUBLISHERS.

Library of Congress
Catalog Card No.: 57–6457

Third printing.......May, 1964

PRINTED IN THE UNITED STATES OF AMERICA

19675-C

# PREFACE

*Dairy Microbiology* was prepared to serve as a useful source of information for the many persons interested in the microbiological quality of dairy products. It should make an excellent working reference for plant operators, fieldmen, laboratory personnel, sanitarians, and others. It also is intended for use by college students who have had an introductory course in general bacteriology.

As its title indicates, the book deals with the relation of microbiology to the dairy industry. It is an interpretative work, one that stresses the broad generalizations that can be drawn from information in the literature. Citations to original papers are used sparingly except for relatively recent information, the source of which might be of interest to the reader.

The first six chapters emphasize the application of well-known facts in the science of microbiology to the various pertinent phases of the dairy industry. The main dairy organisms are described, first according to the classical taxonomic arrangement and then according to physiological groupings in which the various organisms that produce the same changes in milk are placed together. Next, the authors deal with the factors affecting the growth of microorganisms, stressing the means of preventing growth where it is unwanted and of stimulating it where it is desired. They discuss in considerable detail the physical and chemical methods of killing microorganisms in milk and on dairy equipment. General directions for examining dairy products for microorganisms are given, with explanations of underlying principles. The limitations, advantages, and disadvantages of the methods used are discussed. Finally the sources of microorganisms in milk are considered, and emphasis is placed upon means of producing milk of the best possible bacteriological quality.

Chapters 7 to 14 deal with the microbiology of specific dairy products—market milk, fermented milks, cheese, butter, and evaporated, condensed, dried, or frozen products. Sufficient description of the method of manufacture employed for each product is given to permit the reader to understand how microorganisms are affected by the various processes involved. A separate chapter is devoted to a consideration of cultures or starters used for fermented products. The book's final chapter deals with the principles and problems of dairy plant waste disposal and with the utilization of dairy by-products by fermentation.

*Dairy Microbiology* is the result of the concerted efforts of five authors. Each chapter was prepared by the person best qualified to write it, but was reviewed by all the others. The names of the authors are not associated with the individual chapters they have written, for the five authors prefer to consider each chapter, as well as the entire book, as a group project for which they are all equally responsible. The reader should know that the order of the names below, and on the title page, has no special significance.

The authors are indebted to many of their friends and colleagues for help. They are especially appreciative of the cooperation of Mrs. A. D. Orla-Jensen, who kindly placed at their disposal a number of photographs of microorganisms from the collection of the late Dr. S. Orla-Jensen. Sources of other illustrative materials are acknowledged throughout the book.

Special thanks go to the following persons who read sections of the manuscript and pointed out errors and areas for improvement: Dr. Wendell Arbuckle, University of Maryland; Dr. S. T. Coulter, University of Minnesota; Dr. W. C. Frazier, Dr. W. V. Price, and Dr. G. A. Rohlich, University of Wisconsin; Mr. Joe Greenspan, Consolidated Products Co.; Dr. W. L. Mallmann, Michigan State University; Mr. F. J. McKee, Kraft Foods Co.; Dr. J. W. Pette, Nederlands Instituut voor Zuivelonderzoek, Hoorn, Nederlands; Dr. F. R. Smith, Pet Milk Co.; Dr. R. P. Tittsler and Dr. George Holm, United States Department of Agriculture; and Mr. Donald Williams, International Association of Ice Cream Manufacturers.

Finally, the authors are indebted to those who reviewed the entire manuscript and gave the benefit of their criticism and advice. These are Dr. F. W. Barber, National Dairy Research Laboratories; Dr. J. Frank Cone, Pennsylvania State University; Dr. P. R. Elliker, Oregon State College; and Dr. M. E. Morgan, Storrs (Connecticut) Agricultural Experiment Station.

E. M. FOSTER          M. L. SPECK
F. E. NELSON          R. N. DOETSCH
J. C. OLSON, JR.

# CONTENTS

**5**   *Microbiological methods of examining dairy products*   115

*Dairy*

*Microbiology*

# An introduction to
# dairy microbiology

The dairy industry provides an excellent example of an area in which bacteria, yeasts, molds, viruses, and occasionally rickettsiae are very important in determining the quality of the final products. In this industry the control and destruction of undesirable microorganisms as well as their purposeful introduction and utilization are problems which demand much attention. The nutritional qualities of milk and milk products make them desirable foods for humans and young animals. The same nutritional values also permit growth of many microorganisms, some of which cause undesirable changes. Milk is a secretory product of animal origin, and its sanitary qualities are influenced by many factors in the course of its production, processing, and delivery to the consumer. This chapter is a brief review of principles upon which the application of microbiology to the dairy industry is based.

An example of a segment of the dairy industry that is dependent to a large extent on desirable enzymatic changes caused by microorganisms is cheese manufacturing. The flavors and the physical characteristics of cheese are largely ascribed to the alteration of milk constituents by various species acting simultaneously or sequentially. Only a few bacterial and mold species are added deliberately to cheese milk or to the curd during the manufacturing process. Doubtless others would be used if it were known how and when to use them in order to initiate desirable reactions. Probably much of the microbial activity that takes place during cheese ripening is due to species that enter the milk by chance at various points in the manufacturing process. Much remains to be learned about the biological and physico-chemical factors that govern the growth of the mixed populations found in cheese. Ultimately, new techniques will be developed to secure accurate data on these points.

The taste and aroma of good butter are pleasing to most consumers. At present, flavor is the greatest competitive asset of butter. Starter cultures, which are mixed bacterial cultures selected for acid- and flavor-producing ability, are important in the manufacture of some fine flavored butter. The conditions under which optimum flavor develops and the relationships between species are fairly well known, and there is no doubt that the changes brought about by butter starter cultures are desirable.

Yogurt, sour cream, and buttermilk are examples of fermented milks made by the addition of various microorganisms to concentrated milk, cream, and skimmilk, respectively. Each product has a characteristic flora that is responsible, in part, for its distinctive flavor and physical appearance. It is now possible to manufacture these fermented milks with uniform properties from day to day by using starter cultures specially selected for their desirable flavor and acid-producing ability.

The conversion by microorganisms of certain of the constituents of milk into economically valuable products like vitamins, solvents, and food adjuncts can now be done on an industrial scale. There is essentially no limit, except the ingenuity of the experimenter, to the variety of substances which may be obtained in this way. On the other hand, milk constituents which have no economic value, or which are inadvertently wasted, must be changed to stably oxidized and non-obnoxious substances before being discharged into streams or lakes. Here again microbial activity is in large measure responsible for the desired changes in the organic constituents of dairy wastes in the process of sewage treatment.

Microorganisms are undesirable in milk and its products if they are capable of causing deterioration in flavor or physical appearance, if they are able to produce disease, or if they indicate careless or unsanitary handling of the product. Off-flavors produced by microorganisms are not only undesirable per se, but indicate that there has been opportunity for growth. It is important that the dairy microbiologist understand the factors which influence the deterioration of dairy products and the methods by which this deterioration can be prevented. Souring of milk or cream is undesirable under most circumstances, but souring (production of lactic acid) is essential for the manufacture of cheese or cultured milk. Discolorations, sliminess, ropiness, putrefaction, rancidity, gassiness, and many other defects are caused by various microorganisms growing in dairy products.

Milk and some milk products occasionally have been found to be carriers of microorganisms that cause disease. Fortunately these agents of disease can be controlled, and at present only a few outbreaks are reported each year, these usually being due to the consumption of unpasteurized or grossly contaminated products. As new processes and products are developed by the dairy technologist, they must be carefully checked to insure that they are safe from the public health point of view.

Many of the ordinances and other regulations under which milk and milk products are produced and handled specify quantitative, and in some instances qualitative, microbiological standards. These standards are the result of experiences which have shown that under desirable conditions the numbers of microorganisms gaining entrance to the product will not exceed certain levels and, also, that proper handling of the products will not permit growth beyond certain levels. To a certain degree these standards are aesthetic, because the numbers of microorganisms permitted usually are far below the numbers necessary to cause spoilage. However, as increased knowledge of the factors which control microbial populations is applied under practical conditions, higher standards for microbial counts of the various products frequently are employed. Also, procedures for estimating microbial populations have been improved, resulting in a greater proportion of the microorganisms present being enumerated. The result has been a gradual raising of microbiological standards for the various dairy products. Because of this close control, the bottled milk used by most people these days is of very high microbiological quality. The tendency is for the microbiological and other standards, aside from those dealing with gross chemical composition, to be applied less stringently to other dairy products than to market milk. A good case could be advanced for having the same level of sanitary and aesthetic standards apply to all food products. However, custom still supports standards at different levels for the various dairy products. The discussions in this book will be based upon current industrial and regulatory practice, leaving much of the philosophy relative to the adequacy of these standards to be debated under other circumstances.

## CLASSIFICATION OF MICROORGANISMS

Microorganisms may be classified into seven large and perhaps heterogeneous groups—bacteria, molds, yeasts, viruses, rickettsiae, algae, and protozoa. This sequence indicates the relative order of their importance in the dairy industry. The algae and protozoa generally are assumed to be of no major importance.

In order to understand clearly the relationship of microorganisms to other forms of life, it would be well to remember that bacteria, yeasts, and molds are considered to be members of the plant kingdom. Further, they are classified in the phylum *Thallophyta* whose members are defined as undifferentiated masses of tissue devoid of root, stem, or leaf. The phylum *Thallophyta* is divided into the sub-phyla *Algae* and *Fungi,* and it is the latter sub-phylum which includes those classes of microorganisms of interest to the dairy microbiologist. Fungi are *Thallophyta* that are devoid of photosynthetic pigments. Bacteria are placed in the class *Schizomycetes* (from Greek, *schizein,* split or cleave) or fission fungi (1). The class is divided further into orders, families, tribes, genera, and species. All other forms of life are similarly divided into these groups. It is common practice to refer only to the genus and species of an organism, viz., *Streptococcus lactis, Escherichia coli.* The complete classification of the former would appear as follows:

Kingdom: *Plant*
Phylum: *Thallophyta*
Sub-phylum: *Fungi*
Class: *Schizomycetes*
Order: *Eubacteriales*
Sub-order: *Eubacteriineae*
Family: *Lactobacteriaceae*
Tribe: *Streptococceae*
Genus: *Streptococcus*
Species: *lactis*

Molds and yeasts are found in the classes *Phycomycetes, Ascomycetes,* and *Fungi Imperfecti.* A more detailed account of molds and yeasts will be found in Chapter 2. At present, rickettsiae and viruses are placed in the orders *Rickettsiales* and *Virales* respectively in the system of classification tentatively advanced in the sixth edition of *Bergey's Manual* (1). Further detailed characteristics of the microorganisms considered above also will be found in Chapter 2.

SOME BIOLOGICAL PROPERTIES OF MICROORGANISMS

In order to understand why the activity of microorganisms is important, some of their biological properties must be considered. The unit employed when discussing bacterial dimensions is the *micron* ($\mu$). This unit is equal to 0.001 mm or 1/25,400 inch. Most bacteria are of the order of 1 to 5 $\mu$ in length or diameter and 0.5 to 1.0 $\mu$ in width. The general properties of bacteria, such as shape, grouping, internal structure, and physical and chemical properties, are considered in a number of textbooks on general bacteriology, and the student should read these, if necessary (e.g., 2, 3), to supplement the following discussion.

It should be noted that bacteria are considered to be aquatic, plant-like organisms for several reasons. They possess rigid, well-differentiated cell walls, such as are characteristic of plant cells but generally not of animal cells. Further, many bacteria are morphologically similar to the blue-green algae, although they lack the photosynthetic pigments of their algal counterparts. Finally, bacteria are holophytic rather than holozoic; that is, nutrients are taken into the cell only in solution rather than ingested in particulate form; this again is a plant-like characteristic.

The ratio of surface area to volume is known as "specific surface." With the possible exception of viruses and rickettsiae, no other group of living organisms possesses greater surface to volume ratio than do bacteria. To illustrate this concept, let us assume that 2 microorganisms exist, both cubical in form, one being 1 $\mu$ per edge and the other 1,000 $\mu$ per edge. The dimensions of *Streptococcus lactis* and the common cheese mite would approximate these figures. The volume, surface area, and specific surface of these cubes are important factors in their metabolism. The cube with an edge of 1 $\mu$ would have a volume of 1 cubic $\mu$, a surface area of 6 square $\mu$, and a surface to volume ratio of 6. The cube with an edge of 1,000 $\mu$ would have a volume of one billion cubic $\mu$, a surface area of six million square $\mu$, and a surface to volume ratio of 0.006. If these figures were transferred to the organisms suggested above, the cheese mite would have a total surface area one million times greater than a single *Streptococcus lactis* cell, but the latter would have a surface to volume ratio one thousand times greater than the former. To appreciate the significance of this, visualize not one *Streptococcus lactis* cell but a number of them, the volume of which is equal to the volume of a cheese mite (one billion cubic $\mu$); there would then be one billion cells with a total surface area of six billion square $\mu$ or one thousand times the surface area of the larger organism. Bacteria, therefore, have great absorptive surface per unit volume, and this is one reason for their ability to effect rapid transformations of the substances they can utilize for energy or protoplasmic synthesis. Nutrients can be very rapidly absorbed, metabolized, and excreted by this "sheet" of bacterial surface. It has been estimated that a quart of milk soured by *Streptococcus lactis* contains about one trillion ($10^{12}$) cells (about 0.8 g, wet weight), and this number would represent a surface area of approximately 50 square feet. It should be noted that for organisms of bacterial dimensions, high surface to volume values are of advantage only when coupled with large numbers of cells per unit volume. The disadvantage of large surface to volume ratios is that the energy of maintenance is high. The bacterial cell must continually transform substances in order to obtain energy for synthesis of new protoplasm, as well as for replacement of unstable and inactivated compounds. For example, the energy of maintenance for man in terms of kg cal/g N/day is 1, but for bacteria it is about 50.

Another important characteristic of bacteria is their rapid multiplication rate. Under optimum conditions some species of bacteria will divide once every 20 minutes. This rate cannot be maintained indefinitely, since several factors, such as exhaustion of nutrients, accumulation of waste products, and lack of available space, soon become critical. To appreciate the significance of high multiplication rates, assume that each of the 10,000 organisms per milliliter in a vat of milk can divide once every 30 minutes; at the end of 8 hours of multiplication at this rate there would be present, theoretically, 655,360,000 bacteria per milliliter of milk. Many flavor and physical changes in milk may be detected as the result of the growth of certain bacteria to a level of only two to five million per milliliter, and further, 8 hours is less time than that which elapses between the evening milking and the delivery to the processing plant the next day. It is well to keep in mind that bacteria multiply geometrically, and under optimum conditions enormous numbers per unit volume can be reached in a relatively short time. Detailed characteristics of bacterial growth curves are considered in Chapter 3.

The multiplication of bacteria is always accompanied by the chemical alteration of substances used as sources of carbon and nitrogen. The souring of milk, the ripening of cheese, and the acetic fermentation of alcoholic whey are a few of the hundreds of examples of transformations brought about by bacteria in substances of interest to the dairy microbiologist. Bacteria are notable in that they produce chemical changes in carbohydrates and proteins rapidly and apparently in disproportion to the actual mass of living cells involved in the process. The amount of substrate decomposed by microorganisms can be easily determined. If the number of bacteria present in a culture is known, and the amount of substrate present is measured at the beginning and the end of the experiment, the amount of substrate decomposed per bacterium can be estimated. The actual weight utilized per cell will be extremely small, but when compared with the weight of a bacterial cell, the results assume a new aspect. For example, it has been found that some lactic acid bacteria can ferment twice their weight of carbohydrate per hour. These rapid transformations are brought about by bacterial enzymes. The cells of all plants and animals produce these enzymes or catalysts, and even the simplest microorganism possesses a large variety of them. Each enzyme has a unique biochemical function; that is, it is specific. Enzymes are composed in part of protein, and occasionally a non-protein moiety is required for their function. They are easily inactivated by heat and certain chemical and physical agents. In addition, enzymes require certain ranges of temperature, pH, and substrate concentration for optimal activity. Some enzymes are excreted from the cell, and these extracellular enzymes bring about changes in the medium surrounding the cell, whereas other intracellular enzymes are not normally found active outside the intact cell.

Most of the life processes of microorganisms are controlled by enzyme action. One of these activities is concerned with converting chemical compounds into forms utilizable as nutrients by the organism. Enzymes make possible the synthesis of all substances, or protoplasm, from the nutrients that are absorbed into the cell; they also function in the complex mechanisms in which the cell obtains energy for maintenance.

The mechanism of enzyme action may be thought of as the formation of an intermediate complex consisting of substrate and specific enzyme. This intermediate is highly unstable and breaks down into substrate decomposition products and enzyme. The enzyme is left essentially unaltered and is then able to repeat its catalytic action. A small amount of enzyme is capable of transforming relatively enormous amounts of substrate.

Not all types of enzymes are produced by any one microbial species, although some kinds of enzymes seem common to all microorganisms. It is the ability of one microorganism to produce an enzyme that another cannot produce which is, in part, the basis upon which microorganisms are separated into species. *Streptococcus lactis* and *Escherichia coli* both contain the enzyme lactase, which enables them to hydrolyze lactose. However, subsequent enzymatic reactions of the former organism cause end-products of substrate metabolism to appear almost exclusively as lactic acid, whereas in the latter case, carbon dioxide, hydrogen, acetic acid, and lactic acid are the main end-products. Obviously, the enzyme contents of these organisms are different.

The preceding discussion regarding bacteria applies almost equally well to yeasts and molds. Concerning the biological activities of all microorganisms, then, the important characteristics are: (a) their rapid multiplication under optimum conditions, (b) their high surface to volume ratios, and (c) their ability to transform chemically large quantities of material in a short period of time. The physico-chemical environment largely determines the nature and extent of microbial activity, and the interplay between these will be noted in subsequent chapters.

The question of whether microbial transformations are desirable or not is relevant only for man. It is obvious that in all cases the microorganisms are merely carrying out their life processes as governed by their hereditary pattern. Whether certain end-products are "bad" and others "good" is a question that depends upon circumstances. For example, the souring of milk is considered "bad" for the market milk dealer and "good" for the cheese maker. The biology of the microorganisms considered herein is of primary concern, since this book deals with applied microbiology, which is the application of biological principles to development processes of economic importance.

## References

1. Breed, R. S., E. G. D. Murray, and A. P. Hitchens, *Bergey's Manual of Determinative Bacteriology,* 6th Ed. Baltimore: Williams and Wilkins, 1948.
2. Lamanna, C., and M. F. Malette, *Basic Bacteriology—Its Biological and Chemical Background.* Baltimore: Williams and Wilkins, 1953.
3. Thimann, K. V., *The Life of Bacteria.* New York: Macmillan, 1955.

# 2

## The microorganisms of
## milk and dairy products

The microorganisms found in milk and its products can be studied as groups possessing one or more major characteristics in common. They may be divided on the basis of their action on milk constituents as, for example, acid-forming, proteolytic, or inert. Another approach might emphasize sources, and accordingly groups would be composed of microorganisms entering milk from the cow, soil, manure, dairy utensils, or personnel. Finally, a taxonomic point of view would result in considering the microorganisms as morphological groups, for example, micrococci, streptococci, or sporogenous rods. In this chapter the last-mentioned approach will be employed, but not to the complete exclusion of the others. Milk and its products constitute an environment for a diverse collection of microorganisms, and indeed, these organisms may have little in common except their environment. Although some of them are considered part of the "normal flora" of milk and its products, it is probable that other more primitive reservoirs of them exist.

The important microorganisms in milk and milk products are "true" bacteria of the sub-order *Eubacteriineae*, viruses of the order *Virales*, rickettsiae of the order *Rickettsiales,* and yeasts and molds. Microorganisms classified in these groups may play a role either in the spoilage of milk, in disease outbreaks traceable to milk and its products, or in the manufacture of various dairy products. In the sub-order *Eubacteriineae* are found a large number of bacteria of economic or public health significance, and though these bacteria are physiologically diverse, they appear morphologically as rods or spherical cells in various arrangements. Motility, where present, is always by means of flagella, and some species produce endospores. Cell division is always by simple fission. Some species are chromogenic, but none encountered in dairy microbiology is photosynthetic. There is no apparent close phylogenetic relationship to algae, yeasts, or molds.

The families in the sub-order *Eubacteriineae* that are studied by the dairy microbiologist include the following: *Lactobacteriaceae, Micrococcaceae,*

**8**

*Enterobacteriaceae, Pseudomonadaceae, Bacillaceae, Achromobacteriaceae, Bacteriaceae, Corynebacteriaceae,* and *Parvobacteriaceae* (10).

## LACTOBACTERIACEAE

Lactic acid was discovered in sour milk by the Swedish chemist Scheele in 1782. Three-quarters of a century later Pasteur demonstrated that the formation of lactic acid by fermentation involved living microorganisms. A few species of the genera *Bacillus* and *Micrococcus,* as well as members of the *Escherichia-Aerobacter* group, produce some lactic acid from carbohydrates, but these are excluded as true lactic acid bacteria on morphological and further biochemical grounds. The *Escherichia-Aerobacter* group is generally considered to be on the borderline between true lactic and non-lactic bacteria. Its members are sometimes referred to as "pseudo lactic acid bacteria."

The members of the family *Lactobacteriaceae* are gram-positive, nonmotile, microaerophilic or anaerobic rods or cocci which divide like rods in one plane only. Surface growth on most media is generally poor. The nutritional requirements of this group are complex, and in addition to a wide assortment of amino acids and vitamins, a fermentable carbohydrate is essential for growth. Considerable variation is found in the optical type of lactic acid [L (+)-lactic acid, D (−)-lactic acid or DL-lactic acid*] and the quantity of this acid produced by various species (47). Conventionally these organisms are divided into two groups. Those which produce primarily lactic acid from fermentable carbohydrates are known as the homofermentative group. In the heterofermentative group, acetic acid, ethanol, glycerol, carbon dioxide, and other substances are produced in addition to lactic acid.

Lactic acid bacteria are of great importance in applied microbiology (60). They are essential in the manufacture of lactic acid, sauerkraut, pickles, and silage. In the dairy industry they are indispensable in the production of fermented milks, cheeses, and culture-containing butter. Under certain circumstances various species of lactic acid bacteria are considered spoilage agents, for example, in the souring of market milk or cream and in the production of discolorations in Cheddar cheese.

Lactic acid bacteria are widely distributed. Certain plants, some feeds, dairy utensils, manure, and saliva have been found to harbor them. When-

---

*D and L do not refer to optical rotation, but to structural configuration as compared to glyceraldehyde. Optical rotation is designated by (+) for rotation of polarized light to the right (dextrorotatory) and by (−) for rotation to the left (levorotatory). In the case of lactic acid, D (−)-lactic acid has a configuration comparable to D-glyceraldehyde, and is levorotatory; L (+)-lactic acid has a configuration comparable to L-glyceraldehyde, and is dextrorotatory. A racemic substance is designated as DL, even though its configuration may be unknown. In this book it has been presumed that the two forms of lactic acid have been differentiated only on the basis of optical rotation. (For further explanation see Ray Q. Brewster, *Organic Chemistry,* 2nd Ed., p. 356, Prentice-Hall, 1953.)

ever raw milk is allowed to remain at room temperature for some time, it is soured by lactic acid bacteria, and eventually sufficient acid is formed to coagulate the casein. Acidification prevents or retards the growth of many proteolytic organisms, and this reaction may be considered a form of food preservation. The "natural" souring of milk is a universal phenomenon; similarly, the formation of lactic acid from foodstuff carbohydrates, for example, of cabbage leaves, corn and various grasses, or cucumbers, is effective in preserving them as sauerkraut, silage, and pickles respectively.

Lactose is hydrolyzed to glucose and galactose by the enzyme lactase. These monosaccharide units are then phosphorylated and further dissimilated according to the accepted glycolytic scheme. Pyruvic acid is the final intermediate, and it is reduced to lactic acid by the enzyme lactic acid dehydrogenase and by the reduced co-enzyme diphosphopyridine nucleotide, according to the equation:

$$CH_3COCOO^- + DPNH + H_3O^+ \rightarrow CH_3CHOHCOO^- + DPN^+ + H_2O$$

In the homofermentative group 90 per cent or more of the carbohydrate fermented (under acid conditions) is converted to lactic acid, and the over-all reactions shown below, using lactose as an example, are therefore almost quantitative:

$$\underset{\text{lactose}}{C_{12}H_{22}O_{11}} + H_2O \rightarrow \underset{\text{glucose}}{C_6H_{12}O_6} + \underset{\text{galactose}}{C_6H_{12}O_6}$$

$$\underset{\substack{\text{monosaccharide} \\ \text{units}}}{2C_6H_{12}O_6} \rightarrow \underset{\substack{\text{lactic} \\ \text{acid}}}{4C_3H_6O_3}$$

The spherical lactic acid bacteria are classified in the tribe *Streptococceae* in which two genera are well-known to dairy microbiologists: *Streptococcus* and *Leuconostoc*. The rod-shaped lactic acid bacteria are placed in the tribe *Lactobacilleae* of which three genera, *Lactobacillus, Microbacterium,* and *Propionibacterium,* are important (10).

### STREPTOCOCCUS

The word *Streptococcus* is derived from the Greek words *streptos* meaning flexible, and *kókkos* meaning seed or grain—hence, a pliable length of seed, similar to a necklace. Streptococci are cocci remaining united after cell division, and for this reason, they may form chains of cells. In milk many species form only pairs or short chains of cells (22). Generally, the streptococci are divided into "pyogenic," "viridans," "lactic," and "enterococcus" groups (53). Most streptococci produce a group specific polysaccharide (C substance) which enables one to classify them serologically by a precipitin reaction (Lancefield typing, 37). Thus far, groups A, B, C, D, E, F, G, H, K, L, M, N, and O have been described. These group specific polysaccharides can be extracted from the cells with strong acids or alkalies. In the following discussion the Lancefield type of the group will be given wherever possible.

*Pyogenic streptococci.* The pyogenic group, of which *Streptococcus pyogenes* (Group A) and *Streptococcus agalactiae* (Group B) are representative, do not grow at 10°C. or 45°C. (50°F. or 113°F.). They are generally beta-hemolytic causing complete disruption of red blood cells in the area immediately surrounding the colony on a blood agar medium. They usually do not coagulate milk, and litmus milk is reduced slowly, if at all. They do not grow in the presence of 0.1 per cent methylene blue, 6.5 per cent sodium chloride, or at pH 9.6, and ammonia is produced from peptone or arginine. *Streptococcus agalactiae* (Figure 2.1) has frequently been isolated from the milk and udders of animals afflicted with mastitis. This species is not known to be pathogenic for man nor does it survive pasteurization. There are no specific morphological features which differentiate it from other streptococci (22). It may, however, produce alpha-, weakly beta-, or gamma-hemolysis on blood agar. In the case of alpha-hemolysis there is partial destruction of red blood cells surrounding the colony and a greenish discoloration of the blood agar medium. *Streptococcus pyogenes* (Figure 2.2) is a strongly beta-hemolytic organism. It is pathogenic for man and is commonly the cause of septic sore throat, scarlet fever, septicemia, abscesses, and various other pathological conditions. Man can infect the udder of the cow with this organism, causing an acute mastitis. *Streptococcus pyogenes* may be found in the milk of an animal so infected and therefore may give rise to milk-borne streptococcal epidemics in man. Fortunately, this organism is destroyed by proper pasteurization.

*Viridans streptococci.* The viridans group is represented by such species as *Streptococcus thermophilus* and *Streptococcus bovis* (Group D). They do not grow at 10°C. (50°F.) but do grow at 45°C. (113°F.). Some species are alpha-hemolytic on blood agar. Litmus milk is coagulated and reduced. No growth occurs in the presence of 0.1 per cent methylene blue, 6.5 per cent sodium chloride, or at pH 9.6, and ammonia is not produced from peptone or arginine. *Streptococcus thermophilus* is not a thermophilic organism as the species name might imply, since its optimum temperature lies between 40°C. and 45°C. (104°F. and 113°F.); it does not grow at 53°C. (127.4°F.). Pasteurized milk samples may show, upon plating out and incubating at 32°C. (89.6°F.), large numbers of "pinpoint" colonies, many of which may

**Figure 2.1**     *Streptococcus agalactiae.* Methylene blue stain of milk from an animal afflicted with mastitis. The large dark elements are leucocytes. Courtesy R. Brown and USDA.

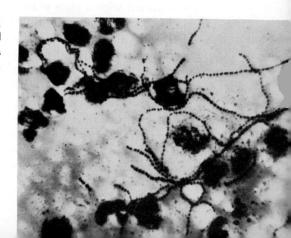

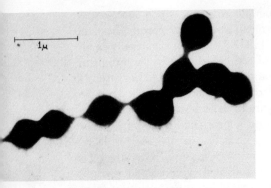

1μ

**Figure 2.2**    *Streptococcus pyogenes.* Electron microscope photograph of a chain of cells. Courtesy S. Mudd, and D. B. Lackman, J. Bact., 41 (1941): 415, and Williams and Wilkins, Baltimore.

be *Streptococcus thermophilus*. *Streptococcus thermophilus* is an important organism in the manufacture of cheese such as Swiss, made with a high cooking temperature, and in fermented milks like yogurt and skyr. It is readily inhibited by as little as 0.01 unit of penicillin or 5 μg of streptomycin per milliliter, and milk to be inoculated with this organism must be carefully selected to avoid difficulties with antibiotics. Various starter strains show marked differences in sensitivity to antibiotics, and these figures are therefore approximations (31). *Streptococcus bovis* is regularly found in cow manure and cow saliva, and it may enter milk from these and other sources. It survives pasteurization and frequently can be isolated from pasteurized milk held at room temperature. It also has been found in some lots of Brick cheese.

    *Lactic streptococci.* Some of the most widely known dairy bacteria are found in the lactic group. *Streptococcus lactis* (Group N) and *Streptococcus cremoris* (Group N) grow at 10°C. (50°F.) but not at 45°C. (113°F.) (12, 13). They reduce litmus milk prior to coagulating it, and growth occurs in broth in the presence of 0.1 per cent methylene blue but not in 6.5 per cent sodium chloride or at pH 9.6.

    *Streptococcus lactis* was first described by Lister. This organism, named *Bacterium lactis* by him, was studied by diluting sour milk until a given volume was calculated to contain one organism. This amount was distributed by a special syringe into boiled fresh milk and incubated in sterile glasses covered with a glass plate until souring occurred. Microscopic examination revealed this organism to be predominant and hence the causative bacterium involved in the "natural souring" of milk. *Streptococcus lactis* occurs in milk as elliptical cocci in pairs or short chains, the individual cells ranging from 0.5 to 1.0 μ in diameter (Figure 2.3). Elongation of cells in the direction of the chain is observable. This species is grampositive, non-motile, asporogenous, and stains easily with common bacteriological dyes. *Streptococcus lactis* may be considered as either useful or harmful in the dairy industry. It is essential in the manufacture of cheese and fermented milk and has been considered as an aid in the "natural" preservation of certain carbohydrate-containing proteinaceous dairy products.

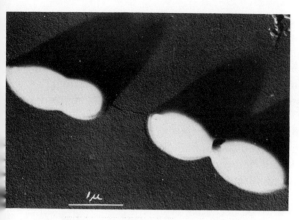 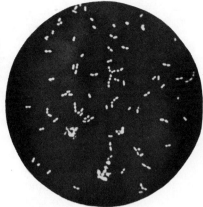

**Figure 2.3** **(left)** *Streptococcus lactis.* Electron microscope photograph showing pairs of cells shadowed with chromium. Courtesy S. S. Breese, Jr. **(right)** *Streptococcus lactis.* Negative stain showing typical cell arrangements. Courtesy S. Orla-Jensen and *det Kongelige Danske Videnskabernes Selskab.*

*Streptococcus lactis* can be recovered from dairy utensils, silage, the cow's coat, and some plants (1, 53). It is easily isolated from sour milk by plating appropriate dilutions on trypticase soy glucose agar, orange serum agar, or yeast extract agar containing a suitable carbohydrate. Tomato juice glucose agar and whey agar also may be used. After incubation at 25°C. to 30°C. (77°F. to 86°F.), small, gray, circular, convex, glistening colonies may be transferred to litmus milk for further study. Litmus milk is acidified and usually completely reduced before coagulation, and the pink band of unreduced litmus that forms at the surface of the coagulated litmus milk increases in depth with aging. No proteolysis or gas production is evident in the coagulated milk. *Streptococcus lactis* may be conveniently kept in screw top vials as stab cultures in the above solid media or in milk plus excess calcium carbonate to neutralize the formed acid. Frequent transfer of cultures is necessary to insure maximum viability. Cultures stored in plain litmus milk remain viable for 3 to 4 weeks.

*Streptococcus lactis* grows well in milk and ferments the lactose to 0.8 to 1.0 per cent acid of which L(+)-lactic acid constitutes nearly all of the acid formed, although traces of acetic and propionic acid may be present. Acid production is depressed by aeration. Although citrate is not normally fermented by this species, closely related species are able to attack this substrate (59). In skimmilk cultures *Streptococcus lactis* produces an increase in amino acids and peptides, and the increase is greatest during the period of rapid proliferation of the culture. Apparently nitrogen degradation products are produced more rapidly than they can be utilized. Among the amino acids found to be thus increased in protein-free filtrates of skimmilk cultures are valine, leucine, isoleucine, threonine, arginine, methionine, histidine, tryptophane, tyrosine, phenylalanine, glycine, glutamic acid, alanine, leucine, proline, and serine (61, 62). *Streptococcus lactis* strains require a number of B vitamins for optimal growth in a synthetic medium; among them are biotin, niacin, thiamine, pantothenic acid, pyridoxine, and folic acid. Among the amino acids, isoleucine, valine, leucine, histidine, methionine, arginine, proline, glutamic acid, and phenylalanine are required (8).

*Streptococcus lactis* has an optimum temperature of 30°C. (86°F.) and a range of 10°C. to 40°C. (50°F. to 104°F.). This species does not survive 63°C. (145.4°F.) for 30 minutes and hence is a post-pasteurization contaminant if found in pasteurized milk. Complete inhibition of many *Streptococcus lactis* strains in milk can be brought about by 0.15 unit of penicillin per milliliter, or 0.5 µg of aureomycin per milliliter. Two to 6 ppm of quaternary ammonium compounds will inhibit *Streptococcus lactis* in broth, but 600 to 1,000 ppm may be necessary in milk.

Some strains of *Streptococcus lactis* elaborate a complex polypeptide or protein, known as nisin, which is inhibitory to *Streptococcus cremoris*, *Streptococcus agalactiae*, streptococcus groups A, B, E, F, G, H, K, M, and certain other gram-positive organisms including species of *Bacillus*, *Clostridium*, and *Lactobacillus* (25, 43). Other antibiotic substances also have been found in *Streptococcus lactis* cultures, but they are not well defined. On the other hand, preparations of autolyzed or sonically treated extracts of *Streptococcus lactis* and *Streptococcus cremoris* stimulate the development of *Lactobacillus casei* and *Leuconostoc citrovorum*. The active principle is filterable and increases both the end-point of fermentation and the final bacterial crop. The substance or substances produced do not stimulate the organisms which produce it (24).

Occasionally organisms are found that vary in some minor way from *Streptococcus lactis,* and these may be considered here. *Streptococcus lactis* var. *maltigenes* produces a malty defect in milk and cream. It has been established that the malty aroma is due principally to 3-methylbutanal and that as little as 0.5 ppm is sufficient to give milk this defect. It is probable that the precursor of the aroma substance is the free leucine of milk, and *Streptococcus lactis* var. *maltigenes* converts this amino acid to the corresponding pentanal (29). *Streptococcus lactis* var. *tardus* differs from *Streptococcus lactis* in that it coagulates milk slowly, and although this property may vary in some strains, it has been generally found to be stable. It can be induced by prolonged incubation periods. *Streptococcus lactis* var. *anoxyphilus* does not reduce litmus milk before coagulating it. This is also a stable characteristic of the variety.

Acetoin-producing organisms similar in most other characteristics to *Streptococcus lactis* have been described. They belong to serological group N but differ from *Streptococcus lactis* in their ability to utilize citrate. They produce carbon dioxide, volatile acids, and various C4 (acetoin) compounds from this substrate but not from glucose or lactose. These citrate fermenting strains have been designated as *Streptococcus diacetilactis* (11, 59).

*Streptococcus cremoris* has many properties in common with *Streptococcus lactis*. It is used in starter cultures and has approximately the same vitamin and amino acid requirements as *Streptococcus lactis*. Despite these similarities, *Streptococcus cremoris* can be differentiated from *Streptococcus lactis* by phage typing and by fermentation of maltose and mannitol and production of ammonia from arginine by the latter species. Recent work on the nutrition of *Streptococcus lactis* and *Streptococcus cremoris* shows that the latter organism requires acetate and oleate for growth in a synthetic medium whereas the former usually does not require them (16). Other studies indicate that *Streptococcus cremoris* will not grow in a synthetic medium plus citrate but that *Streptococcus lactis* does grow under these conditions (35). Some strains of *Streptococcus cremoris* produce diplococcin, an antibiotic effective against *Streptococcus lactis* (25). *Streptococcus lactis* var. *hollandicus* (Figure 2.4) may more properly be considered as *Streptococcus cremoris* var. *hollandicus* (10), distinguished from the normal strains by the production of capsules. This organism may cause ropiness in milk, although the ability to do so is easily lost, especially after cultivation on artificial media.

*Enterococci.* The enterococcus group consists of *Streptococcus fecalis, Streptococcus liquefaciens, Streptococcus zymogenes,* and *Streptococcus durans.* These bacteria grow at both 10°C. and 45°C. (50°F. and 113°F.). The latter two species are beta-hemolytic, and all belong to Lancefield Group D. Litmus milk is reduced prior to coagulation. Enterococci will grow in the presence of 0.1 per cent methylene blue, 6.5 per cent salt and at pH 9.6, and ammonia is produced from peptone or arginine. All species of this group resist 63°C. (145.4°F.) for 30 minutes. *Streptococcus fecalis* is found in the intestinal tracts of man and of animals, in raw milk, pasteurized milk, milk powder, and cheese. Because of its tolerance to salt and heat, it has been tried as a starter culture in the manufacture of Cheddar cheese. *Streptococcus*

**Figure 2.4**     *Streptococcus cremoris* var. *hollandicus.* Negative stain showing capsules. Courtesy S. Orla-Jensen and *det Kongelige Danske Videnskabernes Selskab.*

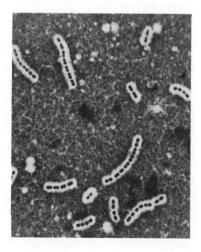

*liquefaciens* is also found in milk and its products, and it coagulates milk and peptonizes the casein at relatively low acidity ("sweet curdling"). *Streptococcus liquefaciens* has been found to produce bitter flavors in milk and soft cheeses. It has been reported to be one of the most numerous organisms in Romano cheese made with raw milk (41). *Streptococcus zymogenes* also has been isolated from Romano Cheese made from raw milk; both this species and *Streptococcus durans* have been isolated from cow feces and udders, and from soil and water. These two species have been found in pasteurized milk and have caused some confusion since they are beta-hemolytic streptococci. However, they are not regarded as pathogenic for man. Since the pathogenic *Streptococcus pyogenes* does not survive pasteurization, milk known not to be contaminated after this treatment need not be looked upon with suspicion even if beta-hemolytic streptococci are found. Further differentiation is provided by the fact that *Streptococcus pyogenes* is in Lancefield Group A and the enterococci are in Group D. The taxonomy of the enterococci is somewhat confusing at the present time. Some investigators prefer to consider all of the foregoing species, with the possible exception of *Streptococcus durans,* as varieties of *Streptococcus fecalis* (1, 51).

### LEUCONOSTOC

This genus was known earlier as *Betacoccus* (47), and the present generic name is derived from the Greek, *leucus* meaning colorless, and *nostoc,* referring to a genus of encapsulated blue-green algae (10). *Leuconostoc dextranicum* and *Leuconostoc citrovorum* are morphologically similar to the blue-green alga *Nostoc,* but they lack the photosynthetic pigments of the latter. Leuconostocs are spherical cells occurring in pairs and chains and may be considered heterofermentative streptococci. They produce acetic acid, ethanol, carbon dioxide, and DL- or L(+)- and D(−)-lactic acid from fermentable carbohydrates. Leuconostocs produce acid from glucose but not from xylose, mannitol, or sorbitol, and ammonia is not produced from arginine. They are not particularly active in milk and rarely coagulate it, some strains being unable to ferment lactose to any great degree (1, 26). The cells are of the same size as *Streptococcus lactis* or, infrequently, smaller. Citric acid is fermented with the production of acetoin, biacetyl, 2, 3-butylene glycol, acetic acid, and carbon dioxide. Leuconostocs found in dairy products are seldom spoilage agents and are illustrative of microorganisms which serve a useful purpose in the dairy industry. Occasionally, however, they may cause "slits" in Cheddar cheese made with butter starters. This defect is caused by the carbon dioxide produced by these organisms.

Differences between *Leuconostoc dextranicum* and *Leuconostoc citrovorum* are minor. The former produces acid in litmus milk and usually slime in sucrose-containing media. Both organisms are gram-positive cocci, 0.6 to 1.0 $\mu$ in diameter. They are aerobic or facultatively anaerobic and require supplements of yeast extract or beef infusion for optimal growth. These species grow best at 25°C. to 30°C. (77°F. to 86°F.) and slowly at 8°C. (46.4°F.) but not 45°C. (113°F.), and they usually do not survive pasteurization. Since leuconostocs are used in starter cultures, it is important to note that they are quite susceptible to antibiotics, and approximately 0.1 unit of penicillin per milliliter is sufficient to impair their development.

Leuconostocs are found on green vegetables, and roots, and in butter, sour cream, and milk. *Leuconostoc dextranicum* is found in the latter two products but rarely *Leuconostoc citrovorum*, which more commonly is recovered only from commercial mixed cultures. To isolate these species, the material is plated out on meat infusion agar containing peptone and glucose and incubated at 21°C. (69.8°F.). Small, gray colonies, not especially distinctive, are transferred to litmus milk for further study. As noted previously, litmus milk may be weakly acidified but not coagulated (1). *Leuconostoc dextranicum* and *Leuconostoc citrovorum* are included in starter cultures for the manufacture of sour cream, buttermilk, and butter. In this regard, the formation of desirable flavor substances from citric acid fermentation is their important function. For this reason these organisms are sometimes termed "aroma bacteria." Biacetyl is the most important of the aroma substances formed. Larger yields of aroma substances result when the pH is low (4.4 to 3.7) and conditions are aerobic. (See Chapter 11.)

LACTOBACILLUS

This word is derived from the Latin *lac*, meaning milk, and *bacillum*, staff or stick; hence a rod-shaped organism from milk. Lactobacilli generally are long, thin, rod-shaped organisms. Orla-Jensen designated the homofermentative rod-shaped lactic acid bacteria with optimum temperatures around 40°C. (104°F.) as *Thermobacterium*, whereas those with optimum temperatures near 30°C. (86°F.) were *Streptobacterium*. The heterofermentative rods were designated as *Betabacterium* (47). *Lactobacillus casei*, *Lactobacillus acidophilus*, *Lactobacillus plantarum*, and *Lactobacillus helveticus* are typical homofermentative lactobacilli of interest to the dairy microbiologist. Lactobacilli are found in feeds, silage, manure, and milk and its products (15, 47). Considerable amounts of acid (mainly L(+)-lactic acid with traces of D(−)-lactic acid) are produced by their fermentation of carbohydrate, and since these organisms are not easily killed by the acid, they have been termed "aciduric." Heterofermentative species may be differentiated from homofermentative ones by incubation in tomato juice yeast extract glucose broth under a vaspar seal. Usually after about a week the heterofermentative types will have produced sufficient gas to raise the seal above the surface of the medium. *Lactobacillus brevis*, *Lactobacillus buchneri*, and *Lactobacillus fermenti* are heterofermentative lactobacilli, but this group is not of great interest to the dairy microbiologist at the present time.

Recently a series of studies has been made on the physiological differentiation of various species of lactobacilli. In one study the tests used included production of gas from glucose and citrate, ammonia from arginine, growth at 15°C., 45°C., and 48°C. (59°F., 113°F., and 118.4°F.), heat survival at 60°C. and 65°C. (140°F. and 149°F.), and tolerance of 4, 6, and 8 per cent salt. Under these conditions the lactobacilli could be separated into eight groups (14). Further physiological work allowed separation of *Lactobacillus acidophilus*, *Lactobacillus bulgaricus*, *Lactobacillus plantarum*, *Lactobacillus helveticus* and *Lactobacillus casei* (65, 66). The value of this work remains to be fully ascertained. Another proposed differentiation of non-gas-forming lactobacilli was based on colony type (R or S), per cent and rotation of acid formed, growth at 16°C. or 45°C. (60.8°F. or 113°F.), vitamin requirements, and final pH in carbohydrate fermentations (49).

*Lactobacillus casei* (Figure 2.5) is a gram-positive, non-motile, asporogenous, rod-shaped organism that forms short chains of cells in milk and longer chains in broth cultures. Granules may be observed when the cells are stained with methylene blue. *Lactobacillus casei*, like all lactobacilli, requires supplemental materials usually derived from yeast extract, tomato juice, carrot, or liver infusions, as well as amino acids and fermentable carbohydrates, for optimal growth. Among the B vitamins, various strains require niacin, pantothenic acid, pteroylglutamic acid, and riboflavin. Because of the variety of vitamins and amino acids required for growth in synthetic media, *Lactobacillus casei* has frequently been used for vitamin and amino acid assay purposes. *Lactobacillus casei* is microaerophilic and has an optimum growth temperature of 30°C. (86°F.) with a range of 10°C. to

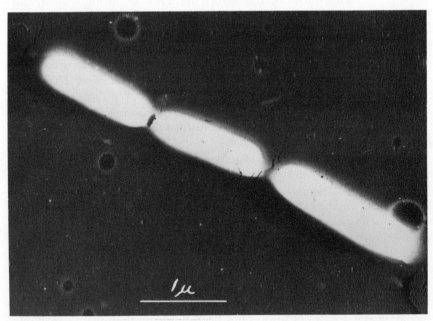

**Figure 2.5**     *Lactobacillus casei.* Electron microscope photograph of a chain of cells shadowed with chromium. Courtesy S. S. Breese, Jr.

40°C. (50°F. to 104°F.). A few strains may survive 63°C. (145.4°F.) for 30 minutes but none survives 60°C. (140°F.) for 90 minutes. Penicillin in concentrations of 0.3 to 0.6 unit per milliliter or streptomycin in concentrations of 5 µg per milliliter inhibit this organism, but various strains will grow in the presence of 5.5 per cent salt. *Lactobacillus casei* grows well in milk and produces up to 1.5 per cent acid in it, and upon prolonged incubation of milk, especially in the presence of calcium carbonate, an increase in soluble nitrogen may be observed. *Lactobacillus casei* is a common organism in raw milk and is important in ripening of cheese and natural souring of milk and cream, where acidities above those produced by *Streptococcus lactis* develop. Cell-free extracts of *Lactobacillus casei* contain proteolytic enzymes active on casein, gelatin, DL-leucylglycylglycine, glycyl-L-leucine, and DL-alanylglycine, but not on D-leucyl-L-tyrosine. This species apparently possesses proteinase, aminopolypeptidase, and dipeptidase, but not carboxypolypeptidase (23).

    *Lactobacillus acidophilus* differs in several ways from *Lactobacillus casei*. The former cannot ferment mannitol although the latter can, and *Lactobacillus acidophilus* has a higher optimum growth temperature—37°C. (98.6°F.)—and will not grow at 20°C. (68°F.). Carbohydrates are fermented with the production of DL or L(+)-lactic acid, and amounts of acid up to 1.8 per cent are produced. *Lactobacillus acidophilus* does not grow in the presence of 4 per cent salt. *Lactobacillus acidophilus* may be observed to grow as long chains of cells (Figure 2.6), and involution forms are common in older cultures. Frequently *Lactobacillus acidophilus* shows granulations when stained with methylene blue. Certain strains of *Lactobacillus acidophilus* have been used in the preparation of fermented milks.

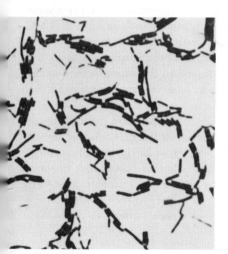

**Figure 2.6**     (**left**) *Lactobacillus acidophilus.* Gram stain. Courtesy A. P. Harrison, Jr. (**right**) *Lactobacillus acidophilus.* Gram stain of a chain of cells. Courtesy A. P. Harrison, Jr.

It can be implanted in the intestinal tract of man and has been used in the treatment of certain intestinal disorders.

Lactobacilli may be isolated by plating dilutions of suitable material on trypticase soy glucose agar, carrot-liver infusion agar, yeast extract glucose agar, tomato juice glucose agar with Tween 80 added, or whey agar and by then incubating at a temperature suitable for the development of the species desired. Small gray or white surface colonies or fuzzy, rough, or lens-shaped, sub-surface colonies may be picked to litmus milk for further study. Cultures may be stored as stabs in screw-top vials in suitable media as cited above but containing an excess of calcium carbonate. Good growth is obtained in sterile skimmilk supplemented with tomato or carrot juice, yeast extract, or tryptone. Some cultures are kept in liquid media in association with film-forming yeasts, since the latter reduce the oxygen tension, supply vitamins, and reduce the acidity and hence contribute to greater viability of the lactic acid organisms. Using precipitin tests on material prepared from lactobacilli or crude acid extracts of them, it is possible to classify them into six groups and one sub-group (50). The division of the serological groups closely concurs with those groups (14, 65, 66) separated on the basis of physiological tests. The lactobacilli apparently possess antigens similar to those of the streptococci.

*Miscellaneous lactobacilli. Lactobacillus thermophilus* (taxonomic status questioned) has been isolated from pasteurized milk, and since it is thermophilic—optimum temperature above 50°C. (122°F.)—it may cause difficulty in obtaining satisfactory reduction of bacterial numbers during pasteurization of milk by the vat (holding) method. This is a rare occurrence and usually aerobic spore-forming bacteria are found in these outbreaks. *Lactobacillus plantarum* var. *rudensis* and *Lactobacillus brevis* var. *rudensis* have been implicated as causes of rusty spot defect in Cheddar cheese. *Lactobacillus helveticus,* which can grow at temperatures as high as 48°C. (118.4°F.), has been used in starter cultures in the manufacture of Swiss cheese. *Lactobacillus bulgaricus* is used in Swiss cheese starter cultures as is *Lactobacillus lactis;* the former is also employed in the manufacture of certain fermented milks, sour condensed whey, and semi-solid buttermilk (see Chapter 8).

*Lactobacillus bulgaricus* and *Lactobacillus acidophilus* are difficult to distinguish readily. Recently (65) the following differential characteristics were suggested: *Lactobacillus acidophilus* will grow in the presence of bile salts, or in 2 per cent but not 4 per cent salt, whereas *Lactobacillus bulgaricus* will not grow in the presence of bile salts or in 2 per cent salt. Generally *Lactobacillus bulgaricus* produces more acid in milk cultures than does *Lactobacillus acidophilus* but there is some variation among cultures.

## MICROBACTERIUM

Brief mention must be made of several other genera that at present are classified in the family *Lactobacteriaceae* (10). They are different in some characteristics from the genera previously considered, but their inclusion here is warranted because of their occurrence in dairy products. Microbacteria (3, 18, 46, 47, 56) are small (1 $\mu$ in length), gram-positive, non-motile, asporogenous, rod-shaped organisms (Figure 2.7). Since they are aerobic, they grow well on the surface of media but poorly in the depths. As microbacteria have irregular forms, appear granular when stained, form "palisades" of cells after fission, produce catalase and only small amounts of acid, they have been considered by some to be thermoduric corynebacteria (3). The most common species is *Microbacterium lacticum*, the only one usually found in this country. This organism produces acid in milk but coagulation is variable. Most of the acid produced is L(+)-lactic acid. It grows optimally at 30°C. (86°F.) and has a range of 15°C. to 35°C. (59°F. to 95°F.). Some strains of *Microbacterium lacticum* survive 80°C. to 85°C. (176°F. to 185°F.) for 10 minutes and are therefore examples of the most heat-resistant asporogenous bacteria known. *Microbacterium lacticum* will grow in the presence of 2.5 per cent salt. *Microbacterium flavum* produces a yellow pigment on solid media and is morphologically distinct from *Microbacterium lacticum* in that it has larger cells not arranged in palisades. It has not been isolated frequently in this country.

Microbacteria are found on dairy utensils and in dry milk, cheese, butter, milk, and cow manure, but not in the udder. They are easily isolated by plating pasteurized samples on proteose-peptone glucose agar or its equivalent and incubating at 30°C. (86°F.) for 3 days. The small colonies contain cells characterized by their palisade arrangement, and granulations may be observed within the cells in methylene blue stains. The microbacteria are very resistant to heat and may be the cause of high bacterial counts in pasteurized milk and milk powder. Since these organisms do not grow well at 35°C. (95°F.), plates incubated at this temperature will not reveal them. It is essential therefore that a lower incubation temperature—30°C. (86°F.)—be employed for their growth and detection.

**Figure 2.7**   *Microbacterium lacticum.* Negative stain showing typical cell arrangements. Courtesy S. Orla-Jensen and *det Kongelige Danske Videnskabernes Selskab.*

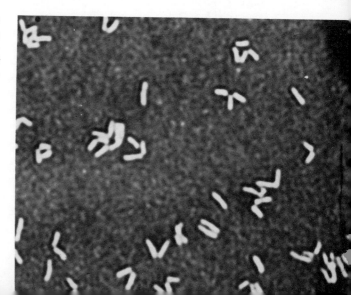

PROPIONIBACTERIUM

These organisms (Figure 2.8 a, b) are essential in the manufacture of Swiss cheese. They are gram-positive, non-motile, asporogenous, coccobacillary organisms and ferment the lactic acid in the cheese to propionic and acetic acids and carbon dioxide (63). Propionic acid formation from succinate has recently been shown (30). Propionibacteria are essen-

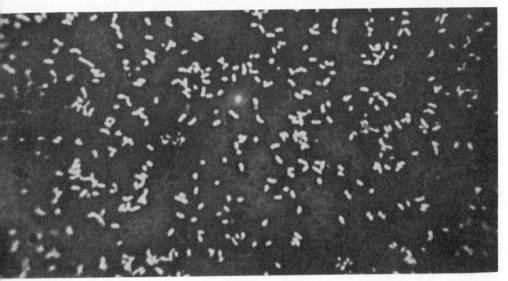

**Figure 2.8a** *Propionibacterium* sp. Negative stain of cells grown anaerobically. Courtesy D. C. Heath and Co. and reprinted from *Biology of Bacteria* by permission of A. T. Henrici and E. J. Ordal, copyright 1948.

**Figure 2.8b** *Propionibacterium* sp. Negative stain of cells grown aerobically. Courtesy D. C. Heath and Co. and reprinted from *Biology of Bacteria* by permission of A. T. Henrici and E. J. Ordal, copyright 1948.

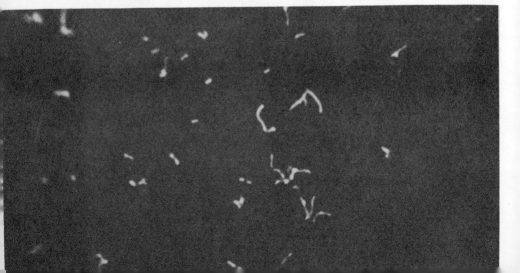

tially anaerobic organisms and require supplements of yeast extract and fermentable carbon compounds for optimal growth (9, 32). They have an optimum temperature of 30°C. (86°F.) with a range of 15°C. to 45°C. (59°F. to 113°F.). *Propionibacterium shermanii* or *Propionibacterium petersonii* are used in starter cultures for Swiss cheese, but they have been isolated from Cheddar cheese as well. *Propionibacterium shermanii* is inhibited by 0.1 unit penicillin or 5 μg streptomycin per milliliter of milk. Salt concentrations of 10 per cent prevent the growth of propionibacteria (9). These species can be isolated by plating suitable material on yeast extract glucose peptone agar and incubating anaerobically or in deep tubes at 30°C. (86°F.) or under an overlay containing 1.5 per cent agar and 0.05 per cent sodium thioglycollate (32). Under these conditions the colonies are rather large and lens shaped, and propionibacteria in the colonies are identified by their similarity in appearance to cells of *Streptococcus lactis,* their catalase production, and their lactate-fermenting ability, although sometimes this is quite weak. Litmus milk is generally acidified and frequently coagulated.

## MICROCOCCACEAE

Bacteria included in this family are spherical or elliptical cells which divide in two or three planes and occur singly, in pairs, packets, or tetrads. They are non-motile, asporogenous, gram-positive, and they produce catalase. All grow well at 22°C. (71.6°F.) and many grow best at 30°C. to 31°C. (86°F. to 87.6°F.). Surface growth on most solid media is good, and some species produce yellow, orange, or red pigments. One genus, *Micrococcus,* is important to the dairy microbiologist.

### MICROCOCCUS

The name is derived from the words *micrus,* meaning small, and *kókkos,* seed or grain, hence, small seed (10). Micrococci are spherical cells (Figure 2.9) arranged in irregular masses but never in long chains (2, 52). Some types of these organisms are found in the lactiferous ducts of the cow's mammary gland and are present in milk obtained from the udder under sterile conditions. Contaminated equipment may be the main source

**Figure 2.9**   *Micrococcus varians.* Methylene blue stain showing typical cell arrangements. Courtesy W. L. Flannery.

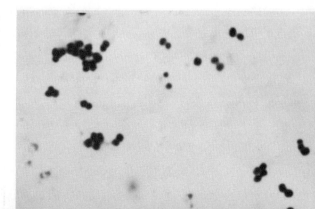

of micrococci in milk. Most species of dairy micrococci are cocci arranged in irregular masses with cells ranging from 0.8 to 1.2 μ in diameter, and there is a tendency for the cells to occur as tetrads in certain species. The colonies are usually greenish-yellow or white, and they are larger than colonies of lactic acid bacteria. Many species of micrococci are heat resistant and survive 63°C. (145.4°F.) for 30 minutes. More species have been reported to survive high-temperature short-time (HTST) than low-temperature long-time (LTLT) pasteurization. It should be noted that true udder micrococci are not resistant to pasteurization temperatures, and the occasional reported exceptions to this generalization need more careful examination by direct heating experiments, for results based upon the somewhat unsatisfactory taxonomy of this group may lead to erroneous conclusions.

Dairy micrococci are coagulase-negative, and although they produce acid from glucose, they fail to produce it from mannitol. They do not produce acetoin from glucose or ammonia from arginine. There are two clearly defined groups; one produces an acid curd in litmus milk, ferments lactose, liquefies gelatin, grows at 37°C. (98.6°F.), and fails to survive 65°C. (149°F.) for 30 minutes and may be considered *Micrococcus luteus;* the other acidifies litmus milk slowly, does not liquefy gelatin, fails to grow at 37°C. (98.6°F.) and survives 65°C. (149°F.) for 30 minutes and may be considered *Micrococcus varians* (2). Unfortunately, a great number of species of micrococci have been inadequately or poorly described, and it is difficult to identify many of them from their characteristics. *Micrococcus freudenreichii* has been isolated from Cheddar cheese made with raw milk and subsequently has been used in attempts to accelerate flavor development of cheese made with pasteurized milk (7). These species and *Micrococcus varians* also have been isolated from Brick cheese smear. Micrococci also have been found to cause thickening of sweetened condensed milk, and they may be important organisms in thermoduric outbreaks in pasteurizing plants. Certain strains of some species in this genus which are coagulase-positive elaborate a heat-stable toxin; *Micrococcus pyogenes* var. *aureus* (Figure 2.10) often produces such a toxin. Although ingestion of this toxin is rarely fatal, the symptoms produced are acute and distressing. These include nausea,

**Figure 2.10**    *Micrococcus pyogenes* var. *aureus.* Electron microscope photograph of a clump of cells shadowed with chromium. Courtesy R. C. Williams and R. W. Wyckoff, Proc. Soc. Exptl. Biol. Med., 59 (1945): 265 and Soc. Exptl. Biol. Med.

vomiting, diarrhea, and abdominal pains, generally of no more than one day's duration. The toxin-producing organisms may be introduced into dairy products via the udder of an infected cow or by human carriers or by contaminated equipment. Subsequent incubation, or failure to refrigerate properly, may allow growth and consequent toxin production by these bacteria in a food made from the infected milk. The presence of toxin does not alter the appearance or taste of the food. Pasteurization kills this species, including all the toxin-producing strains, but the heat treatment does not inactivate the food-poisoning agent. *Micrococcus pyogenes* var. *aureus* and to a lesser extent *Micrococcus pyogenes* var. *albus* also are important as causative agents of mastitis in dairy cows.

## ENTEROBACTERIACEAE

The bacteria in this family are gram-negative, asporogenous rods which are peritrichously flagellated when motile. Surface growth on most solid media is good. The family is divided into a number of tribes of which *Eschericheae* is of principal interest, although occasionally organisms in the tribes *Proteae* or *Salmonelleae* are encountered. The genera of the tribe *Eschericheae* ferment lactose with the production of acid and gas, whereas the genera in the tribes *Proteae* and *Salmonelleae* do not have this ability. The tribes *Proteae* and *Salmonelleae* are differentiated on the basis of urease production by the former.

The tribe *Eschericheae* includes two genera upon which the dairy microbiologist has done much work (17, 68). These are the genera *Escherichia* and *Aerobacter* which collectively comprise the coliform, or colon-aerogenes, group. The name is derived from the Latin *colon,* large intestine, with reference to the common occurrence therein of one of the chief members of the group, *Escherichia coli* (Figure 2.11). Coliform bacteria occur singly, in pairs, and in short chains, but many strains are coccobacillary. They have been defined as aerobic, facultative anaerobic, gram-negative, asporogenous, rod-shaped organisms capable of producing acid and gas from lactose (57). The coliform group is completely undesirable in milk and its products.

**Figure 2.11**    *Escherichia coli.* Gram stain. Courtesy W. L. Flannery.

## ESCHERICHIA-AEROBACTER

*Escherichia coli* and *Aerobacter aerogenes* are two of the most important members of the coliform group. In addition to the characteristics above, it might be noted that *Escherichia coli* is generally motile, whereas *Aerobacter aerogenes* generally is not. These species grow well on nutrient agar, and plates containing their colonies have an unclean odor. They have an optimum temperature of 37°C. (98.6°F.) and a range of 2.5°C. to 45°C. (36.5°F. to 113°F.). Ability to resist 63°C. (145.4°F.) for 30 minutes is extremely uncommon.

*Escherichia coli* and *Aerobacter aerogenes* grow well in milk and ferment the lactose rapidly, but gas is not readily seen unless coagulation occurs early. There may be some degree of coagulation, but peptonization of the casein is not evident. In the absence of a fermentable carbohydrate, *Escherichia coli* may be very mildly proteolytic and produce indol, whereas *Aerobacter aerogenes* is unable to do this. About 35 per cent of the acid produced by *Escherichia coli* is lactic, and other products include ethanol, acetic and succinic acids, carbon dioxide, and hydrogen. The gases are produced in a ratio of 1:1 by *Escherichia coli*. Because of the lactic acid produced, these organisms occasionally have been referred to as "pseudo lactic acid bacteria." The type of lactic acid formed by *Escherichia coli* depends on the sugar fermented and the nature of the nitrogen source. *Aerobacter aerogenes* forms D(−)- or DL-lactic acid. The ratio of carbon dioxide to hydrogen in *Aerobacter aerogenes* fermentations is 2:1; this organism is able to dissimilate acids which it forms, resulting in relatively greater carbon dioxide production. Furthermore, this dissimilation determines whether a final low or high pH is produced and is the basis of differentiation of the genera *Escherichia* and *Aerobacter* by the methyl red test.

*Escherichia coli* is found in manure, dirty utensils, and soil, and it always occurs in the intestinal tract of man and vertebrate animals. *Aerobacter aerogenes* is frequently found in grains and feeds, and also in the intestines of man and of animals. Most raw milk supplies harbor these organisms, which, owing to their unrestricted occurrence, are not necessarily of fecal origin. Because of their wide distribution, coliform bacteria have been used as indicators of sanitation in the dairy industry. Since they almost invariably are destroyed by proper pasteurization, their presence in heat-treated dairy products signifies either inadequate pasteurization or post-pasteurization contamination. A number of selective and differential media (many adapted from water bacteriology techniques) are available for the detection of coliform bacteria.

*Escherichia coli* is differentiated from *Aerobacter aerogenes* on the basis of a series of physiological tests known as IMViC reactions. These letters represent indole production, methyl red, Voges-Proskauer, and citrate utilization tests respectively. *Escherichia coli* is generally positive for the first two and negative for the latter two, whereas *Aerobacter aerogenes* is the reverse. Atypical cultures may, however, show other combinations of positive and negative reactions.

In addition to producing gassy defects in milk and milk products, a number of flavor defects are brought about by these species. The defect "unclean" is particularly important. *Aerobacter aerogenes* produces encapsulated variants and these have been isolated in cases of ropiness in milk. *Escherichia coli* has been recovered from gassy cans of evaporated and sweetened condensed milk (17).

### PROTEUS

The tribe *Proteae* is composed of the single genus, *Proteus*. The organisms of this genus rarely occur in spoilage outbreaks, and since they are readily killed by pasteurization, market milk samples usually are free of them. They do not ferment lactose but do decompose urea rapidly. *Proteus vulgaris* is representative of the species in this genus.

### SALMONELLA

In the tribe *Salmonelleae* is found the genus *Salmonella*. There are a large number of species in this genus, some of which have been implicated in cases of food infection. For example, *Salmonella typhosa, Salmonella paratyphi,* and *Salmonella schottmuelleri* are causative organisms of typhoid and paratyphoid fevers A and B in man. These bacteria are transmitted in foods which have been contaminated directly or indirectly by the fecal material of infected man or rodents. Species of *Salmonella* (*Salmonella typhimurium, Salmonella enteritidis*) produce symptoms much like those described for ingestion of the entertoxin produced by *Micrococcus pyogenes* var. *aureus,* but with *Salmonella* an endotoxin rather than an exotoxin is involved. Twelve to 30 hours may elapse after ingestion of these organisms before symptoms appear. Presumably this represents the period during which the endotoxin is being elaborated following growth of these organisms. This infection is differentiated from food poisoning produced by micrococci because in the latter case the time lapse following ingestion of the exotoxin is much shorter before symptoms appear. These bacteria are readily destroyed by proper pasteurization. Their detection involves a number of diagnostic media and antisera.

## PSEUDOMONADACEAE

In this family only the genus *Pseudomonas* is of interest to the dairy microbiologist. The generic name is derived from the Greek *pseudus,* meaning false, and *monas,* a unit. The reference is to these organisms as a false species of *Monas,* which was an early generic name for a protozoan (10). Species of pseudomonads are gram-negative, asporogenous rods (1 to 4 $\mu$ long) which when motile possess a single polar flagellum or a tuft of flagella (Figure 2.12 a). Most species grow well on solid media and some produce a fluorescent, greenish, water-soluble pigment.

### PSEUDOMONAS

Species of this genus that are important to the dairy microbiologist include *Pseudomonas fluorescens* (Figure 2.12 b), *Pseudomonas fragi, Pseudomonas nigrifaciens, Pseudomonas putrefaciens,* and *Pseudomonas viscosa.* Many pseudomonads described by dairy microbiologists have not been placed in definite species. The presence of these bacteria in milk and its products is completely objectionable, since they are versatile spoilage agents frequently with pronounced biochemical activity, especially on proteins and fats. There is usually little fermentative activity on carbohydrates and the changes effected are mainly oxidative. Pseudomonads may be introduced into dairy products by soil or water contamination, as well as by utensils and equipment. They have optimum temperatures of about 21°C. (69.8°F.) and a range of 0°C. to 37°C. (32°F. to 98.6°F.), varying somewhat with different species. Proper pasteurization destroys all species. At 32°C. (89.6°F.) and below, pseudomonads produce large, reddish-gray, dirty-brown, cream, or porcelain-white colonies. *Pseudomonas fluorescens* colonies color the medium greenish-brown, whereas *Pseudomonas nigrifaciens* colonies impart a black color to the medium.

*Pseudomonas fluorescens* and *Pseudomonas fragi* have been isolated in outbreaks of rancidity in cream and butter. *Pseudomonas fragi* colonies produce a characteristic ester-like odor not unlike that of May apples (28). This odor also has been noted in butter before rancidity is detected. This organism has been found in milk, cream, butter, and bulk condensed milk. In cottage cheese a fruity odor and a flat, rancid or bitter flavor and a white, gelatinous film are produced on the curd particles (20). Acid coagulation and some casein digestion occurs in litmus milk cultures. Exposure to 62°C. (143.6°F.) for 10 minutes is sufficient to destroy *Pseudomonas fragi.*

*Pseudomonas nigrifaciens* has been isolated from mildly salted butter showing reddish-brown or black surface discoloration. *Pseudomonas putrefaciens* is a cause of surface taint in butter and produces cheesy, putrid flavor defects (64). It tolerates 4 per cent salt. Presumably it is introduced from wash water and contaminated equipment. It is easily killed by as little as 1 ppm chlorine (40). Litmus milk is reduced and completely proteolyzed. This species is acid sensitive and is killed at pH 5.3. It grows at 3°C. and 30°C. (37.4°F. and 86°F.) but not at 37°C. (98.6°F.). Unlike *Pseudomonas fluorescens* or *Pseudomonas fragi,* the predominant biochemical characteristic of *Pseudomonas putrefaciens* is not lipolysis but proteolysis. *Pseudomonas viscosa* produces a yellowish- or brownish-colored, slimy film on cottage cheese, accompanied by flat, bitter, or putrid flavors and rotten odors (20). This species is destroyed by proper pasteurization, and as in the case of all other pseudomonad outbreaks, its presence indicates faulty processing or post-

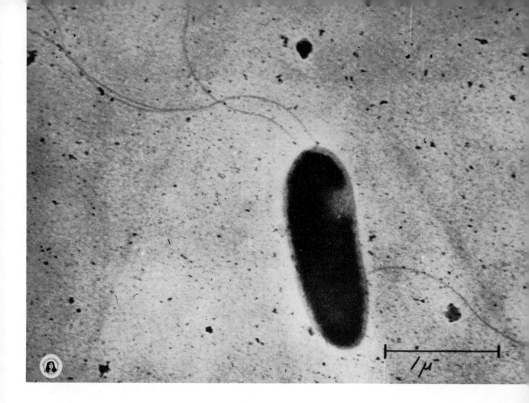

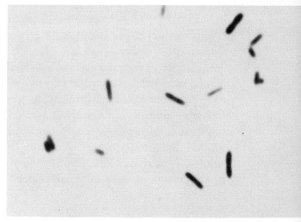

**Figure 2.12a** (above) *Pseudomonas aeruginosa.* Electron microscope photograph showing polar flagella. Courtesy J. W. Bartholomew.

**Figure 2.12b** *Pseudomonas fluorescens.* Gram stain. Courtesy W. L. Flannery.

pasteurization contamination. Milk and dairy products held at refrigeration temperatures may develop bitter flavors because of protein decomposition by cold-tolerant pseudomonads. Some of these produce phosphatase, and their growth causes false positive tests in pasteurized, refrigerated dairy products.

## BACILLACEAE

The family *Bacillaceae* is divided into two genera, *Bacillus* and *Clostridium*, and the dairy microbiologist should be familiar with some of their properties. The genera of this family are sporogenous, rod-shaped cells, and when motile, they possess peritrichous flagella.

### BACILLUS

Bacillus is derived from the Latin *bacillum*, little stick; members of the genus are large, aerobic organisms. They are fundamentally saprophytic soil bacteria (Figure 2.13), and it is only under unusual circumstances that the dairy microbiologist encounters them in large numbers. They commonly are relatively large bacteria (3 to 9 $\mu$ in length) most of which are gram-positive, but a few are gram-negative (55). The spores are ellipsoidal to cylindrical in shape and occasionally bulge the sporangia. The cells occur singly, in pairs, and in long chains (streptobacilli). Typical of the species found in milk and dairy products are *Bacillus cereus* var. *mycoides, Bacillus coagulans,* and, sometimes, *Bacillus polymyxa* (*Aerobacillus*).

*Bacillus cereus* var. *mycoides* grows well on nutrient agar and in most liquid media. Optimum growth temperature is 30°C. (86°F.) and the range is 15°C. to 50°C. (59°F. to 122°F.). This species forms spores which withstand 63°C. (145.4°F.) for 30 minutes. Probably all milk contains spores of this organism, but seldom do conditions favor their germination. In milk *Bacillus cereus* var. *mycoides* does not attack lactose but slowly peptonizes the casein. Some aerobic spore-formers possess a rennet-like enzyme and "sweet-curdle" milk; that is, they coagulate the milk at relatively low acidity. Litmus milk cultures show complete reduction of the litmus (36). Agar colonies are greyish, rhizoid, rough appearing, and large. Requirements for sporulation and germination, as well as conditions governing the heat resistance of spores, are complex and depend on pH, oxygen tension, temperature, and nutritional factors. The aerobic spore-formers generally do not grow at the high acidity produced by lactic acid bacteria, and hence it is only when the lactic organisms are killed or inhibited by some special treatment that the former group need be considered. Thermophilic, aerobic spore-formers may grow in milk foam in pasteurizing vats and in repasteurized milk supplies, causing thermophilic

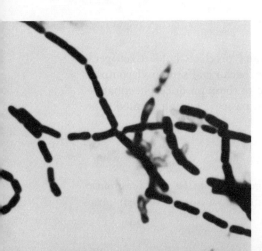

**Figure 2.13**     *Bacillus cereus* var. *mycoides.* Gram stain. Courtesy W. L. Flannery.

outbreaks in pasteurizing plants or wherever milk is held at high temperature for long periods. Spores of *Bacillus cereus* var. *mycoides* have been found in milk powder, sweetened condensed milk, and spoiled evaporated milk. They may cause "broken" or "bitty" cream, a defect in which the cream breaks into particles of varying sizes which do not re-emulsify like those of normal milk or cream (58).

*Bacillus coagulans* is unusual in that in milk it produces L( + )-lactic, acetic, and propionic acids. It was first isolated from an outbreak of coagulated evaporated milk. *Bacillus coagulans* has an optimum temperature of 45°C. (113°F.) and a growth temperature range of 28°C. to 60°C. (82.4°F. to 140°F.). It grows well on proteose-peptone agar, but the colonies formed are not distinctive. It coagulates milk and slowly increases the soluble nitrogen without peptonizing casein actively. Some outbreaks of thermophilic bacteria in pasteurizing plants and cases of coagulated evaporated milk have been ascribed to this organism.

Aerobic spore-formers can be isolated by heating the raw material to 80°C. (176°F.) for 10 minutes and plating on appropriate media. The large, usually rough, colonies formed may then be investigated further. The vegetative cells commonly have no special heat resistance, so heat treatment is specific only for those cells in the spore stage.

### CLOSTRIDIUM

The anaerobic genus *Clostridium* (Figure 2.14) is limited mainly to the soil and intestinal tract of animals, although species may contaminate and become established on equipment. Milk and milk products contaminated with manure will also contain them. Typical of these bacteria are *Clostridium perfringens, Clostridium putrefaciens, Clostridium sporogenes,* and *Clostridium butyricum. Clostridium perfringens* is a gram-positive, motile, sporogenous, rod-shaped organism ranging from 1 to 4 μ in length. Litmus milk is acidified and coagulated, large amounts of gas are produced, and the coagulum is broken up in a reaction appropriately called "stormy fermentation." Proteolysis is not evident, but organisms of this type can produce foul odors and gas in both natural and process cheeses as

**Figure 2.14** *Clostridium* sp. Swollen terminal spores are shown in this preparation. Courtesy General Biological Supply House, Inc., Chicago, Illinois.

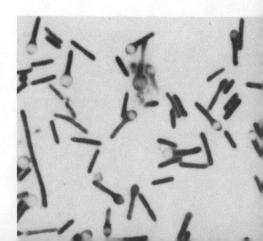

well as in various spreads. The optimum growth temperature of *Clostridium perfringens* is 35°C. to 37°C. (95°F. to 98.6°F.).

## MISCELLANEOUS BACTERIA

The remaining families to be considered do not contain important genera but rather a few scattered species which occasionally are found as agents of economic importance in certain dairy products. A few species are important as etiological agents of diseases which may be transmitted by milk and dairy products.

In the family *Achromobacteriaceae* species of the genera *Alcaligenes, Achromobacter,* and *Flavobacterium* are encountered (10). *Alcaligenes viscosus* (Figure 2.15) is a gram-negative, non-motile, asporogenous, rod-shaped organism varying from 0.8 to 2.6 μ in length. Certain strains possess a large capsule. This organism has an optimum temperature of 20°C. (68°F.) with a range of 10°C. to 37°C. (50°F. to 98.6°F.) and it is killed by heating to 63°C. (145.4°F.) for 30 minutes. It is aerobic, grows well on nutrient agar, and forms dirty-white colonies which are usually of a viscid consistency. No acid or gas is produced from carbohydrates, but the organism is lipolytic, a characteristic frequently overlooked (4, 39). *Alcaligenes viscosus* has been incriminated in outbreaks of ropiness in milk and cream, and in this defect, the fluid may be drawn out into long, mucilaginous strands. The organism is predominantly aerobic, and in some instances only the surface layers of milk are involved. Usually the ropy condition is produced at low temperatures—10°C. to 15°C. (50°F. to 59°F.)—and relatively low acidity. The ability to produce ropiness is variable and may be lost upon subculturing the organism for some time. *Alcaligenes viscosus* is found in feeds, stagnant water, stable dust, dairy utensils, soil, and manure. *Alcaligenes metalcaligenes* forms a white, gelatinous film on cottage cheese curd but with no change in odor or flavor (20). It also is a soil or water organism.

Occasionally outbreaks of rancidity are traced to *Achromobacter lipolyticum.* Usually, circumstances favoring lipolysis must be present. Thus high

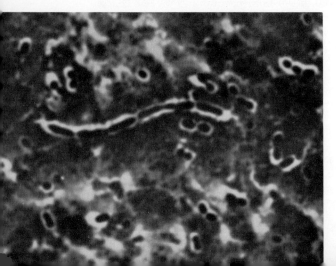

**Figure 2.15**     *Alcaligenes viscosus.* Negative stain showing capsules. Courtesy W. L. Flannery.

fat products such as cream and butter are very likely to be involved. It is considered a soil and water organism. There is some question as to whether this species ought not be transferred to the genus *Bacterium*.

*Flavobacterium aquatile* and certain other gram-negative soil and water forms are occasionally found in milk. They are easily distinguished from other gram-negative rods in that they only feebly attack carbohydrates and are usually non-motile, but when motile, have peritrichous flagella.

In the family *Bacteriaceae* there is an important species, *Bacterium linens*. It is a gram-positive, non-motile, asporogenous, rod-shaped organism ranging from 0.6 to 2.5 $\mu$ in length. It has an optimum temperature of 21°C. (69.8°F.) with a range of 8°C. to 37°C. (46.4°F. to 98.6°F.), and is easily destroyed by heating to 63°C. (145.4°F.) for 30 minutes. This species is aerobic, produces catalase, and grows well on tryptone or trypticase glucose extract agar. Small cream-colored colonies are formed which become brownish-red on aging (6). *Bacterium linens* slowly produces an alkaline reaction in milk, and proteolysis is evident after incubation for several weeks. The amino nitrogen of the milk is increased greatly. *Bacterium linens* will grow in the presence of 15 per cent salt. This organism is widely distributed in hay, feeds, soil, water, and manure and is found in the smears of surface ripened cheeses like Brick, Limburger, and Camembert. It plays a role in the ripening process by producing proteolytic enzymes which diffuse into the cheese mass from the surface. *Bacterium linens* is quite sensitive to acid conditions; it will grow at pH 9.8 but not 5.0; and it is found on surface ripened cheeses, growing in association with salt-tolerant yeasts. The latter decrease the acidity of the curd to a point favorable to *Bacterium linens* (above pH 5.8) and in addition elaborate certain factors required for its growth. *Bacterium erythrogenes,* a non-motile, gram-positive rod, produces a red pigment and can be isolated from the surface smears of soft cheeses, where it presumably functions in the same manner as *Bacterium linens*.

The genus *Corynebacterium* of the family *Corynebacteriaceae* contains three important species. *Corynebacterium diphtheriae* is the etiological agent of diphtheria in man. This organism can be transmitted to milk by carriers or persons having the disease. Formerly it caused epidemics of diphtheria among drinkers of raw milk. It is easily destroyed by proper pasteurization. *Corynebacterium bovis* can be isolated from milk directly from the cow's udder sometimes in large numbers. It is not a pathogenic organism but may produce rancidity in cream. *Corynebacterium pyogenes* has been found in some cases of bovine mastitis. These species are slender, curved, club-shaped rods which are gram-positive, non-motile and asporogenous. They are aerobic and readily recognized by their banded-and-beaded, clubbed appearance in heat-fixed stained preparations. Some thermoduric corynebacteria (microbacteria) have been described earlier in this chapter.

In the family *Parvobacteriaceae* the organisms are small, asporogenous, gram-negative, nutritionally fastidious, rod-shaped bacteria. Nearly all of them are pathogenic. Members of the genus *Brucella* are important as the etiological agents of brucellosis in man and abortion in cows and goats. The chief host of *Brucella abortus* is the cow. There is also *Brucella suis* (porcine host) and *Brucella melitensis* (caprine host). Animals with the disease may shed the organisms in their milk or discharges, from which they then can be transmitted to man. The bacteriological methods involved in the detection of these organisms are elaborate and time consuming; therefore, serological techniques are used to detect infections by *Brucella* species. Fortunately these bacteria are easily killed by proper pasteurization.

*Mycobacterium tuberculosis* var. *hominis* and var. *bovis* are the etiological agents of tuberculosis in man and bovine respectively, although either organism can produce the disease in either host. At present this genus is classified in the order *Actinomycetales* (10). Many of the organisms of this order form branched, elongated cells and, in addition to cell fission, may reproduce by forming conidia or by hyphal fragmentation. *Mycobacterium tuberculosis* is in the family *Mycobacteriaceae*, whose members do not form a mycelium or other special structures. This family is comprised of thin, rod-shaped organisms that occur singly. *Mycobacterium tuberculosis* is non-motile, asporogenous, and acid fast. It is quite resistant to adverse environmental conditions and is the most heat-resistant bacterial pathogen likely to be found in milk and its products. Pasteurization times and temperatures currently in use have been recommended on the basis of the thermal resistance of this organism. *Mycobacterium tuberculosis* may be found in the feces, milk, and udders of infected animals. The detection of this organism in milk or its products requires complicated laboratory procedures.

## BACTERIAL VIRUSES AND RICKETTSIAE

Viruses are classified in the order *Virales* (10). In the field of dairy microbiology interest centers largely on the bacteriophages, which are viruses that parasitize bacterial cells. Those bacteriophages which attack *Streptococcus lactis, Streptococcus thermophilus,* and *Streptococcus cremoris* are of especial interest, since their presence in processes involving acid production by lactic acid streptococci usually means destruction of the latter, resulting in failure of acid production and consequently in economic loss. In the cheese industry, experiences with bacteriophages have been very costly (19, 67).

Bacteriophages (Figure 2.16) are sub-microscopic agents with morphological features similar to a spermatozoan; that is, they consist of an approximately spherical "head" and a "tail." They range in size of head from 10 to 80 m$\mu$ and reproduce only on young, actively growing cells. Bacteriophages active against *Streptococcus lactis* and *Streptococcus cremoris* have head diameters of around 70 m$\mu$, and tails of 150 to 160 m$\mu$ by 7.0 m$\mu$ thickness, with an over-all length of 220 to 230 m$\mu$. After a bacteriophage particle attacks a sensitive host cell (it generally attacks only a specific species or strain), it is reproduced within the cell and, then, is liberated in greatly increased numbers as the cell lyses. Under optimum conditions

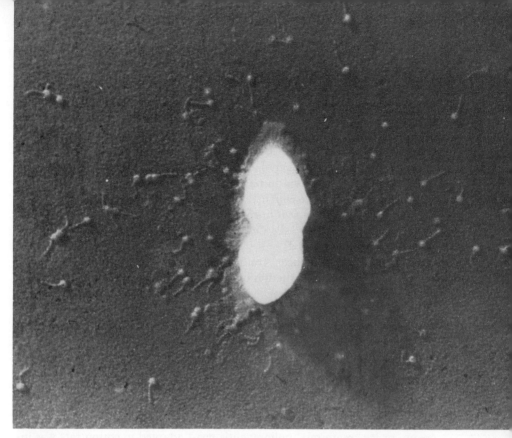

**Figure 2.16** Bacteriophage attacking *Streptococcus lactis*. Electron microscope photograph showing typical morphology of a bacterial virus shadowed with chromium. Reproduced from *J. Bacteriol.*, 57 (1949): 393, by permission of Williams and Wilkins Co., Baltimore.

60 to 80 minutes usually are required from invasion to lysis, and an average of 50 to 150 particles is liberated from the lysed cell; the exact time and the exact number of particles released depend upon many factors. Bacteriophages have no demonstrable physiological activity when not associated with the host cell. They are destroyed by a 500 ppm hypochlorite solution or by heating at 63°C. to 88°C. (145°F. to 190.4°F.) for 30 minutes, the exact temperature needed being dependent upon the strain. These viruses may tolerate a pH as high as 11 and as low as 3 without inactivation. Bacteriophages may be found in material in which lactic fermentation has occurred and in mists from centrifugal separators, whey, milk, and sewage.

The role played by milk and dairy products in the transmission of viral and rickettsial diseases of man is still obscure. Reports dealing mainly with the virus of poliomyelitis and the etiological agent of Q fever, *Coxiella* (*Rickettsia*) *burnetii* have appeared in the literature. Since the latter organism has been studied extensively in this connection during recent years, it will be considered here.

Q fever is an infectious disease of man that may be contracted by the ingestion of raw milk from infected cows, goats, or sheep (21). These animals are infected naturally with the rickettsia of Q fever, and apparently the distribution of the infection is extensive. *Coxiella burnetii* is a small (0.25 by 0.4 μ to 0.5 μ) gram-negative organism that differs from other rickettsiae in that it readily passes through bacterial filters and has no antigenic factors in common with *Proteus* strains (10). It is quite resistant to 0.5 per cent formalin and 1 per cent phenol as well as to heating for approximately the time and temperature used in pasteurization. In this regard commercially vat-pasteurized milk in which the vats were without space heaters have shown viable *Coxiella burnetii* in some samples (27). The holding method of pasteurization probably kills *Coxiella burnetii* when precise time and temperature controls are used.

Experiments have been conducted on the effect of milk and dairy products on the heat destruction of strains of Coxsackie viruses (34). It has been found that these viruses, when present in human stools, were killed at 55°C. (131°F.) for 15 minutes or at 71.1°C. (160°F.) for 15 seconds when suspended in water; when present in milk, cream, or ice cream mix, the temperature necessary for destruction was increased. In milk 61.7°C. (143.1°F.) for 30 minutes or 71.1°C. (160°F.) for 15 seconds was adequate, and 65°C. (149°F.) for 30 minutes was required for inactivation of one of the human strains when suspended in ice cream.

In several epidemiological studies milk has been implicated in the transmission of poliomyelitis (42). However, when suspended in milk, cream, or ice cream mix, poliomyelitis virus adapted to cotton rats was inactivated by the standard vat method of pasteurization. In addition, when the virus from fecal material was suspended in different milk products, it was inactivated by vat or flash pasteurization methods (33).

Most of the evidence incriminating milk as a vehicle for the transmission of viral diseases is circumstantial; more work must be done to establish with certainty the exact role of milk and dairy products in the transmission of such diseases as hepatitis (45), epidemic diarrhea of the newborn (44), poliomyelitis, inclusion conjunctivitis, and foot and mouth disease.

## YEASTS

Yeasts are similar to bacteria in gross colonial morphology, methods of cultivation, and biochemical activity (38, 54). There is no close phylogenetic relationship between yeasts and bacteria, and there is no one taxonomic group in which all have been placed. Yeasts are unicellular, generally ovoid, or elliptical cells; they are gram-positive, non-motile, and large (approximately 10–15 μ) in relation to bacteria. Some yeasts form ascospores (more than 1 per cell and usually 4), but these are primarily reproductive and possess limited ability to resist adverse environmental conditions. Yeasts commonly reproduce by budding, and buds are observed in growing cultures. Yeasts that produce ascospores are known as "true" yeasts;

those in which ascospores have not been observed are termed "false" yeasts. Yeasts grow well in the range of 25°C. to 40°C. (77°F. to 104°F.), and most can tolerate rather high acidities (pH 3.5). They are strongly fermentative or oxidative in their metabolism of carbohydrates and organic acids, and generally they are not considered proteolytic, although a few species are lipolytic.

*Saccharomyces fragilis* (Figure 2.17), an example of a true yeast, is characterized by its ability to produce alcohol and carbon dioxide from lactose. It is an ovoid to elongated organism 1.8 to 5.6 $\mu$ long, and it forms white, glistening colonies on malt extract agar. It produces acid and gas in litmus milk but peptonization is not evident. It has an optimum temperature of 37°C. (98.6°F.), does not grow at 5°C. or 43°C. (41°F. or 109.4°F.), and is destroyed by pasteurization. This species is found in fermented milk drinks such as kefir and kumiss as well as in certain Italian cheeses. Like all lactose-fermenting yeasts, it requires an exogenous source of nicotinic acid. Other species of *Saccharomyces* found in dairy products include *Saccharomyces delbrueckii* (Italian cheese, Dutch buttermilk), *Saccharomyces lactis* (gassy cheese, milk, Italian cheese), and *Saccharomyces chevalieri* (Italian cheese).

*Candida pseudotropicalis* var. *lactosa* (*Saccharomyces kefyr* Beijerinck, *Mycotorula lactosa* Harrison, *Mycotorula lactis*) has properties typical of a false yeast. It forms ovoid to elongated cells 7 $\mu$ to 15 $\mu$ in length. It ferments lactose with the production of alcohol and carbon dioxide and produces gas in litmus milk. Peptonization, however, is not evident. Optimum temperature is near 37°C. (98.6°F.) with no growth at 5°C. or 43°C. (41°F. or 109.4°F.). This yeast has been found in outbreaks of "yeasty" or "gassy" cream—which is characterized by high acidity, excessive foaming, and a yeasty odor—and in kefir grains and buttermilk.

Species of lactose-fermenting yeasts also have been recovered from gassy cans of sweetened condensed milk and yeasty cream. Lactose-fermenting yeasts have been used industrially for the production of ethyl alcohol from whey (See Chapter 15). Other species of *Candida* found in dairy products include *Candida mycoderma,* whose perfect form is known as *Pichia membranefaciens* (yogurt, fermenting butter). *Candida lipolytica* (*Torula, Mycotorula*) has been found in stale margarine (38).

**Figure 2.17**  *Saccharomyces fragilis.* Gram stain. Courtesy W. L. Flannery.

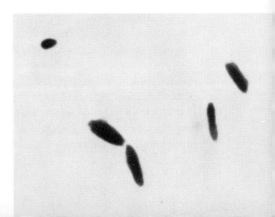

Asporogenous film-forming yeasts are of importance in certain aspects of dairy microbiology. Biochemically, species of *Candida* and *Mycoderma* are primarily oxidative rather than fermentative and seem in some respects to be more closely related to molds than to yeasts. They are characterized by the formation of a heavy, dry pellicle or film on the surface of liquid media, for these organisms are strictly aerobic. Their cells are usually cylindrical, and multiplication occurs by means of bud formation. However, the bud is not separated by fission from the mother cell. These organisms oxidize lactic acid to carbon dioxide and water. *Candida krusei* is grown in association with starter cultures of lactobacilli and *Streptococcus thermophilus*. Here, it oxidizes lactic acid, reduces oxygen tension, and elaborates growth factors, thus maintaining conditions favorable to the viability of starter cultures. *Candida lipolytica* produces lipolytic enzymes and has been used experimentally in the manufacture of Blue cheese. Salt-tolerant yeasts also are found on the smears of surface ripened cheeses, and they undoubtedly bring about favorable conditions for subsequent organisms by elaborating growth factors and reducing the acidity of the curd. Various other yeasts occasionally have been noted in dairy products: *Pichia fermentans* (buttermilk, Italian cheese); *Debaromyces hansenii* (cheese); *Debaromyces subglobosus* (cheese in Holland); *Sporobolomyces salmonicolor, Sporobolomyces roseus, Sporobolomyces pararoseus* (all from the air of dairy plants); *Torulopsis holmii* (buttermilk, yeasty butter); *Torulopsis lactis-condensi* (spoiled sweetened condensed milk); *Torulopsis sphaerica* (imperfect form of *Saccharomyces lactis*) in yeasty cream, whey, and gassy cheese; and *Torulopsis globosa* in gassy, sweetened condensed milk (38).

## MOLDS

Molds are complex, multicellular organisms differing greatly in most respects from bacteria and from the majority of yeasts. However, it should be noted, the methods of cultivation and the biochemical activities of molds are somewhat similar to those of the other two groups. Molds actively dissimilate carbohydrates, fats, and some proteins. They are aerobic and grow over wide ranges of pH, osmotic pressure, and temperature. Most mold colonies appear cottony or wooly and are generally white, cream, green, black, or brownish because of the presence of pigmentation in the long, thread-like strands of protoplasm or in the enormous numbers of aerial asexual spores. *Alternaria, Cladosporium,* and *Hormodendron* have dark mycelia. *Penicillium, Aspergillus, Rhizopus,* and *Geotrichum* have colorless mycelia, but the spores of all but the last-named are usually colored green or black. As with yeasts, mold spores are reproductive and not especially resistant to heat, but they are resistant to drying or desiccation and somewhat resistant to ultraviolet light. Molds are found in soil, stable dusts, feeds, and manure, as well as on poorly cleaned utensils. *Geotrichum candidum* grows best on products soured by lactic acid production. Most molds do not grow rapidly in milk, and seldom is an opportunity presented for their development there.

The individual mold is composed of an aggregate of branching protoplasmic threads known as a mycelium. Individual threads of the mycelium are termed hyphae. The hyphae may or may not possess cross walls, which, if present, would divide it into a number of uninucleate cells. Those portions of the mold involved in securing nutriment from foodstuffs and in attaching to the solid substrate are known as the vegetative hyphae. Molds produce both asexual and sexual spores, the former being produced on fertile aerial hyphae. In some instances the asexual spores (sporangiospores) are produced in large numbers within a sac or sporangium, whereas in others the spores (conidiospores) are produced from the tips of fertile hyphae without being enclosed in any way. All of the mycological terms used in this section may be found defined in an excellent dictionary devoted solely to them (5).

Molds, like yeasts, are easily grown on such media as malt extract agar or potato dextrose agar. Tartaric or lactic acid usually is added just before using to give these media a final reaction of approximately pH 3.5. Molds are identified by morphological examination. This is done with a hand lens or the low power (total magnification x 100) objective of a microscope. The gross appearance of the mycelium, the presence of cross walls, the nature, the arrangement, and the color of the fertile hyphae and spores are used as the basis for mold identification. Among the common mold genera likely to be found in various dairy products are *Rhizopus, Penicillium, Aspergillus, Cladosporium, Alternaria,* and an intermediate yeast-like organism, *Geotrichum candidum.* All except *Rhizopus* have septate mycelia.

*Rhizopus* species (Figure 2.18) have a vegetative mycelium which pro-

**Figure 2.18** *Rhizopus sp.* Mount showing sporangium, sporangiophore, mycelium, and holdfasts. Courtesy Edward Arnold Co. and reprinted from *Industrial Mycology* by permission of G. Smith, copyright 1946.

duces stolons or runners over the substrate. At each point of attachment of the stolon to the substrate there are found "holdfasts" or rhizoids which serve to anchor the mycelium. From these points of attachment, clusters of fertile hyphae develop (sporangiophores). At the tip of these structures there develops a sac (sporangium), which eventually contains an enormous number of asexual spores. The sac soon becomes black due to the maturation and coloration of the spores contained therein, and when the sporangium ruptures, the spores are scattered about. *Rhizopus* species have been found to be involved in the ripening of Gammelost cheese.

*Penicillium* molds (Figure 2.19 a, b) do not produce a mycelium as easily identifiable as that of *Rhizopus*. From various places along the vegetative mycelium, structures known as conidiophores are produced, and from the tip of these structures conidiospores arise. The various branches (sterigmata) of the conidiophore along with the spores superficially resemble a paint brush. The color of these molds is usually blue-green because of the coloration of the mature conidiospores. In the ripening of Camembert and Roquefort cheese, proper species of the genus *Penicillium* are essential. The proteolytic and lipolytic activities of these molds (*Penicillium camemberti* and *Penicillium roqueforti*) are mainly responsible for the characteristic flavor and appearance of these cheeses. Salt-tolerant species may produce surface discolorations on butter.

*Aspergillus* species (Figure 2.20) also produce conidiospores. However, they are easily distinguished from *Penicillium* in that these asexual spores are borne on sterigmata attached to a swollen vesicle. The arrangement is quite characteristic for the genus, and various species produce spores which are black, green, brown, or orange. Species of *Aspergillus* have been recovered from cans of sweetened condensed milk where they grow for a limited time to form "buttons." These are usually small accretions of mold mycelia and coagulated casein.

*Cladosporium* (Figure 2.21) is recognized by the deep olive-green to black of its vegetative mycelium and spores. The spores, usually two-celled, are produced from a branching mycelium. Species of this genus have been found to produce surface discolorations of butter.

*Alternaria* species (Figure 2.22) have relatively short conidiophores with characteristic large size, multicellular spores which are borne in chains. They are pigmented olive or dark brown, and like the genera above, they have been involved in surface discoloration of butter.

*Geotrichum candidum* (Figure 2.23) (*Oospora lactis* and *Oidium lactis* are older synonymous designations.) oxidizes the lactic acid of sour milk and dairy products to carbon dioxide and water, and it rapidly hydrolyses the butterfat of cream. *Geotrichum candidum* grows on the surface of sour cream and cheese as a firm, felt-like, white mass. Microscopically, the cells appear to be large and to have square-cut ends; fragmentation of the primitive mycelium formed by this organism results in the production of these elements, known as arthrospores, each of which is reproductive. *Geotrichum*

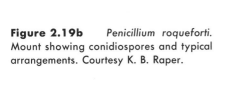

**Figure 2.19a** (above) *Penicillium* sp. Glass model showing vegetative and fertile hyphae. Courtesy Chicago Natural History Museum, Chicago, Illinois.

**Figure 2.19b** *Penicillium roqueforti.* Mount showing conidiospores and typical arrangements. Courtesy K. B. Raper.

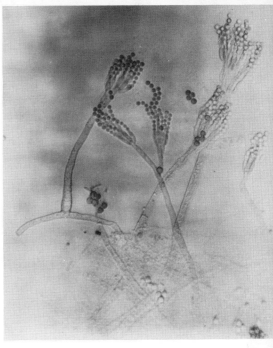

*candidum* may be responsible for the production of yeasty flavors in dairy products, and it sometimes is a part of the surface smear of cheeses. *Geotrichum candidum* is not saccharolytic, and its importance is due to its oxidative and lipolytic characteristics. It is destroyed by pasteurization, and its presence in pasteurized cream and butter is interpreted as an indication of faulty handling methods.

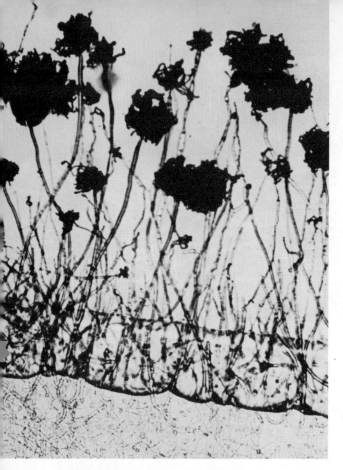

**Figure 2.20** *Aspergillus niger.* Mount showing typical arrangements. Courtesy Harper and Brothers and reprinted from *Microbiology, General and Applied* by permission of W. B. Sarles, W. C. Frazier, J. B. Wilson, and S. G. Knight, copyright 1951.

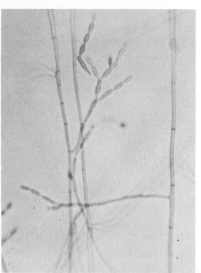 

**Figure 2.21** **(left)** *Cladosporium trichoides.* Although this species is pathogenic, typical structures are shown. Courtesy C. W. Emmons. **(right)** *Cladosporium* spores. Courtesy C. W. Emmons.

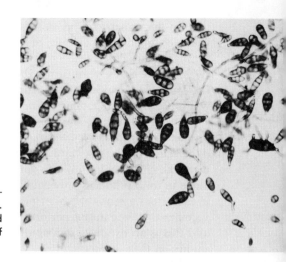

**Figure 2.22** *Alternaria* sp. Septate mycelium and multi-septate conidia are shown. Courtesy Edward Arnold Co. and reprinted from *Industrial Mycology* by permission of G. Smith, copyright 1946.

## ASSOCIATIVE ACTION AMONG MICROORGANISMS

In most cases the microorganisms of milk and its products are present as a mixed flora, and it is therefore necessary to consider some consequences of their interaction. The effects observed in simple cases (involving only two species or groups) have been defined as follows: synergistic, that is, when two organisms produce a change neither could carry out alone; metabiotic, when there is cooperation among the various species resulting in a "food-chain," wherein the metabolic end-products of one are used as a foodstuff for the other; and antibiotic, when the presence of one species inhibits or represses the development of a second. It should be emphasized

**Figure 2.23** *Geotrichum candidum.* Fragmentation of the mycelium is shown. Courtesy Harper & Brothers and reprinted from *Microbiology, General and Applied* by permission of W. B. Sarles, W. C. Frazier, J. B. Wilson, and S. G. Knight; copyright 1951 by Harper & Brothers.

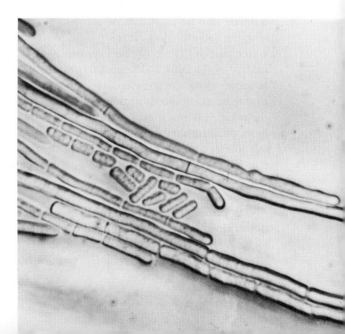

that, in the presence of organisms of a different species, a given bacterium, yeast, or mold may exhibit reactions which differ markedly from those shown in pure culture. There are reactions other than the ones above that two or more species can bring about when they are growing together, but these are not of concern to the dairy microbiologist. The following examples will illustrate the reactions defined above.

In mixed starter cultures containing *Streptococcus lactis, Leuconostoc dextranicum,* and *Leuconostoc citrovorum,* the function of the first species is to produce acid from lactose, and the function of the latter two species is to ferment the citric acid of milk to volatile compounds. *Streptococcus lactis* grown alone in milk produces only small amounts of volatile compounds, and the leuconostocs are unable to ferment citric acid until a low pH is obtained. Together these organisms perform a function that none can carry out alone, and this is an example of a synergistic effect. See Chapter 11 for further studies on these bacteria.

In the manufacture of Swiss cheese, lactic acid bacteria ferment lactose to lactic acid. This compound is then converted to propionic acid by propionibacteria, and it is the salt (propionate) of this acid which is partly responsible for the characteristic flavor of Swiss cheese. This is a metabiotic effect in which the end-products of one species are used as foodstuffs by a second species. Another, and perhaps theoretical, example of metabiosis is suggested by consideration of the fate of raw milk allowed to stand at room temperature. First, lactic acid bacteria of the *Streptococcus lactis* type ferment the lactose until sufficient lactic acid is present to precipitate the casein. When a concentration of 1 per cent lactic acid is present, the lactic cocci become inactive and organisms such as *Lactobacillus casei* continue the fermentation until about 2 per cent lactic acid is produced. *Geotrichum candidum* may establish itself on the surface of the coagulated milk and oxidize the lactic acid to carbon dioxide and water. When the acidity is sufficiently reduced and no more lactose is present for the lactobacilli to ferment, proteolytic sporeformers develop and decompose the casein. Finally, only water, and a little fat (also eventually decomposed) remain. The organic matter of the milk has been "mineralized," that is, reduced to simple inorganic substances such as carbon dioxide, ammonia, and hydrogen sulfide; and these compounds or their oxidation products are again ready to enter the cycle of living things. As a final example, it may be noted that the surfaces of some surface ripened cheeses like Limburger, contain numerous salt-tolerant yeasts, especially during the early ripening stages. These yeasts contribute to the growth of acid-sensitive, proteolytic organisms such as *Bacterium linens* by decreasing curd acidity and secreting growth factors for such organisms (48).

A common example of antibiosis is the acid production, by lactic acid bacteria, which is known to inhibit proteolytic bacteria (particularly sporeformers) by producing an unfavorable pH for their development. Organisms that are "acido-proteolytic" would not be affected in this case. It is necessary that the acid be formed prior to the growth of proteolytic organisms if the latter are to be inhibited. Another example of antibiosis is the inhibition of lactic acid starter organisms when cultured in reconstituted milk. If extensive microbial growth occurred in the milk prior to the drying process, substances inhibitory to the starter organisms might be formed. Some of these substances might not be inactivated during drying and might therefore be present in the reconstituted milk. The production of nisin by *Streptococcus lactis* and diplococcin by *Streptococcus cremoris* has been considered earlier in this chapter.

There are a number of instances in which a defect of milk or dairy products is brought about by the associative action of microorganisms. Some examples of these are the following: *Candida pseudotropicalis* ( *Torula cremoris*) and *Torulopsis sphaerica* have been implicated in outbreaks of yeasty cream. However, when these yeasts act on cream alone, the typical foaming observed under natural conditions does not occur. This is explained by the fact that without coagulation the gas escapes as rapidly as it is produced. However, under practical circumstances, associative action with acid-forming bacteria which produce the necessary coagulation provides the physical conditions required for the appearance of this defect.

In the production of discolorations, examples of associative action are known. *Pseudomonas cyanogenes* does not produce a blue pigment when grown in milk as a pure culture. The reaction of the milk becomes alkaline, and a brownish color is observed. In association with acid-producing microorganisms (such as *Streptococcus lactis*) a definite blue color is observed, presumably owing to the color of the pigment of *Pseudomonas cyanogenes* under acid conditions. The blue color is not produced by *Pseudomonas cyanogenes* alone when in an acid medium but by the two organisms growing together.

## DAIRY MICROORGANISMS
## AS PHYSIOLOGICAL GROUPS

Occasionally it is necessary to know not only the physiological reactions of a particular group of microorganisms, but also the reactions of the groups of microorganisms capable of bringing about a specific change in milk and its products. In this section, the various organisms producing specific changes in milk products and the conditions requisite for these changes will be considered.

Acid formation and acid coagulation by fermentation of lactose in milk can be brought about by organisms from a number of taxonomic groups. *Streptococcus lactis* and *Streptococcus cremoris* (and other lactic streptococci) will produce an acid curd in raw milk which is allowed to stand at room temperature. *Streptococcus thermophilus* will bring about the same change at about 45°C. (113°F.). Lactic acid-forming rods of the homofermentative type may also bring about acid coagulation of raw milk, although they are usually outgrown by other organisms in the mixed population. *Lactobacillus casei* will coagulate milk at room temperature; *Lactobacillus acidophilus* and *Lactobacillus bulgaricus* produce acid optimally at about 40°C. (104°F.) and at even higher temperatures in the case of *Lactobacillus thermophilus*. The maximum acidity produced in milk by cultures of lactic streptococci is approximately 1 per cent, calculated as lactic acid. The lactobacilli produce up to 2 per cent acid and occasionally more. Lactobacilli in raw milk held at suitable temperatures may continue to grow after the lactic streptococci are inhibited by excess acid formation.

The typical clean, sour flavor usually caused by *Streptococcus lactis* and by certain lactobacilli is due to the fact that these organisms are relatively non-proteolytic and non-lipolytic. Other organisms, such as *Streptococcus liquefaciens,* the coliform bacteria, and certain aerobic spore-formers like *Bacillus coagulans,* produce large amounts of lactic acid, but the sour flavor is associated with undesirable flavors—flavors that are the result of partial protein and fat degradation by these organisms, and of their production of volatile acids and other compounds from lactose.

If milk is heated to fairly high temperature, so that most of the lactic acid bacteria are killed, certain lactic-acid-producing aerobic sporogenous bacteria may grow. This is especially true if the heated milk is held at from 37°C. to 55°C. (98.6°F. to 131°F.). In this case *Bacillus coagulans,* if present, may grow and produce sufficient acid to coagulate the milk. Studies on outbreaks of coagulation in evaporated milk have implicated this organism.

In the case of *Streptococcus lactis,* milk is coagulated when pH 4.6–4.7 is reached. This coagulum is smooth and firm with no evidence of whey or bubbles. This is the type of coagulation desired in the beginning of the cheese making process and in the preparation of many cultured milks. The coliform bacteria, such as *Escherichia coli* and *Aerobacter aerogenes,* may coagulate milk, but the curd or coagulum usually will appear shrunken and weak.

Another type of coagulation is known as sweet curdling. *Streptococcus liquefaciens* and certain aerobic spore-formers commonly cause this reaction. An extracellular enzyme similar to rennin is liberated, and this enzyme causes the casein to precipitate in the form of small flecks of curd. The precipitation occurs before any appreciable quantity of acid is produced. Occasionally this type of curdling may be observed in raw cream when it is delivered from the farm and in pasteurized milk and cream which has been stored a long time. Usually a bitter flavor accompanies this type of curdling. If all of the above organisms were absent, *Micrococcus luteus* or related dairy micrococci might acidify the milk without coagulation.

Gas production by microorganisms in milk results in a gassy defect, and carbon dioxide is the most common gas produced. In the manufacture of Swiss cheese and of certain fermented milks, this fermentation is desirable, but for the most part, gas production in dairy products is undesirable. The coliform bacteria, lactose-fermenting yeasts, and certain species of

*Clostridium* are the most important organisms involved in this fermentation.

Gassiness often may be observed in Cheddar cheese (see Chapter 13) and more commonly in certain nondescript Brick types or "beer cheeses." The defect is manifest in the body of the cheese as small holes, about one or two millimeters in diameter, with smooth shiny inside surfaces. "Slits" may be produced in Cheddar cheese made with starters containing leuconostocs, since these heterofermentative lactic acid bacteria produce carbon dioxide.

Gas and acid formation by the *Escherichia-Aerobacter* group is possible wherever excess utensil, feed, soil, or manure contamination exists. These organisms grow well from 10°C. to 37°C. (50°F. to 98.6°F.) and may grow to some degree above and below this range. Gas formation is not conspicuous because the organisms do not coagulate casein during the stages of most vigorous gas production. Lactose-fermenting yeasts—for example, some species of *Candida, Torulopsis,* and *Saccharomyces*—produce alcohol and carbon dioxide in milk and cream. Foaminess develops when these yeasts grow in association with acid-producing bacteria. When milk and cream are partially coagulated, the gas escapes as a foamy mass. These yeasts are introduced by soil, utensil, feed, or manure contamination. In products that have been exposed to high processing temperatures, anaerobic bacteria of the genus *Clostridium* may, occasionally, produce gassy defects. These defects probably occur when manure and soil contamination has been heavy. Gassy defects in cheese have been ascribed to *Clostridium pasteurianum, Clostridium butyricum,* and *Clostridium sporogenes.* Aerobic spore-formers like *Bacillus polymyxa* ferment lactose to carbon dioxide and hydrogen plus volatile substances. This organism has been found to cause gassy defects in cheese.

Proteolytic reactions (casein decomposition) may be brought about by a variety of organisms. Aerobic and anaerobic spore-formers will bring about proteolysis in products heated sufficiently high to kill off bacteria which form lactic acid. In the case of certain reconstituted milk powders, holding at room temperature for a short time results in the proteolysis of the casein and concomitant off-flavors. Pseudomonads, if present, are active in milk and cream stored under refrigeration. They may attain enormous numbers after a period of storage at low temperatures and may initiate proteolytic changes with the production of very objectionable odors and flavors.

Certain flavors may be pronounced for several hours or days, depending upon the product, the temperature of storage, and other environmental factors. Often a flavor will appear only to disappear shortly afterwards, thus indicating that a series of reactions is taking place. Proteolysis by microorganisms to the extent of flavor change may be desirable in cheese ripening, but it is highly objectionable in other dairy products. Mild proteolysis, which is detectable only by chemical analysis, is brought about by many microorganisms usually not considered to be proteolytic.

*Streptococcus liquefaciens* coagulates milk at low acidity and then attacks the casein. Generally it is of slight importance in raw milk and cream. If it did grow, bitter flavors due to products of proteolysis would result. Other lactic acid cocci and rods show weak proteolytic activity; for example, the lactic organisms involved in ripening certain cheeses. The acid-proteolytic coccus, *Micrococcus caseolyticus,* produces changes similar to those of *Streptococcus liquefaciens.*

Hydrolysis of fats is termed lipolysis (fat splitting). A number of bacterial and mold species are lipolytic. Butterfat is characteristic in that it contains lower chain fatty acids such as butyric and caproic acids. When these are present in free form in dairy products, they usually are objectionable because of the rancid flavor which they impart to the product.

Among the lipolytic organisms of interest in dairy microbiology are *Pseudomonas fragi, Pseudomonas fluorescens, Achromobacter lipolyticum, Candida lipolytica, Geotrichum candidum,* and *Penicillium roqueforti.* Since fatty acids arise from the hydrolytic action of lipase on fats, rancid flavors may result, especially when butyric acid is a component of the fat, as is the situation with butterfat. Caproic, caprylic, and capric acids may contribute to a lesser extent to rancidity. The organisms mentioned above occur in soil, water, air, and utensils. Some of them develop at temperatures down to freezing. Cream and butter made from cream infected with lipolytic organisms can develop rancidity during storage at refrigeration temperatures.

Ropiness in milk and cream is due to the synthesis of capsular material (mucins and galactans) by microorganisms. There is an increase in viscosity of the material, and it may be pulled into threads or strands. This defect is noted most frequently in milk held at about 13°C. (55.4°F.). Organisms implicated are *Alcaligenes viscosus, Streptococcus cremoris* var. *hollandicus, Escherichia-Aerobacter* group, *Micrococcus* species, and *Lactobacillus bulgaricus.* These organisms enter the milk supply as contaminants from water, feed, soil, manure, or utensils. Species of lactobacilli and *Streptococcus cremoris* var. *hollandicus* show ropiness when acid develops. Pure cultures gain or lose this property capriciously.

The growth of microorganisms in dairy products may bring about a number of flavor changes. One of the most common, yet seldom recognized unless pronounced, changes that may be observed in raw milk and cream as they are delivered from the dairy farm is the development of a malty flavor. This flavor is often called burnt or caramel. Maltiness occurs most frequently during the summer months, and its presence almost invariably indicates a lack of proper cooling. This is understandable, for *Streptococcus lactis,* including the *maltigenes* variety when present, usually outgrows other species in milk at a temperature of approximately 21°C. (69.8°F.). Lack of proper cooling will allow extensive growth of this organism. Maltiness may be observed in butter (see Chapter 14), and when associated with other off-flavors, a musty-like odor may occur. The malty principle has been identified as 3-methylbutanal (29). There is evidence to indicate that almost any type of flavor in milk may be caused or duplicated by microbial activity. At any rate, there is a host of miscellaneous, but distinct and at times troublesome, flavor changes which may occur in milk. The occurrence of these changes often results in rejection of milk at the receiving platform, or in complaints by consumers. Perhaps the most common of these miscellaneous changes are the "barny" and "cowy" flavors. Both of these may be due to absorption of odors from the barn, but they are often caused by bacterial action on butterfat.

Bitterness in milk may be caused by several bacterial species and by certain yeasts. When caused by the latter, a yeasty or fermented odor is associated with the bitterness. *Streptococcus liquefaciens* often is the causative organism of bitter flavor in milk, cream, and cheese, and certain aerobic spore-formers closely related to *Bacillus subtilis* are particularly troublesome in evaporated milk.

An odor similar to that of potatoes occasionally may be observed in raw milk or cream. This defect has been ascribed to two bacterial species, *Pseudomonas graveolens* and *Pseudomonas mucidolens*. Fishy, fruity, and metallic flavors often are of bacterial origin.

There are a number of microorganisms that produce color changes in dairy products. For the most part, color development is objectionable. Surface discoloration of butter and cheese is a rather common defect. On butter this change is usually due to the colored mycelium or spores of mold species belonging to the genera *Penicillium, Alternaria,* and *Cladosporium.* In extreme cases, mold growth may be visible throughout the body of butter packed in tubs or boxes. A particularly objectionable black surface discoloration of butter is caused by a bacterial species, *Pseudomonas nigrifaciens.* On cheese the colored molds, particularly the green *Penicillium* species, appear in the cracks of the wax coating or beneath the wrapper. In aged cheese, mold growth may extend some distance along the fissures that form as the cheese dries out. Certain yeasts may produce pink or brownish discolored spots on the surface or in the interior of cheese.

Color changes in milk and other fluid milk products are rarely observed, and consequently they are of little practical importance. In past years, when raw milk was widely distributed, a number of outbreaks of blue coloration of milk occurred. These outbreaks usually were due to *Pseudomonas cyanogenes.* The blue pigment produced by this organism is water soluble and is discernible only in the presence of acid.

Yellow and red colorations of milk have been reported, but these, like the blue coloration, are of no practical importance. The organisms most commonly reported as being involved in the yellow and red colorations are *Pseudomonas synxantha* and *Serratia marcescens,* respectively.

Attention should be directed to a group of organisms which, though not taxonomically homogeneous, pose a common problem. These are cold tolerant or psychrophilic bacteria. Distinction is sometimes made between those bacteria which are able to grow at 20°C. (68°F.) or below but which grow better at higher temperatures and those which grow best at 5°C. to 10°C. (41°F. to 50°F.). It is probable that the differences are quantitative rather than qualitative. Species of asporogenous, gram-negative rods such as *Pseudomonas* have been most often involved in outbreaks of spoilage encountered at refrigeration temperatures. Occasionally species of soil and water forms like *Alcaligenes, Achromobacter,* and *Flavobacterium* are found. Most cold tolerant organisms are killed by pasteurization so that their appearance in products so treated must be ascribed to unsanitary utensils or to contaminated water supply. It is obvious that products coming in contact with such water—for example, butter and cottage cheese—will be susceptible to the action of these organisms. Thus cases of "surface taint" of butter caused by *Pseudomonas putrefaciens* and rancid, fishy, and fruity defects caused by other pseudomonads might arise from this source. Discolorations and off-odors in cottage cheese have been traced to pseudomonads and species of *Alcaligenes.* Coliform bacteria may also grow at 10°C. (50°F.). Equipment is freed from these organisms by the use of hypochlorite solutions containing 100 to 200 ppm available chlorine.

In addition to cold tolerant organisms, two groups distinguished on the basis of thermal relationships are the thermoduric and the thermophilic bacteria. The thermoduric bacteria constitute a miscellaneous group with the common property of being able to survive normal pasteurization temperatures. Among the thermoduric bacteria are species of *Micrococcus, Streptococcus, Bacillus, Microbacterium,* and *Lactobacillus.* Thermophilic bacteria are those that have an optimum growth temperature above 50°C. (122°F.). These organisms would be able to grow in milk pasteurized by the vat method or in any other products held at 50°C. (122°F.) for some time. Most of the thermophilic bacteria are species of *Bacillus,* but *Lactobacillus thermophilus* is an exception.

In this discussion several species of bacteria have been mentioned, each of which is responsible for a specific flavor or physical change in milk. Many other changes just as important also occur, as was indicated in the previous section, through the synergistic activity of two or more species. Changes that result from this associative activity often are difficult to reproduce experimentally; yet they occur with great regularity under natural conditions. This presents a challenging problem to the dairy microbiologist, who often is concerned with the elimination of the cause, and with the control, of defective products.

It is significant that, in the case of many defects in dairy products, there is no way of predicting with any great degree of certainty whether the defect will occur. All too often the first indication of the presence of the defect is obtained through the senses of taste and smell, and at which time it is much too late to apply control measures. Very little success has been obtained through the use of qualitative or quantitative, analytical chemical or bacteriological procedures for the detection of predisposing conditions which would indicate future development of defective products. There is need for further investigations in this regard.

# References

1. Abd-el-Malek, Y., and T. Gibson, Studies in the bacteriology of milk, I: the streptococci of milk, *J. Dairy Research,* 15 (1948): 233–248.

2. ———, Studies in the bacteriology of milk, II: the staphylococci and micrococci of milk, *J. Dairy Research,* 15 (1948): 249–260.

3. ———, Studies in the bacteriology of milk, III: the corynebacteria of milk, *J. Dairy Research,* 19 (1952): 153–159.

4. ———, Studies in the bacteriology of milk, IV: the gram-negative rods, *J. Dairy Research,* 19 (1952): 294–301.

5. Ainsworth, C. G., and G. R. Bisby, *A Dictionary of the Fungi,* 3rd Ed. Surrey, England: Commonwealth Mycological Institute, 1950.

6. Albert, J. O., H. F. Long, and B. W. Hammer, Classification of organisms important in dairy products, IV: *Bacterium linens, Iowa Agr. Exp. Sta. Research Bull. 328,* 1944.

7. Alford, J. A., and W. C. Frazier, Effect of micrococci on the development of flavor when added to Cheddar cheese made from pasteurized milk, *J. Dairy Sci.,* 33 (1950): 115–120.

8. Anderson, A. W., and P. R. Elliker, The nutritional requirements of lactic streptococci isolated from starter cultures, I: growth in a synthetic medium, *J. Dairy Sci.,* 36 (1953): 161–167.

9. Babel, F. J., and B. W. Hammer, Bacteriology of cheese, IV: factors affecting the ripening of Swiss-type cheese made from pasteurized milk, *Iowa Agr. Exp. Sta. Research Bull. 264,* 1939.

10. Breed, R. S., E. G. D. Murray, and A. P. Hitchens, *Bergey's Manual of Determinative Bacteriology,* 6th Ed. Baltimore: Williams and Wilkins, 1948.

11. Briggs, C. A. E., A note on the serological classification of *Streptococcus diacetilactis* (Matuzewski et al.), *J. Dairy Research,* 19 (1952): 167–168.

12. Briggs, C. A. E., and L. G. M. Newland, The serological classification of *Streptococcus cremoris, J. Dairy Research,* 19 (1952): 160–168.

13. ———, Observations on the serological typing of group N ('lactic') streptococci, *J. Dairy Research,* 20 (1953): 189–197.

14. Briggs, M., The classification of lactobacilli by means of physiological tests, *J. Gen. Microbiol.,* 9 (1953): 234–248.

15. Briggs, M., and C. A. E. Briggs, The lactobacilli: a review of the literature with special reference to taxonomy, *Dairy Sci. Abstr.,* 16 (1954): 252–268.

16. Collins, E. B., F. E. Nelson, and C. E. Parmelee, Acetate and oleate requirements of the lactic group of streptococci, *J. Bacteriol.*, 59 (1950): 69–74.

17. Crossley, E. L., The coliform flora of milk and dairy products, *J. Dairy Research*, 14 (1946): 233–282.

18. Doetsch, R. N., and M. J. Pelczar, The microbacteria, I: morphological and physiological characteristics, *J. Bacteriol.*, 56 (1948): 37–49.

19. Elliker, P. R., The problem of bacteriophage in the dairy industry, *J. Milk and Food Technol.*, 14 (1951): 13–16, 44.

20. ———, Fine points of sanitation that up cottage cheese quality, *Food Eng.*, 26 (1954): 79–82.

21. Enright, J. B., R. C. Thomas, and P. A. Mullett, Q fever and its relation to dairy products, *J. Milk and Food Technol.*, 16 (1953): 263–266.

22. Frost, W. D., and M. A. Engelbrecht, *The Streptococci, Their Descriptions, and Distribution, with Special Reference to Those Found in Milk*. Madison, Wisc.: Wildorf, 1940.

23. Gonshery, L., and P. A. Hansen, Proteolytic activity of crude extracts of *Lactobacillus casei, Virginia J. Sci.*, 2 (1951): 307.

24. Hansen, P. A., A study in cheese ripening: the influence of autolyzed cells of *Streptococcus cremoris* and *Streptococcus lactis* on the development of *Lactobacillus casei*, *J. Dairy Sci.*, 24 (1941): 969–976.

25. Hirsch, A., The evolution of the lactic streptococci, *J. Dairy Research*, 19 (1952): 290–293.

26. Hucker, G. J., and C. S. Pederson, A study of the physiology and classification of the genus *Leuconostoc*, *Zentr. Bakteriol. Parasitenk. Abt. II*, 85 (1931): 65–114.

27. Huebner, R. J., W. L. Jellison, M. D. Beck, and F. P. Wilcox, Q fever studies in southern California, III: effects of pasteurization on survival of *C. burnetii* in naturally infected milk, *Public Health Repts. (U. S.)*, (1949): 499–511.

28. Hussong, R. V., H. F. Long, and B. W. Hammer, Classification of organisms important in dairy products, II: *Pseudomonas fragi, Iowa Agr. Exp. Sta. Research Bull. 225*, 1937.

29. Jackson, H. W., and M. E. Morgan, Identity and origin of the malty aroma substance from milk cultures of *Streptococcus lactis* var. *maltigenes*, *J. Dairy Sci.*, 37 (1954): 1316–1324.

30. Johns, A. T., The mechanism of the propionic acid fermentation, *J. Gen. Microbiol.*, 5 (1951): 337–345.

31. Johns, C. K., Differences in sensitivity of lactic starters to antibiotics, *J. Dairy Sci.*, 36 (1953): 1241–1247.

32. Kambar, C. S., G. W. Reinbold, and R. V. Hussong, A plating method for the isolation and enumeration of propionibacteria, *J. Dairy Sci.*, 35 (1952): 915–919.

33. Kaplan, A. S., and J. L. Melnick, Effect of milk and cream on thermal inactivation of human poliomyelitis virus, *Am. J. Public Health*, 42 (1952): 525–534.

34. ———, Effect of milk and other dairy products on the thermal inactivation of Coxsackie viruses, *Am. J. Public Health*, 44 (1954): 1174–1184.

35. Kizer, D. E., and M. L. Speck, Observations on the acetate and citrate metabolism of *Streptococcus lactis* and *Streptococcus cremoris*, *J. Dairy Sci.*, 38 (1955): 96–102.

36. Knight, B. C. J. G., and H. Proom, A comparative survey of the nutrition and physiology of mesophilic species in the genus *Bacillus, J. Gen. Microbiol.,* 4 (1950): 508–538.

37. Lancefield, R. C., A serological differentiation of human and other groups of hemolytic streptococci, *J. Exp. Med.,* 57 (1933): 571–595.

38. Lodder, J., and N. J. W. Kreger-Van Rij, *The Yeasts: A Taxonomic Study.* New York: Interscience, 1952.

39. Long, H. F., and B. W. Hammer, Studies on *Alcaligenes viscosus, Iowa State Coll. J. Sci.,* 10 (1936): 261–265.

40. ———, Classification of organisms important in dairy products, III: *Pseudomonas putrefaciens, Iowa Agr. Exp. Sta. Research Bull. 285,* 1941.

41. Maskell, K. T., R. E. Hargrove, and R. P. Tittsler, A preliminary report on the bacteriology of Provolone and Romano cheese (abstract), *J. Dairy Sci.,* 34 (1951): 476.

42. Mathews, F. P., Poliomyelitis epidemic, possibly milk-borne, in a naval station, Portland, Oregon, *Am. J. Hyg.,* 49 (1949): 1–7.

43. Mattick, A. T. R., and A. Hirsch, The streptococci and antibiotics. *XIIth International Dairy Congress, Papers and Communications,* Volume 2, Section II (1949): 546–550.

44. Meiklejohn, G., Viral studies on the etiology of epidemic diarrhea of new born, *Calif. Med.,* 67 (1947): 238–240.

45. Murphy, W. J., L. M. Petrie, and S. D. Work, Outbreak of infectious hepatitis, apparently milk borne, *Am. J. Public Health,* 36 (1946): 169–173.

46. Nashif, S. A., and F. E. Nelson, Some studies on microbacteria from Iowa dairy products, *Appl. Microbiol.,* 1 (1953): 47–52.

47. Orla-Jensen, S., *The Lactic Acid Streptococci.* Copenhagen: Munksgaard, 1919.

48. Purko, M., W. O. Nelson, and W. A. Wood, The associative action between certain yeasts and *Bacterium linens, J. Dairy Sci.,* 34 (1951): 699–705.

49. Rogosa, M., R. F. Wiseman, J. A. Mitchell, M. N. Disraely, and A. J. Beaman, Species differentiation of oral lactobacilli from man including descriptions of *Lactobacillus salivarius* nov. spec. and *Lactobacillus cellobiosus* nov. spec., *J. Bacteriol.,* 65 (1953): 681–699.

50. Sharpe, M. E., A serological classification of lactobacilli, *J. Gen. Microbiol.,* 12 (1955): 107–122.

51. Shattock, P. M. F., The faecal streptococci. *XII International Dairy Congress, Papers and Communications,* Volume 2, Section II (1949): 598–604.

52. Shaw, C., J. M. Still, and S. T. Cowan, Staphylococci and their classification, *J. Gen. Microbiol.,* 5 (1951): 1010–1023.

53. Sherman, J. M., The streptococci, *Bacteriol. Revs.,* 1 (1937): 1–97.

54. Skinner, C. W., C. W. Emmons, and H. M. Tsuchiya, *Henrici's Molds, Yeasts, and Actinomycetes,* 2nd Ed. New York: Wiley, 1948.

55. Smith, N. R., R. E. Gordon, and F. E. Clark, Aerobic sporeforming bacteria, *USDA Monograph No. 16,* 1952.

56. Speck, M. L., A study of the genus *Microbacterium, J. Dairy Sci.,* 26 (1943): 533–543.

57. *Standard Methods for the Examination of Dairy Products,* 10th Ed. New York: American Public Health Association, 1953.

58. Stone, M. J., and A. Rowlands, "Broken" or "bitty" cream in raw and pasteurized milk, *J. Dairy Research,* 19 (1952): 51–62.

59. Swartling, P. F., Biochemical and serological properties of some citric acid fermenting streptococci from milk and dairy products, *J. Dairy Research,* 18 (1951): 256–267.

60. Tittsler, R. P., C. S. Pederson, E. E. Snell, D. Hendlin, and C. F. Niven, Symposium on the lactic acid bacteria, *Bacteriol. Revs.,* 16 (1952): 227–260.

61. Van Der Zant, W. C., and F. E. Nelson, Proteolysis by *Streptococcus lactis* grown in milk with and without controlled pH, *J. Dairy Sci.,* 36 (1953): 1104–1111.

62. ———, Amino acids and peptides in the protein-free fraction of milk before and after incubation with *S. lactis, J. Dairy Sci.,* 37 (1954): 790–794.

63. van Niel, C. B., *The Propionic Acid Bacteria.* Haarlem, Netherlands: Boissevain, 1928.

64. Wagenaar, R. O., The bacteriology of surface taint in butter: a review, *J. Dairy Sci.,* 35 (1952): 403–423.

65. Wheater, D. M., The characteristics of *Lactobacillus acidophilus* and *Lactobacillus bulgaricus, J. Gen. Microbiol.,* 12 (1955): 123–132.

66. ———, The characteristics of *Lactobacillus plantarum, L. helveticus* and *L. casei., J. Gen. Microbiol.,* 12 (1955): 133–139.

67. Whitehead, H. R., Bacteriophage in cheese manufacture, *Bacteriol. Revs.,* 17 (1953): 109–124.

68. Yale, M. W., "Bacteria of the *Escherichia-Aerobacter* group in dairy products," in *B. W. Hammer Panegyric.* Ames, Iowa: Collegiate, 1937.

# 3

# Factors affecting growth of microorganisms

The term growth, as applied to higher organisms such as animals, commonly is concerned with increase in protoplasmic mass and does not apply to reproduction or to increase in numbers. In microbiology the term has acquired a somewhat different meaning; although increase in protoplasmic mass may be meant, increase in numbers of organisms (reproduction) more often is the criterion of growth. The situation is complicated further by the fact that the increase in numbers may be determined in more than one way. An increase in "total" count may be determined by enumerating all cells; procedures such as direct microscopic count or estimation of numbers by the increase in optical density of a suspension may be employed. The "viable" count may be used, the cells enumerated being those capable of forming colonies under the specific conditions employed for plating and incubation. An increase in enzymatic activity, such as might be measured by acid production, may be a measure of growth. These various procedures may not give the same results, because changes in one criterion of growth may not be paralleled by changes of similar magnitude in another criterion. Considerable space could be devoted to a discussion of reasons for the lack of complete parallelisms, but such discussions are beyond the scope of this presentation. Some of the factors influencing population estimates will be discussed in Chapter 5. For more detailed discussions the reader should consult one or more of the textbooks on bacterial physiology (4, 19, 24).

Milk as it comes from the udders of healthy cows already contains some bacteria. As will be discussed in Chapter 6, additional bacteria and other microorganisms get into milk almost from the moment it leaves the udder. The numbers of these microorganisms are not great under favorable conditions of production and handling; under unfavorable conditions the numbers may be large. The count of these microorganisms may increase very rapidly if the product is held under conditions favorable for growth. Spoilage may result if the microorganism populations become great enough to effect considerable change in the product. Under some conditions disease-producing organisms, if present, may grow; their growth would increase the possibility that disease might result from consumption of the product. The presence of microorganisms of certain types may be inhibitory to growth of desirable organisms. In many dairy products the aim is to minimize microbial growth; in other products the purpose is to foster the growth of desirable organisms while inhibiting the development of those that are undesirable. Proper control of conditions in the environment may be used either to minimize development of undesirable microorganisms or to promote development of desirable types. Knowledge of how these factors may be used in controlling development of microorganisms in dairy products is essential for intelligent handling and processing.

### MICROBIAL GROWTH

Bacteria increase in numbers by a process of simple binary fission. One bacterial cell increases in size and divides into two similar cells. Each of the new cells may in turn divide to become two cells. Each division produces what is termed a "new generation" of cells. Theoretically, there are 2, 4, 8, 16, 32, 64, 128 and 256 cells in the second, third, fourth, fifth, sixth, seventh, eighth and ninth generations, respectively. This is what is known as a logarithmic series, for the population doubles with each successive generation. Under very favorable conditions, some bacteria produce a new generation in 15 minutes or less; under unfavorable conditions, 24 hours or more may be needed for each generation. Bacteria from an old culture, when they are placed in an adequate medium at a temperature favorable to growth, require some time to become adjusted before beginning to reproduce at the maximum rate. This period of adjustment is known as the lag phase. The lag phase is represented by section AB of the idealized growth curve shown in Figure 3.1. In this figure the numbers of bacteria are plotted on a logarithmic scale. This means that each ten-fold increase occupies the same distance on the vertical scale (an increase from 100,000 to 1,000,000 occupies the same space as an increase from 1 to 10). This form of plotting is necessary because, with the doubling of population in each generation, a simple arithmetic scale would be inadequate for plotting the large populations of the later generations. The period during which the successive generations are appearing at a relatively constant rate is the period of logarithmic increase; the straight line CD in Figure 3.1 shows this period. Eventually a time is reached when conditions are less favorable for the appearance of new generations. The rate of population increase becomes less rapid. A point finally is reached where the number of new cells produced just equals the number of old cells dying because of unfavorable conditions. This period is the maximum stationary phase and is shown by EF. The unfavorable conditions continue, and the cells in the culture begin to die off rather rapidly; thus phase GH of the growth curve is entered. If the culture is not transferred to a new medium under favor-

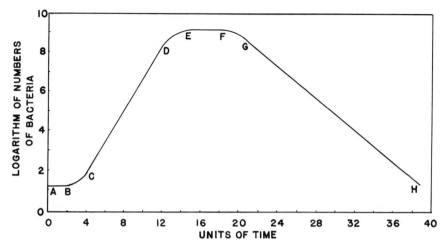

**Figure 3.1**    An idealized growth curve, showing the logarithm of bacterial population plotted against time.

able conditions, the old cells all will die eventually and the culture will be lost.

Many factors influence the shape of the growth curve. The curve of Figure 3.1 is presented for illustration only; most curves obtained experimentally would deviate somewhat from this example. Various organisms differ considerably in their reactions to a standardized set of conditions. Some bacteria will not grow at all under conditions that may be optimum for others. Variations in medium composition, associated organisms, moisture level, temperature, oxygen supply, and pH are only a few of the many factors that may influence noticeably the shape of a growth curve. Proper control of one or more of these conditions may be used either to minimize development of undesirable microorganisms or to promote development of desirable types. Knowledge of how these factors may be used in controlling development of microorganisms in dairy products is essential for intelligent handling and processing.

The yeasts and the yeast-like organisms important in dairy products nearly all reproduce by a process known as budding. Figure 2.17, page 37, illustrates one phase of this process. The original yeast cell or "mother" cell forms a small sac or "bud" into which one portion of the divided nucleus moves. The bud continues to grow in size until it becomes as large as the mother cell and is essentially indistinguishable from it. The resulting "daughter" cell may split from the mother cell before either cell begins the budding process all over again, or it may remain attached for a time. In the case of some yeasts, a chain of cells known as a "pseudomycelium" may form if the conditions are correct. However, the yeasts do not form the true mycelium of the more highly organized molds. Because the yeasts reproduce primarily by a system in which one independent cell becomes two independent cells, the same general conditions which apply to the growth curve for bacteria apply to the growth curve for yeasts. Ascospores, both sexual and asexual, are formed by some yeasts, but they are not important among those yeasts found in dairy products and thus will not be discussed here.

Molds usually initiate growth by means of a spore that germinates in much the same manner as does a seed of higher plants. In most molds the spore is a single cell. This germinated spore forms a mold filament which increases in length by growing out from one end. The filament branches and rebranches as it grows, being similar to a tree in this respect. When the new cells form, they usually remain attached to the old cells. The filaments become differentiated into vegetative and reproductive types as the mold colony develops. Some molds go through a sexual reproductive cycle, but such a cycle usually is not important under the conditions that prevail in dairy products. In asexual reproduction, the aerial filaments may simply pinch off conidia or "spores" at the end, as in the case of *Geotrichum candidum;* they may undergo special branching followed by the pinching off of conidia, as in the case of *Penicillium* species; they may produce special sac-like structures within which the spores are produced, as with *Mucor* and *Rhizopus* species. Because of the multicellular and otherwise more complex nature of the mold, growth usually is measured either by diameter of the colony or by weight of the total mycelium. The growth curve of single-celled organisms such as bacteria and yeasts is not applicable to molds because of the multicellular nature of the latter. However, growth of all three of these microorganism types is controlled by the same factors, although these factors sometimes are operative at different levels with the several organism types.

## THE CONCEPT OF MICROENVIRONMENT

In considering the conditions which permit growth of microorganisms, one is apt to think in terms of the average values for the entire mass of material in which growth takes place. This concept undoubtedly would be correct in the middle of a large container of completely dissolved chemicals where the system was completely homogeneous. However, very few situations exist in which at least minor differences in physical or chemical environment are not found. Even in a container of water, the conditions where the water contacts either the container or the air are different from those in the mass of the water. Where the surfaces of the microorganisms are in contact with the water surrounding them, the conditions may be quite different from those in most of the solution. Nutrients, toxic products, and other materials may accumulate at the organism-solution interface, or the oxidation-reduction potential or the hydrogen ion concentration may be different.

Because of the usually small size of the cells of microorganisms and because of the non-uniform character of many of the materials in which the organisms may be found, the conditions prevailing in an extremely small part of the total system may determine whether growth occurs at all or whether growth is slow or rapid. Because of these considerations, the term "microenvironment" is introduced. The term covers the conditions existing in a very small section immediately adjacent to the organism. Whether the organism will grow or die, the rate at which it will grow, and the type of change that it will cause depend upon the microenvironment. The average conditions in the mass of material (the macroenvironment) may be quite unsatisfactory for organism growth, even though the localized conditions of the microenvironment will permit extensive development and biochemical activity. As will be discussed in greater detail in Chapters 13 and 14, the concept of microenvironment is particularly important in cheese and in butter because of the internal heterogeneity of these products. In butter, for example, an organism may grow well in a moisture droplet into which no salt has been worked. However, there may be a droplet in fairly close proximity that is infected but that will not permit organism growth because the salt concentration is above that tolerated by the organism. Similar considerations could apply to pH, oxidation-reduction potential, concentration of nutrients, and many other determining factors.

### WATER RELATIONSHIPS

Metabolic activity, as it exists on the earth, can occur only in the presence of water. This is true whether the organism being studied is a man, a tree, or a bacterium. Water serves as the medium in which food for the organism is dissolved; without such solution, the nutrients could not reach and enter into the cells in which they are to be used either for energy production or for synthesis of protoplasm. Water serves as the material in which waste products of cell metabolism are carried away. Water enters directly into many of the chemical reactions necessary for life processes. In the hydrolysis of proteins, fats, and complex carbohydrates, the hydrogen and hydroxyl ions of water are introduced into the reaction as the simpler compounds are formed from the more complex. An example is the hydrolysis of a simple peptide bond in a protein according to the following scheme:

$$R^1{-}\underset{\substack{|\\ C\diagdown_{OH}^O}}{\overset{\substack{H\ N\\ |\ \ |}}{C}}{-}N{-}O{-}\underset{\substack{|\\ H}}{\overset{\substack{O\ \ NH_2\\ \|\ \ |}}{C}}{-}C{-}R^2 + HOH \rightarrow R^1{-}\underset{\substack{|\\ NH_2}}{\overset{\substack{H\ O\\ |\ \ \|}}{C}}{-}C{-}OH + R^2{-}\underset{\substack{|\\ NH_2}}{\overset{\substack{H\ O\\ |\ \ \|}}{C}}{-}C{-}OH$$

By a series of these hydrolyses, the individual amino acids are freed to become available to the microorganism. Also, in the successive oxidative breakdowns of simple compounds such as the monosaccharides to yield energy for the metabolic functions of the organisms, water frequently is necessary for the hydration of some of the intermediate compounds in order to provide the necessary substratum for subsequent reactions. Water is the final end-product of the oxidation of hydrogen from organic compounds to yield energy for microbial growth. Thus, water is known to be essential for microbial activity; the question becomes one of how much water is needed for the various metabolic processes of different types of micro-organisms.

One way of keeping bacteria and many other organisms viable over long periods of time is to dry them carefully under the proper conditions. Even some of the most delicate bacteria and viruses can be held for months if they are frozen first and then dried under vacuum without thawing. For best results the culture to be dried must be at a favorable level of physiological activity and in a suitable medium. The culture must be dried by sublimation of water from the solid state to a very low level of moisture content, and it must be sealed off from oxygen. The sealing presumably avoids oxidation of critical metabolic systems during holding. The optimum conditions vary to some degree with different organisms. Many different processes based on these general principles are in use.

The minimum moisture level at which a microorganism will grow depends upon many interrelated factors. The nature of the organism concerned, the concentration of materials which influence osmotic pressure, the specific chemical nature of the dissolved materials, and the extent to which other nutritional and physical conditions approach optimum for the organism all have an influence. Thus, it becomes impossible to present figures which define the absolute levels of moisture that will permit microbial growth. Growth will not occur unless there is more water present than is necessary to hydrate proteins and other hydrophilic components of the medium and to dissolve the soluble materials. In other words, there must be "free" water, in addition to the water needed for hydration and solution, if the microorganisms are to grow.

Mossel and Westerdijk (13) have summarized considerable material that indicates that osmotic pressure is the determinant of whether the water level is high enough to permit microorganisms to grow in an environment that is otherwise favorable. The relative humidity, or relative water vapor pressure of the system, is a more easily determined measurement, and this is related mathematically to osmotic pressure. The Mossel-Westerdijk survey indicates that bacteria, yeasts, and molds usually will not grow when the relative humidity levels of the system (the atmosphere in equilibrium with the substance) decline below 95, 85 and 70 per cent, respectively, for the 3 groups of organisms. Saccharophilic yeasts and molds and halophilic bacteria are responsible for growth at the lower humidity levels for their groups of organisms. Because various products differ in their abilities to take up water, one can give no limiting moisture percentages for microbial growth except for individual products under specified conditions.

Fluid milk contains adequate amounts of water for the development of all microorganism types. The same is true of nearly all other dairy products except sweetened condensed milk and dried products of milk and whey. Dehydration, as employed for dried milks and whey, reduces the moisture level to well below that which will permit microbial growth. The moisture levels that are reasonably inhibitory to undesirable chemical changes in these products are more than adequate to control microbial growth. In sweetened condensed milk, the level of available moisture has been reduced by the addition of sugar to a point where bacteria and most yeasts will not grow because of the high osmotic pressure. Osmophilic yeasts may grow at room temperature, or somewhat above, and molds of several types will develop on the surface of the product unless air is excluded (see Chapter 9). In most of the other dairy products, moisture level is not a limiting factor for any of the organism types.

The presence of moisture is an extremely important factor in the growth of potential contaminants on utensils and equipment. If the equipment is handled and treated so that water does not remain on the metal surfaces or in any joints or possible similar pockets, then those microorganisms which may survive the sanitization treatments will be unable to grow. If incomplete drainage, high humidity, or inadequate washing permits moisture to remain or collect in equipment, opportunities will exist for development of microorganisms, which then may contaminate products subsequently handled in such equipment.

### NUTRIENT REQUIREMENTS

The substrata upon which microorganisms grow must contain the following: (a) a source of energy (an exception is the photosynthetic bacteria, which derive their energy from light and are of little or no concern in dairy products); (b) sources of the substances or the precursors of the substances which make up the cell protoplasm; and (c) minerals and possibly other soluble materials which are essential for normal functioning of enzymes and, at least in some instances, for maintenance of the proper physico-chemical state of the cell and its components. Among the various microorganisms, marked differences are shown in the types of materials which are essential for growth. Some, such as many molds and certain of the gram negative bacteria of soil and water, require only a medium containing an ammonium salt, glucose, and traces of several inorganic ions in a water solution. Energy is derived primarily from the oxidation of glucose, frequently to carbon dioxide and water. Nitrogen for the synthesis of protoplasmic proteins and related compounds comes from the ammonia and is attached to carbon from the glucose. Phosphorus, sulfur, and the other ionic substances incorporated into the protoplasm come from the small quantities of inorganic ions present in the medium. The final product is a complicated structure of proteins, carbohydrates, fat, enzymes, vitamins, nucleic acids, and other complex materials which, in the organized structure of the cell, are able to carry on the processes known as life.

Increasing nutritional requirements result as organisms lack the ability to synthesize one or more of the materials needed in carrying out either metabolic or growth processes. Certain yeasts, bacteria, and molds can use the simple compounds for most syntheses but are unable to synthesize one or more members of the vitamin B complex. For such organisms to grow, the vitamin must be added to the simple nutrient solution. Some bacteria can synthesize only a portion of a vitamin molecule and need to have the other portion already formed; an example of this is the synthesis by certain pathogenic micrococci of the thiazole portion of thiamin, while the pyrimidine portion must be supplied in the medium. In some instances certain of the vitamins of the B group must be present as complexes or conjugates before growth of the organism is possible. An example of this is *Lactobacillus bulgaricus,* some strains of which cannot grow when pantothenic acid is added to the medium but which require that the conjugate pantethine be present in an otherwise adequate medium. Most of the B vitamins seem to be needed by microorganisms for the synthesis of enzymes required in the metabolic processes of the organisms. This is true whether these vitamins are synthesized by the organism or must be present in the medium because they cannot be synthesized by the organism.

Many of the bacteria which will develop in a medium containing ammonia or nitrate as the nitrogen source grow much better if amino acids are added. The rate of synthesis of one or more amino acids apparently may be a limiting factor in growth in a simple medium. Other microorganisms must have one or more amino acids present in the medium to permit any growth, presumably because the organism lacks the ability to synthesize that amino acid. In still more complex cases, an entire group of amino acids plus a number of purine and pyrimidine bases, as well as vitamins, may be necessary for growth.

Asparagine, glutamine, unsaturated fatty acids, acetic acid, certain amines, and carbon dioxide are all known to be required by certain lactic acid bacteria for growth in defined media.

An interesting aspect of microbial nutrition is that the absolute requirements of an organism may change with variations in such factors as temperature of incubation. This phenomenon has importance in the use of microorganisms for assays of amino acids and vitamins. Undoubtedly this will extend to the commercial use of microorganisms, such as in the dairy industry.

An approach to the ultimate in nutritional complexity is exemplified in the reproduction of bacteriophages such as those attacking lactic streptococci. The bacteriophage particles are incapable of reproduction in any known medium except the protoplasm of the living susceptible cell.

Even under these conditions the particle loses its identity during the reproductive process, so it can not be said to reproduce at all in the manner characteristic of most of the other microorganisms which are of concern in dairy products. Instead the particle breaks down into simpler components at one stage in the process. These components combine with many other complex substances, and finally organize into a considerable number of new bacteriophage particles within the host cell.

Milk and most milk products contain the nutrients needed for growth of all microorganisms that are of concern to the dairy industry, with the exception of bacteriophages, other viruses, and rickettsiae. Non-nutritional factors usually will be the most important causes of restricted growth. However, this does not mean that certain modifications of, or additions to, milk and milk products may not improve the growth of the microorganisms which may gain entry to the product.

The belief, still held by some, that an organism must be able to utilize lactose to grow well in milk or milk products, is incorrect. Many organisms that are important in dairy products are unable to ferment lactose. Some of these organisms apparently use hydrolytic products of proteins or fats as their source of energy and carbon. Other organisms may use lactic acid or similar compounds produced from lactose by other microorganisms. Addition of glucose to milk is stimulatory to some organisms, including species of *Leuconostoc,* because this carbohydrate is used by many organisms which either do not utilize lactose or utilize it slowly.

The sources of nitrogen in milk are adequate for most microorganisms. Many of the organisms which grow in milk are considered to be either non-proteolytic or very weakly proteolytic. Some of these organisms apparently can utilize certain of the simpler non-protein nitrogenous compounds, such as the ammonia nitrogen, the limited amounts of free amino acids, the smaller peptides, and the nitrogen bases normally present in milk which has not undergone microbial proteolysis. The growth of bacteria such as *Streptococcus lactis* results in a considerable increase in the amounts of non-protein and amino nitrogen in milk, even early in the growth cycle (23). On the other hand, additions of peptones or certain amino acids to milk will improve the growth of many strains of *Streptococcus lactis, Streptococcus cremoris,* lactobacilli, and a number of other organisms. Presence of the more readily available protein degradation products presumably reduces the dependence of the organisms on their own mild proteolytic activities to free amino acids from the native proteins. In a mixture of two or more organisms, the more (most) proteolytic organism may stimulate growth of the other organism(s) by producing protein degradation products. Such stimulation may be important to an organism growing simultaneously with a more proteolytic type. Also, the degradation products formed by one may stimulate subsequent growth of another organism. This latter situation is important during the ripening of certain cheeses, where proteolysis by *Streptococcus lactis,* as well as by rennin, apparently stimulates growth of lactobacilli during the later stages of ripening.

Milk contains nearly all of the members of the water-soluble B group of vitamins. Many microorganisms are not stimulated by the addition of these vitamins or their conjugates to milk. However, the addition to milk of yeast extract or vegetable juices is stimulatory to many of the more fastidious members of the family *Lactobacteriaceae*. Probably some of this stimulation is due to unknown growth factors present in such materials. Vitamin secretion by one organism may stimulate the simultaneous or subsequent growth of another organism. Unquestionably, this is a factor of importance in the sequence of organisms appearing in the smear of some varieties of cheese, although part of the effect observed has been shown to result from changes in pH resulting from utilization or neutralization of substances responsible for some of the acid reaction. Utilization of lactic acid and of fatty acids may be looked upon as a phase of nutrition because the energy derived from such utilization would be available, at least in part, for synthetic functions of the cell. Similar considerations would apply to the utilization of other intermediates of protein, carbohydrate, and fat degradation.

Whether an organism can cause lipolysis apparently is not a major factor in determining whether it can grow in milk or milk products; many strongly fat-splitting organisms can grow very well in the absence of fat. If fat is present and is attacked by lipase, either, or both, the glycerol and the fatty acids freed by the hydrolytic enzyme may be utilized by the organism. Such a source of carbon might be quite stimulatory to some microorganisms. This is especially true whenever carbohydrates, or readily utilizable breakdown products of carbohydrates, are not available. Some of the lactic streptococci and lactobacilli are stimulated specifically by oleic acid, although there is little evidence that the organisms are able to free this acid in detectable amounts from the butterfat.

The relatively complex mineral content of milk apparently is an adequate source of most of the inorganic ions required by microorganisms. A few reports indicate that small additions of certain ions may provide stimulation under special circumstances. Additions of some ions, particularly in excessive quantities, also may prove inhibitory to development of some organisms. A field that has not been explored extensively with regard to dairy products concerns the influence of fermentation patterns by a control of the amounts and balances of certain ions. The control of ions has been found to be important with respect to certain industrial fermentations. Preliminary reports indicate this might be a desirable area for further investigation (9).

pH

The pH of a medium may be measured colorimetrically with indicators such as brom thymol blue and brom cresol purple. Electrometric procedures also are used, where the difference in potential between a noble metal electrode in contact with the system and a calomel reference electrode is determined potentiometrically. The system measured usually is considered to be the molar concentration of the effective hydrogen ions. From this value the pH level usually is defined as the logarithm of the reciprocal of the effective hydrogen ion concentration. The common formula is: $pH = \log_{10} \dfrac{1}{[H^+]}$.

The small size of the individual microbial cell makes almost impossible the determination of the pH of the cellular protoplasm. Because the cells are bounded by a semi-permeable membrane inside of which are retained proteins and other complexes which influence ionic equilibrium, one can be almost certain that the pH of the interior of the cell is not the same as that of the surrounding medium. The magnitude and direction of the differences remain to be determined. Undoubtedly the cell tends to resist changes in internal pH when the pH of the medium with which the cell is in contact is changed. Also, there is no assurance that the cell protoplasm is uniform in pH.

The pH of the medium is one of the most important factors affecting growth, physiological activity, and death of microorganisms. Most of the common organism types will grow well in the pH range from 5.6 to 7.5, and many types will grow beyond this range. *Thiobacillus thiooxidans,* one of the sulfur-oxidizing bacteria, grows best at pH 3–4, but it can survive after producing enough acid to bring the reaction below pH 1. One of the criteria used for differentiating some of the streptococci by the procedures of Sherman (21) is the ability of the enterococci to grow at pH 9.6. Most strains of lactic streptococci, such as *Streptococcus lactis,* will not begin growth in a medium more acid than pH 4.8. However, after they start growing well, they may produce enough lactic acid to bring the reaction to pH 4.3 or below (18). Probably this is a case of continuing enzyme activity after cell multiplication has been stopped by an adverse pH level. The considerably more acid-tolerant lactobacilli often found in milk and cream are able to initiate growth at pH levels which stop acid production by *Streptococcus lactis;* some strains of *Lactobacillus bulgaricus* can bring the final reaction well below pH 4.0. Many of the proteolytic and lipolytic bacteria have their growth markedly retarded, or actually stopped, by the pH levels produced by the lactic streptococci. This is important in controlling the growth of undesirable microorganisms in the manufacture of various milk products where the lactic fermentation is desirable. However, this antibiotic effect of acid is sometimes overrated because in many cases a considerable growth of the undesirable organisms may accompany the growth of the acid-producing organisms.

Yeasts and molds usually are able to develop at relatively low pH levels. One of the common procedures for enumeration of these organisms depends upon the ability of most of them to grow at pH 3.5 on suitable media, whereas this reaction prevents the growth of nearly all bacteria. Studies by Olson (16) have shown that yeast and mold counts may be higher on some samples when antibiotics, rather than low pH, are used for inhibition of bacteria. Possibly this is due to the low pH being inhibitory to some of the yeasts and molds.

Yeasts and molds may have a considerable influence on the sequence of organisms growing in a mixed culture because of their ability to utilize some of the products responsible for the acid reaction. Upon occasion some bacteria may help achieve this result. By action of these organisms the pH may be raised to a level that will permit growth of bacteria that otherwise could not develop. An example of this is the growth of yeasts and micrococci on the surface of Limburger cheese; these organisms raise the pH from approximately 5.0 to 5.8 or above, thus permitting *Bacterium linens* and related bacteria to develop. Without a rise in pH, attributable either to these early microorganisms or to the washing of the cheese with a dilute solution of ammonia, the development of *Bacterium linens* and the resulting marked increase in soluble nitrogen would not occur.

Microbial enzyme production and activity also are influenced considerably by pH. Some of these relationships have been studied in detail, but others are known only by effects upon flavor and other organoleptically determinable characteristics. The influence of acidity on the production of flavor and aroma constituents of butter and cheese cultures is discussed in Chapter 11. The influence of pH on rennin activity and curd formation is discussed in Chapter 13. In table 3.1 are shown the pH ranges for activity of some of the enzymes of bacteria and other microorganisms of importance in dairy products. Information of the type given in the table is not available for many of the enzyme systems important in these products. Enzymes which are of the same type but which are produced by different organisms may have their optima for activity at different pH levels. Some of the differences may be due to variations in techniques employed by the investigators; however, many of the differences probably are attributable to real differences between the various enzymes. These data show very definitely that, although comparatively narrow, the pH range encountered in dairy products is sufficiently wide to influence markedly the activities of representative enzyme systems.

The literature contains a number of references to the influence of pH on changes brought about by microorganisms growing in dairy products. The dependence of flavor and aroma in lactic cultures on adequate acid production by the lactic streptococci is well known. Acid production by *Streptococcus lactis* is necessary for the development of a pronounced bitter flavor in cream by a yeast identified as *Rhodotorula mucilaginosa* (5). Acid production by *Streptococcus lactis* is inhibitory to the release of tyrosine and tryptophan-active compounds in cream by *Bacillus subtilis* and *Pseudomonas fragi* (7).

**Table 3.1** The pH levels at which certain enzymes of organisms important in dairy products are active

| ENZYME | SUBSTRATUM | ORGANISM | pH OF OPTIMUM ACTIVITY | APPROX. pH RANGE OF 50% OF OPTIMUM ACTIVITY | INVESTIGATOR |
|---|---|---|---|---|---|
| Proteinase | Casein | S. liquefaciens | 7.4–7.5 | 6.6–9.0 | Dudani (Thesis, Iowa State Coll, 1950) |
| Proteinase | α-casein | S. lactis | 6.5 | 5.5–8.0 | van der Zant & Nelson (J. Dairy Sci., 36: 1212. 1953) |
| Proteinase | Casein | B. linens | 7.0 | 6.5–8.0 | Thomasow (Kieler milchw. Forschungsberichte, 2:35. 1950) |
| Proteinase | Casein | L. casei | 6.0 | <4.0–>8.0 | Brandsaeter & Nelson (J. Bact., 72: 68. 1956) |
| Peptidase | DL-alanylglycine | S. liquefaciens | 7.0<br>8.3 | 6.2–7.7<br><7.8–>9.0 | Dudani (ibid.) |
| Peptidase | Glycyl-L-leucine<br>DL-leucylglycine<br>DL-alanylglycine<br>Glycylglycylglycine | S. lactis | 6.5–7.5<br>8.5<br>8.0<br>8.0 | 5.0–9.0<br>5.5–8.3<br>5.0–9.2<br>6.7–8.7 | van der Zant & Nelson (J. Dairy Sci., 37: 1. 1954) |
| Peptidase | DL-alanylglycine<br>Glycyl-DL-alanine<br>Alanylglycylglycine | L. casei | 7.0–7.5<br>8.0<br>7.0 | 5.5–8.3<br>7.0–8.5<br>5.5–7.5 | Brandsaeter & Nelson (J. Bact., 72: 73. 1956) |
| Deaminase | Serine | L. casei | 7.0(52°C.)<br>8.3(46°C.) | 5.7–8.5<br>7.2–9.3 | Kristoffersen & Nelson (Applied Microbiol., 3:268. 1955) |
| Lipase | Butterfat | C. lipolytica | 6.2–6.5 | 5.5–7.2 | Peters & Nelson (J. Bact., 55:593. 1948) |
| Lipase | Coconut oil | P. fragi | 7.0–7.2 | 6.3–8.0 | Nashif & Nelson (J. Dairy Sci., 36:459. 1953) |
| Lipase | Butterfat | G. candidum | 6.0 | <5.0–>8.0 | Nelson (J. Dairy Sci., 35:455. 1952) |
| Lipase<br>Protease | Butterfat<br>Casein | P. roqueforti | 5.3–7.5<br>5.8–6.3 | 4.5–9.0<br>4.8–7.5 | Thibodeau & Macy (Minn. Agr. Exp. Sta. Tech. Bull. 152. 1942) |

## OXIDATION-REDUCTION POTENTIAL

Because an understanding of oxidation-reduction potentials is basic to the discussion of oxygen relationships of microorganisms, certain factors which influence these potentials will be discussed first. Oxidation-reduction potential is fundamentally a measure of the tendency of a reversible system to give up or to take up electrons. Oxidation is the process involving loss of electrons, and reduction is the process involving gain of electrons. The reaction involving the ferrous and ferric ions may be written as follows: $Fe^{++} \underset{\text{reduction}}{\overset{\text{oxidation}}{\rightleftharpoons}} Fe^{+++} + e$, where $e$ represents an electron. The electron must be taken up or accepted by another substance, such as oxygen. The formula for this may be written $\frac{1}{2}O_2 + 2e \underset{\text{oxidation}}{\overset{\text{reduction}}{\rightleftharpoons}} O^{--}$. Combining these two equations and considering the $Fe^{++}$ to have been the ferrous oxide, $2Fe^{++}O^{--} + O_2 \rightarrow Fe_2^{+++}O_3^{--}$. Because of the chemical affinities involved, this oxidation can be reversed only when the hydrogen becomes the electron acceptor at temperatures of about 300°C. (570°F.). The formula for this change would be $Fe_2^{+++}O_3^{--} + H_2 \rightarrow 2Fe^{++}O^{--} + H_2^{+}O^{--}$.

In biological systems, such as in cultures of microorganisms, simultaneous oxidations and reductions are the sources of energy for the cell processes. The products of the fermentation are the result of the oxidation-reduction reactions which have taken place. Biological oxidations are visualized most easily if they are considered to involve a loss of hydrogen or a gain of oxygen, both of which amount to a loss of electrons. Conversely, reduction involves gain of hydrogen or loss of oxygen, these being manifestations of a gain of electrons. In complex molecules, certain carbon atoms may be reduced (the H:O ratio is greater than 2:1), while other carbon atoms may be oxidized (the H:O ratio is less than 2:1). When all the valences of carbon are satisfied by oxygen to give $CO_2$, the atom is completely oxidized and only then can yield no more energy. Some types of organisms are able to break glucose down to $CO_2$ and water by using oxygen as the final electron acceptor. Because oxidation has been complete, the energy yield of this reaction is very high. The equation for this reaction is as follows: $C_6H_{12}O_6 + 6O_2 \rightarrow 6CO_2 + 6H_2O + 674$ kg cal. On the other hand, the breakdown of the same glucose may proceed in the absence of oxygen to give lactic acid and a low energy yield according to the following equation: $C_6H_{12}O_6 \rightarrow 2CH_3CHOHCOOH + 22.5$ kg cal. This is anaerobic oxidation, with one carbon atom being oxidized while another is reduced. A similar type of change may occur when anaerobic bacteria obtain energy by oxidizing one amino acid while reducing another. The intermediate stages in these oxidations and reductions are the important reactions from the standpoint of energy production. In many instances the responsible reactions are not known completely and the mechanisms postulated are conclusively provable only with equipment or methods not now available. Many of the schemes postulate phosphorylated intermediate complexes which yield energy by the subsequent breakage of energy-rich phosphorus bonds. The changes are under the control of enzymes and the associated co-enzymes, the latter frequently serving as energy transfer agents. The terms "hydrogen transfer" and "hydrogen acceptor" are very often used in discussing this type of reaction, because the end-products usually are explained by movement of hydrogen from one carbon atom to another, frequently with some apparent movement of oxygen. The apparent oxygen movement usually can be explained on the basis of dehydrogenation of a hydrated compound. An example is

$$
\underset{\substack{|\\ \mathrm{H}}}{-\mathrm{C}}=\mathrm{O} + \mathrm{H_2O} \;\rightleftharpoons\; \underset{\substack{|\\ \mathrm{H}}}{-\mathrm{C}}\!\!<\!\!{}^{\mathrm{OH}}_{\mathrm{OH}} \;\xrightarrow{\text{acceptor}}\; -\mathrm{C}\!\!<\!\!{}^{\mathrm{O}}_{\mathrm{OH}} \;+\; \mathrm{H_2} = \text{acceptor.}
$$

Com-

pounds such as glutathione, cysteine, ascorbic acid, methylene blue, and resazurin may serve as hydrogen acceptors for many of the bacteria which lack the necessary enzyme systems, such as cytochrome, to use oxygen as a hydrogen acceptor. These compounds also may be used by the many micro-organisms for which oxygen ordinarily is the final acceptor, when these organisms find themselves without free oxygen.

Culture media in general are reducing; e. g., they have a low oxidation-reduction potential in the absence of oxygen and a high oxidation-reduction potential when in equilibrium with oxygen. When litmus milk is first removed from the autoclave, the color of the litmus indicator is almost completely gone. This is because the oxygen has been driven off, and the litmus, which is an indicator of oxidation-reduction potential, as well as of pH, has been reduced. As the milk cools and the oxygen is dissolved, the litmus again becomes colored through oxidation. Some bacteria, such as *Streptococcus lactis,* can establish a reducing potential in milk sufficient to reduce litmus in all except a narrow band at the surface of the milk. This usually occurs after acid coagulation reduces convection currents, which otherwise bring oxygen into the depths of the medium. The reduction of methylene blue or resazurin in the dye reduction tests depends upon the ability of many of the organisms common to dairy products to bring about reducing conditions in the milk in which they are growing and metaboliz-ing actively. Inversion of the tubes just at the time that reduction of the dye is beginning often retards the color change because introduction of oxygen raises the oxidation-reduction potential.

Prevention or retardation of rise of potential in culture media is neces-sary for growth of certain bacteria that are sensitive to high oxidation-reduction potentials. Addition of agar to minimize convection currents, and thus reduce oxygen solution, is one procedure used in conjunction with deep layers of the medium. Vaseline, agar plugs, or other mechanical agents sometimes are used to seal the surface from actual contact with air. Substances such as thioglycollic acid, cysteine, glutathione, and ascorbic acid may be added to the medium to decrease the susceptibility to oxidation, for these compounds serve as electron donators or reducing agents.

### OXYGEN RELATIONSHIPS

Oxygen supply is one of the most important factors controlling the growth and the viability of microorganisms. From the standpoint of growth in the presence of oxygen, microorganisms are divided into four groups. An aerobic organism is one which grows only in the presence of atmospheric oxygen. An anaerobic organism is one which grows only in the relative absence of free or atmospheric oxygen. A facultative organism is one that grows either in the presence of free oxygen or in its absence. A microaerophilic organism is one that grows best in a reduced oxygen pressure. Figure 3.2 shows how the growth of organisms of each of these four types is distributed when deep tubes of agar are inoculated with the organisms, mixed thoroughly, permitted to solidify and then incubated. As is common in biology, sharp lines of demarcation between types are not possible in all instances. The facultative organisms may be of two types. One type, of which *Streptococcus lactis* is representative, apparently uses little or no free oxygen in its physiological processes, but it does tolerate the presence of oxygen. A second type, of which *Escherichia coli* is an example, will use free oxygen in its metabolism if the gas is present, but it also can carry on an anaerobic metabolism if oxygen is not present. The energy yields from these metabolic types were discussed earlier.

Bacteria which fall into each of the four classes described above are known. If the class into which an organism falls is known, methods for encouraging or discouraging microbial growth may be worked out to some degree on the basis of oxygen relationships alone. When this factor is employed in combination with others, the possibilities of control are broad-

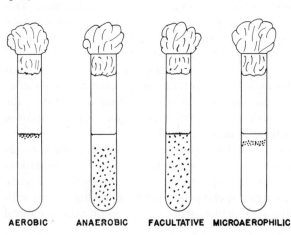

**Figure 3.2** A diagram of the growth of aerobic, anaerobic, facultative, and microaerophilic organisms in deep agar shake tubes, showing the relationship of growth of these organisms to atmospheric oxygen.

AEROBIC     ANAEROBIC     FACULTATIVE   MICROAEROPHILIC

ened immensely. Certainly no one would attempt to grow a member of the genus *Acetobacter* under anaerobic conditions or a member of the genus *Clostridium* under aerobic conditions. However, so many bacteria and yeasts are facultative that oxygen control is far from being a highly selective procedure.

Molds are almost completely aerobic in character. However, some species tolerate less completely aerobic conditions than do others. One of the reasons *Penicillium roqueforti* can grow in the inside of Roquefort-type cheese, although many of the molds find conditions there unsatisfactory, is the greater tolerance of the former for semi-anaerobic conditions. This situation may be complicated by relative carbon dioxide content within the cheese. One of the most effective procedures for control of mold growth is the exclusion of oxygen. In some instances, the replacement of air with carbon dioxide has reduced considerably the development of molds on foods in storage. Paraffining or plastic wrapping of cheese, reduction of head space in cans of sweetened condensed milk, and minimizing of surface-volume ratio in the case of cream are some of the methods used in the dairy industry for control of mold growth by exclusion of oxygen.

Yeasts range from aerobic to facultative in their oxygen requirements. The mycoderm type, which frequently is grown with *Lactobacillus bulgaricus* and *Streptococcus thermophilus* to increase viability, is aerobic, as are some of those types encountered in surface smears of slime-ripened cheeses. On the other hand, the common bread and beer yeasts and most of those yeasts responsible for defects in cream employed for butter making are facultative.

Oxygen markedly influences the survival of bacteria in cultures and in dried preparations. Oxygen generally has no obvious deleterious effect upon organisms so long as they are metabolically active and thus presumably able to maintain their protoplasm in a reduced condition. As the culture ceases to be metabolically active, sensitivity to oxygen increases. The resulting rise in oxidation-reduction potential, which undoubtedly occurs as the oxygen penetrates the cell, may inactivate some of the enzyme systems necessary for continuing viability. Dried cultures, including those dried from the frozen state, usually remain viable much longer if they are stored in the absence of oxygen rather than in its presence.

Color production by microorganisms often is affected considerably by oxygen supply, even when other characteristics are affected to a much lesser degree. This phenomenon is most apparent in the case of bacteria such as *Bacterium linens,* where absence of abundant oxygen may decrease chromogenesis considerably. In Blue cheese, reduced oxygen pressure may result in lessened or changed color in the mold which develops, bringing on a decrease in salability of the product. In this case, merely allowing the cut cheese to stand in the air often will permit the mold to change from an unnatural yellowish-green to the deeper blue-green characteristic of this cheese.

TEMPERATURE

Temperature is one of the most important means for controlling microbial growth. Microorganisms are known whose development under refrigeration is limited only by a degree of cold which reduces the free water content of the material to an extremely low level. Some molds, because they can develop in the presence of less free water, grow at slightly lower temperatures than do low-temperature yeasts and bacteria. Other microorganisms can grow in hot springs or in pasteurizing vats. The importance of the character of the substratum in determining growth under extreme conditions makes it undesirable to attempt to give definite minimum or maximum temperatures for specific organisms. Also, temperatures for growth must be differentiated clearly from temperatures which merely permit survival.

Complete freezing does stop microbial growth. While a product is thoroughly frozen, it is protected from microbial spoilage, although it is not protected from some forms of chemical deterioration. However, freezing does not kill many of the microorganisms which were in the product at the time of freezing. After thawing, the surviving organisms usually are able to grow much as if they never had been frozen. This latter situation is not appreciated by many. Whether frozen peas or ice cream is the product concerned, microbial growth will begin as soon as the product reaches a temperature at which any of the surviving bacteria can grow.

Because of the much wider use of refrigeration in stores and homes and because of some changes in the patterns of distribution of dairy products, many dairy products are held for considerably longer times before consumption now than was the case only a few years ago. These newer situations mean that dairy products are much more subject to spoilage by those microorganisms that may develop in the product under refrigeration conditions. Microorganisms which grow at unusually high temperatures usually are relatively much less important to the dairy industry.

Microorganisms which are heat resistant are known as thermoduric. In the dairy industry this term often is applied to microorganisms, particularly bacteria, which will survive normal pasteurization temperatures. Those bacteria which have their optimum temperature for growth in the range above 50°C. (122°F.) are classed as thermophilic or heat-loving. Some of these bacteria will not grow at temperatures below 45°C. (113°F.), although others may grow at 25°C. (77°F.). Those bacteria known as mesophilic are defined as having their optimum growth temperature in the range of 20°C. to 40°C. (68°F. to 104°F.). They usually will not grow at temperatures below 10°C. (50°F.), and some species may not grow at 20°C. (68°F.). Some of the organisms in this group may be thermoduric. Those microorganisms classified as psychrophilic (cold-loving) grow best at 20°C. (68°F.) or below. Many of them will grow at temperatures of 0°C. (32°F.) or below as long as a portion of the water remains in the free state. Usually, they will not grow above 32°C. (89.6°F.). Many of the so-called psychrophilic bacteria in dairy products actually are somewhat between mesophilic and psychrophilic in that they will grow at temperatures of 5°C. (41°F.) and below, and in that they will grow poorly, if at all, above 30°C. (86°F.); however, their optimum is at about 25°C. (77°F.), rather than at 20°C. (68°F.) or below. Also there is a tendency to term psychrophilic those bacteria growing in dairy products held at 8°C. to 10°C. (46.4°F. to 50°F.). This may seem to be ultra-fine separation, but it does have importance in later practical considerations of the problems of psychrophilic bacteria. Sherman (21) defines the lactic and enterococcus groups of the streptococci partially on the basis of ability to grow at 10°C. (50°F.). Both of these types are mesophilic, based upon optimum growth being above 30°C. (86°F.). The enterococci are pasteurization resistant. Neither of these two types of organism will grow on plates incubated at 5°C. (41°F.), but they will increase in numbers in milk and milk products held at 8°C. to 10°C. (46.4°F. to 50°F.) and then show up in counts subsequently made at 21°, 25°, 32°, or 35°C. (69.8°, 77°, 89.6°, or 95°F.). Some strains of micrococci and bacilli apparently behave similarly. Some strains of coliform bacteria will grow at 3°C. to 5°C. (37.2°F. to 41°F.), and most of these show good colony development on selective media incubated at 35°C. (95°F.). These strains thus tend to combine psychrophilic and mesophilic characteristics.

Rates of growth, as indicated by generation times, show a definite relationship to temperature. An organism growing at approximately 0°C. (32°F.) usually requires 24 hours or longer per generation, whereas an organism growing at 65°C. (149°F.) may produce a new generation in approximately 10 minutes. Of course, not all organisms growing at a given temperature will give the same generation time, the individual characteristics of the different strains being very important in this respect. The lag phase of the growth curve also tends to be lengthened at low temperatures and shortened at the higher temperatures. The total yield of cells per unit volume tends to be greatest at a temperature below that giving the minimum generation time. Also, production of enzymes sometimes is greater at temperatures below the optimum as determined by minimum generation time. The data of Nashif and Nelson (14) on production of lipase by *Pseudomonas fragi* demonstrate this point. From these discussions one may conclude that in each instance one must define very accurately the criteria employed for the determination of optimum temperature for an organism.

The factors which determine maximum and minimum growth temperatures or, more properly, multiplication temperatures are not well understood. One interpretation of maximum multiplication temperature is that the reactions for multiplication are accelerated by increases in temperature, as are nearly all chemical reactions. On the other hand, reactions destroying enzyme systems necessary for multiplication increase in rate with rising temperatures much more rapidly than do the reactions necessary for multiplication. At the upper limit for multiplication of an organism the boundary then is defined by the balance between acceleration of multiplication processes and acceleration of destruction of key enzymes. The relative rates of the two reactions are so different that a curve showing rate of multiplication plotted against temperature declines much more steeply above the optimum rate of multiplication than below the optimum. As will be shown in Chapter 5 under the discussion of the influence of temperature on plate counts, the sharp restriction of multiplication with rising temperature frequently causes a considerable decline in plate count to be associated with an increase in incubation temperature in the range from 34°C. to 39°C. (93.2°F. to 102.2°F.). Thus, the upper limits of multiplication temperatures influence markedly not only multiplication rate of organisms in dairy products but also enumeration results.

In mixed populations, such as those usually encountered in dairy products, the temperature at which the products are held markedly influences, both directly and indirectly, the sequence of population development and the final results of that development. The detailed changes will depend considerably upon the character of the initial flora, but a few generalizations can be made. Since *Streptococcus lactis* grows over the range from 10°C. to 40°C. (50°F. to 104°F.), some acidity nearly always develops in products containing this organism when they are stored in this temperature range. Toward the upper end of this bracket, such organisms as the coliform and spore-forming bacteria develop more rapidly than does *Streptococcus lactis*. The common lactose-fermenting yeasts do not multiply as rapidly, but they are more acid tolerant and their increase in numbers will continue for a longer period of time than does that of *Streptococcus lactis*. Other organisms also may multiply rapidly and be somewhat acid tolerant, the result being that a pure lactic fermentation seldom occurs at the higher temperatures and that many off-flavors may accompany the acid formation.

As the temperature drops toward 10°C. (50°F.), many bacteria can multiply faster than does *Streptococcus lactis*. This is particularly true of the gram-negative soil and water types, of which many members of the genus *Pseudomonas* are examples. As the temperature goes below 10°C. (50°F.), acid production may stop almost completely. The changes usually will occur relatively slowly in the product, unless there has been a massive initial inoculum, because of the slow growth at the lower temperatures. However, the low temperatures and relative lack of developed acidity frequently permit the multiplication of defect-producing microorganisms which could not compete as favorably at somewhat higher temperatures.

Another example of temperature influence on relative multiplication rates is the necessity of growing most mixed-strain lactic cultures for use in butter and cheese at temperatures of 20°C. to 25°C. (68°F. to 77°F.) to avoid disturbing the effective balance between those bacteria that produce acid and those that produce flavor and aroma only in the presence of an adequate amount of acid.

ANTIBIOTICS

Many of the bacteria used in making cheese, cultured milk, and other fermented dairy products are quite sensitive to the action of antibiotics. A compendium of some of the data available on sensitivity to antibiotics is presented in Table 3.2. The data show that some decrease in sensitivity can be achieved by training.

Antibiotics have become important therapeutic agents for combatting mastitis. These agents act, with varying degrees of success, to reduce growth of the causative bacteria in the bovine udder. Normal body defense mechanisms thus have a better chance of success in controlling the infection. Different antibiotics are of various degrees of usefulness against the several types of microorganisms which may cause mastitis. Penicillin, streptomycin, and aureomycin have been used most extensively. Penicillin in particular has been used in a number of different forms in attempts to maintain the active antibiotic at a high level in the udder for the longest possible time from a single injection or a very limited number of injections.

Much of the antibiotic is excreted in the first milking after therapeutic use. Diminishing quantities are excreted in subsequent milkings. Such factors as kind of preparation used, amount injected, production level of the animal, anatomy of the udder ducts of the individual animal, completeness of milking, and frequency of milking influence the pattern of antibiotic elimination in the milk. The extent to which milk from treated quarters is diluted with other milk is an important factor in determining antibiotic concentration at the processing plant. Because of these variables, exact statements as to how soon after the antibiotic has been injected the milk will be suitable for manufacturing use are not possible. The common recommendation is to withhold the milk for the first 72 hours after the last injection.

The farmer or the veterinarian who may have administered the antibiotic frequently does not realize the extent to which normal processing of products involving lactic fermentation is disrupted by presence of antibiotic in milk. The producers of antibiotic products for treatment of bovine mastitis apparently have not seen fit to emphasize to producers and veterinarians that milk from treated quarters should be discarded for several milkings after completing the antibiotic treatment. In order to minimize this problem the processor should include, in his producer education program, information on the problems that may arise from the use of antibiotics for mastitis therapy. The Food and Drug Administration has ruled that milk containing antibiotics is adulterated, a point deserving some emphasis in educational programs.

Reliable, quick, platform tests for antibiotics in milk are not available. The usual cup test in which the zone of inhibition on an agar plate seeded with a sensitive test organism is measured requires at least 2 hours. The time will be somewhat longer unless the plates inoculated with the test organisms have been prepared earlier, incubated for 2 hours, and then refrigerated to have them available when needed. A test depending upon the sensitivity of *Streptococcus thermophilus* to antibiotics has been described in Europe (3) and is used to some extent in the United States. A heavy broth culture of the organism is mixed with the suspected milk to which resazurin

**Table 3.2** Inhibitory concentrations of antibiotics in milk on various dairy organisms

| Investigator | Organism tested | Antibiotic | Minimum inhibitory concn.* per ml. |
|---|---|---|---|
| Hunter (*J. Dairy Research*, 16: 391. 1949) | *S. cremoris* HP | Penicillin | 0.1 unit |
| | *S. cremoris* K | Penicillin | 0.25 unit |
| | *S. cremoris* $R_1$ | Penicillin | 0.05 unit |
| | *S. cremoris* $R_6$ | Penicillin | 0.05 unit |
| | *S. cremoris* $E_8$ | Penicillin | 0.1 unit |
| | Intermediate $ML_1$ | Penicillin | 0.1 unit |
| | *S. lactis* $ML_2$ | Penicillin | 0.15 unit |
| | *S. lactis* $ML_3$ | Penicillin | 0.15 unit |
| | *S. lactis* $L_{10}$ | Penicillin | 0.15 unit |
| | *S. lactis* 2B | Penicillin | 0.15 unit |
| Katznelson & Hood (*J. Dairy Sci.*, 32:961 1949) | 4 mixed strain starters | Penicillin | 0.05 unit |
| | Adapted starter | Penicillin | 2.4 units |
| Johns (*J. Dairy Sci.*, 36:1241. 1953) | 20 mixed strain starters | Penicillin | 0.2 unit |
| | | Aureomycin | 0.05 µg. |
| | | Dihydrostreptomycin | 0.4 µg. |
| Hargrove et al. (*J. Dairy Sci.*, 33:401. 1950) | *S. thermophilus* | Penicillin | 0.01 unit |
| | *S. thermophilus* | Streptomycin | 5 µg. |
| | *L. bulgaricus* | Penicillin | 0.1 unit |
| | *L. bulgaricus* | Streptomycin | 1 µg. |
| | *P. shermanii* | Penicillin | 0.1 unit |
| | *P. shermanii* | Streptomycin | 5 µg. |
| | *S. thermophilus* † | Penicillin | >3 units |
| | *S. thermophilus* † | Streptomycin | >500 µg. |
| | *L. bulgaricus* † | Penicillin | >3 units |
| | *L. bulgaricus* † | Streptomycin | >500 µg. |
| | *P. shermanii* † | Penicillin | >1 unit |
| | *P. shermanii* † | Streptomycin | >200 µg. |
| Wilkowske & Krienke (*J. Dairy Sci.*, 34:1030. 1951) | *L. bulgaricus* | Penicillin | 0.3–0.6 units |
| | *L. acidophilus* | Penicillin | 0.1–0.3 unit |
| | *L. casei* No. 1 | Penicillin | 0.3–0.6 unit |
| | *L. casei* 7469 | Penicillin | 0.3–0.6 unit |

\* Reduction of 0.1% or greater in titratable acidity at end of test period.

† Strains in which antibiotic resistance had been developed by subculture in presence of increasing amounts of antibiotic.

also is added; the time required to reduce the resazurin is noted and compared to a control known to be free from antibiotic. The culture used must be prepared well in advance and must be in the proper active state, but even then the test requires about 45 minutes for completion. A somewhat similar test involving a milk culture and use of 2, 3, 5-triphenyltetrazolium chloride as indicator requires incubation for 2.5 hours (15).

Results of these tests for antibiotics are available too late to be of much use in deciding to accept or reject a particular lot of milk. The tests probably are of some psychological value because the producers know their milk is being examined. One of the limitations of testing is that a supply which was perfectly satisfactory one day may contain antibiotic the next, as the result of treatment in the interval. Likewise, milk unsatisfactory today may be satisfactory tomorrow because the antibiotic has been eliminated to a sufficient degree. Incorporation into the antibiotic preparation of a readily detectable indicator such as a dye has been suggested to permit a simple test at the plant for detecting the use of antibiotic preparations. Such suggestions have not been accepted.

Presence of antibiotics also would be undesirable because of the possibility that they might sensitize people so that later use in treatment of a diseased condition would have undesirable side reactions. Many disease-producing bacteria are able to develop resistance to some of the antibiotics; if the antibiotics frequently were present in milk, they might be instrumental in establishing a dominance of resistant disease-producing types in the human body. Such resistant organisms would not then respond to treatment with antibiotics should the disease process continue to a point where such treatment might be indicated. Additional information in this area would be very desirable.

Antibiotics might be present in such quantities that they would cause a considerable increase in the time required for reduction of methylene blue or resazurin in dye reduction tests. Under these conditions the milk would be graded higher than it should be for the level of microorganisms present and the sanitation employed. Along a similar line, an increase in keeping quality might be found in some cases where antibiotics were present, particularly if they were present in large quantities. Especially with penicillin, action of the antibiotic might reduce development of the milk-souring streptococci, while permitting essentially uninhibited growth of some gram-negative, defect-producing bacteria, such as the coliform organisms or *Pseudomonas fragi*.

Antibiotics offer some possibility of selective inhibition of undesirable microorganism types in dairy products. Studies are being made in Europe to control butyric acid bacteria in Swiss and similar sweet types of cheese by incorporating selected antibiotics, or the organisms that produce the antibiotics, into the cheese during manufacturing. In the United States some work has been done on use of antibiotics to control mold growth on the surface of certain types of hard cheese (20). Whether such usage will prove desirable and will be permitted by regulatory agencies remains to be seen.

Antibiotics have been suggested for improving the storage life of human milk in the European centers where such milk is distributed. Streptomycin has been used in most instances because it is inhibitory to the development of many types of bacteria.

### SULFONAMIDES

The sulfonamides constitute another group of compounds which has been used to some extent for the treatment of mastitis. These compounds also may inhibit the development of desirable organism types used in dairy fermentations. Many of the same considerations which apply to antibiotics also apply to these compounds. The sulfonamides, as such, are not used often at the present time. They are employed primarily in combination with antibiotics to increase the efficacy of the treatment. Therefore space will not be taken to discuss in detail their relationship to dairy processes.

### THE GERMICIDAL PROPERTY OF MILK

Normal raw milk contains varying quantities of several substances which inhibit normal development of certain bacteria and which may even kill the bacterial cells. At least three factors have been demonstrated. The level of activity varies markedly between milk samples, even between samples obtained from the four quarters of the same cow. Jones and Simms (8) named the inhibitory factor lactenin and arrived at some characterization of the material. Auclair and co-workers (1, 2) since have demonstrated that lactenin is made up of two components. Bovine colostrum is the primary source of lactenin 1, and lactenin 2 occurs mainly in milk. The former is slightly more heat-labile than the latter and also precipitates out at a lower acetone concentration when a whey concentrate is heated with increasing amounts of acetone. The two components acting together are more bactericidal than either one alone. Lysozyme activity is almost nonexistent in milk with high lactenin activity. Lactenin is most active against *Streptococcus pyogenes,* and this organism commonly is used for test purposes. Aside from the variable lactenin levels in different milk samples, one possible reason for the ability of *Streptococcus pyogenes* to grow in the udder is that lactenin has little activity under anaerobic conditions such as prevail there. Additions of glutathione, cysteine, and other reducing compounds also decrease the bactericidal activity in the same manner as anaerobiosis does. The ability of *Streptococcus agalactiae* to cause mastitis so readily may be due not only to the reduced activity of lactenin under the anaerobic conditions of the udder, but also to the presence in milk, and especially in colostrum, of factors stimulatory to this organism (2).

Lactenin activity is reduced by the addition of whole blood or peptone to milk and also by a temperature of 22°C. (71.6°F.), rather than 37°C.

(98.6°F.) (26). However, other investigators have shown that the effect of lactenin lasts longer at low temperatures, even though the level of activity may be lower at any one time.

A specific factor active against certain strains of coliform bacteria has been demonstrated in milk (12). This factor was inactivated by 53°C. (127.4°F.) for 30 minutes, whereas another form of activity, presumably that of lactenin, was but partially destroyed by 65°C. (149°F.) for 30 minutes and was completely inactivated only at 70°C. (158°F.) for 30 minutes.

The practical importance of the germicidal activity of milk probably is very slight. Certainly it can not be depended upon to prevent, or even to retard significantly, the development of mixed populations of microorganisms in raw milk. The marked variations in sensitivity to the factor(s) displayed by the different types of bacteria which may be present might mean that some types would be inhibited markedly, although other types would grow rapidly under the same conditions. With some strains of lactic streptococci, the germicidal factor may be important because acid development in the cheese vat or in lactic cultures may be retarded. Pasteurization exposures only partially inactivate lactenin. One of the reasons for heating milk to be used for carrying cultures to temperatures above 80°C. (176°F.) is to inactivate lactenin.

## QUATERNARY AMMONIUM COMPOUNDS

Quaternary ammonium compounds are used in the dairy industry in combination detergent-sanitizers for farm use in some areas and as bactericidal agents on previously cleaned equipment. At times they are used for controlling mold development on walls of cold storage rooms and similar surfaces, a solution of 200 to 500 ppm frequently being used. The term quaternary ammonium compounds (frequently shortened to "quats" or "QAC") covers a group of compounds of closely related structures. These compounds may all be considered to be derived from simple ammonium salts such as ammonium chloride by substitution of organic groups for the four hydrogen atoms in the ammonium ion. In some of these compounds the nitrogen is contained in the pyridine ring, three of the valences being satisfied by the ring structure and the fourth by a long-chain alkyl group, such as the cetyl group. If the nitrogen is not in the ring structure, two or three of the valences may be satisfied by methyl or occasionally ethyl groups, one or two by long-chain alkyl groups, and one possibly by a benzyl group. In some of the compounds substitutions may be made in one or more of the groups attached to the nitrogen. Examples are alkyldimethylbenzylammonium chlorides, diisobutylphenoxyethoxyethyldimethylbenzylammonium chloride, oleyldimethylethylammonium bromide and cetyl pyridinium chloride. Some of these structures are shown in Figure 3.3. Within certain limits of variation in structure, quaternary ammonium compounds have bactericidal activity at relatively high concentrations (200 ppm) and bacteriostatic ability at low concentrations.

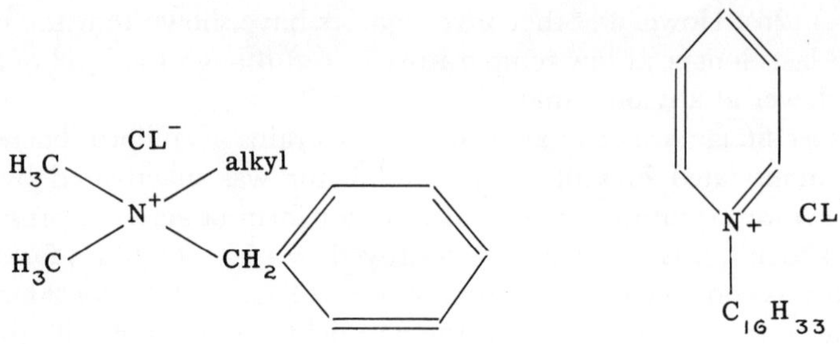

**Figure 3.3**    The chemical structures of representative quaternary ammonium compounds.

As is true of most chemical and physical agents which help control microorganisms, quaternaries do not have the same level of activity against all of the microorganisms against which they may be employed. Differences in chemical structure also influence the relative activity against different organisms. The uses of these compounds in the sanitization of equipment will be discussed in other sections; the concern here will be with their influence upon the growth of bacteria in milk and milk products.

Quaternary ammonium compounds may find their way into milk accidentally when residues of germicidal rinses containing them gain entrance into the product; usually this is the result of incomplete drainage or of incorrect positioning of a valve in a pipeline or tank outlet. The quaternary ammonium compounds are relatively stable in the presence of milk and other organic residues. Although attempts have been made to add these compounds to milk to reduce or prevent microbial growth, their presence can be detected by their bitter flavor at bacteriostatic concentrations.

The bacteria usually employed in a mixed lactic culture, such as is used for cottage cheese or for cultured milk, are quite sensitive to quaternary ammonium compounds. The flavor- and aroma-producing bacteria are even more sensitive than the acid-producing bacteria in the culture. In some areas producers have been asked not to use these compounds for sanitization because of difficulties which seemingly have been traceable to their presence in milk used for making cheese and other dairy products in which fermentation is important. The quantities of quaternary ammonium compound which can cause trouble in fermented products are of the order of five parts per million (11). Some people feel that concentrations slightly above this level are detectable by taste, but opinions upon this point vary. The tests used for determining strength of bactericidal solutions containing quaternary ammonium compounds are not sufficiently delicate to detect the smaller amounts which may cause trouble in fermented products. A more sensitive test based upon use of an eosin indicator and titration of the resultant color with a standard solution of anionic surface-active compound has been developed by Furlong and Elliker (6); this test procedure seems to be the method of choice at the present time.

SALT

Sodium chloride seems to influence microbial growth in a specific chemical manner, in addition to its effect upon osmotic pressure and the availability of water. The effect of sodium chloride on bacterial growth is sufficiently pronounced to permit classification of some bacteria. A specific case is the ability of members of the enterococcus group of the genus *Streptococcus* to grow in the presence of 6.5 per cent sodium chloride, although other groups within this genus can not grow at this salt concentration. Many of the bacteria capable of causing pronounced proteolytic and lipolytic defects in butter are sensitive to moderate salt concentrations in the particular portion of the butter serum in which the organisms are located. Differences in salt tolerance provide one of the most useful means for controlling development of both desirable and undesirable microorganisms on, and in, cheese. As an example, *Bacterium linens,* some of the other bacteria, and some of the yeasts which make up the normal surface smear of Limburger and related cheeses are unusually salt tolerant; they develop readily on the heavily salted surfaces of the cheese, whereas most undesirable types of microorganisms are inhibited.

FATTY ACIDS

Fatty acids, such as oleic acid in the salt or ester form, are stimulatory to certain bacteria, particularly to the lactic streptococci and the lactobacilli. However, the lower fatty acids, even in the salt form in which they usually occur after being freed from the glycerides of butterfat, are inhibitory to many bacteria, including the lactobacilli and the lactic streptococci. Many of the lipolytic bacteria are thought to die off more rapidly in the presence of the fatty acids which they have freed than they would in an environment which did not contain free fatty acids. When free fatty acids result either from the action of the natural milk lipase or from the lipolytic activity of certain microorganisms, development of lactic acid by the lactic streptococci frequently is inhibited to a definitely measurable degree. However, this factor unquestionably is not of major importance in the abnormally slow acid development in cheese and other fermented products.

Some microorganisms are able to utilize free fatty acids in their metabolism and thus may reduce the effective concentration of these acids in the immediate environment. Certain of the molds, such as *Penicillium roqueforti,* as well as a number of the gram-negative nonsporulating bacteria, are able to utilize considerable amounts of these acids. Probably one reason why the highly lipolytic mold *Geotrichum candidum* usually is not associated with organoleptically detectable rancidity is that the lower fatty acids may be utilized by the mold; the higher fatty acids accumulate and can be demonstrated by titration of the fat or by the tests for water-insoluble acids. Recent data indicate that the lipase of *Geotrichum candidum* is quite specific and that it does not attack glycerides containing butyric acid to the same extent that glycerides of the higher fatty acids are attacked (25). Thus the utilization of the lower fatty acids may be a less important factor in relative absence of rancidity than had been postulated earlier. *Streptococcus lactis* can utilize oleic acid to an extent great enough to be detected by the test for water-insoluble acids in cream (7).

The free fatty acids in dairy products usually result either from the action of milk lipase or from the growth of microorganisms which produce lipases acting upon milk fat. Milk lipase may be inactivated by pasteurization and the usual lipase-producing microorganisms are killed by this process. Early pasteurization of milk or milk products thus will minimize activity of the milk lipase and destroy most lipase-producing microorganisms. Delayed pasteurization may permit fat splitting to a degree that the resulting free acids will be quite inhibitory to the growth of desirable bacteria.

### MISCELLANEOUS AGENTS

Many agents other than those mentioned so far may influence microbial development in milk or milk products. Included among these agents are light, smoke, propionates, sorbic acid, physiological abnormalities of the producing animals, and leucocytes.

Light is not required for growth and physiological activity by the microorganisms usually encountered in dairy products. However, light may influence microorganisms. As will be discussed in another area, certain wavelengths of ultraviolet light will kill many types of microorganisms. A number of organisms are influenced considerably in their pigment production, both as to types and amounts, by the amount and the type of light in their environment. On the other hand, most of the organisms of importance in dairy products grow equally as well either in the absence or in the presence of light in the visible portion of the spectrum.

Smoke has been used in dairy products to an extremely limited extent, principally with certain cheese types. The heavier smokes, such as those used with hams, are considered to impart some keeping quality other than that attributable to drying and heating. However, the level of smoking that would be needed to affect keeping quality probably would not be used with any dairy products.

The propionates, principally the calcium and sodium salts of propionic acid, have been used to some degree for limiting growth of microorganisms, especially molds, on a variety of food products. Used under appropriate conditions, propionates on butter wrappers definitely reduce the amount of mold growth on butter (17). Such a procedure never should be used to replace any sanitary practices, but rather to supplement desirable levels of cleanliness and care in plant operations. Direct incorporation of propionates into dairy products to control subsequent mold development has not met with approval by regulatory officials.

Sorbic acid ($CH_3CH{=}CH{-}CH{=}CH{-}COOH$) has been given tentative approval as a fungistatic agent to be used with food products such as cheese. Reports (22) show that the mixture of 0.05 per cent of sorbic acid into process Cheddar cheese is sufficient to inhibit mold growth. From 2.5 to 5 g of sorbic acid per 1,000 square inches of thermoplastic-coated cellophane is practical for wrapping small packages of process or natural Cheddar cheese, provided the details of the packaging procedure are watched carefully, especially the sealing processes. Such additions of sorbic acid impart no objectionable taste, odor, or color to the product.

# References

1. Auclair, J. E., and N. J. Berridge, The inhibition of microorganisms by raw milk, II: the separation and electrophoretic examination of two different inhibitory fractions, *J. Dairy Research,* 21 (1953): 370–374.

2. Auclair, J. E., and A. Hirsch, The inhibition of microorganisms by raw milk, I: the occurrence of inhibitory and stimulatory phenomena. Methods of estimation, *J. Dairy Research,* 21 (1953): 45–59.

3. Berridge, N. J., Testing for penicillin in milk, *Dairy Inds.,* 18 (1953): 586.

4. Buchanan, R. E., and E. I. Fulmer, *Physiology and Biochemistry of Bacteria,* Vol. II. Baltimore: Williams & Wilkins, 1930.

5. Chinn, S. H. F., Non-lactose fermenting yeasts and yeast-like fungi from cream and butter. Unpublished thesis, Iowa State College Library, Ames, Iowa. 1946.

6. Furlong, T. E., and P. R. Elliker, An improved method of determining concentrations of quaternary ammonium compounds in water solutions and in milk, *J. Dairy Sci.,* 36 (1953): 225–234.

7. Harmon, L. G., and F. E. Nelson, Interrelationships of microorganisms in cream, I: *Streptococcus lactis, Pseudomonas fragi,* and *Geotrichum candidum. J. Dairy Sci.,* 38 (1955): 1189–1198.

8. Jones, F. S., and H. S. Simms, The bacterial growth inhibitor (lactenin) of milk, I: the preparation in concentrated form, *J. Exptl. Med.,* 51 (1930): 327–339.

9. Knight, S. G., W. H. Mohr, and W. C. Frazier, White mutants of *Penicillium roqueforti, J. Dairy Sci.,* 33 (1950): 929–933.

10. Lamanna, C., and M. F. Mallette, *Basic Bacteriology.* Baltimore: Williams & Wilkins, 1953.

11. Miller, D. D., and P. R. Elliker, Effect of quaternary ammonium compounds on activity of lactic acid starter bacteria in milk and cheese, *J. Dairy Sci.,* 34 (1951): 279–286.

12. Morris, C. S., The presence in raw milk of a bactericidal substance specific for certain strains of coliform organisms and the comparative rate of growth of bacteria in raw and pasteurized milk, *Dairy Inds.,* 10 (1945): 180–181.

13. Mossel, D. A. A., and J. Westerdijk, The physiology of microbial spoilage in foods, *Antonie van Leeuwenhoek J. Microbiol. Serol.,* 15 (1949): 190–212.

14. Nashif, S. A., and F. E. Nelson, The lipase of *Pseudomonas fragi,* II: factors affecting lipase production, *J. Dairy Sci.,* 36 (1953): 471–480.

15. Neal, C. E., and H. E. Calbert, The use of 2, 3, 5-triphenyltetrazolium chloride as a test for antibiotic substances in milk, *J. Dairy Sci.,* 38 (1955): 629–633.

16. Olson, H. C., The use of aureomycin as a bacterial inhibitor for yeast and mold counts (abstract), *J. Dairy Sci.,* 37 (1954): 643.

17. Olson, J. C., Jr., and H. Macy. Propionic acid, sodium propionate and calcium propionate as inhibitors of mold growth, I: observations on the use of propionate-treated parchment in inhibiting mold growth on the surface of butter. *J. Dairy Sci.,* 28 (1945): 701–710.

18. Overcast, W. W., F. E. Nelson, and C. E. Parmelee, Influence of pH on proliferation of lactic streptococcus bacteriophage, *J. Bacteriol.,* 61 (1951): 87–95.

19. Porter, J. R., *Bacterial Chemistry and Physiology,* New York: Wiley, 1946.

20. Rusoff, L. L., and A. J. Gelpi, Jr., Manufacture of cheese. U. S. Patent 2,585,501. 1952.

21. Sherman, J. M., The streptococci, *Bacteriol. Revs.,* 1 (1937): 1–97.

22. Smith, D. P., and N. J. Rollin, Sorbic acid as a fungistatic agent for foods, VII: effectiveness of sorbic acid in protecting cheese. *Food Research,* 19 (1954): 59–65.

23. van der Zant, W. G., and F. E. Nelson, Proteolysis by *Streptococcus lactis* grown in milk with and without controlled pH, *J. Dairy Sci.,* 10 (1953): 1104–1111.

24. Werkman, C. H., and P. W. Wilson, ed., *Bacterial Physiology.* New York: Academic Press, 1951.

25. Wilcox, J. C., W. O. Nelson, and W. A. Wood. The selective release of volatile acids from butterfat by microbial lipases, *J. Dairy Sci.,* 38 (1954): 775–781.

26. Wilson, A. T., and H. Rosenblum, The antistreptococcal property of milk, I: some characteristics of the activity of lactenin *in vitro.* The effect of lactenin on hemolytic streptococci of the several serological groups; II: the effects of anaerobiosis, reducing agents, thiamine, and other chemicals on lactenin action; III: the role of lactenin in milk-borne epidemics. The *in vivo* action of lactenin, *J. Exptl. Med.,* 95 (1952): 25–59.

# 4

# *Destruction of microorganisms by physical and chemical agents*

Some microorganisms usually are present in milk as it comes from the udder of the cow. In the subsequent handling of milk or in the processing of it into other milk products, microorganisms gain entrance because it is not practical to handle the products under completely sterile conditions. As pointed out in Chapter 3, milk and milk products, as well as the materials with which they come in contact, frequently provide an environment which is satisfactory for considerable increases in microbial population. The microorganisms in dairy products may cause spoilage or human disease; they frequently are used as an index of the sanitary conditions under which the products are handled. A study of the conditions under which microorganisms can be destroyed or removed therefore is essential to an understanding of the satisfactory handling of the product. In some instances the product must be treated to destroy all the organisms of a particular type, destruction of other types being somewhat incidental; an example of this is pasteurization to destroy potential pathogens, although some other bacteria often survive to cause spoilage under the proper circumstances. Under other conditions, such as with canned evaporated milk, practical sterility is required, because survivors may be able to grow under some conditions under which the product might be held. Various levels of destruction also are employed in cleaning operations. A level satisfactory for handling raw milk on the farm would not be suitable for handling sterilized milk which was to be canned aseptically.

Because a considerable number of different methods of destroying or removing bacteria have been employed with various materials, the background for some of these procedures, along with some preliminary statements concerning their application, will be given in this chapter. The hope is that this background material will provide a basis for understanding that will permit more intelligent applications of these processes to the various dairy products and materials with which they come in contact.

## DESTRUCTION OF MICROORGANISMS BY HEAT

Heat is one of the most widely employed methods for the destruction of microorganisms; it is used in the treatment of a wide variety of materials. Heat commonly is used in the bacteriology laboratory to provide sterile materials with which to work. Inoculating loops are sterilized by heating them to red heat in the flame of a Bunsen burner. Petri dishes and pipettes are placed in a hot air oven which is maintained at 170°C. (338°F.) for an hour. Agars and broths are sterilized by steam under pressure in an autoclave, an exposure of 20 minutes at 121°C. (249.8°F.) (15 pound pressure) being used for many media and some equipment. Heat treatments for dairy products range from pasteurization to destroy potential disease-producing organisms to sterilization to destroy all microorganisms present.

The effect of heat on living cells depends upon temperature (intensity of heat) and, in addition, upon the period of exposure at that temperature. Therefore it must be kept in mind, when considering the relation of heat to microbic life, that both temperature and the time of exposure to that temperature are operating.

It was learned long ago that the destruction of bacteria by heat takes place in an orderly manner with time. Investigations in this regard have led to the conclusion that the order of death of bacterial vegetative cells and spores by heat is logarithmic. This orderly destruction is illustrated in Figure 4.1 which shows a hypothetical rate of destruction curve for bacteria. If a given population of bacteria is subjected to heat and the number of survivors is determined after successive intervals of time, plotting the logarithms of the number of survivors against the time gives a "straight line" curve. Such a curve indicates that the order of death is logarithmic and that the death rate is constant. From Figure 4.1 it may be observed that a reduction in population from 1,000,000 (initial population) to 100,000 in the first five minutes of exposure represents 90 per cent destruction. In the next five minute interval the population is reduced to 10,000 which again represents 90 per cent destruction (this time, 90 per cent of 100,000) or a survival of ten per cent. This constant rate of destruction continues with the elapse of time, but theoretically the population of an infinite number never is reduced to zero. The slope of the survivor curve will depend upon a number of factors, temperature being one of them. Naturally the higher the temperature of exposure, the steeper the curve, for destruction will occur more rapidly per unit of time at a high temperature than at a lower one.

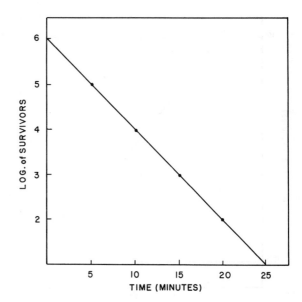

**Figure 4.1**    Hypothetical
bacterial rate of destruction
curve.

## THERMAL DEATH TIME

For many years the standard of comparison of heat resistance
among bacteria was the thermal death point, i.e., the lowest temperature
at which a given suspension in a known environment is killed in ten minutes. Certain difficulties inherent in the determination of thermal death
point have resulted in its replacement by a more useful standard of comparison, the thermal death time. The thermal death time is the time required to kill an organism at a given temperature and in a known environment. Knowing the thermal death time of an organism at several
different temperatures will make possible the construction of a *thermal
death time curve*. This is illustrated in Figure 4.2, wherein thermal
death times are plotted on graph paper having a logarithmic scale
for the time factor and an arithmetic scale for temperature. Such a
line characterizes the thermal resistance of an organism under the specific
conditions of its exposure to heat. The symbol $z$ is used to express the slope
of a thermal death time curve (1).* More specifically, $z$ represents the degrees Fahrenheit which are necessary to reduce the thermal death time ten-

---

* Various other symbols have been introduced for use in calculating thermal processing
times. Ball (1) introduced the symbols $z$ and $F$; the latter indicates the thermal death time of an
organism at 250°F. The $F_o$ value, which often is used, was intended originally to express the $F$
value when $z$ equalled 18. The symbol $F'$ was introduced to represent the thermal death time at
150°F. The use of symbol $\mathcal{Z}$ was suggested to characterize the slope of the bacterial rate of destruction curve. This value is expressed as minutes. The symbol $D$ also was introduced to replace
the symbol $\mathcal{Z}$ thus avoiding confusion with the lower case $z$. For further information about the
meaning and origin of these terms, see reference (15).

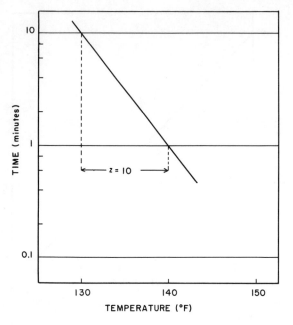

**Figure 4.2** Hypothetical thermal death time curve.

fold; for example, an examination of Figure 4.2 shows that a decrease in thermal death time from 10 minutes to 1 minute required an increase in temperature of 10.0°F. Thus the $z$ value of this curve is 10. If one point on the curve (one thermal death time) and the $z$ value are known, a thermal death time curve may be constructed, and from this the thermal death time at any other temperature may be determined. Such curves may be used to establish thermal processing times necessary to accomplish the extent of bacterial destruction desired. Among the data that exist, those which are most adaptable for analysis indicate that $z$ values for non-spore-forming bacteria range from approximately 10 to 14. There is evidence to indicate that $z$ values are greatest among the more heat-resistant non-spore-formers. In the case of spore-forming bacteria, $z$ values of approximately 18 are common, and this value often is used in the calculations of food processing times.

### FACTORS WHICH INFLUENCE HEAT RESISTANCE

In the definition of thermal death time, the qualifying phrase, "in a known environment," should be emphasized. When a thermal death time value is given for any organism, the conditions under which the value was obtained should be indicated, for there are a number of factors which affect heat resistance. Those which are most pertinent to present purposes are discussed below.

*Number of cells or population.* The effect of this factor may be understood by an examination of Figure 4.1. If the initial population of the suspension was 10,000,000 rather than 1,000,000, the first point on the curve would be plotted at the intercept of zero time and the logarithm of 10,000,000 or 7. At the end of 5 minutes exposure the population would be 1,000,000; after 10 minutes, 100,000; after 15 minutes, 10,000; and so on until at the end of 25 minutes 100 would remain. On the other hand, the curve which is shown in Figure 4.1 indicates that, by starting with an initial population of 1,000,000 bacteria, 100 cells would remain after 20 minutes of exposure. Thus, a tenfold increase in population has increased the time required for the same destructive effect by 5 minutes. While the above example is hypothetical, the principle is sound, for it has been demonstrated experimentally many times and is employed in practice. The effect of population on the thermal death time of a suspension of bacteria is one of the reasons why all precaution should be used in keeping the number of bacteria to a minimum in any product to be processed.

Processing time at a given temperature (the heat treatment) is based upon extent of bacterial kill that is desired. Since the number of bacteria present in the product to be processed will influence the processing time, it is essential that the bacterial population be kept below the maximum figure which was used in calculating or determining the processing time to be applied. This factor of population or "bacterial load" applies generally, but it is particularly important in the development of processing times designed to result in commercially sterile products such as evaporated milk.

*Nature of the medium.* Generally speaking, a concentrated medium affords bacteria greater protection to heat than do more dilute solutions. This effect may not be entirely explainable on the basis of heat penetration, but it is most likely the major reason, other factors being equal. Figure 10.2 (Chapter 10) shows the much greater resistance of *Micrococcus freudenreichii* to destruction by heat when suspended in ice cream mix than in milk. Other species are affected somewhat similarly. The high concentration of sucrose in ice cream mix may be a factor in protecting organisms against heat. Fay (6) and others have shown that bacteria suspended in high concentrations of sugar solutions show greater than normal heat resistance. The mechanism which accounts for the increased resistance is not clear, although the increased osmotic pressure of such a system—resulting in partial dehydration of the organisms—is thought by some to be the cause. This is one of the reasons why higher heat treatments are used in the commercial pasteurization of ice cream mix than generally are applied to fluid milk.

*Type of organism.* Different species vary greatly in heat resistance. Generally, pathogenic bacteria, with the exception of those which produce spores, are relatively heat sensitive. As was noted before, spores are very heat resistant. Probably the most heat resistant species among the non-spore-forming bacteria are those which belong to the genus *Microbacterium.* Recent studies at the University of California would indicate that

*Coxiella burnetii,* the causative organism of Q fever, is considerably more heat resistant than most pathogens likely to be present in milk.

Variations in heat resistance occur among species of the same genus as well as among strains of the same species. This is illustrated in Table 4.1, which shows the distribution of 139 coliform cultures according to their heat resistance in milk when exposed to a temperature of 57.2°C. (135°F.). The data in this table show that heat resistance not only varies greatly among closely related species, but also among different strains of the same species. Generally, organisms such as coliforms and species of *Pseudomonas, Achromobacterium, Alcaligenes,* and others have low heat resistance. This enhances the value of heat treatments such as pasteurization.

*Growth temperature.* The temperature at which bacteria are grown markedly affects their heat resistance. Most studies in this regard have shown that heat resistance increases with an increase in growth temperature.* The effect of growth temperature on heat resistance is illustrated in Figure 4.3. The culture of *Escherichia coli* grown at 20°C. (68°F.) was much less resistant than those grown at 30°C. or 37°C. (86°F. or 98.6°F.). The data in this figure also show how prior growth temperature of the bacteria in milk may affect the efficiency of pasteurization. The knowledge of the effect of growth temperature on heat resistance may be applied in practice by keeping milk at low storage temperatures prior to heat processing. By doing so, the heat resistance of the bacteria which may be present may

**Table 4.1**    Distribution of coliform cultures which survived various periods of exposure at 135°F.*

| CLASSIFICATION [a] | LESS THAN 5 MINUTES | | 5–10[b] MINUTES | | 10–20[c] MINUTES | | 20–40[d] MINUTES | | 40–60[e] MINUTES | | 60 OR MORE MINUTES | |
|---|---|---|---|---|---|---|---|---|---|---|---|---|
| | (No.) | (%) | (No.) | (%) | (No.) | (%) | (No.) | (%) | (No.) | (%) | (No.) | (%) |
| A. aerogenes section | 10 | 38.5 | 14 | 48.3 | 24 | 60 | 9 | 52.9 | 1 | 6.3 | 0 | 0 |
| E. coli section | 1 | 3.8 | 2 | 6.9 | 10 | 25 | 5 | 29.4 | 15 | 93.7 | 10 | 90.9 |
| Intermediate section | 15 | 57.7 | 13 | 44.8 | 6 | 15 | 3 | 17.6 | 0 | 0 | 1 | 9.1 |
| Total | 26 | 100.0 | 29 | 100.0 | 40 | 100.0 | 17 | 99.9 | 16 | 100.0 | 11 | 100.0 |

[a] according to Parr (16).
[b] 5–10 = survived 5 but not 10 minutes.
[c] 10–20 = survived 10 but not 20 minutes.
[d] 20–40 = survived 20 but not 40 minutes.
[e] 40–60 = survived 40 but not 60 minutes.
* Taken from data of Olson et al. (15).

---

* This may not hold true for growth temperatures at, or close to, the maximum. This seems evident from an investigation made by Theophilus and Hammer (26), who found that certain spore-forming bacteria important in the spoilage of evaporated milk possessed greatest heat resistance when grown at their optimum growth temperature.

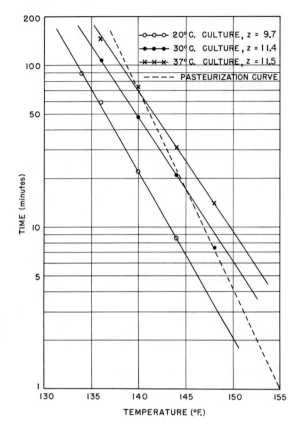

**Figure 4.3**    Effect of growth temperature on heat resistance as shown by TDT curves for *Escherichia coli* after growth at three different temperatures. Taken from data of Olson et al. (15).

be kept at a minimum. The desirability of this has been emphasized in the past (23).

*Miscellaneous factors.* A number of other factors have been shown to influence heat resistance of microorganisms. Microorganisms are killed by heat more easily in an acid medium than in one which is neutral or slightly alkaline. The application of this factor is limited owing to the altering of the stability of milk constituents to heat by relatively small changes in pH; however, it undoubtedly is a major factor in the "cooking" of certain varieties of cheese where some acidity has developed. The low pH of certain processed products prepared from cheese also contributes to heat destruction of microorganisms during the heating employed in processing.

The tendency for some species to clump or to occur as aggregates provides protection to those in or near the center of the clump. This may allow the survival of some cells that otherwise would have been killed had they been uniformly dispersed. The age of the culture, or of individual cells, is a factor since young, actively growing cells are more sensitive to heat than old cells.

PASTEURIZATION

The term pasteurization is defined in the *Milk Ordinance and Code*, recommended by the United States Public Health Service (11) as follows: "The terms 'pasteurization,' 'pasteurized,' and similar terms shall be taken to refer to the process of heating every particle of milk or milk products to at least 143°F., and holding at such temperature continuously for at least 30 minutes, or to at least 161°F., and holding at such temperature continuously for at least 15 seconds, in approved and properly operated equipment: *provided* that nothing contained in this definition shall be construed as barring any other process which has been demonstrated to be equally efficient and which is approved by the State health authority." The laws, regulations, and ordinances of various states and municipalities contain identical or very similar definitions. When milk is pasteurized at 143°F. for 30 minutes, the process is commonly referred to as the low-temperature, holding (LTH) method; when 161°F. for 15 seconds is used the process is called the high-temperature, short-time (HTST) method.

The application of this relatively mild heat treatment to milk is based upon the work of Louis Pasteur, who, during the period from 1860 to 1864, demonstrated that souring and other abnormal fermentations of wine could be prevented by heating at approximately 57.2°C. (135°F.) for a few minutes. Some years later, Pasteur showed that abnormal fermentations of beer could be prevented by the application of mild heat. Soon mild heat treatments were applied to milk and to other foods; hence, the term pasteurization.

In the commercial application of the two pasteurization processes, the heat treatment given would be greater than that implied by the minimum time-temperature standards for pasteurization. It takes a considerable period of time to bring milk to the pasteurization temperature and then to cool it. During the heating and the cooling, milk is exposed for appreciable time to temperatures which can contribute to the total effect of the heat destruction of bacteria. The magnitude of this additional time factor will, of course, depend upon the type of pasteurization unit and the effect that other factors may have in determining the time consumed in raising or cooling milk to, or from, the holding temperature. Some of these factors are the following: temperature of heating or cooling water; temperature of milk before heat is applied; efficiency of heat transfer; size of unit and speed of milk flow (dependent upon pump speed, pipe diameter, and space volume between plates).

*Objectives of pasteurization.* Present day objectives for pasteurization of milk and other dairy products are (a) to destroy pathogenic microorganisms which may be present and (b) to enhance the keeping quality of the products. The latter objective is attained through the destruction of many microorganisms and certain naturally occurring enzymes (particularly lipase) which are capable of causing the deterioration of milk.

Pasteurization is effective in accomplishing both of these objectives. There are, of course, certain non-biological considerations which are important, but these are beyond the scope of this discussion.

As the technology of milk processing advanced, a variety of temperature-time relationships for heat processing came into use. As a result it became necessary to establish the adequacy of these heat treatments for the destruction of pathogens and to determine the destructive effect of these treatments on the rest of the microflora likely to be present. In the discussion to follow, emphasis is placed largely upon the destruction of pathogens. Additional discussions of the effect of various heat treatments on the destruction of the normal flora of raw milk may be found in subsequent chapters pertaining to the various dairy products.

*Basis for temperature-time requirements.* At the time standards were being developed, *Mycobacterium tuberculosis* was regarded as the most heat resistant of the pathogenic microorganisms likely to be present in milk; consequently, the heat treatment necessary for its destruction in milk and other products was the primary determining factor in the establishment of pasteurization standards. Another factor which had to be considered was the effect of the heat treatment upon the flavor and the chemical and physical characteristics of milk. Since excessive heat treatment alters these characteristics, it was important that a minimum heat treatment be established, one which would assure the destruction of pathogens while causing a minimum of change in flavor and in chemical and physical properties.

More than one hundred reports of the thermal destruction of *Mycobacterium tuberculosis* have appeared in the scientific literature of the world. The results of these studies are quite variable. An excellent review of the most important of the studies which were reported prior to 1927 was given by North and Park (13). Many of these studies indicated that *Mycobacterium tuberculosis* was not killed after heat treatments which were supposedly equal to, or greater than, the temperature-time relationships that were given above in the definition of pasteurization. On the other hand, more carefully controlled studies showed that suspensions of tuberculosis bacilli were destroyed by heat treatments less severe than these requirements. Earlier in this chapter, several factors which influence heat resistance of microorganisms were considered. It is evident that the reasons for the variable results which have been reported for the destruction of *Mycobacterium tuberculosis* have been due to certain of these factors, as well as (a) errors in time measurement, particularly when short intervals of exposure were made at high temperatures (above 150°F.); (b) insufficient agitation to prevent pellicle formation (denatured protein) on the surface of milk, which affords protection to cells trapped therein; and (c) failure to maintain the foam, which often forms on the surface of milk, at the same temperature as the milk.

This confusion over the destruction of *Mycobacterium tuberculosis* in milk existed for many years after the commercial introduction of heat treatment for milk. The situation finally was resolved by the work of North and Park (13) reported in 1927. Two years earlier, the results of an extensive cooperative study involving six laboratories, including those of North and Park, had been reported (14). This report was criticized, particularly in regard to the results of the first series of experiments, which were inconclusive. Although they were not in accord with the critics, North and Park nevertheless began another extensive series of experiments. From these studies they concluded that a minimum temperature of 142°F. for a minimum time of 30 minutes afforded ample margin of safety insofar as the destruction of *Mycobacterium tuberculosis* was concerned. This was essentially the same conclusion that previously had been reported from the cooperative study mentioned above. A summary of the results obtained by North and Park is shown in Table 4.2. Thus the early work of several investigators (21, 22, 24) was confirmed, and a sound basis for the present requirement for pasteurization of milk by the low-temperature, holding method was established.

The use of the high-temperature, short-time method for pasteurizing milk did not become extensive until late in the 1930's. Considerable work had been done previously, showing the effect of temperatures in the region of 160°F. for various periods of time in the destruction of *Mycobacterium tuberculosis*. From most of these studies, it is difficult for several reasons to determine the exact time required for destruction. Even in the carefully controlled experiments of North and Park, the minimum times at temperatures above 155°F. were not determined (see Table 4.2). Later work (8, 10, 27) was more explicit and has shown the adequacy of the present standard for HTST pasteurization of milk. This method now is in common use. It should be mentioned, however, that a lag in the development of adequate control mechanisms, which would assure proper heat treatment of every particle of milk in HTST equipment, caused a reluctance on the part of milk control officials to accept this method of pasteurization. This delayed its early acceptance somewhat.

**Table 4.2**  Temperature-time relationships for destruction of *Mycobacterium tuberculosis*[*]

| Temperature (°F.) | Time | Temperature (°F.) | Time |
|---|---|---|---|
| 130 | 60 min. | 150 | 2 min. |
| 132 | 60 min. | 155 | 30 sec.[a] |
| 134 | 40 min. | 160 | 20 sec.[a] |
| 136 | 30 min. | 170 | 20 sec.[a] |
| 138 | 20 min. | 180 | 20 sec.[a] |
| 140 | 10 min. | 200 | 20 sec.[a] |
| 142 | 10 min. | 212 | 10 sec.[a] |
| 145 | 6 min. | | |

[*] From North and Park (13).
[a] Shorter exposure times were not used.

*General effectiveness of LTH vs. HTST pasteurization.* Comparative studies have shown that bacterial destruction by the high-temperature, short-time process of milk pasteurization generally is not as great as that obtained by the low-temperature, holding method. The explanation for this is based on the relationship of bacterial thermal death time curves to the pasteurization curve, the latter being a line drawn between two points representing the temperature-time relationships for LTH and HTST pasteurization (see Figure 4.3). Thermal death time curves which have levels of position near the level of the pasteurization curve would have $z$ values greater than that of the latter. Therefore, the thermal death time curve of a culture may be located in a position relative to the pasteurization curve which would indicate destruction by the LTH method but survival by the HTST process. The curve for the 30°C. (86°F.) culture shown in Figure 4.3 illustrates such a case. The time-temperature combinations represented by points on the pasteurization curve which lie above that point at which the thermal death time curve intersects the pasteurization curve would be sufficient to destroy the organism, whereas those which lie below the point of intersection of the two curves would permit survival. If a certain proportion of the bacterial population in a raw milk supply was of such a nature, then it is conceivable that differences in bacterial destruction by the two pasteurization processes would occur. If the bacterial population in a raw supply consisted of relatively heat-sensitive types (i.e., the usual pathogens, gram-negative rods, and the lactic streptococci) characterized by thermal death time curves having a position considerably below the pasteurization curve, it would be expected that the processes would appear to be equal in bacterial destruction. The latter situation, then, provides a logical explanation for instances in which differences in bacterial destruction by the two pasteurization processes were not evident.

Additional discussions of the temperature-time requirements for pasteurization as applied in the manufacture of other dairy products may be found in subsequent chapters.

### STERILIZATION

The application of a procedure which results in complete destruction of all living organisms is called sterilization. Heat is the most commonly used sterilizing agent, although other agents may be used.

Sterilization may be accomplished more easily by moist heat than by dry heat. This is due to the more rapid penetration of heat in a moist environment. Moist heat may be applied with hot or boiling water or with steam. With boiling water or with steam not under pressure the temperature will be near 100°C. (212°F.), depending upon the atmospheric pressure; thus, excessively long periods of time may be required to sterilize material containing spores. For this reason steam under pressure is used rather than atmospheric steam. It is emphasized that pressure, of itself, contributes nothing bactericidal, for microbes are capable of withstanding extreme fluctuations in pressure. At any given temperature, saturated steam is steam which is at the maximum pressure and density possible. Its temperature cannot be reduced without lowering the pressure nor can it be increased without increasing the pressure. Consequently, steam under pressure is used solely for the purpose of attaining high temperatures. Air mixed with steam will materially lower the temperature attainable at any given pressure. The extent to which this occurs is shown in Table 4.3. For this reason sterilizing equipment such as autoclaves and retorts must be provided with proper devices to allow air to escape when steam is introduced.

Most bacteriological media and solutions are sterilized by moist heat in an apparatus known as an autoclave. This is equipped with a thermometer, a pressure gauge, and with devices that allow air and condensate to escape and which automatically admit sufficient steam to maintain the desired temperature and pressure in the chamber during operation. Usually a temperature of 121°C. (249.8°F.) maintained for 15 to 20 minutes is sufficient for sterilization of media, dilution water, and other miscellaneous solutions.

Dry heat is used in the laboratory to sterilize materials such as glassware, powders, and other materials which are not injured by high temperatures or which may be corroded, or deteriorated, by moisture. Specially designed ovens which are heated by electricity or gas are used. For practically all purposes, 170°C. (338°F.) maintained for at least 1 hour will accomplish sterilization of most laboratory materials commonly subjected to dry heat. For further discussion of specific applications of heat sterilization of laboratory equipment see *Standard Methods for the Examination of Dairy Products* (25).

Different dairy products require different heat treatments, depending upon their composition, their use, and the length and type of storage to which they may be subjected. Products which are sealed, such as evaporated milk and canned chocolate or whole milk, are expected to remain

**Table 4.3**   Temperature of Air and Steam Mixtures *

| Gauge Pressure | Pure Steam | | ⅔ Air Discharge (20″ vacuum) | | ½ Air Discharge (15″ vacuum) | | ⅓ Air Discharge (10″ vacuum) | | No Air Discharge | |
|---|---|---|---|---|---|---|---|---|---|---|
| (lbs.) | °C. | °F. | °C. | °F. | °C. | °F. | °C. | °F. | °C. | °F. |
| 5 | 109 | 228 | 100 | 212 | 94 | 202 | 90 | 193 | 72 | 162 |
| 10 | 115 | 240 | 109 | 228 | 105 | 220 | 100 | 212 | 90 | 193 |
| 15 | 121 | 250 | 115 | 240 | 112 | 234 | 109 | 228 | 100 | 212 |
| 20 | 126 | 259 | 121 | 250 | 118 | 245 | 115 | 240 | 109 | 228 |
| 25 | 130 | 267 | 126 | 259 | 124 | 254 | 121 | 250 | 115 | 240 |
| 30 | 135 | 275 | 130 | 267 | 128 | 263 | 126 | 259 | 121 | 250 |

* Courtesy of American Sterilizer Company.

free of spoilage caused by microorganisms during storage at ordinary temperatures. Thus, the processing of such products requires the application of a sterilizing procedure either after the containers are sealed or just prior to aseptically filling or packaging the product. Commercial sterilization processes are designed to provide adequate preservation against spoilage, yet to provide for sufficient retention of quality factors such as flavor and physical appearance so as not markedly to impair acceptance of the products by the consumer. The extent of heat treatment necessary to achieve commercial sterility will vary depending upon a number of factors as previously described (see "factors which influence heat resistance" ). For further discussion of this subject see Chapter 8.

## DESTRUCTION BY RADIATION

Microorganisms are affected by various types of radiation. The types of radiation which cause destruction of bacteria without the generation of appreciable heat are of primary interest because of the possibility of accomplishing sterilization of many food products, drugs, and biologics which are affected adversely by sterilizing heat treatments.

Ordinary visible light may be harmful to bacteria, but the amount of exposure required for any destructive effect is much greater than that required when radiations of shorter wave length are applied. Visible light, therefore, is of little or no practical significance in the destruction of bacteria.

Within the electromagnetic spectrum those radiations of wave lengths greater than those of visible light, such as infrared rays, produce bactericidal effects by the heat produced in the material being treated. Those radiations such as x-rays, which have wave lengths shorter than those of visible light, produce bactericidal effects directly by contact or direct hit of a vital cell constituent by the radiation. No heat of any consequence is produced by these radiations.

### IONIZING RADIATION

The term ionizing radiation refers to the ability of certain types of radiation to ionize atoms and molecules which they traverse. An evaluation (18) of several of these may be summarized as follows:

*Ultraviolet light.* Ultraviolet light is effective only for surface sterilization because such rays have very little capacity for penetrating matter. Lamps which emit ultraviolet rays have found some use in the control of mold on walls and ceilings of refrigeration rooms, surfaces of meat during aging, and in the control of the bacterial population of the air in operating rooms and in rooms specially designed for culture transfer and manipulation. Some use of ultraviolet lamps may be found in dairy and food plants, particularly for the purpose of controlling the bacterial population of the air in rooms where finished products are packaged. Quite commonly such lamps are installed above conveyer lines carrying empty containers to filling machines or carrying filled containers to capping machines.

*X-rays.* Although x-rays are germicidal and are capable of relatively great penetration, the production of x-rays is relatively inefficient in terms of electron energy required for their production. No radioactivity is produced in the irradiated product; hence such radiation is safe.

*Cathode rays.* Beta rays or cathode rays are high energy electrons. Their production is relatively efficient. Sterilization can be accomplished in a very short time, a second or less. Penetration of matter by cathode rays is less deep than penetration by x-rays, but it is sufficiently deep to be applicable for sterilization of many products. Radioactivity in irradiated products is not produced except at voltages well above those necessary for sterilization. Therefore, this type of radiation is efficient, safe, and commercially applicable.

*Neutrons.* Neutrons are electrically neutral particles having the mass of the hydrogen atom. Their penetrating effect is relatively great, but they create induced radioactivity. This and the inefficiency of neutron production limit their application for food sterilization.

*Alpha particles.* These are doubly charged positive nuclei of helium atoms. They have little penetrating effect and consequently may be eliminated from consideration for food sterilization purposes.

*Gamma rays.* These are high energy radiations from certain radio-active isotopes. Like x-rays, they are capable of great penetration into matter. Waste fission products from nuclear reaction installations are potential sources of this type of radiation for sterilization purposes.

A theory known as the "target theory" has been advanced to account for the bactericidal effect of ionizing radiations. When, for example, high energy cathode rays are projected directly into a medium containing bacteria, there is a possibility that electrons will strike various atoms of a bacterial cell. The collisions will cause the electrons to lose energy which, in turn, causes ionization of atoms of the cell constituents. The result may cause death of the cell or impairment of normal cell functions. If a vital area of the cell is hit, death may occur; collisions in less vital areas may affect enzyme mechanisms, rendering them inactive but not necessarily causing their death. Also, there is the possibility of an "indirect effect" caused by electrons that traverse matter near the organism. In such an event, ionization of atoms of the medium may occur. These then may possess sufficient energy, in turn, to ionize atoms of cell constituents and thus affect the organism. In this manner the effect of the electron beam may be extended beyond its directed path through material being irradiated.

Since efficient production, safety, and practicality are three characteristics that radiation sources should possess in order for them to be of use for commercial sterilization of foods, it seems evident from the above discussion of radiation sources that high energy cathode rays have the greatest potential for this purpose. However, energy in the form of gamma rays emitted from waste fission products from nuclear reaction installations may have application for sterilizing purposes. Much current research is being done in this field.

### DESTRUCTION OF BACTERIA IN MILK BY RADIATION

Only a few results of the destruction of microorganisms in dairy products by radiation have appeared in the literature. Most of these have been included with results obtained from the irradiation of a number of other food items and bacterial suspensions. A summary of several of these reports is shown in Table 4.4.

More extensive investigations have been made by Gaden et al. (7) and by Proctor and O'Meara (20). The former group found that the keeping quality of raw milk samples which received doses* of 36,400 and 73,000 R was approximately 1.5 and 2.0 times as great, respectively, as that which occurred in unirradiated samples. Greater differences were obtained at higher doses, but with such doses off-flavors occurred. Proctor and O'Meara irradiated milk by cathode rays produced at 3,000,000 rep. Milk so treated at a temperature within the range of 10°C. to 16°C. (50°F. to 60.8°F.) acquired an off-taste and an off-odor. These defects decreased on storage, but they could be minimized by irradiation of the milk when in the frozen state. These investigators also found a difference in the amount of bacterial destruction in raw milks irradiated in the frozen and unfrozen state as shown in Table 4.5.

The use of electromagnetic radiations for food sterilization is a new technological development. The results so far, as they apply to the sterilization and preservation of milk, are meager. Many problems require solution before this means of destroying microorganisms in milk can be widely applied in commercial dairy plant operations.

## EFFECTS OF SONIC ENERGY, ELECTRICITY, AND PRESSURE

### SOUND

The effect of sound vibrations below frequencies of approximately 10,000 cycles per second (audible sound) has been shown to have little effect on bacteria unless the intensity is very great. Supersonic waves (10,000 to 200,000 cycles per second) and ultrasonic waves (above 200,000 cycles per second) readily affect bacteria and other microorganisms. Such vibrations are so rapid that the cells may shatter, resulting in lysis and

---

\* Radiation dose may be expressed in terms of the "roentgen" (R) and the "roentgen equivalent physical" (rep). The roentgen is the unit of x-ray energy, and is defined as the amount of x-radiation which produces one electrostatic unit of electric charge in 1 cc of air at standard conditions. The roentgen equivalent physical, or rep, is defined as the amount of energy producing in a medium other than air an amount of ionization equivalent to a roentgen.

**Table 4.4**  Summary of results of radiation experiments reported by various investigators

| Product | Original Bacterial Count | Dose | Amount of Sample | Results | Remarks | Investigation |
|---|---|---|---|---|---|---|
| Fluid milk | ? | one impulse, approx. one millionth sec. duration from 3,500,000 volt Capacitron | 50 ml | Sterility | No change in appearance | Brasch & Huber (3) |
| Fluid milk | ? | same as above but with 6 impulses | ? | 6 days storage time at 37.5°C. | good taste and appearance | Brasch & Huber (3) |
| Fluid cream | ? | same as above but with 8 impulses | ? | 8 days storage time at 37.5°C. | taste good; odor fair* | Brasch & Huber (3) |
| Powdered cream | ? | same as above but with 6 impulses | ? | 20 days storage time at 37.5°C. | taste good; odor fair* | Brasch & Huber (3) |
| Cream cheese | ? | same as above but with 12 impulses | ? | 12 days storage | taste good; odor fair* | Brasch & Huber (3) |
| Milk, raw | 1,500,000 per ml | 1,000,000 Roentgens | ? | sterility | ? | Dunn, et al. (5) |
| Milk, pasteurized | 15,000 per ml | 1,000,000 Roentgens | ? | sterility | ? | Dunn, et al. (5) |
| Milk, raw | 37,000,000 per ml | cathode rays produced at 2,000,000 volts. | milk under continuous flow in 4 mm ID glass tubing | 2 per ml | irradiated milk used to prepare cottage cheese. Flavor of cheese normal. | Dunn, et al. (5) |
| Whole milk powder | 1,300 per gm | 1,330,000 rep. | 20–60 gm | 0 per 0.2 gm after incubation of plates at 37°C. and 55°C. | ? | Proctor, et al. (19) |

? Indicates information incomplete.
* Off taste occurred unless deaerated followed by irradiation at low temperatures.

death. Sonic vibration of bacteria has been used rather extensively in obtaining information about the structure of bacteria and in isolating unaltered bacterial constituents which otherwise would be changed by more drastic treatment with heat and chemicals. As yet, the application of sonic treatment to foods for the purpose of destroying bacteria has not been practical.

ELECTRICITY

When a current of electricity is passed through a suspension of bacteria, heat and chemical changes may occur in the suspension medium. This may affect the bacteria and mask any direct effect of the current on the bacteria. Numerous experiments have been performed wherein bacteria have been subjected to electric currents and in which the temperature has been eliminated as a destructive agent. Such experiments have resulted in bacterial destruction. The mechanism of destruction is not clear nor has it been determined with certainty that the effect resulted directly from the passage of the current through the cells.

Pasteurization of milk and the sterilization of water by electricity has been advocated but has not found wide usage. Such units, when used for the pasteurization of milk, must generate sufficient heat to satisfy the temperature-time requirements of pasteurization.

Magnetic forces have little, if any, effect on bacteria.

PRESSURE

Very high pressures are capable of adversely affecting bacteria. Generally hydrostatic pressures in the region of 600 times the normal atmospheric pressure will inhibit growth, and even cause death, of many terrestrial species. On the other hand, marine bacteria found near the ocean floor grow readily at such pressures. Thus it appears that the nature of the habitat governs to a considerable extent the response of bacteria to pressure.

**Table 4.5**   Effect of freezing and irradiation by supervoltage cathode rays on the survival of microorganisms in raw milk *

| Dose | UNFROZEN MILK | | FROZEN MILK | |
| | *Bacterial count* | *Survival* | *Bacterial count* | *Survival* |
| (rep) | (per ml) | (%) | (per ml) | (%) |
| Control | 275,000 | —— | 300,000 | —— |
| 100,000 | 9,000 | 3.3 | 30,000 | 10.0 |
| 200,000 | 700 | 0.25 | 9,000 | 3.0 |
| 300,000 | 130 | 0.05 | 2,700 | 0.9 |
| 500,000 | 5 | 0 | 34 | 0.01 |
| 750,000 | 0 | 0 | 4 | 0 |
| 1,000,000 | 0 | 0 | 0 | 0 |

* From Proctor and O'Meara (20).

Under ordinary conditions pressure is of no consequence in the destruction of bacteria. As mentioned previously, pressure is used in the application of heat sterilizing processes; however, in this instance pressure is used merely to increase the temperature of the steam.

In the dairy and food industry, milk and other products commonly are homogenized by forcing the product through small orifices under high pressure. This often is done at temperatures which are lethal to many bacteria, and reductions in bacterial populations result. When homogenization is performed at non-lethal temperatures no bacterial destruction is evident; in fact, some increases as measured by the agar plate method may occur. This is a false or apparent increase, however, owing to the breaking up of bacterial clumps, thus providing additional sources of colonies in the medium.

## EFFECTS OF SURFACE FORCES

Surface tension refers to the surface forces existing at a liquid-air interface. At the surface of liquids there exists an attraction between molecules which tends to hold them together. A substance in the form of a sphere possesses the smallest amount of surface area per unit of volume. Thus the attractive forces between the molecules of a liquid will tend to cause the liquid to assume the shape of a sphere as is the case with a drop of water in air. Force is required to disrupt the surface—to overcome the cohesive forces of the molecules at the surface.

Surface tension therefore is the force necessary to overcome the attraction between the molecules of a liquid at a liquid-air interface. This may be measured by the du Noüy tensiometer and results are expressed in dynes per square cm.

Interfacial tension is a similar phenomenon but differs from surface tension in that it refers to a liquid-liquid or liquid-solid interface.

Although surface tension can be measured, as can the interfacial tension of liquid-liquid systems, a satisfactory method for measuring interfacial tension of liquid-solid systems such as bacteria suspended in water or in a broth has not been developed. Nevertheless, the forces which act at the surfaces of bacteria as well as at the surfaces of the intracellular constituents affect bacteria greatly (see discussion of "specific surface" in Chapter 1).

The surface tension of pure water is approximately 72 dynes per square cm. Addition of nutrients as in the preparation of media will lower the surface tension. Most bacteria grow well within a range of 50–65 dynes per square cm. Some bacteria (such as the enterococci and enteric bacilli) are capable of growth at low surface tension. This fact is made use of in the selective culture of such organisms through the use of bile salts and other surface tension depressants in culture media. Other types are more sensitive, and exposure to liquids of low surface tension results in growth inhibition and even lysis. In the case of bacteria, which characteristically form a pellicle on the surface of media, or of molds, which form a mat of growth on the surface, the addition of surface tension depressants causes the growth to be dispersed through the body of the medium.

Although microorganisms respond in various ways to changes in surface tension of the medium in which they may be suspended, it is not known with certainty that such effects are the result of altered surface tension per se. Since a bacterium-medium interface is involved, the change in surface tension may be viewed only as an indirect measure of the change in interfacial tension at the bacterium-medium interface.

## DESTRUCTION BY CHEMICALS

### DEFINITIONS

Several terms are commonly used to describe the action of various agents, chemical and physical, in killing and inhibiting microorganisms.

The term disinfectant usually means a chemical agent which destroys organisms capable of causing infection but which does not necessarily kill all types of microorganisms or spores. This term usually is used in connection with the treatment of eating and drinking utensils from contagious-disease wards in hospitals, of floors, and of other inanimate-equipment surfaces suspected of harboring infectious agents. It is commonly used in connection with the treatment of water supplies. The term antiseptic implies protection against sepsis, decay, or putrefaction; it applies to an agent which prevents the growth of microorganisms either by inhibiting or killing them. This term is used to describe agents commonly applied to living tissue. The term germicide means any agent which destroys microorganisms. The term bactericide is more restricted, meaning any agent which kills bacteria but not, necessarily, bacterial spores. The terms fungicide, viricide and sporicide are terms meaning agents which kill fungi other than bacteria, viruses, and bacterial and mold spores, respectively.

Many agents which are known to be excellent disinfectants or germicides may cause other effects, depending upon the conditions of use. For example, when bacteria or other microorganisms are exposed to very small concentrations of certain chemicals, their effect may be stimulatory and actually accelerate growth. Somewhat higher concentrations may be inhibitory but not destructive in the sense that killing occurs rapidly; only when applied in relatively high concentration is a truly germicidal effect obtained. Those substances which do not kill microorganisms rapidly but which inhibit or prevent multiplication for an extended period are called bacteriostatic agents. Actually there is no sharp differentiation between bacteriostatic and germicidal action by various agents. The effect produced is dependent largely upon the conditions of use and often upon the type of organisms to which the agents may be applied. The distinction between the two effects is quite arbitrary and is made for convenience of discussion and designation. Various agents or conditions which often cause bacteriostasis include desiccation, low temperature, sulfonamides, certain dyes, antibiotics, and quaternary ammonium compounds.

### ACIDS

Bacteria are inhibited or destroyed by high acidity. This destructive effect of acidity is due to the hydrogen ions and the undissociated acid molecules. The pH of a solution is a measure of the concentration of the hydrogen ions. Strong acids such as hydrochloric acid are highly dissociated with correspondingly low pH values. Their destructive effect is due primarily to the high concentration of hydrogen ions or the low pH produced. Weak acids such as most of the organic acids, i.e., acetic acid, are much less dissociated and have a much higher pH value. In addition to the effect of the hydrogen ions, the undissociated molecules in solutions of organic acids have been shown to be inhibitory and even destructive. As pH is lowered (concentration of hydrogen ions increased) until a pH of approximately 3.5 is reached, most bacteria are inhibited and many destroyed. Most molds and yeasts are sufficiently resistant to low pH levels and at pH 3.5 will grow readily. Care, therefore, must be taken in the preparation of culture media to control the pH in order to assure growth of the maximum number of organisms, especially when total counts of a mixed flora are sought. The selective effect of pH on bacteria, molds, and yeasts may be utilized in the selective culture of molds and yeasts from materials heavily laden with bacteria. Yeasts, being somewhat more rapid reproducers than molds, often can be isolated from plates of an acidified medium before being overgrown with mold colonies.

Many food products owe their keeping quality to the presence of acidity, with both low pH and undissociated acid contributing to the preservative effect. Lactic and acetic acids are the principal acids produced during the fermentation of products such as sauerkraut, pickles, fermented milks, and silage. Retention of desirable characteristics of these products during storage is due in large measure to the presence of these acids. In the manufacture of many varieties of cheese, the initial acid fermentation results in inhibition of potential spoilage organisms.

### ALKALIES

Bactericidal property of alkalies in general depends upon the concentration of hydroxyl (OH) ions. Therefore the extent of dissociation is a governing factor in the effectiveness of various alkalies. Potassium hydroxide and sodium hydroxide, both highly dissociated, are markedly germicidal. Ammonium hydroxide, which is much less dissociated, is only slightly germicidal. The cation in certain alkalies, such as the barium in barium hydroxide, also is toxic. Therefore both the cation and the anion contribute to germicidal effect in the case of such compounds.

Alkalies are widely used for cleaning and germicidal purposes. The ability of strong alkalies to hydrolyze proteins makes their use of great importance in the cleaning of many types of food equipment. This property permits concurrent destruction of many microorganisms. For example, sodium hydroxide is a common ingredient in milk and other beverage bottle-washers and in solutions used for in-place-cleaning of pipelines and other food and dairy processing equipment.

The acid-fast group of bacteria is one notable exception to the general destructive effect of alkalies upon bacteria. The ability of this group of bacteria to withstand high concentrations of strong alkalies is made use of in selective isolation of them from materials containing a mixed flora and other interfering substances. The alkali dissolves the extraneous material and destroys the non-acid-fast types, leaving the acid-fast organisms unaffected.

## METALS AND THEIR SALTS

Certain metals in the form of their salts or of complex organic compounds are very toxic to microorganisms. In general the bivalent metals are more toxic than the monovalent metals, and the heavier metals such as mercury and silver are more toxic than the lighter metals such as calcium and sodium. For this reason compounds of mercury, silver, bismuth, and arsenic were among the first to be used to combat infections.

Many of these agents have specific uses in the control of certain types of infections. Examples are the application of silver nitrate to the eyes of newborn babies to prevent infection by the gonococci and the use of colloidal preparations of silver as disinfectants on mucous membranes such as the nasal passages. The use of compounds of bismuth and arsenic in the treatment of syphilis was common before the advent of the antibiotics. Organic mercury compounds such as Mercurochrome, Metaphen, and Merthiolate are widely used as antiseptics for skin abrasions, cuts, and wounds.

Mercuric chloride, often known as corrosive sublimate or bichloride of mercury, is an effective germicide. It is irritating to the skin, however, and is poisonous if taken internally. Mercuric chloride is widely used in the dairy industry to preserve composite milk and cream samples for butterfat testing. The chemical does not interfere with the butterfat test; yet it destroys the bacteria and prevents deterioration of the sample.

The toxicity to humans of metallic salts or compounds having germicidal properties has resulted in the use of relatively few such compounds as preservative agents in foods. Notable exceptions to this are sodium chloride, sodium benzoate, sodium propionate, and calcium propionate. The use of brine solutions for the preservation of foods is well known. Sodium benzoate is widely used in small amounts as a preservative in tomato products and in some margarines. Calcium propionate is used as an ingredient in bread to control moldiness and, to some extent, the ropy defect of bread.

Also, some use is made of this agent in the control of surface molding of butter and of cream cheese.

## HYDROGEN PEROXIDE

Hydrogen peroxide ($H_2O_2$) has been used as a germicide for many years. Because of its instability, its use for that purpose is limited. It is effective, however, when applied to deep wounds and to skin abrasions containing dirt and other extraneous material. The bubbling action of the $H_2O_2$ solution that aids in removal of debris probably is of just as much, if not more, value than its germicidal property. The germicidal action of $H_2O_2$ apparently is due to its oxidizing effect.

Recently its use for destroying bacteria in milk has been studied extensively, particularly by the Italians. Relatively few studies have been reported by investigators in this country, although attempts have been made to use $H_2O_2$ to supplement heat in the production of sterile canned milk and some concerns have used it rather extensively in the treatment of milk for cheese making.

The use of chemical additives of any kind for the destruction of microorganisms in milk has not been generally accepted either by the dairy industry or by regulatory officials. The possible residual toxic effects of added chemicals and the general desire to maintain dairy products unadulterated have been the principal reasons for this attitude. Recently, however, there has been a growing tendency toward a re-examination of this viewpoint. The increased knowledge which has accrued over the years in the field of nutrition has stimulated an interest in the possible utilization of certain chemicals to improve the nutritional value of dairy products and to enhance keeping quality.

The use of $H_2O_2$ has received attention in this regard. The addition of $H_2O_2$ to milk will effectively reduce the bacterial population. Furthermore, $H_2O_2$ may be easily eliminated from milk after its germicidal action has occurred by the addition of the enzyme catalase, which decomposes $H_2O_2$ to water and to molecular oxygen. The results of studies which have been reported in the literature show that destruction of approximately 85 per cent of the total bacterial flora may readily be attained by adding 0.2 per cent edible $H_2O_2$ solution (30 per cent–35 per cent $H_2O_2$) to milk at 48.9°C. (120°F.), and by allowing the milk to stand for 10 to 15 minutes before inactivating the $H_2O_2$ with catalase. The data available on the destruction of specific species of bacteria are much more variable. It seems apparent that anaerobic sporeformers are affected greatly, as are the coliforms, although available data show considerable discrepancy in that regard (4, 12). Temperature, pH, concentration of $H_2O_2$, and number of organisms are important factors which influence the bactericidal effect of $H_2O_2$. These factors have not been fully appreciated; consequently, many of the data available lack specificity.

Recent studies (12) have shown that milk treated with $H_2O_2$ gave excellent results in the manufacture of Swiss cheese. This was attributed largely to the destruction of undesirable gas formers, presumably anaerobic and coliform bacteria. A combination of $H_2O_2$ and heat treatment is the basis for the recently developed "Winger Process" (17) for canned sterile whole milk.

Undoubtedly other applications of $H_2O_2$ for the destruction of microorganisms in various foods will be developed. Products such as whey (to inhibit acid production while awaiting further processing), evaporated and dried milks, egg products, and ice cream mix are possibilities for such a development.

$H_2O_2$ treatment of milk should not be considered as a substitute for pasteurization, primarily because (a) it cannot be depended upon to sterilize milk when used in any practical manner and (b) destruction short of sterilization cannot be depended upon to destroy pathogens selectively when in the presence of other bacteria; therefore, pathogens may be present among the survivors of a non-sterilizing treatment.

### HALOGENS

Chlorine and iodine, members of the halogen group of elements, are very active oxidizing agents. Various preparations containing these elements are powerful germicides. Fluorine, another member of this group, is not used for this purpose because of its extreme reactivity. Certain preparations of fluorine, however, are used as insecticides. Recently bromine preparations have been suggested for use as germicides, but, as yet, these have not received wide acceptance.

*Chlorine.* Elemental chlorine is used commercially as a gas. Hypochlorites are available as powders containing calcium hypochlorite ($CaO_2Cl_2$) and sodium hypochlorite (NaOCl), and as solutions of sodium hypochlorite. The strength of hypochlorite powders and solutions is commonly determined by titration procedures and is expressed as per cent "available chlorine."

The bactericidal action of chlorine is probably due to its strong oxidative property; however, direct combination of chlorine with cell proteins also is thought to play a part.

Powders and solutions containing varying concentrations of available chlorine are used in water purification processes, treatment of swimming pool water, and effluents from sewage-treatment plants; they are also used as laundry and household bleaches; as household disinfectants; and as sanitizing agents for restaurant eating and drinking utensils, dairy farm milking utensils, and dairy and food processing equipment.

Several factors affect the practical use of chlorine solutions as germicides. In general the bactericidal effectiveness decreases with increase in pH of solutions. Nevertheless, most hypochlorite solutions are used in the alkaline range for reasons of stability. Chlorine solutions are irritating to the skin, some people being particularly sensitive. Continued use of chlorine solutions for sanitizing the udders and teats of cows often results in chapped and irritated teats. Chlorine powders in tightly closed containers are relatively stable. Hypochlorite solutions, however, deteriorate in storage, especially when exposed to the air and to light. Chlorine solutions are corrosive, and for this reason sanitizing rinses should be applied just prior to use of the equipment. This will prevent long exposure of the metal surfaces to the corrosive action of the chlorine.

When in the presence of organic matter, chlorine is dissipated rapidly from solutions. For this reason maximum effectiveness is obtainable only when surfaces are physically clean. To many the odor of chlorine is objectionable. When added to milk, it may impart a flavor. The concentration of chlorine in milk which will cause an off-flavor corresponds fairly closely to that concentration which has a bactericidal effect in milk. Consequently little difficulty may be expected from the addition of chlorine to milk for the purpose of maintaining low bacterial counts. Increasing the temperature increases the effectiveness of chlorine solutions; however, these solutions should be used at moderate temperatures since elevated temperatures hasten their deterioration and increase their corrosiveness.

Another chlorine compound known as chloramine-T is used commercially as a germicidal agent. The chemical name of this product is paratoluene sulfonchloramide. Its stability to moderate heat and to light are primary advantages; however, slow germicidal action in comparison to that of hypochlorites has resulted in limited use of the compound.

*Iodine.* The use of iodine as a germicide has been limited largely to use in the form of aqueous or alcoholic solutions for topical application to cuts and wounds. A much wider application has resulted from the availability of preparations known as iodophors. These are complex compounds consisting of combinations of iodine and synthetic detergents, the detergent acting as the iodine carrier and, in addition, giving increased stability to the product. The nonionic rather than ionic detergents are most commonly used as carriers. They are very effective bactericides and also have good detergent properties. This dual property has resulted in certain iodophor preparations being known commercially as detergent-sanitizers.

The use of iodophors as sanitizing agents for restaurant utensils, milking utensils, and dairy and food plant equipment is increasing rapidly. Stability when compared with chlorine, negligible odor, and the dual-purpose property of detergent and bactericidal action are major advantages.

The bactericidal effectiveness of iodophors decreases greatly with an increase in pH. For maximum activity solutions should be used at pH 5.0 or lower. Activity is relatively slow at pH 7.0. This is of practical importance for in-use dilution where the concentration of iodine is low, since the water used may cause an increase in pH sufficient to reduce materially the effectiveness of the iodophor.

## QUATERNARY AMMONIUM COMPOUNDS

Quaternary ammonium compounds (quats) are surface active agents. When added to water the surface tension is lowered, and the wetting properties of water are increased. Hundreds of quaternary ammonium compounds are possible, but relatively few are used commercially.

There are three broad classes of surface active agents: anionic, nonionic and cationic. Anionic surface active agents contain the active principle in the anion. Sodium salts of fatty acids (soap) and of sulfated primary alcohols are examples of anionic agents. Nonionic surface active agents do not ionize. They are composed of a hydrophobic or fatty-like group in combination with a hydrophilic group, usually of ether linkage, containing hydroxyl radicals. The latter group confers water-soluble properties to such compounds. Cationic surface active agents contain the active principle in the cation, or positively charged, ion of the molecules. Quaternary ammonium compounds are cationic surface active agents. The chemical structure of quaternaries may be represented by the following formula:

$$\left[ \begin{array}{c} R_1 \\ R_2 \\ \diagdown N \\ R_3 \diagup \\ R_4 \end{array} \right]^+ \; Cl^-,$$

where $R_1$, $R_2$ and $R_3$ represent alkyl groups such as $CH_3$

and $C_2H_5$ or a phenyl group and $R_4$ represents a long chain alkyl group containing 8 to 18 carbon atoms. In general, quaternaries with the above chemical structure are actively germicidal. It is this property which has been primarily responsible for the rapid increase in their commercial use.

Since the active principle is the cation portion of the molecule, the quaternary ammonium compounds are incompatible with anionic compounds such as soaps and synthetic anionic detergents. They are, however, compatible with nonionic detergents. Thus, nonionic detergents are sometimes combined with quaternaries in the preparation of detergent-sanitizers.

In general, quaternary ammonium compounds used as bactericidal agents have the advantages of being nontoxic, essentially odorless and colorless, noncorrosive and nonirritating, stable to heat, relatively stable in the presence of organic matter, and active over a wide range of pH although, generally, they are more effective in the pH range of 7.0 to 8.0 than at higher or lower pH. The effect of pH of quaternary solutions is influenced considerably, however, by the species of organisms involved. Major disadvantages are noncompatibility with anionic detergents and certain water-hardness compounds, lack of good rinsing property, and some selectivity in bactericidal effects. In general, gram-negative bacteria are more resistant than gram-positive types. Recently, proprietary preparations of quaternaries have been formulated to contain sequestering or chelating agents. These agents are added for the purpose of preventing interference of water-hardness compounds with the germicidal activity of the quaternary.

Specific applications of iodine, chlorine, and quaternaries are discussed further in Chapter 6.

## CLEANING AND SANITIZATION

Dairy and food equipment must be maintained in proper sanitary condition. When products are handled or processed in unclean equipment, residues which may be dislodged may be deleterious to the products. Large numbers of microorganisms, often intimately associated with soiled surfaces, must be removed or destroyed for reasons previously discussed. Pathogens, if present, must be destroyed or removed from equipment surfaces to prevent their gaining access to products being handled or processed.

The maintenance of equipment in proper sanitary condition involves two highly important processes, cleaning and sanitization. Both of these when properly applied will result in extensive removal and destruction of microorganisms.

### CLEANING

A variety of surface active synthetic compounds (see discussion of "quaternary ammonium compounds"), available singly or in various combinations, are marketed as synthetic detergents and wetting agents. They are widely applied for various cleaning operations including those involving dairy and food equipment. Various formulations containing these agents are available, and these range from proprietary compounds containing high causticity for use where drastic cleaning treatments are necessary to those suitable for hand washing of equipment. In addition, various synthetic detergents may be combined with chlorine, iodine, or quaternary ammonium compounds to produce a detergent-sanitizer, a product that has both cleaning and bactericidal properties. Preparations containing synthetic detergents and caustic also have cleaning and germicidal activity, the latter due primarily to the sodium hydroxide content; however, the compounds commonly known as detergent-sanitizers contain little or no free caustic and are used principally in hand cleaning operations such as those employed in restaurants, taverns, on dairy farms, and in dairy and food plants.

While some bactericidal effects may be exerted by the synthetic detergents per se, their primary value lies in their ability to lower the surface tension of water and to give water the property of increased "wetness." This permits the solution to contact soiled surfaces more intimately, thus assisting greatly in removal of material including microorganisms from surfaces during the cleaning operation. This principle also is applied in the use of various chemicals for bactericidal purposes to permit more rapid and intimate contact between the germicide and the bacterial cell.

### SANITIZATION

The terms "sanitize" and "sanitization" are commonly used in connection with the care of equipment used in handling milk and milk products and other foods and beverages. The dictionary definition of the word "sanitize" is "to make sanitary." This is a broad definition which would include cleaning and proximate sterilization. As commonly used, however, the term means the application of a bactericidal process sufficient to render equipment approximately sterile. It is also implied that proper sanitization will result in the destruction of pathogens likely to be found associated with dairy equipment and eating and drinking utensils. Cleaning is the first essential in the sanitary care of food equipment, and approximate sterilization is the last. The broader meaning of the word sanitize has given way to the more restricted meaning as given above, and the word, therefore, is descriptive of the final step in the sanitary preparation of dairy and food equipment. Heat and chemicals are used in the sanitization of dairy and food equipment. Heat may be used in the form of hot air, hot water, or steam. The extent of heat treatment applied should be sufficient to destroy pathogens and the more resistant non-pathogenic vegetative bacterial cells as well.

Only three chemical agents are generally acceptable at the present time for sanitizing purposes. These are chlorine in various forms; iodine, usually in combination with certain non-ionic compounds; and certain quaternary ammonium compounds. These chemical agents have been discussed previously in this chapter, and the reader is referred to later chapters for more detailed applications of heat and chemicals in sanitizing procedures.

## MISCELLANEOUS METHODS
## FOR REMOVAL OF MICROORGANISMS

### GRAVITY

When a bacterial suspension is allowed to stand undisturbed, the bacterial cells usually accumulate at the base of the tube or other container. There are exceptions to this however. Motile species will remain uniformly suspended until death or until loss of motility becomes significant, at which time the dead or non-motile cells begin to settle out. The nature of the suspension medium will affect the sedimentation rate. An extreme example of this may be observed in the case of bacteria in milk and cream, where the vast majority of the bacteria actually rise to the surface layers. This is caused by the sweeping action of the fat globules, which, as they rise and cluster, act as a movable filter, carrying the bacteria upward to the cream layer. The reverse of this occurs in the sedimentation beds in water-purification systems where flocs of chemical-precipitating or clarifying agents hasten the settling of suspended material including many cells of microorganisms.

CENTRIFUGAL FORCE

The application of centrifugal force, which in effect accelerates the force of gravity, is of significance in the field of microbiology. Differences in specific gravity and in size of particles are primary factors which affect the rate of sedimentation. This, plus the fact that the amount of centrifugal force (speed of centrifuge) which may be applied can be varied, makes the technique of differential centrifugation possible. Applications of this technique are made in determining particle size of viruses or of inanimate objects, in separating bacteria from viruses, and in obtaining relatively high concentrations of a particular organism or group of organisms from a mixed suspension so as to permit easier isolation.

*Separation and clarification of milk.* The process of mechanical separation of milk has an effect on the distribution of microorganisms in the various fractions obtained. Three fractions (skimmilk, cream, and slime) result from centrifugal separation of milk. With this process many bacteria are removed, as evidenced by the high counts in the separator slime. If the separator itself is clean and free of microorganisms, the bacterial count of cream usually will be somewhat higher than that of either the skimmilk or whole milk. For example, results from 100 separation trials reported by Leete (9) showed that, in 70 trials, bacterial counts of cream were greater than those of the whole milk; in 23 trials, the reverse occurred; and in 7 trials, no differences were observed.

Frequently, the total bacterial population as determined by the plate count of skimmilk and cream combined exceeds that of the whole milk which was separated. Such observations may be explained by realizing the distinction between bacterial count and content. If the separator is not a source of contamination, the total bacterial content of the cream and skimmilk will be less than that of the whole milk, for large numbers of bacteria are found in the separator slime. Agitation during separation (and clarification) may break up clumps of bacteria, thus increasing the number of sources and the number of colonies which may be observed on agar plates prepared from the cream and skimmilk. Separation, therefore, increases the bacterial count but not the bacterial content.

The same effect holds for clarification of milk. In this process, two fractions result, the slime and the clarified milk. Many bacteria as well as other extraneous matter are thrown out in the slime fraction; hence, the bacterial content of clarified milk would be lower than that of unclarified milk. Agitation which results in breaking up clumps has the same effect on bacterial counts as in the case of separation.

FILTRATION

Filtration is the passage of liquids through devices having small porosity. Particles suspended in the liquids either will be retained by the filter or will pass through, depending for the most part upon the electric charge associated with the filter material, upon that associated with the particles in suspension, and upon the porosity of the filter.

Bacteriological filters are made from various materials including compacted diatomaceous earth, special clays, and asbestos fibers; also, filters made of glass which is finely ground and then heated to the sintering point (sintered glass) are available. These are prepared in various sizes and shapes, depending upon use.

Filtration is widely used in the laboratory and in industrial processes. Media which would be altered by a sterilizing heat treatment may be sterilized by passing through small laboratory filters. Viruses may be separated from bacteria by filtration. This is an important technique in determining causes of starter (lactic cultures) failure and is discussed elsewhere. Certain biologics such as serums and solutions, i.e., glucose for intravenous feeding, may be sterilized by filtration.

Water may be purified as it seeps through the soil. This principle is applied in municipal water treatment where suspended material, including most microorganisms, is removed by passing the water through beds of sand and rock.

Cloth filters are sometimes inserted in miik lines, and they are used at farms having pipeline milkers; also, such filters sometimes are used in milk-processing plants to filter the raw milk prior to processing. These filters have little effect in removing bacteria, being used only to remove extraneous matter of larger size. Although effective for this purpose, they may constitute a problem. Bacteria may grow in the filters if they are used for a period of too many hours with milk flowing through at temperatures favorable to bacterial growth.

Many of the agents and principles which have been covered in this chapter will be discussed in later chapters, wherever specific applications are pertinent to various methods of handling and processing milk and milk products.

## References

1. Ball, C. O., Thermal process time for canned foods, *Nat'l. Research Council Bull.* (1932): Volume 7, Part 1, Number 37.

2. ———, Short time pasteurization of milk, *Ind. Eng. Chem.*, 35 (1943): 71–84.

3. Brasch, A., and W. Huber, Ultrashort application time of penetrating electrons, *Science*, 105 (1947): 112–117.

4. Curran, H. R., F. R. Evans, and A. Leviton, The sporicidal action of hydrogen peroxide and the use of crystalline catalase to dissipate residual peroxide, *J. Bacteriol.*, 40 (1940): 423–434.

5. Dunn, C. B., W. L. Campbell, H. Fram, and A. Hutchins, Biological and photochemical effects of high energy, electrostatically produced roentgen rays and cathode rays, *J. Appl. Phys.*, 19 (1948): 605–616.

6. Fay, A. C., The effect of hypertonic sugar solution on the thermal resistance of bacteria, *J. Agr. Research*, 48 (1934): 453–468.

7. Gaden, E. L., Jr., E. J. Henley, and V. P. Collins, Preservation of milk by radiation, *Food Technol.,* 5 (1951): 506–509.

8. Holmquist, C. A., High temperature short time pasteurization. International Association Dairy and Milk Inspectors, 20th Annual Report (1931): 79–100.

9. Leete, C. S., Relation between the bacterial count of whole milk and that of cream and skimmilk separated from it, *J. Agr. Research.,* 31 (1925): 695–699.

10. Mattick, A. T. R., Experiments in the destruction of tubercle bacilli and streptococci. National Institute for Research in Dairying (England) Annual Report, 1937.

11. *Milk Ordinance and Code: Public Health Bull. 220,* (USPHS), 1953.

12. Morris, A. J., P. B. Larsen, and J. D. Johnson, Hydrogen peroxide has a place in the making of high quality Swiss cheese, *Farm and Home Science* (1951): 79–80. Utah Agr. Exp. Sta.

13. North, C. E., and W. H. Park, Standards for milk pasteurization, *Am. J. Hyg.,* 7 (1927): 147–173.

14. North, C. E., W. H. Park, V. A. Moore, M. J. Rosenau, C. Armstrong, A. B. Wadsworth, and E. P. Phelps, Commercial pasteurization, *United States Public Health Service Bull. 147,* 1925.

15. Olson, J. C., Jr., H. Macy, and H. O. Halvorson, Thermal death-time studies of coliform bacteria in milk, *Minn. Agr. Exp. Sta. Tech. Bull. 202,* 1952.

16. Parr, L. W., Coliform Bacteria, *Bacteriol. Rev.,* 3 (1939): 1–48.

17. Patterson, P. J. and E. B. Williams, Whole milk in cans, *Butter, cheese, & milk products J.,* 43 (1952): (No. 2) 30–31.

18. Proctor, B. E. and S. A. Goldblith, Food processing with ionizing radiations, *Food Technol.,* 5 (1951): 376–380.

19. Proctor, B. E., S. A. Goldblith, and H. Fram, Effect of supervoltage cathode rays on bacterial flora of spices and other food materials, *Food Research,* 15 (1950): 490–493.

20. Proctor, B. E. and J. P. O'Meara, Unpublished data, cited by B. E. Proctor and S. A. Goldblith in *Advances in Food Research,* 3 (1951): 119–196.

21. Rosenau, M. J., Thermal death points of pathogenic microorganisms in milk, *Hygienic Laboratory Bull. 42.* Washington, D. C.: Public Health and Marine-Hospital Service, 1908. (United States Public Health Service)

22. Russell, H. L. and E. G. Hastings, Thermal death point of tubercle bacilli under commercial conditions. Wisc. Agr. Exp. Sta. 17th Annual Report (1900): 147.

23. Sherman, J. M., C. N. Stark, and P. Stark, An unappreciated but important factor in the pasteurization of milk, *J. Dairy Sci.,* 12 (1929): 385–393.

24. Smith, Theobald, The thermal death point of tubercle bacilli in milk and other fluids, *J. Exptl. Med.,* 4 (1899): 217.

25. *Standard Methods for the Examination of Dairy Products,* 10th Ed. New York: American Public Health Association, 1953.

26. Theophilus, D. R. and B. W. Hammer, Influence of growth temperature on the thermal resistance of some bacteria from evaporated milk, *Iowa Agr. Exp. Sta. Research Bull. 244,* 1938.

27. Workman, T. W., Short time high temperature pasteurization, Assoc. Bull. Int'l. Assoc. Milk Dealers, No. 22 (1941): 585–588.

# 5

## Microbiological methods of examining dairy products

There are several factors that contribute to the value of quantitative microbiological examinations of milk and milk products. Produced by a living animal (and the only food which can be consumed directly from the animal), milk is handled by a number of employees and is transported varying distances for processing. Any minor exception to approved handling methods may permit the entrance of unwanted bacteria, anywhere along the route from the cow to the consumer. Furthermore, bacteria may enter the milk as it undergoes the numerous processing operations to which it is subjected, because of practices employed during these operations which are not consistent with public health. However, as a result of the constant vigilance of those concerned with milk sanitation and because of the improvement of mechanical devices used in milk production and processing, milk and its products are only rarely involved in human illness.

The acceptance of milk as a nutritious and safe food has been followed by a demand that the product, and those made from it, possess desirable flavor. Milk is an excellent medium for the growth of a large variety of bacteria. Unless proper refrigeration is used to prevent their growth or heat is applied to destroy them, the bacteria will increase readily. When bacteria grow in milk, the flavor usually deteriorates in proportion to the extent of such growth. This deterioration is not the result of the loss of milk constituents so much as the addition of products normally excreted by the growing bacteria. Such products include acids of various types and decomposition products of protein, fat, and other milk constituents. The proper application of bacteriological techniques can locate causes and sources of bacterial contamination and can thus prevent loss of product by the producer and avoid delivery of an unsavory product to the consumer.

Microbiological standards for various dairy products have been developed so that health officials, processors, and producers can judge the sanitary quality of such products and evaluate the sanitation procedures used in making them. These standards are not unattainable goals, goals reserved for those especially equipped to meet them; they are reasonable requests based on proven attainments consistent with certain quality specifications for the milk product concerned. Laboratories and technicians charged with the responsibility of examining milk and milk products microbiologically should realize that the standards set for these products are based on the use of definite and approved laboratory procedures. The abandonment of what seems to be an inconsequential step in a procedure usually leads to a short-cut in technique which has a definite, detrimental effect on the accuracy of the results obtained. Therefore, the approval or disapproval of any product should be based on a laboratory procedure that follows the prescribed method unreservedly. *The Standard Methods for the Examination of Dairy Products* (26) contains recommended procedures that should be followed by all laboratories conducting microbiological examination of milk and milk products. This manual has been prepared by committees from the American Public Health Association and the Association of Official Agricultural Chemists. From time to time new editions of the manual are published in which new procedures, based on research, are presented as approved methods. In any legal consideration of milk analysis, the methods in this publication have priority, for milk ordinances are based on results obtainable by compliance to these prescribed methods.

Certain states have organized programs for certifying laboratories that are qualified to conduct various analyses of milk. The Public Health Service also has such a program for laboratories concerned with examining interstate shipments of milk. In order for a laboratory to qualify under these programs, the methods used must be those recommended in the current edition of *Standard Methods for the Examination of Dairy Products* (26), and qualified personnel must be employed to conduct the analyses.

There are numerous quantitative and qualitative bacteriological examinations that are valuable in evaluating the quality of milk and milk products. The microbiological quality of milk is probably best judged by determining the total number of bacteria present, since the types that may enter depend upon the sources of contamination and the types that grow depend upon many factors. When the production methods used keep the total population to a minimum, there is not only less likelihood of pathogens being present, but there is also greater possibility of having a high quality product with good organoleptic characteristics. The methods used for such determinations include the following: (a) the plate count, which gives an estimate of the numbers of viable bacteria present; (b) the direct microscopic count, which estimates total numbers present, including some dead bacteria in addition to the viable; and (c) the dye reduction tests, by which bacteriological quality of milk is measured by the activity of the bacteria present. The dairy bacteriologist and sanitarian do, however, examine for certain bacteria or groups of bacteria which may indicate that sources of contamination are present whereby pathogens may also enter the product. The detection of other groups of specific microorganisms is part of laboratory control in locating and eliminating specific sources of contamination that can lower the quality of a product. Tests for certain types or groups of bacteria may be quantitative, such as those for coliforms, thermoduric bacteria, thermophiles, and pyschrophiles; at times only qualitative examination is made, for example, when testing for mastitis, brucellosis, and similar conditions.

## BACTERIAL SAMPLES

The proper bacteriological analysis of dairy products is dependent upon the reliability of the sample and the sampling procedure. A sample can be valid only when it meets the following requirements: (a) it is representative of the product sampled; (b) equipment used in handling and collecting it is free from microorganisms; (c) aseptic measures are used in collecting the sample; (d) the sample is stored in a manner to prevent growth or destruction of the bacteria prior to analysis.

The sampling of fluid products requires thorough agitation to distribute the microorganisms homogeneously through the product. Small containers can be shaken, and moderately large volumes can be stirred manually with a can stirrer. Products in tanks can be agitated by mechanical stirrers, but special care must be taken to avoid the use of stirrers incapable of thoroughly mixing large volumes. Air agitators are being increasingly used to mix fluids in large tanks or vats where mechanical stirrers are relatively ineffective (Figure 5.1). The conditions required for obtaining replicate samples with equal bacterial populations should be determined for a given vat and stirring assembly, and these conditions should be used for the collection of any subsequent samples. Solid products are sampled by collecting a representative portion, going from the outer layers to the center. Care is taken that the outer portion has not been contaminated subsequent to the manufacture and packaging of the product.

Containers for samples can be sterilized by conventional laboratory procedures. Sampling tubes, triers, or milk-thieves can be similarly sterilized. Dippers and hand agitators may, after being rinsed in a can of flowing water, be sanitized by being placed in a can containing a chemical bactericide. Any viable bacteria that might survive such treatment would

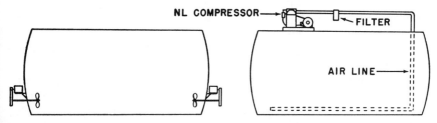

**Figure 5.1**     Schematic diagram for the agitation of milk in a horizontal tank by the use of air and mechanical agitators. Courtesy of Ingersoll-Rand Co., Phillipsburg, N. J.

be sufficiently diluted in the product sampled so as not to be detectable. Larger agitators can be cleaned and then disinfected by heat or by "fogging" with a chemical disinfectant.

During the collection of samples reasonable asepsis must be practiced. Excessive air currents that may be dust laden, splashings, the drippings of condensate, and similar factors can easily be avoided.

Immediately after its collection, a fluid sample can best be stored in a mixture of ice and water. This will maintain a temperature near 0°C. (32°F.), which will prevent growth, or destruction, of the bacteria in the sample. Fluid samples should not be frozen since this and the subsequent thawing prior to testing may kill some microorganisms. It is customary to examine liquid samples within 4 hours from the time of sampling. Samples of frozen products should be kept in the frozen condition until tested.

For details of recommended sampling procedures the reader is referred to the latest edition of *Standard Methods for the Examination of Dairy Products* (26).

## QUANTITATIVE METHODS FOR TOTAL BACTERIA

### THE STANDARD PLATE COUNT

The standard plate count is one of the oldest and most frequently used methods for enumerating bacteria. When it was originally proposed, its purpose was to count all of the bacteria contained in the portion of milk plated. Actually, however, counts obtained are only estimates, since the conditions of the test (incubation temperature, medium, oxidation-reduction potential, existence of clumps of bacteria, and so forth) impose limitations that may prevent the growth of some of the bacteria in a sample. Certain of the factors have been adjusted over the years so that the present method is superior to older ones for obtaining an estimate of the total bacterial population in milk samples; further improvement is, however, still possible. In making plate counts there are numerous manipulations, variations in which can affect the accuracy of the count obtained. For this reason every detail pertaining to apparatus, technique of plating, incubation, counting, and reporting of counts is presented in detail in the current edition of *Standard Methods for the Examination of Dairy Products* (26). Anyone engaged in performing plate counts should follow completely the method outlined in this manual. Bacterial standards fulfill their purpose only when plate counts are obtained in this manner and, furthermore, counts obtained this way in any given laboratory can be accepted as authoritative by all persons concerned.

The sterility of all glassware, dilution blanks, and media is essential in this procedure. Liquids are autoclaved at 121°C. (250°F.) for 20 minutes, and dry glassware is sterilized, preferably in metal cans, at 170°C. (338°F.) for at least 1 hour. Media and glassware should be checked periodically to be sure that the proper sterilization is being obtained.

Dilution blanks prepared with buffered distilled water (pH 7.2) are preferable to tap water, unless continuous observations indicate that the tap water is not toxic or bacteriostatic to bacteria. The presence of high concentrations of chlorine and certain minerals, such as copper, make some tap water supplies unsuitable for use in bacteriological procedures. The volume of the dilution blank often is reduced as a result of evaporation during sterilization. The volume used should be such that the final volume after autoclaving is $99 \pm 2$ ml. Screw cap closures prevent contamination at the lip of the bottles; leak-proof rubber liners in the caps are desirable in order to prevent evaporation during storage and leakage during shaking when samples are diluted.

Two media have been approved officially for plating milk samples, and either of these can be used. Both are clear, permitting easy count of colonies, and give essentially equal results when used with the same milk sample (19). The two media and their composition are as follows:

(1) Plate count agar (Bacto No. 479).

| | |
|---|---|
| Bacto-yeast extract | 2.5 g |
| Bacto-tryptone | 5.0 g |
| Bacto-dextrose | 1.0 g |
| Bacto-agar | 15.0 g |
| Distilled water | 1,000.0 ml |
| Final pH | $7.0 \pm 0.1$ |

(2) Milk-protein hydrolysate medium (BBL No. 298).

| | |
|---|---|
| Milk-protein hydrolysate | 9.0 g |
| Glucose | 1.0 g |
| Agar | 15.0 g |
| Distilled water | 1,000.0 ml |
| Final pH | $7.0 \pm 0.1$ |

Petri dishes that have flat bottoms will permit the medium to have a uniform depth, will promote a more uniform distribution of colonies in the plate, and will facilitate counting. The use of pipettes that conform to American Public Health Association specifications and the discarding of those with broken tips are necessary to assure accuracy in volumetric measurements.

Plates which contain an amount of milk sample that will yield between 30 and 300 colonies provide the most accurate counts. Plates containing over 300 colonies may be too crowded for an accurate count, and some colonies may not develop owing to by-products of growth from adjacent colonies. In plates containing less than 30 colonies the chances of having a representative count are decreased. Since most raw and pasteurized milk will give a plate count greater than 300 per milliliter, the sample of milk must be quantitatively diluted so that an exact smaller amount of milk can be placed in the petri dish. Experience within a laboratory will establish the dilutions required to obtain the proper number of colonies per plate; usually two dilutions of each sample are plated. Samples are diluted and placed in the petri dishes as outlined in Figure 5.2. A series of plates with the proper dilutions is prepared. Melted and tempered standard plating medium is added and then the dish rotated or tilted gently to mix thoroughly the sample and the agar. Care should be given to melting the medium completely, without heating it over an extended length of time. The agar subsequently must be tempered thoroughly in a water bath to 43°C. to 45°C. (109.4°F. to 113°F.). After the dishes are poured and the medium has solidified completely, the dishes are inverted and then incubated at 32°C. (89.6°F.) or 35°C. (95°F.) for 48 ± 3 hours.

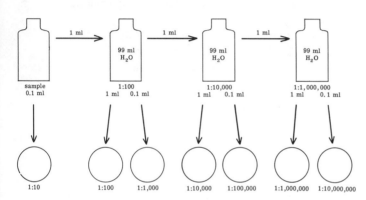

**Figure 5.2**    Protocol for preparing dilutions of a milk sample, indicating volumes to be added to dilution blanks and petri dishes.

At the end of the incubation period all of the colonies are counted in those dishes containing between 30 and 300 colonies (Figure 5.3). By multiplying the number of colonies by the dilution used for a given dish, the standard plate count per milliliter for a given sample is obtained. Definite rules for counting are presented in *Standard Methods for the Examination of Dairy Products* (26); these rules should be consulted particularly for information on the following: (a) counting of duplicate plates; (b) selection of dilutions to be counted; (c) use of plates having spreaders; (d) plates showing less than 30 or more than 300 colonies; (e) laboratory accidents. Counts obtained by use of the standard procedure are reported as Standard Plate Count (or SPC) per milliliter or gram, the latter being used when working with gravimetric measurements on the original sample.

The plate count is particularly useful for low count milk, since 1 ml or more can be examined, as well as fractions thereof. For this reason pasteurized milk counts are obtained almost exclusively by this technique. It also usually is selected for use when premiums are paid to producers for raw milk that meets rigid standards of low count. It is preferred by some workers because colonies of bacteria are easily discernible, and it will detect only the viable bacteria present (i. e., those capable of developing under the test conditions).

There are several factors with which a worker should be familiar in order to realize the limitations of accuracy inherent in the standard plate count procedure. Measurements involving a complete biological system (bacterial cell) are always subject to variations. Furthermore, the bacterial cells in milk will exist in varying ages and stages of division. The different types which may be present also will have varying growth requirements.

The nutrient composition of the medium used for counting is not adequate for the growth of certain bacteria. Furthermore, the yeast extract and protein hydrolysates of the plating media are not synthetic compounds; rather, they are derived from naturally occurring materials by processes which require careful control to assure the same composition in replicate batches. As a result, a reference medium composed of pure chemicals has been developed by which manufacturers can test the performance of each batch of medium (18). This should aid in eliminating any differences which formerly may have been observed in different lots of the medium. It should be recognized that this reference medium is not intended to en-

**Figure 5.3**  Bacterial colonies on an agar plate prepared from milk. Present are between 30 and 300 well distributed colonies, which provide for accurate enumeration.

able all bacteria in the sample to grow; it was formulated to enumerate essentially the same percentage of bacteria as shown by acceptable batches of the standard plating media. Another factor often overlooked is the pH of the medium, even when prepared from dehydrated complete medium. Workers frequently do not check this, or do not check it accurately, and it has been observed that batches have varied appreciably in pH after the medium has been rehydrated and prepared for use.

It should be borne in mind that the temperature of incubation (32°C. or 35°C.) may not permit the growth of all bacteria which may be in milk. For psychrophilic bacteria the 35°C. (95°F.) temperature is definitely too high; 32°C. (86.6°F.) may also be too high to permit growth of some of these bacteria. For some thermophilic bacteria these temperatures are too low. Special incubators must be provided when detection of these groups, the enumeration of which will be discussed later, is desired. The standard incubation temperature formerly was 37°C. (98.6°F.), but it has been shown that the temperatures now in use permit the development of more colonies. In regulatory laboratories where both diagnostic bacteriology and plate counts of milk are performed, the need for the lower temperature for the milk plates often is not appreciated. Usually these laboratories maintain incubators at 37°C. (98.6°F.) for the growth of pathogenic bacteria and do not have other incubation temperatures available. More recent studies have indicated that even lower temperatures of incubation may be more effective for obtaining bacterial counts in milk (3). For raw milk plates, incubation for two days at temperatures in the range of 26°C. to 32°C. (78.8°F. to 89.6°F.) gave the highest count; for pasteurized milk 32°C. (89.6°F.) gave the highest count (Figure 5.4). Thus in choosing be-

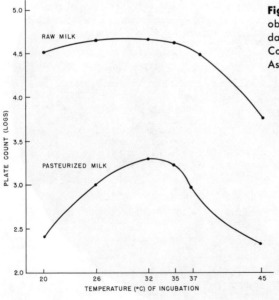

**Figure 5.4** The plate count of milk obtained by incubation of plates for 2 days at different temperatures. From Committee of American Dairy Science Assoc. Report (3).

tween the present allowable temperatures, the 32°C. (89.6°F.) incubation would yield the higher results.

The colonies of bacteria appearing on a plate usually are considered as having originated from a single cell. However, a number of colonies may originate also from pairs, chains, or clumps of cells that have not been separated during the diluting and plating processes. In order to minimize some of the effects of inconsistent disruption of groups of cells, the standard plating procedure recommends that dilution blanks be shaken 25 times over a distance of 1 foot during a period of 7 seconds. Although this standardizes the technique, it should be recognized that a number of the colonies still originate from more than one cell.

If one uses the standard plate count, keeping in mind its limitations of application, and at the same time adheres to the details of the standardized procedure, the results obtained yield valuable information regarding the sanitary quality of the milk sample. Furthermore, the data obtained in different laboratories under such conditions are of value for examinations by other investigators and by regulatory officials.

### THE DIRECT MICROSCOPIC COUNT

The purpose of this method is similar to that of the plate count in that an attempt is made to determine the total bacterial population of a sample of milk. The bacteria as well as the body cells and leucocytes in the sample are more or less selectively stained, and the bacteria in a representative portion are enumerated. In order to attain accuracy, however, an exact volume of milk is used for staining, and this must be spread over an exact area so that each microscopic field examined represents a quantitative aliquot of the sample. The method has the advantage of being rapid, as well as of revealing the types of bacteria present. The latter information is very useful in locating sources of contamination during production. On the other hand, the method has the limitation of being of little use for low count milk, and one must remember that, because of the small volume used, it is necessary to have a representative aliquot for counting. The laboratory worker should be completely familiar with the technique and procedure for this method as given in *Standard Methods for the Examination of Dairy Products* (26).

Glass slides which have a frosted area lengthwise on which the sample can be identified are very satisfactory. Slides 3 inches x 1 inch on which 4 films can be prepared or those 3 inches x 2 inches that accommodate up to 15 films are satisfactory. The slides should be cleaned so as to remove all soil, particularly traces of grease or oil film. Washed slides that have been treated in acid dichromate solution or in 95 per cent alcohol plus 3 per cent glacial acetic acid, dried, and then passed through a gas flame several times usually are satisfactory. Unless the slide is thoroughly cleaned, the film of milk will not adhere to it during staining and washing. The slide is then laid over a guide plate which has areas of 1 cm$^2$—100 mm$^2$—outlined in contrasting colors. Slides also are available that have round areas covering 1 cm$^2$ delineated by a fused line or etching. The latter has the advantage of allowing each film to be identified by pencil.

A special pipette (Breed) which is calibrated to deliver 0.01 ml of milk is used to measure the sample to be counted. This pipette has a very small bore and must always be rinsed, cleaned, and sanitized after each using to prevent the accumulation of solids that otherwise would produce inaccurate measurements and also contaminate successive samples from the previous ones. The milk is drawn somewhat above the 0.01 ml mark and held there while milk adhering to the outside of the pipette is removed with a clean cloth. Then by touching the tip of the pipette to the cloth the milk is drawn by capillarity to the 0.01 ml gradation. The 0.01 ml of sample is placed in the center of the 1 cm$^2$ area by blowing gently on the pipette, which is raised from the slide while the tester is still blowing to prevent re-entrance of the milk by capillarity. The milk is then spread over the 1 cm$^2$ area with a flamed wire needle, and the film is dried within approximately 5 minutes. The drying should be accomplished quickly enough to prevent growth of bacteria, but not so rapidly as to crack the milk film.

Recently a stainless steel syringe-type pipette has been developed whereby measurement of the 0.01 ml sample is facilitated (16). The 0.01 ml portion of milk is drawn into the measuring tube by a spring-actuated piston connected to a plunger. Excess milk adhering to the tip is wiped off. When the plunger is pressed down, the milk is discharged ahead of the piston. When the piston discharges the 0.01 ml aliquot, it protrudes beyond the tip of the pipette and can be used to spread the milk over the 1 cm$^2$ area. This pipette is shown in Figure 5.5.

Loops calibrated to deliver 0.01 ml of milk are available, but this method of measurement is susceptible to sufficient errors due to variations in milk composition, to the manner of withdrawing the loopful of milk, and to other factors to discourage its use in the grading of milk. The loop measurement may be satisfactory for screening a large number of samples in order to get an approximation of the level of bacterial population, but it is not acceptable for grading purposes.

The dried milk film is defatted by the method appropriate for the procedure chosen and then is dried. The next step involves staining with methylene blue. There have been numerous stains proposed for this, some of which like the Newman-Lampert stain, contain the fat solvent and the fixative in order to combine the three steps into one.

Some stains are formulated so that, while the bacteria are stained blue (by methylene blue), the milk background is stained pink (by basic fuchsin); examples of this type of stain are the Gray and the Broadhurst-Paley stains. Comparative studies have shown, however, that the acid-and-water-free stain, the aniline oil methylene blue stain, or the polychrome methylene blue stain reveals a larger number of bacteria than the other stains com-

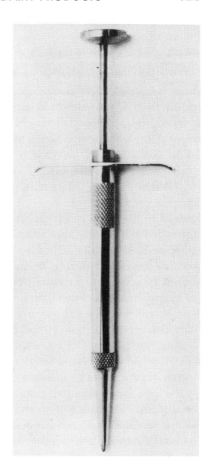

**Figure 5.5**     A syringe pipette for delivering 0.01 ml volume of milk in preparing films for the direct microscopic count. Courtesy of Applied Research Institute, New York, N. Y.

monly used, or proposed, for the direct microscopic count of milk (17). These three staining procedures all now have official status (26).

After the milk film is dried, the enumeration of bacteria can be made immediately, using the oil immersion objective of the microscope (approximately $970 \times$ magnification). Since it is impracticable to examine every portion of the milk film, a sufficient number of representative microscopic fields is examined; the bacterial clumps are counted; and the average number per field is calculated. Therefore, in order to determine the total number of clumps in the whole film one must know the area of the field observed through the microscope. As the area of a circle $= \pi r^2$, one has only to measure the diameter (in mm) of the field by the use of a stage micrometer. The area of the milk film—100 mm²—divided by the area of the microscope field yields the number of microscopic fields in the film. Since the film contains 0.01 ml of milk, the number of fields per film multiplied by 100 gives the number of fields per milliliter of milk, or what is termed the microscopic factor. A simple formula which represents the foregoing arithmetical calculations is the following: $\dfrac{10,000}{3.1416(r^2)} =$ microscopic factor.

As long as the objective, draw tube, and ocular of the microscope remain unchanged, the microscopic factor remains constant and need not be recalibrated. If the calibrated instrument is binocular and the persons using it have interpupillary distances varying greatly from the average (60–65 mm), the microscopic factor should be redetermined by such individuals. Multiplication of the average number of bacteria per field by the microscopic factor yields the number of bacteria per milliliter of sample.

When the 0.01 ml of milk is deposited on the slide, many clumps of bacteria present seem to be concentrated in the surface of the milk and to adhere to the slide at the point of original contact. Clumps of bacteria suspended in the milk appear to concentrate in the center of the dried film either because it is thicker at this point or because the clumps are propelled towards the center during drying (12). For this reason the fields counted should be chosen at random over the film so as to give as representative an examination as is possible, and caution should be taken to see that no field is counted more than once. For the number of fields to be counted with a given microscopic factor, the worker should consult *Standard Methods for the Examination of Dairy Products* (26). A sequential grading plan has been developed which requires fewer observations to obtain results with a given degree of precision (12). In this method a sequential grading table is used which lists, for consecutive numbers of fields counted, the number of bacterial clumps indicative of compliance or non-compliance by a milk sample with a certain grade requirement. After examining varying numbers of fields, the cumulative number of bacterial clumps is compared with the compliance or non-compliance limits for the total fields counted. Counts are continued until it is determined whether or not the milk sample complies with requirements for a certain bacteriological grade.

The direct microscopic count offers certain advantages over other methods for determining the quality of milk. The results are obtained quickly by one skilled in the technique. Once the films have been counted, they can be stored as a permanent record to which one may refer later for any purpose. The total equipment required for this method is less expensive than that required for the standard plate count. Probably the most outstanding advantage is that, when excessive bacteria are present in a sample, their morphology gives valuable clues to the practice which permits the bacteria to be present in the milk.

There are at least four types of contamination which can be recognized by observation of the bacteria present during enumeration in the microscopic count (Figure 5.6). These are the following:

(1) *Improperly cleaned utensils.* Milk aseptically drawn from the udder contains micrococci predominantly. When milk is not removed from utensils, its normal flora always provides bacteria that will develop even on

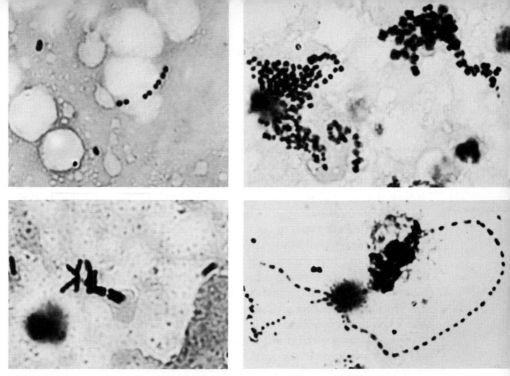

**Figure 5.6** Types and probable sources of microorganisms detectable by the direct microscopic count of milk: (top left) improperly refrigerated milk; (top right) inadequate cleaning and sanitization of milking utensils; (left) dust and soil contamination; (right) milk from cow with mastitis.

residues where the amount of milk solids available is extremely small. Therefore, the presence of cocci, particularly when in clumps of varying sizes, indicates that the sample under observation has been handled in improperly cleaned utensils. Rod forms may also accompany the cocci, but the latter are predominant in this type of contamination.

(2) *Dusty or dirty environment.* Rod forms of bacteria normally are present in large numbers in the soil and manure. Conditions such as dirt on cows, dust in the milking barn originating from feeding, and unclean floors, walls, and bedding will provide sources of this type of bacteria. The need for the correction of such conditions is indicated by high counts caused by the presence of rods in milk.

(3) *Improper cooling of milk.* Milk contains the necessary nutrients for the growth of most of the bacteria that may occur in it. Therefore, temperature is the principal factor controlling the growth of the bacteria present. When the temperature is allowed to rise sufficiently above refrigeration temperatures, the bacteria will begin to grow and multiply more rapidly. The primary manifestation of growth is division of one cell into two daughter cells that adhere together for a period after the first evidence of fission occurs. When a sample of milk contains bacteria that are primarily in pairs or short chains (usually *Streptococcus lactis* or *Streptococcus cremoris*), it can be safely concluded that the milk has been improperly cooled.

(4) *Mastitis.* Bovine mastitis may be caused by any one of a number of bacteria, but in many of the cases the causative organism is *Streptococcus agalactiae.* This organism appears in rather long chains. Leucocytes are present in abnormally large numbers (more than 500,000 ml) in most cases of mastitis. Often the increased leucocyte count precedes the appearance of the bacteria in large numbers, and this means of detecting mastitis early may aid in the treatment of the disease. High leucocyte counts may persist during the chronic stages of the disease, although bacterial numbers are not great enough to be readily detectable by microscopic procedures.

By noting the types of bacteria present in a sample, the regulatory or dairy laboratory is able to expedite the correction of conditions that are undesirable in the production of milk. Often the producer develops a more cooperative attitude toward processors and regulatory officials when he realizes that the bacteriological examination to which his milk is subjected will aid him in locating sources of trouble when it arises.

The microscopic count is not ordinarily considered useful for counting bacteria in pasteurized milk, for several reasons. The viable bacteria that normally are present are so low in numbers that an inordinately large number of fields must be examined before detecting them. The small number of cells also may be distributed unevenly in the film. Another consideration is that bacteria killed by pasteurization retain their ability to be stained for some time after pasteurization. Thus counts performed within about 24 hours after pasteurization may include non-viable bacteria. Some plants, particularly those using the vat method of pasteurization of 61.7°C. (143°F.) for 30 minutes, have found it advantageous to perform microscopic counts on pasteurized milk in efforts to detect the presence of thermophilic bacteria in their products. The thermophilic bacteria present in pasteurized milk are characteristically rod shaped, and the presence of such organisms, particularly with an increase in numbers during the progress of processing, indicates thermophilic contamination.

### THE METHYLENE BLUE REDUCTION TEST

The methylene blue reduction method is an indirect method of estimating the total bacterial content of milk. Instead of counting bacteria directly, a correlation is made between the time required to reduce methylene blue dye to a colorless form in the milk and the probable bacterial population level of the sample. Generally, the time required for reduction of the dye is inversely proportional to the number of bacteria present in the milk. The method is adaptable to the examination of a large number of samples in a comparatively short time with a small amount of equipment and materials, and it has been used widely for the grading of raw milk. The method does not, however, give any information concerning the probable source of contamination if the bacterial population is high (i.e., when the reduction time is short). As with other methods, the technician must observe strict rules of procedure as outlined in *Standard Methods for the Examination of Dairy Products* (26) in order to gain the proper information on samples of milk.

The glassware used for this test need not be sterile, but its contamination should be reduced to a minimum by treatment with boiling water or free-flowing steam. When a 10 ml dipper is used for transferring samples to the tubes, it may be rinsed in a can of clean running water, and then sanitized by immersion in 100 ppm chlorine solution. The very few bacteria that might remain on apparatus after this procedure will not be sufficient to alter the results of the test.

Essentially the procedure is to add 10 ml of milk sample to 1 ml of methylene blue dye solution and to keep the mixture refrigerated until all samples have been so prepared. The tubes are then tempered to 37°C. (98.6°F.) within 5 minutes and incubated at this temperature in a constant temperature bath. After the tempering period, the tubes are inverted gently 3 times to redistribute the cream, and this point is used as the starting time of the test. The initial observations for reduction are made after 30 minutes, and at hourly intervals thereafter. At each observation those tubes which show reduction are removed and recorded, and the remaining ones are inverted 1 time and reincubated. Those reduced at the initial 30 minute observation are recorded as reduced in 30 minutes; those reduced between the 0.5 and the 1.5 hour times, as reduced in 1 hour; those between the 1.5 and 2.5 hours, as reduced in 2 hours, and so forth.

Methylene blue thiocyanate is used since this compound can be prepared with a reproducible dye content. The concentration used is 1 part of dye in 300,000 parts of milk. To obviate differences attributed to weighing, the dye can now be obtained in tablet form; one tablet dissolved in 200 ml of hot, distilled water produces the stock dye solution for addition to the milk tubes. Although this solution is stable when it is refrigerated and protected from light, it is safer to prepare the solution weekly. The susceptibility of the dye to light, natural or artificial, makes it mandatory that the dye solution be stored in low actinic glass and that the reduction test be conducted in a water bath that can be covered tightly to exclude light. Constant temperature baths designed specifically for this test are available.

The inversion of the tubes at the specified intervals has aided materially in overcoming the earlier objectionable feature of creaming. Bacteria normally are carried to the top as the cream rises, making the reduction of the dye irregular throughout the tube. These effects are minimized by the present technique. The inversion of the tubes must be gentle, otherwise the incorporation of oxygen in the milk will cause oxidation of the dye. Since the change from the blue (oxidized) form of the dye to the colorless (reduced) form is reversible, unnecessary agitation of the sample will cause an extended reduction time and will give results indicative of a higher quality than actually exists. The exposure of the surface of the milk to the oxygen in the air above it will cause that part of the milk to remain

blue for some time after the remainder is reduced. For this reason the reduction time is taken to be the time required to reduce the color in four-
fifths of the milk.

Milk as it exists in the udder has a sufficiently low oxidation-reduction
potential to reduce methylene blue immediately. The incorporation of oxygen into the milk during milking, cooling, dumping, and so forth, raises
the potential to about +0.3 volt. At this potential, methylene blue will
exist in the oxidized form, i.e., have a blue color. As the bacteria in the
milk grow during the progress of the test, the potential is lowered; and the
methylene blue is reduced to the colorless form when the oxidation-reduction potential reaches approximately +0.06 to −0.01 volt. Different explanations have been offered regarding the mechanism of the dye reduction
during the test. There are, possibly, several factors interrelated in this
process. Oxygen is removed from the milk by the respiratory process of the
bacteria. This results in a shift of the oxidation-reduction potential since
the oxygen ordinarily maintains a positive potential. As the potential falls,
hydrogen presumably is transferred from milk constituents and bacterial
metabolites to the methylene blue, causing its reduction. Bacteria such as
*Streptococcus lactis* and *Escherichia coli* lower the potential rapidly; others
lower it much more slowly. Although the dye is reduced at a higher oxidation-reduction potential at lower pH values, the abilities of an organism
to produce acid and to reduce methylene blue are not necessarily correlated.

The methylene blue test has found many uses in the grading of raw
milk for pasteurization and of milk to be used as evaporated milk. Its simplicity and the rapidity with which data are obtained are definitely in its
favor. There are, however, definite limitations in the accuracy of the
method, limitations of which the technician and those concerned in the
evaluation of the results should be fully aware. First, the 37°C. (98.6°F.)
temperature of incubation is not favorable for the metabolism of all the
bacteria contained in milk. Second, the different bacteria have varying
abilities with regard to lowering the oxidation-reduction potential of milk.
Thermoduric bacteria frequently are relatively inactive in the test for the
above two reasons. This is probably the most important objection to the
method, for thermoduric bacteria constitute a very important problem for
the processor. Psychrophilic and thermophilic bacteria would show little or
no activity in this test. Inhibitory materials in milk also will prevent the
growth of many bacteria and will cause the test to give an indication of
higher quality than may actually exist. For these reasons, counting methods
will reveal certain bacteria which would not be detected by the methylene
blue test. On the other hand, there may be circumstances wherein the dye
reduction technique would be more indicative of the quality than actual
counts by the plate method. Involved here would be the ability of certain
bacteria to grow in milk, but their inability to form visible colonies on the
standard plating medium. Furthermore, the individual cells of a clump,
which would form just one colony by the plate count, would be more in

evidence by the dye reduction test since each cell would be metabolizing and the cumulative effect of all the cells would be noted. From a practical standpoint, these factors are not considered important since the results of the dye reduction test more frequently indicate lower bacterial populations than are revealed to be the case by counting methods.

The value of the methylene blue test can be expanded somewhat by making a microscopic examination of those samples that reduce the dye sooner than the limit permitted by the grade for which the milk is intended. This gives information on the types of bacteria present in such samples and facilitates remedial procedures. In Great Britain the milk samples are held at atmospheric temperatures, but not exceeding 18.8°C. (65°F.), for about 18 hours prior to performing the test. This not only shortens the time required for dye reduction, but it is considered to give more accurate information on the keeping quality of the original milk.

### THE RESAZURIN REDUCTION TEST

This test is similar to the methylene blue test, but it uses the indicator resazurin to measure the bacteriological quality of milk. After being reported in the United States in 1935 (22), the resazurin test has gained popularity primarily because it requires a maximum of only 3 hours and because, through it, abnormal milk can be detected. Many studies have attested to the value of the method, and it is now recognized by many regulatory agencies as valid in the grading of raw milk.

Resazurin has certain characteristics that make its use as an indicator very useful. The color of resazurin at the normal pH of milk is blue. This compound is reduced to resorufin, which is pink, the color changing gradually during the reduction process from the initial blue through shades of purple and lavender to the full pink color. This phase of reduction is not reversible, and the change to the resorufin occurs at an oxidation-reduction potential between $+0.2$ and $+0.05$ volt. The resorufin is then reduced to hydroresorufin, which is white. This reaction is reversible, the change occurring between $+0.15$ and $0$ volt. In conducting the test, however, the first reaction is of chief concern. In the one-hour test the color of the milk is compared with color standards prepared for blue, the intermediate shades of purple and lavender, and for pink; the grade of the milk depends on the color of the milk after one hour of incubation. In the three-hour test, comparisons of the tubes at intervals of one hour are made with a standard lavender color (Munsell color standard P 7/4), and the grading is done on the basis of the time required to reach this color.

In performing the test 10 ml of milk is added to a screw-capped vial plus resazurin to give a concentration of about one part of dye in 180,000 parts of milk. Standardized tablets of resazurin, each containing 11 mg of dye, are now commercially available. By dissolving one tablet in 200 ml of water and adding 1 ml of the dye solution to 10 ml of milk, the correct amount of resazurin is easily obtained. The tubes are then incubated in a water bath at 37°C. (98.6°F.). After the samples reach this temperature, they are gently inverted three times and returned to the bath; and then the time of incubation begins. In the one-hour test, the tubes are removed from the bath and each tube is compared with a set of four color standards (Munsell). The tubes are graded in the following manner:

> Grade 1—Colors from initial to P B P 7/5.5 (purple shade)
> Grade 2—Colors from P B P 7/5.5 to P R P 7/8 (lavender shade)
> Grade 3—Samples showing pink color
> Grade 4—Samples decolorizing dye completely.

These grades were established at a time when Grade 1 would correspond with a methylene reduction time of not less than 5.5 hours, and the other grades with the corresponding methylene blue class. Applying this grading system to present standards of milk quality would allow more leniency than is now permitted.

The three-hour, or triple reading test, is more commonly used. After the first hour of incubation those tubes having a color of P 7/4 (Munsell color standard) are removed and recorded. The remainder of the tubes are inverted once gently and reincubated. At the end of the second and third hours of incubation the comparison to the color standard of P 7/4 and the inversion of remaining tubes are repeated. The assignment of the milk to grades is then made on the basis of the time in which the resazurin is reduced to the color of P 7/4. This modification of the test is considered to yield results that are more indicative of the bacterial quality of the milk than the one-hour test, particularly since some types of bacteria may not be so rapid in initiating growth.

In conducting the test, the glassware and the dye solution are prepared as described for the methylene blue test. Protection from light also should be provided during the test. Vials containing the correct amount of dry resazurin are now commercially available. In addition, the vials are convenient, and the resazurin in the dry form is stable for long periods and is not particularly sensitive to light.

Since the color changes that are used as end-points of the test occur at higher oxidation-reduction potentials than those for the methylene blue test, the resazurin test can be done in a shorter period of time. Furthermore, colostrum and milk from cows that have diseased udders or from cows that are being dried up reduce the resazurin very quickly. In such milk the oxidation-reduction zone of dye reduction is shifted more to the positive side than is required for normal milk. It is generally assumed that leucocytes or substances associated with leucocytes are responsible for this shift. Reduction in such instances is not always associated with high bacterial content, but the ability of the test to detect such milk is certainly a point in its favor. Even though milk of this nature may not be unsafe, its flavor is undesirable, and the quality of normal milk should be maintained by excluding abnormal milk from it. Knowledge of the effect of milk from diseased udders on resazurin has been employed to advantage in locating mastitic cows, the resazurin reduction test being used as a screening test for mastitis on milk from individual quarters (11).

## QUANTITATIVE TESTS FOR SPECIFIC TYPES OF MICROORGANISMS

### THERMODURIC BACTERIA

The term thermoduric bacteria is applied to any bacterial species that resists a particular process involving heat. In the dairy industry the term is used almost exclusively to categorize those bacteria surviving pasteurization processes. It should be emphasized that, for an organism to be considered thermoduric, it need only survive pasteurization; its growth at pasteurization temperatures is not implied. Actually the optimum temperature for the growth of most thermoduric bacteria is about 30°C. to 32°C. (86°F. to 89.6°F.). Their action on milk constituents is frequently not very pronounced, some acid or proteolysis being the common change produced and this only after an extended incubation period. This fact probably has led some people to think that thermoduric bacteria in milk are of relatively little importance. However, a processor may purchase raw milk that meets a certain bacteriological grade requirement only to find that, after pasteurization, the thermoduric flora has survived to the extent that the pasteurized product contains more bacteria than allowable for the grade for which it was purchased. For this reason those concerned with milk sanitation generally hold that milk offered as meeting the requirements for a cetrtain grade when raw should be capable of also meeting the specifications for the corresponding pasteurized grade. This is justified by the fact that large numbers of thermoduric bacteria enter milk by practices of poor sanitation and carelessness. Dirty utensils, unclean cows, and dirty conditions in the milking barn are primary sources of contamination on the producing farm. Elimination of such conditions usually will solve the thermoduric problems as far as producers are concerned. Unsanitary plant conditions may, however, cause high thermoduric counts too, and the processing plant should be certain that such conditions are also eliminated.

In locating sources of thermoduric bacteria, samples of raw milk are collected, and about a 10 ml portion of each is pasteurized in a screw-cap vial at 61.7°C. (143°F.) for 30 minutes. Then each sample is plated, using the standard plate count procedure. Since the usual standard for Grade A pasteurized milk is 30,000 bacteria per milliliter, any sample exceeding this count after pasteurization contains more thermodurics than the Grade allows. In order to allow for adventitious sources of bacteria in pooled pasteurized milk, a standard of 5,000 to 10,000 per milliliter often is used for laboratory pasteurized samples of an individual producer's milk. This is a reasonable standard, and counts exceeding such standards usually can be lowered by eliminating the afore-mentioned sources of these bacteria.

In order to economize on time, media, incubator space, and pipettes and to eliminate dilution blanks, an oval tube technique has been proposed, particularly for use when large numbers of samples are to be examined for thermoduric bacteria (13). In this method the samples (5 ml) of raw milk are pasteurized at 61.7°C. (143°F.) for 30 minutes and are cooled; the vials are shaken vigorously not less than 50 times. This is not only to redistribute the bacteria in the milk, but also to break the clumps of bacteria that usually occur in the dilution blanks. By inserting a welded loop (calibrated to hold 0.01 ml or 0.001 ml) into the vial 2 to 3 mm below the surface of the milk and by then withdrawing it vertically, a satisfactory quantitative sampling of each tube can be made. The loopful of milk is then placed in 4 ml of melted and tempered agar (standard plating medium, contained in oval, cotton-plugged tubes) and is shaken back and forth to remove all the milk. The tubes are slanted on the flat side to allow the medium to flow 2 or 3 inches from the bottom of the tube. When solidified, the medium is in a reasonably thin layer, and the tubes are incubated in an inverted position in a wire rack for 48 hours at 32°C. or 35°C. (89.6°F. or 95°F.). After this period the colonies which develop are counted. This method has shown close agreement with counts made by the regular plating method, and it permits the examination of a large number of samples at one time quite economically (5). See Figure 5.7.

The calibrated loop measurement of laboratory pasteurized samples has been used in certain other ways to determine relative levels of thermoduric bacteria. The loopful of milk can be mixed with melted agar medium in round culture tubes. The tubes can then be rolled until the agar solidifies, forming a thin film on their inner surfaces. In less precise methods the loopful of milk can be smeared on the surface of an agar slant or agar medium in a petri dish. Estimates are made of the number of colonies present after incubation for 48 hours at 32°C. or 35°C. (89.6°F. or 95°F.).

### THERMOPHILIC BACTERIA

Thermophilic bacteria are those that have their optimum growth temperature above 45°C. (113°F.). In the dairy industry the term is more specifically applied to those bacteria which grow actively at the pasteurization temperature of 61.7°C. (143°F.). The species usually found are *Lactobacillus thermophilus* and certain members of the genus *Bacillus.* In the holder method of pasteurization these bacteria can develop into large populations; and in addition to causing high counts, they also can cause increased acidity of the milk, for most of them ferment lactose. Furthermore, *Lactobacillus enzymothermophilus* (probably a variant of *Lactobacillus thermophilus*) produces phosphatase in milk during pasteurization at 61.7°C. (143°F.) for 30 minutes. This phosphatase can be distinguished in subsequent testing by reason of its thermostability.

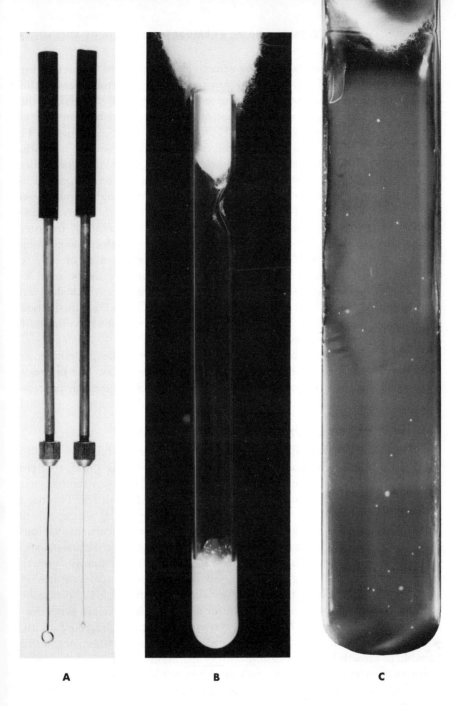

**Figure 5.7**　The oval tube method for making thermoduric counts. (A) Calibrated loops used for delivering milk (0.01 and 0.001 ml) to the medium; (B) a side view of an oval tube of agar medium; (C) colonies of thermoduric bacteria from pasteurized milk growing in an oval tube.

Thermophilic bacteria can be selectively enumerated by incubating plates at 55°C. (121°F.), a temperature at which only members of this group can grow. When the detection of thermophiles is desired in the routine counting of milk samples, a set of plates for the sample under examination is incubated at 55°C. (121°F.), as well as at 32°C. or 35°C. (89.6°F. or 95°F.). These bacteria may appear to be present in insignificant numbers in producers' or plant line samples, but one must remember that, when milk is held at elevated temperatures for prolonged periods, a small number of these bacteria may develop into a very high number in a relatively short period of time. This group of bacteria, therefore, is primarily the concern of the processor rather than of the producer. In order to differentiate between those thermophiles which can develop into colonies on agar media only at 55°C. (121°F.) and those which may be able to grow at 61.7°C. (143°F.), samples of suspected milk may be held at 61.7°C. (143°F.) for several hours before plating. Samples which show an increase in the 55°C. (121°F.) count after the 61.7°C. (143°F.) incubation are the ones that indicate that remedial measures are needed to eliminate the sources of the thermophiles.

The direct microscopic examination of milk from the pasteurizer or points beyond also may be useful in detecting thermophiles. The presence of large numbers of rods, or the increase in the number of these as processing proceeds, is usually indicative of thermophilic contamination.

### PSYCHROPHILIC MICROORGANISMS

Psychrophilic microorganisms are those which are able to develop comparatively rapidly at temperatures below 15°C. (59°F.). There is a definite need for more knowledge to distinguish between the bacteria that may be strictly psychrophilic and those that are facultative. This need for increased knowledge is especially great when bacteria that are capable of growing in milk at refrigeration temperatures are concerned. Various species of the genera *Pseudomonas, Streptococcus, Flavobacterium, Alcaligenes,* and *Achromobacter* and certain coliforms are capable of rather extensive growth at low temperatures, but grow equally as well or better at temperatures up to 20°C. to 30°C. (68°F. to 86°F.). Certain yeasts and molds also may be found growing on products such as butter and cheeses of various types during refrigerated storage. Therefore, the term psychrophilic microorganisms, when used in relation to the dairy industry, concerns those organisms capable of growth at refrigeration temperatures, even though their actual optimum temperature may be more in the mesophilic range.

The increased length of time for holding milk under refrigeration, necessitated by every-other-day collection from the farm and the 3-times-a-week delivery to the home, has increased the importance of psychrophilic microorganisms in dairy products. Furthermore, they may influence the storability of unsterilized concentrated milk, cream, cottage cheese, and butter to a great extent. The presence of psychrophiles may easily be overlooked when making standard plate counts, particularly when the incubation temperature is 35°C. (95°F.). Even counts made at 32°C. (89.6°F.) at times do not enumerate all of the bacteria that will develop at lower incubation temperatures. Furthermore, psychrophilic types of coliform bacteria are often unable to form gas and may produce atypical colonies on selective media at temperatures of 35°C. to 37°C. (95°F. to 98.6°F.). For the enumeration of psychrophiles, therefore, it is recommended that plates be incubated at 5°C. (41°F.) for 7 days (26). Some workers report that 25°C. (78°F.) for 3 days is reliable, too, for detecting these bacteria. Also by incubating a given sample at the refrigeration temperature in use at a specific plant and by making a direct microscopic count before and after the incubation, one can ascertain the presence of bacteria capable of growing under available refrigeration conditions, provided that the count reaches sufficiently high levels to be detected.

The keeping quality of milk can be judged by incubation of samples at 45°F. to 50°F. for several days. The examination of these samples, by the direct microscopic count or the plate count provides a sensitive test for psychrophiles. The presence of psychrophiles not only indicates lower keeping quality of the milk, but also points up unsatisfactory sanitary conditions in the plant.

### COLIFORM BACTERIA

The presence of coliform bacteria (i.e., species of the genera *Escherichia* and *Aerobacter*) in raw milk does not have the same significance as in water supplies, shellfish, and similar environments. In the latter their presence indicates fecal pollution and the possible presence of intestinal pathogens. In raw milk, however, the coliforms that are present usually originate from the intestinal tract of the cow, which is not subject to the enteric infections common to man. Although it is desirable to keep as many of these bacteria out of milk as is possible, milk free from them can be produced only by using extremely sanitary precautions. The presence of these organisms in raw milk is therefore not considered objectionable, unless they are present in such large numbers as to indicate negligence during production. There have been occasional instances of udder infections caused by coliform bacteria, although this source may be expected to occur rarely.

Proper pasteurization is adequate to destroy coliform bacteria, although very uncommonly a somewhat heat-resistant strain may be encountered. The conclusion regarding the susceptibility of these bacteria to pasteurization has been the result of sampling milk from the pasteurizer and finding that coliforms consistently are absent when this unit is operated properly. Also laboratory studies have shown the inability of these bacteria to survive pasteurization when the pasteurization is done in air-tight vials and rigid temperature controls have been employed (1). As a result of such data, the coliform test on pasteurized milk has been used advantageously to indicate recontamination of the product after pasteurization or inadequate pasteurization. Since the phosphatase test can be performed to detect improper pasteurization, the coliform test is used primarily as an index of post-pasteurization contamination. Undoubtedly coliform bacteria that gain entrance to pasteurized milk originate largely from the raw milk, perhaps being transferred from the raw milk equipment to the pasteurized milk equipment by the hands of the workers, utensils, cleaning aids, and so forth. By the same means, however, other bacteria, possibly harmful ones, may be transferred to the pasteurized milk. Another possible source of these bacteria in pasteurized milk is the human intestinal tract, from which they may be carried to the milk by unsanitary practices of the worker. Since there are no practical ways of differentiating coliform bacteria of bovine and human origin, either or both of the above sources can be suspected when coliform bacteria are present in pasteurized milk.

Coliform bacteria can grow slowly at refrigeration temperatures. For this reason it is of little consequence to count coliforms in samples other than those that have been collected within a few hours after pasteurization. In older samples the presence of large numbers of these bacteria may be the result of the growth of a very few that were originally present and may be no indication of the extent of recontamination after pasteurization.

Coliform bacteria can be enumerated by plating aliquots of the sample, as is done in the standard plate count, and by using a selective nutrient agar which will permit distinctive colonies of coliform bacteria to develop. For this method desoxycholate lactose agar and violet red bile agar are recommended by *Standard Methods for the Examination of Dairy Products* (26). Plates prepared with these media should have a thin over-lay of the sterile medium so that all colonies will be sub-surface. This will avoid the confusion in recognizing coliform colonies that might arise if surface colonies were present. Plates should be incubated 18–24 hours at 35°C. (95°F.). In the desoxycholate lactose agar, the lactose-fermenting coliform bacteria will be red with some precipitation of the desoxycholate around the colony. In violet red bile agar the colonies will be purplish-red and will have a zone of precipitated bile adjacent to the colony (Figure 5.8). During the 18–24 hour incubation period gram-positive bacteria generally are inhibited by these media, although some strains of micrococci and streptococci may appear as small red colonies in 24 hours or longer. For this reason counts preferably should be made at about 20 hours; only colonies having a diameter of 0.5 mm or greater should be counted. There are times when coliform bacteria present in products such as ice cream may form colonies smaller than 0.5 mm in diameter. Confirmatory tests are required in such instances to find out if the colonies are of coliform organisms. The inhibitory properties of the bile or bile salt are attenuated by excessive heating, and instructions for the preparation and sterilization of these media must be followed to prevent the growth of non-coliform bacteria in plates poured with these media.

Liquid media also can be used to detect coliform bacteria. Brilliant green lactose peptone bile broth and formate ricinoleate lactose peptone broth are accepted as standard. These media are placed in fermentation tubes, and samples containing coliform bacteria will show gas production after 24 to 48 hours. In brilliant green bile broth the brilliant green dye and the bile have been added to prevent the growth of gram-positive bacteria, whereas gram-negative bacteria are not inhibited; the lactose-fermenting coliforms can grow; and the gas produced in the cleavage of the lactose is collected in the fermentation tube. In formate ricinoleate broth the sodium ricinoleate inhibits the growth of gram-positive bacteria, but does not interfere with the growth of gram-negative bacteria. Coliform bacteria will produce gas from the lactose and formate, and their presence in samples can thus be detected. The formate permits the early appearance of gas and provides for the production of a large total volume of gas. During the fermentation of the sodium formate the medium is buffered so that the pH usually will not drop below 6.0; this favors more extensive growth of the coliform organisms.

When using these liquid media, some information can also be obtained concerning the number of coliform bacteria present by inoculating dilutions of the sample into a series of tubes. By using five tubes for each dilution and selecting dilutions so that at least one tube is positive and one negative in the entire series, a statistical interpretation can be made of the most probable number of coliforms per sample. Tables for evaluating such

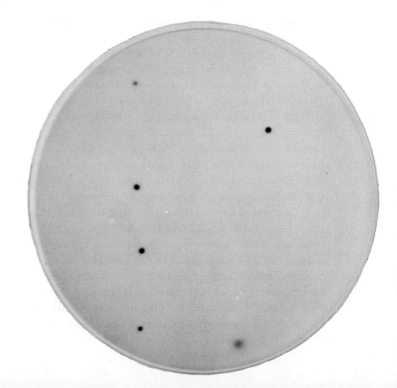

**Figure 5.8**    Coliform colonies on violet red bile agar.

data are available in *Standard Methods for the Examination of Dairy Products* (26). Certain localities have established standards of less than one coliform per milliliter, and here the liquid media are used to determine the coliform population level. In these instances the liquid media are used because a larger volume of sample can be examined and conformance with the standard can more accurately be determined than if 1 or 2 ml of sample were examined.

With any of the foregoing solid or liquid media, positive results for the coliform group are considered presumptive. Although this evidence usually is sufficient to conclude that coliforms are present, colonies from the solid media or those isolated from the liquid media after streaking on eosin methylene blue agar should be checked occasionally to confirm that the bacteria actually are gram-negative, lactose-fermenting, non-sporulating types. There is evidence of false positive tests being encountered in the examination of ice cream flavored with fresh fruit. Non-coliform bacteria, normally present on the fruit, ferment the sucrose added to the selective media and produce coliform-like colonies on the agar media or gas in the fermentation tube test. In instances such as this, confirmation of the presumptive test is mandatory.

The sensitivity of these presumptive media, plus the tendency of coliform bacteria to be present in many sources, makes this group of bacteria a particularly useful index of recontamination following pasteurization. Naturally, contamination of milk may occur from sources that may not have coliforms present, but this is considered to occur sufficiently rarely so as not to detract from the significance of the coliform test as an index of the sanitary measures used in producing a pasteurized product.

### LIPOLYTIC BACTERIA

Milk fat is one of the major constituents of milk and is subject to the lipolytic action of various bacteria, primarily of the genera *Pseudomonas, Achromobacter, Alcaligenes, Serratia* and *Micrococcus*. The action of these bacteria is particularly important in products such as cream, butter, and cottage cheese during extended periods of refrigeration. Lipolytic bacteria frequently are psychrophilic, and this makes them doubly objectionable in the afore-mentioned products. The liberation of free fatty acids from the fat during hydrolysis contributes pungent odor and flavor to the product, although these may be preceded by fruity odor.

Methods used in testing for lipolytic bacteria are based on the detection of free fatty acids from fat added to the culture medium. The indicator nile blue sulfate is normally used in such tests, since it stains the normal fat globules pink, and when the fat is hydrolyzed by lipolytic colonies, stains them blue. Excessive dye in the medium may be toxic for various bacteria, and to avoid this the following procedure is suggested. First, neutral fat is stained by being shaken with 10 per cent by volume of nile blue sulfate or chloride (7). Then excess dye is removed by washing the fat several times with water, and the stained fat is sterilized. One per cent of the stained fat is added to the tempered medium, just prior to plating. It is important to obtain a fine emulsion of the fat in the agar medium. Careful observation of the plates is frequently needed to detect the delicate color changes of the fat, particularly with weakly lipolytic bacteria.

The use of a fat, rather than tributyrin (or similar glyceride), frequently is preferred as the test substrate for lipolytic bacteria, since tributyrin is more easily hydrolyzed. Thus the hydrolysis of tributyrin should not be interpreted to mean conclusively that the organism will also hydrolyze butterfat or any other fat in question.

### PROTEOLYTIC BACTERIA

The proteolysis of casein in milk and milk products by certain bacteria frequently results in the production of a very unsavory product. On the other hand certain types of protein digestion are promoted in the manufacture of cheese. For these reasons a knowledge of the types of proteolytic bacteria in a product or of the source of these bacteria in certain operations is needed. As casein is the main protein of interest in such instances, it usually is used as the substrate for determining the presence of the bacteria. The addition of 5 per cent skimmilk to an otherwise suitable medium provides adequate casein and imparts a cloudy appearance to plates poured with it. When a sample is plated with such medium, colonies of proteolytic bacteria will have a clear zone surrounding them as a result of the conversion of the opaque casein into soluble nitrogenous compounds by proteolytic enzymes. These enzymes, secreted by the bacteria, diffuse into the medium. A clear zone may be produced by certain non-proteolytic bacteria that produce slight acidity in the medium. In these instances the casein is not digested, but is peptized by a combination of the acid and salt. However, if sufficient acid is formed, the casein will again precipitate as the pH of the medium reaches the isoelectric point of the casein. By flooding the plates with dilute acid, the true proteolytic colonies will have a clear zone of hydrolyzed casein around them that will persist; the zone will disappear around the non-proteolytic colonies.

### ACID-PRODUCING BACTERIA

It is frequently important to determine the presence of acid-forming bacteria in certain products or to determine the ratio of acid-formers to those not able to produce acid. By plating such samples with a medium containing the carbohydrate concerned, acid-producing colonies can be detected by having a pH indicator such as brom cresol purple in the medium, or by flooding the plate with it after the colonies have developed. The latter procedure is not suitable when the colonies are to be picked, and in most instances having the indicator present in the medium when the plates are poured is preferable unless the indicator is toxic to the

bacteria. A medium of the following composition may be used for enumerating acid-producers (27).

| | | |
|---|---|---|
| Tomato juice | 300 | ml |
| Yeast extract | 5 | g |
| Glucose | 0.5 | g |
| KH$_2$PO$_4$ | 0.5 | g |
| K$_2$HPO$_4$ | 0.5 | g |
| CaCO$_3$ | 5 | g |
| Brom cresol purple (1.6% in alcohol) | 2 | ml |
| Agar | 15 | g |
| Distilled H$_2$O to | 1,000 | ml |
| pH adjusted to 7.0 | | |

The CaCO$_3$ is added in the form of a slurry, and during the pouring of
plates it is kept well distributed; the plates are cooled quickly after pouring
to minimize the settling of the CaCO$_3$.

Acid-forming colonies will change the brom cresol purple surrounding
the colony from the original purple to a yellow color. When sufficient acid
is produced, the CaCO$_3$ will be converted to a soluble salt which will cause
a clear zone around such colonies. Alkali-producing colonies will produce
a deeper purple color adjacent to the colonies than was originally present
in the medium. The presence of the CaCO$_3$ in the medium causes the acid
from the acid-forming colonies to be confined to a narrow zone around the
colonies, thus preventing diffusion of the acid throughout the medium
where it might obscure the differentiation of acid-formers and non-acid
formers.

A more selective medium for the enumeration of lactic-acid forming
bacteria (e. g., lactobacilli, streptococci, leuconostocs) has been studied.
This has the following composition (4):

| | | |
|---|---|---|
| V-8 vegetable juice (filtered) | 500 | ml |
| Tryptose | 10 | g |
| Lactose | 5 | g |
| Beef extract | 3 | g |
| Agar | 15 | g |
| Brom cresol green | 0.1 | g |
| Distilled water to | 1,000 | ml |
| pH adjusted to 5.7 | | |

On this medium bacteria producing lactic acid form colonies that are dark
green to jet black. After incubation at the appropriate temperature, high
acid-producing colonies have a halo of bright yellow caused by the change
of the brom cresol green; colonies producing smaller amounts of acid cause

less color change. Members of the genera *Bacillus, Micrococcus,* and *Sarcina* apparently are unable to grow in this medium.

A selective medium for the isolation and enumeration of enterococci has been developed. This has the following formula (23):

| | |
|---|---|
| Yeast extract (Difco) ................ | 10 g |
| Trypticase (BBL) ................... | 10 g |
| Sodium citrate ..................... | 20 g |
| Agar ............................. | 15 g |
| Distilled water to ................... | 1,000 ml |

pH adjusted to 7.0

autoclave at 121°C. (250°F.) for 20 minutes

To 100 ml of melted medium, tempered at 43°C. (109.4°F.), are added 1 ml of 0.1 per cent sterile aqueous ditetrazolium chloride and 1 ml of 1.0 per cent sterile aqueous sodium azide. After the plates are poured, a thin over-lay of the same medium is added to each plate. After 72 hours at 37°C. (98.6°F.) the enterococci will have formed blue colonies that can be enumerated or isolated. Extended incubation enables lactobacilli to grow. This medium is based on the ability of the enterococci to use citrate as a carbon source and to convert ditetrazolium chloride to a blue diformazan, and the ability of most enterococci to grow in the presence of 0.01 per cent sodium azide. Some enterococci are not able to grow well in this concentration of azide, but lower concentrations permit the growth of gram-negative rods.

### YEAST AND MOLD COUNTS

For certain dairy products the yeast and mold count is used as an index of proper plant sanitation and high quality raw products. In making butter, bacteria normally are added to produce the desired flavor, and these bacteria, as well as undesirable ones, would appear in a total bacterial count. The yeast and mold counts of this product have been found to

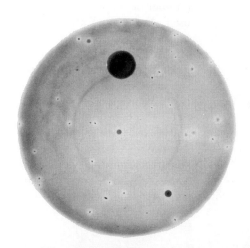

**Figure 5.9**     Acid-forming colonies on tomato juice-yeast extract calcium carbonate medium.

correlate reasonably well with the sanitary quality of the product, although such counts do not give very useful information concerning the keeping quality of the product. The yeast and mold content of soft, uncured cheeses may, however, be an index of storability as well as of sanitary qualities, for spoilage of these products by yeasts and molds does occur.

When examining butter, one should place a quantity of the product in a sterile jar and should warm this in a bath at 40°C. (104°F.) until the butter melts. Then a 1:10 dilution is prepared by adding 11 ml of the melted butter to a 99 ml water blank, from which other dilutions can be made. It is well to have all glassware and dilution blanks tempered to 45°C. (113°F.) until just before use to facilitate the handling of the sample and to prevent any solidification. The pipetting of the diluted sample should be done immediately subsequent to shaking while the fat droplets are evenly distributed. This will aid in preventing errors caused by the coalescing of the fat and by uneven distribution of organisms adhering to the fat droplets.

Yeast and mold counts can be made by using potato dextrose agar or malt agar with the pH adjusted to $3.5 \pm 0.1$. At this pH bacterial growth is inhibited although most yeasts and molds are uninhibited owing to their preference for an acid reaction (Figure 5.10). The pH is adjusted with a predetermined amount of sterile 10 per cent tartaric acid after the medium is melted and tempered, and then the plates are poured in the usual manner. The medium should not be acidified before sterilization or melting, for the acid will hydrolyze the agar and destroy its ability to solidify. Extended holding of the acidified melted agar will prove undesirable for the same reason. The plates are incubated at 21°C. or 25°C. (69.8°F. or 78°F.) for 5 days and the count is reported as "yeast and mold plate count per milliliter" of butter. Differentiation in the population level of the yeasts and molds can be made if desired.

### MOLD MYCELIA COUNT

The plate method just described obviously determines the number of viable yeasts and molds that grow under the cultural conditions used. As pasteurization of the raw products will kill these organisms, no information is obtained on the original quality of the product. Information of this type can be obtained by making a mold mycelia count. In this method a 1 g sample of the butter is obtained after removing ⅛ inch of the surface layer, and placed in a sterile 50 ml beaker. Using a 0.75 per cent carob bean gum or 3 per cent pectin or algin solution tempered to 50°C. to 60°C. (122°F. to 140°F.), 7 g of the gum solution is added to the butter and mixed until the fat droplets are 0.1–0.2 mm in diameter. A portion of this mixture is mounted in a clean Howard cell, with care being taken to spread the sample evenly over the disc. The slide is then examined with a microscope so adjusted that the field area is 1.5 square mm (obtained with a field diameter of 1.382 mm), and the illumination incident to the flat

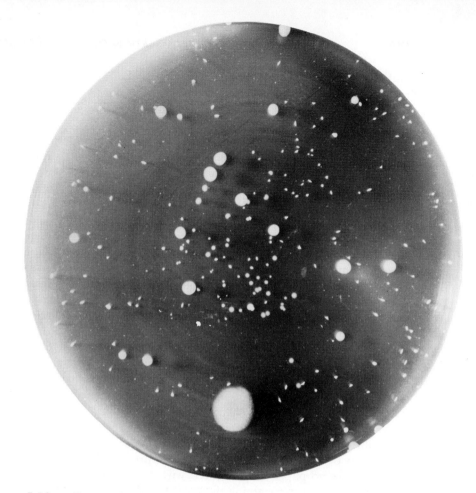

**Figure 5.10** Yeast and mold colonies on potato dextrose agar medium. The filamentous colony is mold, and the others are yeast colonies.

mirror is 125 foot candles. The fields are counted positive for molds when a single filament or the combined length of any three filaments exceeds ⅙ the field diameter (26). After counting 25 fields in two or more mounts, the percentage of positive fields is recorded.

## QUALITATIVE TESTS FOR CERTAIN GROUPS OF MICROORGANISMS

### MASTITIS BACTERIA

The onset of the udder infection, mastitis, is characterized by the accumulation of leucocytes to combat invading bacteria. Blood constituents gain entrance to the milk. As a result, the composition of milk becomes more like that of blood. Mastitis tests, therefore, are based on (a) the detection of the causal organisms (direct microscopic observation, blood agar plate, Hotis test) or (b) the detection of changes in composition of milk toward that of blood (higher pH, chloride, catalase). The infection may be caused by a number of bacteria. Until recent years, *Streptococcus agalactiae* was the most common etiological organism. More recently *Micrococcus pyogenes* var. *aureus* (*Staphylococcus aureus*) is being encountered more frequently. This situation is believed to be the result of widespread use of antibiotics in mastitis therapy. *Micrococcus pyogenes* var. *aureus* not only is more resistant than *Streptococcus agalactiae* to antibiotics, but also has been shown to develop high resistance to these drugs. In some instances species of the genus *Pseudomonas* and coliform bacteria have been shown to be the etiological agents. Other types may be involved less frequently. In early stages of mastitis the bacteria may not be observed microscopically, although the leucocyte, catalase, and chloride content of the milk usually show a definite increase. The pH of the milk may also become more alkaline. When a producer uses a strip cup to test the first few streams of milk, the appearance of flakes or curd particles on the cup screen is probably the first evidence of acute mastitis. Even though much diagnostic information is obtained from the chemical tests, identification of the bacteria causing the infection is also part of the diagnosis and is particularly useful in selecting the proper therapeutic measures.

The pH of the milk may be observed by mixing 1 ml of a 0.04 per cent solution of brom thymol blue (aqueous) with 5 ml of milk. With normal milk (pH 6.6) the mixture will show a grass-green color. Mastitic milk usually is more alkaline (pH 6.8 and above) and will cause the mixture to become blue-green, the intensity of the blue becoming more pronounced with the severity of the infection. Paper blotter impregnated with spots of brom thymol blue and paper strips treated with the same indicator also have been developed for determining the presence of mastitis by the use of milk samples as they are taken directly from the cow. Mastitic milk causes color changes on the paper similar to those described above for mixtures of milk and brom thymol blue.

An increase in leucocyte content of milk usually accompanies mastitis infections. The geometric average cell count of milk from healthy cows has been found to be about 70,000 per milliliter (9). When 40 per cent of the animals in a herd were infected with mastitis, the cell count of the milk was approximately 1,000,000 per milliliter (10). There are factors, not associated with mastitis, that cause an increase in the leucocyte count and, therefore, it is difficult to determine a particular level that definitely is indicative of mastitis infection. For instance, leucocytes usually are more abundant in colostrum and milk from the later stages of lactation; in mechanically drawn milk, especially when the milking machine is left on the cow too long; and in milk from certain cows with no observable evidence of infection.

The Hotis test (6) is used to confirm the presence of streptococcal and micrococcal mastitis when clinical evidence indicates the presence of the infection. Samples of milk are collected aseptically from suspected quarters of the udder. To 9.5 ml of the milk in a sterile test tube is added 0.5 ml of a 0.5 per cent aqueous solution of brom cresol purple and mixed. Mastitic milk, being more alkaline than normal milk, will cause the color to be a deeper purple than will normal milk. The tubes are then incubated at 37°C. (98.6°F.) for 24 hours. *Streptococcus agalactiae,* if present, will show the development of yellow flocculent precipitate or yellow buttons on the sides of the tube. Also the milk will become more acid as a result of the growth of the streptococci. Infections caused by micrococci may show rust colored spots in the milk. The interference from possible contaminants must be considered, although confining the test to a 24 hour incubation period and using aseptic technique in the collection and handling of the samples will minimize such effects. Microscopic examination of the milk after incubation is used to confirm the type of bacteria present.

When mastitis has advanced in the animal, a microscopic examination of unincubated milk will usually reveal the bacteria causing the infection. In such instances the bacteria are usually intimately mixed with the leucocytes present, and frequently bacteria that were undergoing phagocytosis at the time of staining can be observed. The presence of the long-chained streptococci in the direct microscopic count of milk frequently is observed when the milk from one or more cows with a mastitic infection is mixed with herd milk. The non-infectious micrococci commonly present in milk may obscure the presence of staphylococcic mastitis under such conditions of examination, however, unless one gives careful attention to the level of the leucocyte count.

The inoculation on blood agar, by streak or pour plates, with suspected milk taken from individual quarters usually is considered the most reliable method for detecting the common bacteria causing mastitis. Frequently the milk samples are first incubated overnight at 37°C. (98.6°F.) to allow the causative organism, if present, to develop higher numbers for more certain detection. Small colonies showing alpha- or beta-hemolysis are usually presumptive evidence for *Streptococcus agalactiae,* although occasional non-hemolytic strains also are encountered; beta-hemolysis by this organism occurs as a very narrow band around the colonies. *Streptococcus dysgalactiae,* which may be found as the infectious organism, produces alpha-hemolysis on blood agar; otherwise, this organism has characteristics of the human Lancefield C types (*Streptococcus equisimilis*). *Streptococcus uberis* also may be associated with mastitis, but on blood agar it has no action; the classification of this organism is not clear, but it seems to show much similarity to *Streptococcus fecalis.* Colonies of *Micrococcus pyogenes* var. *aureus* are larger than the streptococci and cause beta-hemolysis in rather wide zones around the colony. In addition to morphological identification, other tests must be employed to identify the causative organism that may be present in a given case of bovine mastitis.

The CAMP test can be used to identify strains of *Streptococcus agalactiae* (2, 13). In this test a blood agar plate is streaked across the center with a beta toxin producing strain of staphylococcus (*Micrococcus pyogenes* var. *aureus*). Suspected streptococci are streaked at an angle to, but avoiding contact with, the staphylococcus. The plate is incubated at 37°C. (98.6°F.) overnight. Hemolytic or non-hemolytic Lancefield Group B streptococci, of animal or human origin, will produce a clear zone between the streaks of staphylococcus and streptococcus (Figure 5.11). Since *Streptococcus agalactiae* is the only Lancefield Group B streptococcus associated with bovine mastitis, the CAMP test is specific for this organism.

**Figure 5.11**     The CAMP test for *Streptococcus agalactiae*. The streak of growth in the center is *Micrococcus pyogenes* var. *aureus,* and the eight perpendicular streaks are cultures of streptococci. Five of the streptococci show a positive test for *Streptococcus agalactiae* as indicated by the broad clear zone surrounding the streptococci in proximity to the *Micrococcus pyogenes* var. *aureus* culture. Note that one of the streptococci is very beta-hemolytic and several others are weakly beta-hemolytic, and that hemolysis is quite distinct from the broader clear zone existing around the streptococci showing the positive CAMP reaction. Courtesy James M. Murphy, Cornell University, Ithaca, N. Y.

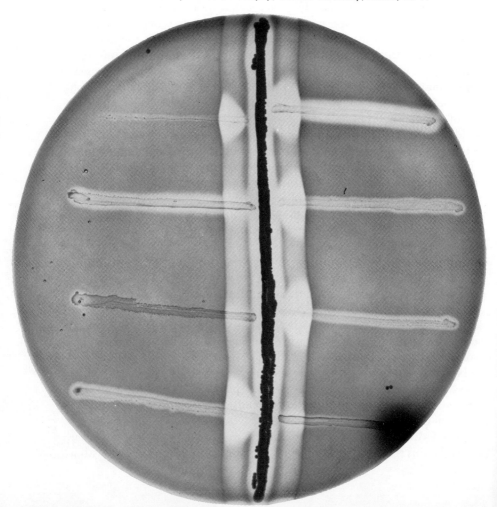

The reader should consult the review on bovine mastitis by Plastridge (20) for further details on the diagnosis of this disease and bacteria associated with it.

### BRUCELLA RING TEST

The detection of brucellosis in cattle usually is restricted to the serological determination of the blood antibody titres of individual animals against *Brucella abortus*. This work is done, under the supervision of veterinarians, at regular periodic intervals in order to confine the disease by the isolation and treatment of affected animals or by slaughtering, if necessary. Within the past several years a rapid test, the ring method, has been developed which may be used directly on milk as it is received at the dairy (24). It is based on the observation that milk from animals with brucellosis contains antibodies for the infecting organism. Aliquots from each can of a producer's milk are collected, mixed, and then 2 ml is added to a 10 x 100 mm tube. To this is added 2 drops of a specially prepared and hematoxylin-stained suspension of *Brucella abortus*. After mixing, the tube is incubated at 37°C. (98.6°F.) for 1 hour. If antibodies for the organism are present, the stained cells are agglutinated and carried to the top of the milk in the cream layer. Thus a blue-violet color in the cream layer with the milk beneath becoming white indicates the presence of brucella antibodies. If no antibodies are present, the stained bacteria remain suspended in the milk, and the cream layer is white. Samples showing intermediate colors of the cream and bottom layers are classified into two levels of a positive reaction (Figure 5.12). This has provided a rapid means of locating herds with possible infection. There are, however, certain questions regarding the accuracy of the test which remain unsolved. For instance, the test usually will show a positive reaction in the milk from cows that have been cured from the disease or vaccinated against it. This may not prove to be too serious an objection. After locating suspected herds by use of the ring test, the veterinarian can then concentrate his time and effort on locating infected animals by blood testing.

**Figure 5.12** The Brucella ring test. The reaction in the tubes, reading left to right, are (1) and (2) negative; (3) and (4) + + reaction; (5) + + + reaction; (6) + + + + reaction. Courtesy of M. H. Roepke, University of Minnesota, St. Paul.

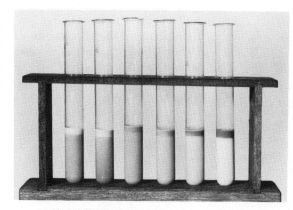

BACTERIOPHAGE

The occurrence of bacteriophage in milk being made into fermented products has been found to be a major cause of the failure of the cultures being used to promote the intended fermentations. Although phage may enter the milk from several sources, the failure of milks to undergo desired fermentations also may be caused by other factors (i. e. antibiotics, quaternaries, fatty acids, sulfa drugs). In order to apply the proper corrective procedures, it is important to know whether cultures are being inhibited by phage or other inhibitory substances. Phage is almost as sensitive to heat as are vegetative cells of bacteria; therefore, milk or other material being tested must not be heated. This property of heat-lability has been used, however, to make a broad differentiation between phage and inhibitors such as antibiotics that may be present in milk, for the latter are relatively stable at high temperatures and may be active after boiling.

In order to separate the bacteriophage from non-susceptible bacteria that may obscure its presence, the material being tested is filtered through a bacteriological filter that will retain the bacteria while allowing the phage to pass through in the filtrate. A Selas filter of No. 03 porosity is suitable for this purpose. When milk is being examined the casein must first be removed or the filter will clog. To accomplish this, add to the milk sufficient 10 per cent lactic acid to curdle the milk; mix well; and allow to stand for 30 minutes. Filter the whey first through the filter paper and then through the Selas filter. In many instances the whey from cheese vats may be examined, and in such instances filtration through the Selas filter only is required. A quantitative estimate of the phage in the filtrate can be made by plaque counts or by a limiting dilution technique.

In making plaque counts 12 ml of an agar medium (e. g., tomato juice-peptonized milk agar) appropriate for the test culture is poured in a petri dish and allowed to harden; one plate is made for each dilution of the phage filtrate to be tested (21). Place 3 ml of 3.25 per cent $CaCl_2 \cdot 2H_2O$ in a 16 x 125 mm sterile test tube as the cell diluent; 2 drops (0.1 ml) are added of an 18 hour phage susceptible culture or the culture being used in the plant for the preparation of a given fermented product. Then 3 ml of whey, diluted to the desired concentration, in sterile distilled water, is added to the tube. Finally 3 ml of the melted agar medium at 65°C. (150°F.) is added, and the tube is inverted 6 times to mix the contents thoroughly. Three ml of this mixture is added to the solidified under-lay medium; this is distributed evenly over the surface; and the plates are put on a level surface to solidify uniformly. After this layer has solidified, incubate it in an upright position at 30°C. to 32°C. (86°F. to 89.6°F.) for about 18–20 hours. Each clear area, where lysis of the bacterial culture has occurred, is considered to represent one phage particle in the original filtrate (Figure 5.13). Multiplying the number of plaques per plate by the

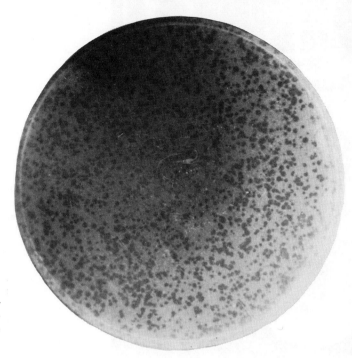

**Figure 5.13** Bacteriophage plaques on medium seeded with *Streptococcus lactis.*

dilution of the whey in the plate will give the phage titer per milliliter of the original whey.

For many purposes the bacteriophage titer of a bacteria-free filtrate can be determined sufficiently accurately by using a limiting dilution technique. For each decimal dilution of the phage to be tested, 5 tubes of medium are each inoculated with a drop of the bacterial culture and a measured amount of the diluted phage filtrate. After an 18–20 hour incubation at 30°C. to 32°C. (86°F. to 89.6°F.), the tubes are observed for absence or retardation of growth (Figure 5.14). The most probable number of bacteriophage particles in the phage filtrate can then be determined from a probability table.

A preliminary test without filtration sometimes is used on whey as it comes from the cheese vat, for detection of the presence of bacteriophage. The procedure is the same as that followed with bacteria-free whey. Usually the whey and the test culture are added to milk, and the acid developed after incubation is compared to that in a control containing no whey. Examination for plaque formation can be made also. The examination of unfiltered whey, however, is considerably less desirable than examination of filtered whey, since phage-resistant bacteria may be present in the former. The resistant bacteria can mask the lysis of sensitive bacteria by producing acid in the milk test or by growing on plates being examined for plaque formation. In view of these limitations the testing of unfiltered whey is

**Figure 5.14** The lysis of a broth culture of *Streptococcus lactis* by bacteriophage. The cells in the tube on the right have been lysed; the tube on the left has had no bacteriophage added to it.

used as a screening test, primarily when facilities for ultra-filtration are unavailable.

## QUALITATIVE TESTS FOR INHIBITORY MATERIALS IN MILK

There are many materials that may enter milk being used for the preparation of fermented milk products and subsequently inhibit starter cultures (see Chapter 2). These are usually antibiotics and sanitizing compounds; bacteriophage has been discussed previously. Usually a vat of milk fails to develop acidity and has to be discarded before plant operators suspect the presence of inhibitory substances. Therefore, it is desirable to test milk to be used in making fermented products for freedom from materials that would interfere with the normal activity of starter cultures. Furthermore, a test for inhibitors in milk should require only a short time, so that there is no long period of storage before determining the milk's suitability for making a given product.

The Leber culture activity test (8) has been used for detecting milk that will inhibit or fail to support normal development of starter cultures. In this test 9 ml of the milk sample is mixed with 1 ml of resazurin solution, such as is used in the resazurin reduction test. One ml of the starter culture is added, the contents are mixed, and the tube is incubated in a 37°C. (98.6°F.) water bath. Low heat non-fat dry milk, reconstituted to 10 per cent solids with water, are used for a control. A satisfactorily active culture should reduce the resazurin completely in the control tube in 30–65 minutes, provided that no inhibitory materials are present in the dried milk. When milk samples, tested along with the control, require more than 30 minutes longer than the control for resazurin reduction, the milk can be suspected of containing materials that will seriously impair the proper activity of the culture in making fermented milk products. The performance of this test, which uses 10 per cent inoculum and a high incubation temperature, requires only a short interval of time. One should not, however, expect to detect lower concentrations of inhibitors, although these may retard the activity of the culture appreciably under conditions of lower inoculum and lower temperature such as are normally used in making certain products.

The measurement of rate of acid produced in milk has also been used to detect starter culture inhibitors. In one method (25), 10 ml of milk to be tested is pasteurized in a sterile test tube at 82.2°C. (180°F.) for 5 minutes. Then 1 ml of an active culture, diluted with pasteurized milk to facilitate measurement, is added and mixed well with the milk; 5 ml is withdrawn immediately to determine the per cent titratable acidity. The remaining 6 ml is incubated in a water bath at 33.3°C. (92°F.) for 4 hours, and the acidity produced is measured. Non-fat dry milk, known to be free of inhibitory substances, is reconstituted to 10 per cent solids and used for a control. If the acidity produced in the test milk is below 80 per cent of that produced in the control milk, inhibitors in the milk under test are indicated.

A test requiring about 2.5 hours for completion has been developed using 2, 3, 5-triphenyltetrazolium chloride (15). Metabolizing cells of a culture will change this dye from a colorless leucoform state to formazane, which is red in color. Materials antagonistic to the bacteria prevent the development of this red form of the dye. In performing the test 9 ml of milk is pasteurized at 80°C. (176°F.) for 5 minutes and quickly cooled to 37°C. (98.6°F.). The tube is then inoculated with 1 ml of a 1:1 dilution of a 12 to 14 hour culture, inverted twice, and incubated at 37°C. (98.6°F.) for 2 hours. Then 0.3 ml of a 1:25 dilution (in distilled water) of 2, 3, 5-triphenyltetrazolium chloride is added, and the tube reincubated at 37°C. (98.6°F.) for 30 minutes. Control tubes prepared with non-fat dry milk (known to be free of inhibitors) reconstituted to 10 per cent solids are used along with the milk under test. The color of the test milk is then compared to that of the control milk, which should be red. This test has been shown to detect 0.04 unit of penicillin, 0.2 gamma of aureomycin, 0.25 gamma terramycin, and 4.0 gamma of streptomycin per milliliter of raw milk when *Streptococcus thermophilus* was used as a test culture. Using a commercial starter culture the test detected 0.3 unit of penicillin, 0.3 gamma of aureomycin, 1.0 gamma of terramycin, and 0.6 gamma of streptomycin per milliliter of raw milk. The test can be performed using either culture, although it frequently may be desirable to use *Streptococcus thermophilus* for detection of the smaller concentrations of penicillin, aureomycin, and terramycin.

# References

1. Buchbinder, L., and E. C. Alff, Studies on coliform bacteria in dairy products, *J. Milk and Food Technol.*, 10 (1947): 137–148.
2. Christie, R., N. E. Atkins, and E. Munch-Petersen, A note on a lytic phenomenon shown by group B streptococci, *Australian J. Exp. Biol. and Med. Sci.*, 22 (1944): 197–200.
3. Committee of the Manufacturing Section of the American Dairy Science Association, Report, 1953 (F. J. Babel, E. B. Collins, J. C. Olson, I. I. Peters, G. H. Watrous, M. L. Speck, Chairman), The standard plate count of milk as affected by the temperature of incubation, *J. Dairy Sci.*, 38 (1955): 499–503.
4. Fabian, F. W., R. C. Fulde, and J. E. Merrick, A new V–8 medium for determining lactobacilli, *Food Research*, 18 (1953): 280–289.
5. Fischer, J. B., and C. K. Johns, A comparison of various methods for detecting thermoduric bacteria in milk, *J. Milk Technol.*, 5 (1942): 269–275.
6. Hotis, R. P., and W. T. Miller, A simple method for detecting mastitis streptococci in milk, *USDA Circular* 400, 1936.
7. Knaysi, G., On the use of basic dyes for the demonstration of the hydrolysis of fat, *J. Bacteriol.*, 42 (1941): 587–589.
8. Leber, H., A resazurin starter activity test, *Milk Plant Monthly*, 39 (1950): (9) 40–42.
9. MacLeod, P., and E. O. Anderson, A study of milk from healthy cows, *Storrs Agr. Exp. Sta. Bull. 290*, 1952.
10. MacLeod, P., W. N. Plastridge, E. O. Anderson, V. N. Gullet, and H. H. Hale, Leucocyte count of herd milk compared to the incidence of mastitis, *J. Dairy Sci.*, 36 (1953): 1267–1271.
11. McBride, C. A., and N. S. Golding, A study of resazurin reduction in freshly drawn mastitic-like milk, *J. Milk & Food Technol.*, 14 (1951): 27–30.
12. Morgan, M. E., P. MacLeod, E. O. Anderson, and C. I. Bliss, A sequential procedure for grading milk by microscopic counts, *Storrs Agr. Exp. Sta. Bull. 276*, 1951.
13. Munch-Petersen, E., R. Christie, and R. T. Simmons, with the technical assistance of H. A. Beddome. Further notes on a lytic phenomenon shown by group B streptococci, *Australian J. Exp. Biol. and Med. Sci.*, 23 (1945): 193–195.
14. Myers, R. P., and J. A. Pence, A simplified procedure for the laboratory examination of raw milk supplies, *J. Milk Technol.*, 4 (1941): 18–25.
15. Neal, C. E., and H. E. Calbert, The use of 2, 3, 5-triphenyl-tetrazolium chloride as a test for antibiotic substances in milk, *J. Dairy Sci.*, 38 (1955): 629–633.

16. Newman, R. W., The Smith 0.01 ml syringe in the microscopic grading of milk, *J. Milk and Food Technol.*, 15 (1952): 101–103.

17. Olson, J. C., Jr., and L. A. Black, A comparative study of stains proposed for the direct microscopic examination of milk, *J. Milk and Food Technol.*, 14 (1951): 49–52.

18. Pelczar, M. J., and J. H. Brown, Synthetic culture media for reference use in dairy bacteriology, *J. Milk & Food Technol.*, 14 (1951): 90–91, 97.

19. Pessin, V., and A. H. Robertson, Observations on the colony productivity of six milk plating media, *J. Milk & Food Technol.*, 15 (1952): 104–109.

20. Plastridge, W. N., "Bovine Mastitis," *Advances in Veterinary Science,* ed. C. A. Brandley and E. L. Jungherr, I, 221–282. New York: Academic Press, 1953.

21. Potter, N. N., and F. E. Nelson, Effects of calcium on proliferation of lactic streptococcus bacteriophage, I: Studies on plaque formation with a modified plating technique, *J. Bacteriol.*, 64 (1952): 105–111.

22. Ramsdell, G. A., W. T. Johnson, and F. R. Evans, Investigation of resazurin as an indicator of the sanitary condition of milk, *J. Dairy Sci.*, 18 (1935): 705–717.

23. Reinbold, G. W., M. Swern, and R. V. Hussong, A plating medium for the isolation and enumeration of enterococci, *J. Dairy Sci.*, 36 (1953): 1–6.

24. Roepke, M. H., K. G. Paterson, F. C. Driver, L. B. Clausen, L. Olson, J. E. Wentworth, The *Brucella abortus* ring test, *Am. J. Vet. Research,* 11 (1950): 199–205.

25. Silverman, G. J., and F. V. Kosikowsky, Systematic testing of inhibitory substances in milk, *J. Milk and Food Technol.*, 15 (1952): 120–124, 137.

26. *Standard Methods for the Examination of Dairy Products,* 10th Ed. New York: American Public Health Association, 1953.

27. Wade, W. E., K. L. Smiley, and C. S. Boruff, An improved method for differentiating acid-forming bacteria, *J. Bacteriol.*, 51 (1946): 787–711.

28. Watrous, G. H., Jr., F. J. Doan, and D. V. Josephson, Some bacteriological studies on refrigerated milk and cream, *Penn. State Agr. Exp. Sta. Bull. 551,* 1952.

# 6

## *Microbiology of milk on the producing farm*

The prevention of the entrance and subsequent growth of bacteria in milk presents a constant challenge to those concerned with producing and processing this product. Over the years methods have been developed for more sanitary handling of milk, and these have resulted in a steady and marked improvement in quality. Yet the same opportunities exist for contaminating milk as formerly existed. There must be no relaxation in applying improved handling methods. The fact that milk is a biological product taken from animals offers the first problem. When milk is collected from the cow, bacteria that dictate limitations on ways in which the milk must subsequently be handled are already present. Furthermore, many people are involved in the production, transportation, and processing of milk before it reaches the consumer. Fortunately, the need for making these people conscious of the acceptable ways of performing their tasks is being increasingly met, through educational, rather than regulatory, channels.

It must be realized that the nutritive values of milk make care in its handling mandatory. The bacteria that are normally in milk when it is taken from the cow must be prevented from growing. Furthermore, the bacteria in the milk can contaminate utensils just as can those from air, dust, and similar sources. When utensils are not properly cleaned and sanitized, the bacteria remaining provide the initial contamination. The residual milk, although seemingly small in amount, furnishes adequate nutrients for bacterial growth. The temperatures at which utensils are stored when not in use are usually favorable for the growth of the adhering microorganisms, as well as the growth of those that are added from other sources. In addition, many of the bacteria in raw milk are able to grow appreciably unless the product is frozen, although they do grow slowly at 4.4°C. (40°F.) and below. Therefore, milk must not be stored for extended periods of time.

The present high level of milk sanitation and the efforts to improve it have been the result of better informed producers, who maintain herds in a better state of health and sanitation and who use more sanitary methods for the collection of the product. The mechanization of numerous operations and the improved equipment for handling milk also have made these conditions easier to realize.

Control of milk contamination involves integrated control of many factors. However, these many factors can be resolved into only a few fundamentals regarding the sources and growth of bacteria. By applying such fundamentals in the numerous milk handling operations, milk of high sanitary quality can be produced consistently.

## CONTAMINATION FROM THE COW

### THE INTERIOR OF THE UDDER

Until 1891 it was generally accepted that milk was sterile as it was removed from the udder. At this time it was shown that fore milk contains many bacteria, although the numbers usually decrease as milking progresses. Later it was demonstrated that the normal udder usually harbors bacteria throughout the lactiferous ducts and thus provides for the entrance of bacteria into milk as soon as it is secreted. This is readily understood by a consideration of the fact that the milk duct system begins with the teat opening and extends back through the teat canal, the gland cistern, and the milk ducts, to the alveolus, where the milk is originally secreted (Figure 6.1). The bacteria present in the udder presumably enter at the teat opening and are distributed internally by their own growth as well as by physical movement. Thus the interior of the udder is open to

**Figure 6.1** Cross section of a cow's udder showing teat canal, milk cistern, and ducts. Courtesy Iowa State College, Ames, Iowa.

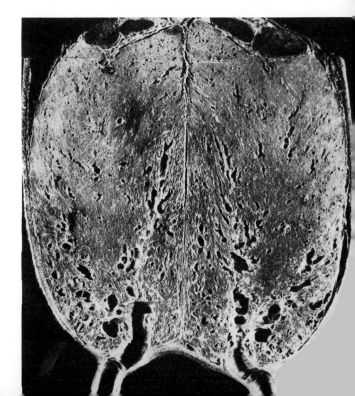

invasion by bacteria with which the opening of the teat comes in contact. It is surprising, however, that relatively few types of bacteria are normally found in aseptically drawn milk and that these are in small numbers compared to the population level they are able to attain after the milk is drawn.

### BACTERIA IN ASEPTICALLY DRAWN MILK

In the literature dealing with the numbers of bacteria present in milk as it is taken aseptically from the udder, one will find varying figures reported, although the numbers found usually are comparatively low. Numbers of bacteria vary in milk from different animals and even from different quarters of a given animal. (Naturally, infected udders will usually yield milk with very high counts.) Counts have been reported from less than 100 to approximately 10,000 per ml in aseptically drawn milk from normal udders, but the anticipated average is probably between 500 and 1,000 per ml. There are reports of exceptional cows which have appeared normal yet consistently gave milk with counts regularly over 100,000 ml. It is fortunate that such animals appear to be rare, for their common occurrence could cause considerable trouble for producers attempting to meet rigid standards for bacterial counts.

During the progress of a milking, bacteria are present in the largest numbers at the beginning and gradually decrease (13, 15). This is the result of mechanical dislodgement of the bacteria, particularly in the teat canal where their numbers are probably highest. Discarding of the first few streams of milk results in a somewhat lower count of the milk (approximately 5 per cent); this may be combined with use of a strip cup for a systematic check for acute mastitis. Furthermore, this first milk commonly has an unsavory flavor that may affect somewhat adversely the flavor of the total milking. Even though the reduction in count gained by eliminating the fore milk may seem questionable, the practice is consistent with other efforts to lower bacterial counts. The other cited advantages aid in maintaining healthy cows as well as the production of a high quality product.

Factors such as age of the cow, stage of lactation, type of feed, and the different quarters of the udder have been investigated with regard to their effects on the numbers of bacteria in the milk. None of these has been found to have any significant effect, although colostrum milk at times has had a somewhat lower count than milk produced later in the lactation period. Milk from different quarters of the udder often varies in numbers and types of bacteria present; there is some evidence that these differences appear with some regularity over rather long periods of time for single quarters.

As indicated earlier, the species of bacteria found in milk as it comes from the udder are limited to relatively few genera (10, 13). The micrococci generally are present in the greatest proportion, followed by streptococci and rods, primarily of the diphtheroid type. A number of species of the micrococci in aseptically drawn milk have been identified (4), and although some of the names of species have been abandoned or changed since these studies were made, a number of them appear to be the same as those more recently identified as occurring in the thermoduric flora of milk and milking utensils. Whether or not the micrococci occurring in the udder are actually thermoduric can not, therefore, definitely be stated. Many of these bacteria are comparatively slow growing, but if allowed to grow in milk, they cause proteolysis and acid formation, resulting in a very distasteful product. The occurrence of micrococci that are pathogenic seems to be limited to animals infected with staphylococcic mastitis; sub-clinical cases of mastitis may have led some to believe that isolations of these bacteria were from normal udders. In the absence of more details, one suspects that the reported presence of pathogenic micrococci in normal udders may have occurred in cases of cows recovering from mastitis or those in which the incipient infection was not recognized by the usual observations or tests for mastitis.

The streptococci in uninfected udders occur less frequently than the micrococci, but they are more important owing to their action in milk as well as to their relation to the health of the udder. *Streptococcus agalactiae* is the organism commonly present, even though no clinical evidence of mastitis is present in the cows. Thus this organism appears to be a normal inhabitant of the healthy udder (1, 20). It often increases in numbers prior to the time that the udder shows inflammation, and it persists after the recovery of the animal from active mastitis. This organism is not pathogenic for humans, and it is killed by pasteurization. The association of a thermoduric streptococcus with udder infections has been reported, the streptococcus causing markedly increased counts of a pasteurized milk supply when the milk from the affected cows was included (7). No evidence has been observed of its pathogenicity for humans, and the characteristics of the organism have not been given except that it was heat resistant and produced an alpha reaction on blood agar. *Streptococcus zymogenes* has also been found in milk taken directly from the udder of a cow with no evidence of mastitis or past history of an udder infection (28). This beta-hemolytic organism was present in the milk at a level of about 200 per ml and was evidently existing harmlessly in the udder. It should be noted that *Streptococcus lactis* has never been associated with the udder flora, and it is agreed that this organism enters milk from external sources.

The presence of diphtheroids in aseptically drawn milk may be overlooked, since they grow slowly and form very small colonies on the usual milk counting media; the use of enriched media (e. g., with added blood serum) aids in their growth and detection. These organisms have been described by various names, viz., *Bacillus abortus* var. *lipolyticus* (14), *Bacterium lipolyticus,* and "primitive forms of bacteria." They are now identified as *Corynebacterium bovis,* a gram-positive rod which produces rancidity by hydrolysis of the fat in milk (3). This organism has at times been found in very high numbers in milk direct from the udder, but it has not been found from other sources such as feces, milk products, and so forth. There is no evidence that the organism is pathogenic for humans or animals, although early workers associated it with the genus *Brucella.*

The foregoing discussion has dealt primarily with bacteria that have been reported in milk taken aseptically from the normal udder. One would expect that more varied types would be found considering the opportunity for contamination via the teat canal. The general agreement among the various investigators on the types present, however, indicates that relatively few bacterial types are able to endure the conditions present in the interior of the healthy udder.

## THE COW AS A POSSIBLE SOURCE OF PATHOGENS

There are various pathogenic bacteria that may be present in the milk of infected cows, and the organisms may be present in certain cases before clinical evidence of the infection is observed. Many of these pathogens can cause infections in humans who consume milk containing them. Outbreaks of human diseases transmitted by milk have been greatly reduced in recent years owing to improvements in detecting infected cattle, quarantine methods used in the purchase of cows, effective vaccination procedures, the improved therapeutic value of new drugs and antibiotics, the better sanitation methods used by the dairymen in the handling and housing of cattle, and the widespread use of pasteurization. Immunization methods for many of these diseases are not effective, and newer infections that previously have not been diagnosed are being recognized. It is necessary, therefore, that everyone concerned with sanitation in the dairy industry be fully informed of the potential health hazards wherein milk may be involved. Animal diseases also constitute the biggest problem encountered by dairymen because of lowered quantity and quality of milk and of loss of animals.

Mastitis infections often shed a large number of bacteria into the cow's milk. Although *Streptococcus agalactiae,* the infectious organism present in many cases, is not pathogenic for humans, the milk is abnormal in composition and has an undesirable flavor. Mastitis that is caused by *Streptococcus pyogenes* or *Micrococcus pyogenes* var. *aureus* constitutes a danger for man, for these organisms can also infect humans. Furthermore, *Micrococcus pyogenes* var. *aureus,* if allowed to grow in milk, may produce a toxin that is not inactivated by pasteurization exposures and that causes a food-poisoning syndrome in humans.

Brucellosis is another disease that may occur in cattle, causing the appearance of the infectious organism, *Brucella abortus,* in the milk of affected cows. This disease is very infectious and is the cause of contagious abortion in cattle and undulant fever in humans. *Brucella suis* causes a similar disease in swine, and *Brucella melitensis* similarly infects goats. All three organisms may cause brucellosis in humans, although *Brucella suis* is the most infectious for man. *Brucella suis* also is highly infective for cattle and may be the cause of the disease in a herd where swine are not completely segregated from cattle. Although humans contract the disease by drinking milk from infected animals, infection can also result from the handling of infected animals or carcasses. Under the latter circumstances, the organisms often enter the body by means of superficial scratches or wounds on the worker's hands. The disease may be detected through the use of an agglutination test on the blood serum of the animal or a ring test on milk. The control of brucellosis in animals involves strict adherence to quarantine measures for newly purchased animals, calfhood vaccination, elimination and proper disposal of infected animals, and the pasteurization of milk.

Tuberculosis in cattle has been reduced greatly in recent years because of the use of the tuberculin test for detecting the disease and of better management in the care of animals to prevent their contracting the infection. The disease is, however, still sufficiently prevalent to constitute a hazard to humans who drink raw milk. There are two types of the causative organism *Mycobacterium tuberculosis*. The human and the bovine types primarily infect humans and cattle, respectively. The disease in humans, however, has been shown to be caused also by the bovine type; this type has occurred more frequently in cases of tuberculosis in children. When the organism enters the milk from infected animals, it frequently originates in sputum, which may pass through the digestive tract into the manure; the manure may enter the milk from the coat of the cow or from bedding. Other sources of the organism may be from lesions in the intestinal tract, from infected uteri, or from lesions in the udder when more advanced stages of the disease are reached.

Q fever is a febrile disease of man caused by the rickettsia-like organism, *Coxiella burnetii* (12). Epidemiological studies have implicated cows, sheep, and goats as sources of the infectious organism in humans. When these animals are infected, their milk contains *Coxiella burnetii;* and this, therefore, represents a possible important mode of transmission of the organism from animal to man. The disease in naturally occurring outbreaks in the United States was first recognized in 1946. Comparatively little is known concerning the prevalence of the disease in this country. It is endemic in California and has been recognized in several other states. During the infection in humans a febrile condition exists, often accompanied by pneumonitis; mortality is low. *Coxiella burnetii* resembles the rickettsia morphologically and in staining reactions, but differs in that it is filterable and does not produce a soluble antigen or stimulate the production of agglutinins for the "X" strains of *Proteus vulgaris*. The organism is more resistant to heat and certain chemicals than are most other rickettsiae. There have been indications that *Coxiella burnetii* may be sufficiently heat resistant to withstand the usual pasteurization exposures to which milk is subjected. Studies are now in progress to obtain information on this question.

In recent years leptospirosis in man and animals has been increasingly observed, largely because of better techniques available to detect and diagnose the disease. Certain animals appear to be the reservoir for a given species of the organism; from this reservoir, other animals and also humans may become infected. *Leptospira canicola* and *Leptospira icterohaemorrhagiae* are found primarily in infections of canines and *Leptospira pomona* in cattle and swine (16, 22). All of these species can infect humans, and the course of the infection is essentially the same in man and in animals. The organisms may enter the body through broken skin, the conjunctival sac, the nares, or the oral route; and a leptospiremia of several days' duration is established. As antibodies for the organism are formed, the leptospiras tend to disappear from the blood but localize in the kidneys. Here they multiply and are eliminated in the urine. In man the disease is termed infectious jaundice (Weil's disease). When the infection occurs in lactating cattle, milk production decreases or may even stop; and an atypical mastitis is often observed. The udder usually remains flaccid, but the small flow of milk may appear yellow, bloody, or thickened. Leptospiras have been isolated from such milk. In these infections the organism could also enter milk from the coat of the cow, having been deposited there from contact with the animal's urine. The importance of milk as a vector of this infection is still obscure, but its possible role in disseminating the causative organism should not be overlooked.

### THE EXTERIOR OF THE UDDER

The cleaning from the udder of soil, bedding, and manure is a practice consistent with good sanitation since it helps prevent the entrance of many types of bacteria into the milk during the milking operation. In many sections, particularly those operating under the United States Public Health Service Ordinance and Code (24), the cleaning is done by wiping the udder with a disinfectant solution. The value of chlorine for this purpose may be questionable, owing to the presence of soil that can dissipate the chlorine before it accomplishes its intended bactericidal purpose. It has been shown that mastitis organisms (*Micrococcus pyogenes* var. *aureus* and *Streptococcus agalactiae*) inoculated on to teats were not completely killed by dipping the teats in a solution containing 400 ppm of available chlorine plus 1 per cent of skimmilk (29). Chlorine is irritating to the hands as well as to the teats and may thus predispose tissues to infection. Quaternary ammonium compounds may be a more effective sanitizer for the udder, since they are less affected by the presence of organic matter and are less harmful to tissues. Soaps can be relied upon only for their detergent action and not for bactericidal properties. It has been shown that, in a herd where mastitis infections recurred periodically, the use of hypochlorite (200 and 400 ppm) or a quaternary ammonium compound (200 ppm) was ineffective in preventing the development of the infection in the herd (21).

Special care must be given to the cloths used for the cleaning of the udder. The re-use of cloths for cleaning and sanitizing offers opportunities for recontamination of the udders. Each cloth should be used for one cow only and should be moistened thoroughly with the sanitizing solution to be used. Many producers find that single-service paper towels are more satisfactory because they eliminate the necessity for the washing, sanitizing, storage, and handling that is required for cloths. The clipping and grooming of the udder will not only make the cleaning easier, but also make the sanitizing more effective.

### THE COAT OF THE COW

The coat of the cow may serve as a vehicle of contamination by adding bacteria directly to the milk during milking. By clipping the coat over an area posterior to a line from the pinbones to the navel, including thighs, flanks, udder, and tail, except for the switch, researchers obtained the comparative counts listed in Table 6.1. It was concluded that clipping lowered the count of milk when milking was done by hand but that the effect was statistically non-significant when a milking machine was used. Considering that the milk is exposed beneath the cow during hand-milking but that it is relatively unexposed during machine-milking, it is reasonable to expect that clipping may be of more importance for the former method of milking.

The coat of the cow also can increase the bacterial population of the air by bringing additional soil into the barn. This source of bacteria becomes extremely important in cold, wet weather when the washing of the cows as they come in from the pasture may be discontinued. At such times it is not uncommon to find an increase in the population of members of the genus *Bacillus* in the milk. The cow's coat also may carry bacteria from stagnant pools of water, and it may be the source of various water forms of bacteria, including those causing ropy milk. Coliform bacteria may gain

**Table 6.1**   Weighted arithmetic mean count per milliliter of composite samples of milk from clipped and un-clipped groups of cows *

| TIME OF MILKING | CLIPPED | | UNCLIPPED | |
|---|---|---|---|---|
| | *No. samples* | *Av. count/ml* | *No. samples* | *Av. count/ml* |
| MACHINE-MILKED | | | | |
| Evening | 8 | 1590 | 8 | 2381 |
| Morning | 8 | 1254 | 8 | 1245 |
| HAND-MILKED | | | | |
| Evening | 6 | 566 | 7 | 1250 |
| Morning | 8 | 771 | 8 | 1000 |

* Data from Hird, Reiter, Weckel, and Allen (19).

entrance into milk from the coat of the cow because of the presence there of soil and manure. Periodic clipping plus daily brushing and at least partial washing of the cow are practices that now are being followed by many dairymen concerned with producing high quality milk.

## THE ROLE OF MILKING UTENSILS IN MILK SANITATION

The various utensils used for milking and handling are the most important sources from which bacteria gain entrance into milk. The increased use of equipment such as milking machines, permanent pipelines, and farm storage tanks has aided in producing milk more economically while preventing exposure of the milk to dust, insects, and similar sources of external contamination. By the use of such equipment, milk of high bacteriological quality can be produced consistently if constant care is given to thorough cleaning and sanitization of the equipment. It has been shown that cleanliness of milking utensils is related directly to lower counts of raw milk and to lower thermoduric counts of pasteurized milk (8); the data in Figure 6.2 show these relationships.

   The value of having equipment that can be cleaned readily and thoroughly is recognized by all concerned with milk sanitation. The use of stainless steel for the fabrication of utensils has provided highly polished and hard surfaces that can be cleaned easily and satisfactorily. All cleaning procedures should be designed to maintain the surfaces of equipment in their original smooth and polished condition so as not to impede the

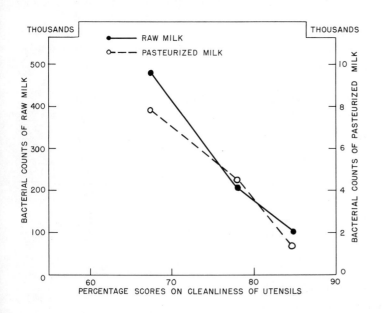

**Figure 6.2** Relationship of scores on physical cleanliness of utensils on farms to the bacterial counts of raw and pasteurized milk. From Dahlberg, Adams and Held (8).

cleaning process. For this reason utensils should be handled with care to avoid dents and scratches. Scouring with abrasive materials should also be avoided, or else numerous scratches and pits, which collect milk residues and make cleaning more difficult, will be made. Most milk cans in current use have tinned surfaces. The tin will gradually wear off and the metal beneath will rust when exposed, causing spots that are difficult to clean. To avoid trouble from such sources, cans should be retinned periodically to keep the surfaces smooth and free from rust spots. Aluminum and stainless steel cans may be used to avoid the need for retinning.

To facilitate cleaning, some utensils now available are made without seams and sharp corners. When seams and joints are present in cans, they should be soldered and smoothed flush with the adjoining surface; any development of breaks in the joints and seams should also be repaired immediately. The importance of such factors in milk sanitation is so well recognized that specifications regarding the construction of many milking utensils are now itemized in most milk ordinances or regulations.

### CLEANING METAL MILKING UTENSILS

Any effective procedure for the care of milk handling equipment must be founded on the following basic considerations: (a) the physical removal of most bacteria and the elimination of residual milk to deny to any bacteria remaining a source of nutrient for their subsequent growth; (b) the prevention of bacterial growth by dry storage of equipment; (c) the destruction of bacteria before use of equipment by the application of a chemical germicide or heat.

First, and the most important step in cleaning utensils, is the rinsing off of as much of the milk as possible immediately after use. This is done preferably with tepid water, which keeps the fat from solidifying on the surface and yet is not hot enough to precipitate proteins. If milk is allowed to dry on the utensils, the proteins and minerals that are deposited on the surfaces are very difficult to remove, and they form surfaces to which milk adheres easily when the utensils are next used, resulting in the gradual formation of milk stone.

The next step is the dismantling of equipment and the brushing with an alkaline detergent containing a wetting agent compatible with the water supply being used. The temperature of this solution should be about 50.6°C. to 54.4°C. (125°F. to 130°F.) for best results, and all of the surfaces that contact the milk must be carefully cleaned. This will emulsify the fat and dissolve the casein so that it can be rinsed easily from the utensils. The use of soaps should be avoided since they are more difficult to rinse from the utensils and usually leave a film consisting primarily of insoluble calcium or magnesium salts of the higher fatty acids. Stiff-bristled brushes should be selected for the scrubbing, appropriate sizes and shapes designed for the various utensils being used to aid in this important step.

An accumulation of milk stone can be removed by brushing with an acid cleaner before using the alkaline detergent. Organic acids such as hydroxyacetic, gluconic, tartaric, and citric mixed with a compatible wetting agent are used. They are mild enough so that they cause no corrosion of metal equipment. The acid will dissolve the calcium and magnesium phosphates that are insoluble in alkaline solutions. The alkaline cleaner that follows will then remove the remaining fat and protein. The value of the acid cleaners is sufficiently established that many producers use what is termed alternate cleaning. In this method about every fourth day an acid cleaner is used in the place of the alkaline detergent. This seems to be effective in preventing the formation of milk stone.

The rinsing of the washed utensils is best done in hot water. Care should be given to the rinsing off of all detergent wash solution. Following rinsing, the equipment should be stored in such a manner that it will drain dry with a minimum of air and dust contamination. The utensils are rinsed with a sanitizer immediately before use to destroy bacteria that have developed in residual moisture or that have entered from air and dust during storage.

### SANITIZATION OF MILKING UTENSILS

The choice of the sanitizing treatment to be used may be decided on a basis of personal preference, although in certain milk sheds the regulations may stipulate the procedure to be used. The proper use of either heat or chemicals will accomplish the purpose, but in each type certain precautions are required to avoid unsatisfactory sanitization. One of the advantages of heat is that, in addition to destroying the bacteria, it will cause evaporation of the water and provide for dry storage of the utensils. When moisture is present on utensils, traces of nutrients that may permit extensive bacterial growth during the storage period usually also are present. Whenever heat is used, it should be sufficient to heat the utensils so that residual moisture will be evaporated. Closures on containers, such as cans, should not be placed on containers until the trapped moisture has evaporated; inversion of hot and wet pails may cause condensation to form on the bottom and sides as the vapors rise. Any process short of sterilization, which is actually impractical under farm conditions, will permit spores, certain heat-resistant micrococci, and microbacteria to survive. The only certain method to prevent these survivors from growing is to deprive them of water.

Various forms of heat sanitization are used, i. e., hot water, steam, or hot air (24). For the hot water treatment, utensils are immersed in water at 76.7°C. (170°F.) or higher for at least 5 minutes. Since these utensils will cool the water as they enter it, the original temperature should be sufficiently high so that it will not drop below 76.7°C. (170°F.). Exposure to steam in special cabinets or in a special room so that a temperature of 76.7°C. (170°F.) for 15 minutes or 93.3°C. (200°F.) for 5 minutes is attained also is a recommended procedure. In using hot air, a temperature of at least 82.2°C. (180°F.) for 20 minutes may be employed.

The use of heat for sanitizing utensils has, to a large extent, given way to the use of chemical agents. Several factors have been involved in this change. For instance, when hot water treatment is used, the immersion of all utensils in an ample quantity of water at the required temperature for the proper time is a requirement that frequently is not met. The subsequent handling of the hot utensils in transferring them to the storage racks is a very uncomfortable task. When hot-air or steam cabinets are used for sanitizing equipment, the necessary temperature frequently is not reached. The costs of the fuel and of the special cabinets are factors that make chemical sanitation preferable to heat sanitization from the economic standpoint.

Chemical sanitizers developed for dairy utensils are relatively fast-acting germicides, require no special equipment in their use, and are economical to use. As a result, there generally is a preference for their use rather than heat in the treatment of farm milking utensils. Of the various chemical sterilizing agents, chlorine has been accepted more widely than any other. Two types of chlorine products have been used, the hypochlorites and the chloramine-T compounds. The latter are much slower in their germicidal action, but are more stable, considerably less corrosive to metals, and not as appreciably affected by organic material. As a germicide must act rapidly when used for rinse treatment of milking utensils, the hypochlorites are more appropriate for dairy farm and plant sanitization. The required concentration of the chlorine compound varies with the product used and the equipment to be treated; usually a solution containing 200 ppm of available chlorine is used. With this solution an exposure of 1–2 minutes will kill nearly all of the bacteria on a clean surface. The rate of killing is increased at higher temperatures, and for this reason some regulations concerning the sanitizing of equipment with chlorine stipulate the use of a hot solution of this germicide. The effectiveness of hypochlorites is dependent upon the concentration of undissociated hypochlorous acid in the solution. However, this acid is very unstable and also corrosive to metals at the pH values below neutrality. For these reasons hypochlorites are used in alkaline solution. Thus, the alkaline reaction of solutions of hypochlorites, although it favors the stability of the solution and lessens corrosiveness, tends to reduce the germicidal activity. The practical effects of this, however, are not serious unless extreme alkalinity is obtained. For this reason the higher pH obtained by increasing the concentration of a hypochlorite solution over that recommended by the manufacturer may result in poor germicidal activity.

The physical condition of a utensil can alter markedly the effectiveness of hypochlorites. Milk or other organic residues react with the chlorine as do bacteria. Treating an unclean utensil with chlorine may, therefore, dissipate the chlorine to the extent that it is relatively ineffective for its intended purpose of killing bacteria. Utensils that have pitted, scratched, or rusted surfaces, broken seams, dents, or similar damage usually harbor milk solids that escape the cleaning and that make the subsequent germicidal treatment relatively ineffective; the milk solids react with the chlorine and protect entrapped bacteria. Although organic material is detrimental to hypochlorites, inorganic compounds such as occur in hard water do not adversely affect them. Hypochlorites are as effective in water containing as much as 400 ppm hardness as they are in distilled water.

The use of chlorine is most effective on equipment that has been rinsed after cleaning. The chlorine solution is sometimes used to rinse the detergent from utensils, but this is not recommended for two reasons. First, the alkalinity of the detergent may lessen the available chlorine for germicidal purposes. Second, the milk solids contained in the detergent solution will also weaken the chlorine solution.

Chlorine solutions normally have a comparatively high surface tension that makes their application on equipment with large surfaces difficult. Smaller utensils can be immersed or rinsed so that the chlorine contacts all parts of the surface, but too often, when it is applied to large equipment, the chlorine runs in rivulets and covers only a part of the total surface. For equipment such as vats and tanks, an apparatus that atomizes the chlorine into a fog that settles uniformly on the total surface accomplishes the sanitization most effectively.

There has been much interest in the compounding of certain halogens in a manner so as to use their germicidal effectiveness and to minimize their instability and corrosiveness. Chlorine has been synthesized into the product 1,3-dichloro-5,5-dimethylhydantoin. This compound is blended with inorganic salts, wetting agent, and acidic material to give a slightly acid solution when dissolved in water. The acidic solution provides for rapid germicidal action of the chlorine as it is released from 1,3-dichloro-5,5-dimethylhydantoin. The chlorine is liberated more slowly from this compound than from hypochlorites, but it appears to be about as lethal to bacteria as are hypochlorites. Solutions of the organic chlorine compound are more stable in the presence of organic material and less corrosive to metal than are hypochlorites. Stability in solution at a slightly acidic pH and low corrosiveness combined with rapid germicidal activity are desirable features of a chlorine-type dairy equipment sanitizer. This form of chlorine has appeared to give satisfactory sanitization of dairy utensils by field trial experiments.

Iodine, a very effective germicide, possesses the properties of instability and corrosiveness as noted for chlorine. It has been found that iodine can be loosely combined with high molecular weight water-soluble polymers and surface-active agents that act primarily as carriers of the iodine. The combination product of the iodine and carriers is referred to as an iodophor. Iodine is released slowly when the iodophor is in aqueous solution; it is stable and is not corrosive. The iodine in such solution, however, has been found to have rapid germicidal action. Field trials have indicated that iodine in the form of an iodophor can be used satisfactorily for the sanitization of dairy equipment.

The quaternary ammonium compounds are germicides which have made a recent entry into the dairy sanitation field. Quaternaries are quite stable in the concentrated form as well as in the diluted. They do not have the corrosive property of the hypochlorites. Thus there is less danger of damaging metal utensils and of causing irritation to the hands of workers. These compounds are comparable in their activity to the hypochlorites, and although they overcome some of the objectionable features of chlorine, they may be adversely affected by certain factors that do not affect hypochlorites.

Quaternaries are not inhibited as markedly by organic matter as are hypochlorites; their deterioration in the presence of milk solids occurs more gradually. Usually quaternaries are more active with increasing alkalinity. The foregoing properties are characteristics that permit their use with alkaline materials in compounding detergent-sanitizers. Another property of quaternaries is to lower the surface tension of a solution. This permits the germicidal solution to have more thorough contact with the surfaces to be sanitized. The film that these germicides leave on surfaces of utensils is an advantage in controlling bacterial growth during storage periods.

Quaternaries are more effective in the destruction of gram-positive bacteria than are hypochlorites. As the thermoduric bacteria are almost solely gram-positive types, these compounds have been effective in lowering thermoduric counts of milk. Quaternaries are not, however, as lethal for gram-negative bacteria as are the hypochlorites. Pseudomonads and coliform bacteria have been observed to be particularly resistant in certain instances. Recent studies have shown that the resistance of various bacteria to quaternaries may be explained by the pH of the germicidal solution being used (27). Thus gram-positive bacteria were very susceptible to quaternaries at pH values above 7, but were resistant below pH 6; *Escherichia coli* was resistant below pH 6 and at pH 8, but susceptible at pH 6–7; *Pseudomonas aeruginosa* was readily killed at low pH values, but was resistant at pH 7 and above. Since most quaternaries are used in a basic solution, the survival of certain gram-negative bacteria is not surprising in view of these findings.

Various compounds react with quaternary ammonium compounds and neutralize their germicidal activity. Salts of iron, calcium, and magnesium are particularly incompatible, and therefore, care must be given to the water available for the preparation of solutions of quaternaries for use.

Although there has been some question concerning the toxicity of quaternary ammonium compounds, animal feeding studies that have been performed have indicated that those studied were non-toxic in concentrations as high as 0.25 per cent of the diet (17). The trace amounts remaining on sanitized milking utensils would, therefore, be considered of no danger to human health.

The practical effects obtained by terminal disinfection of properly cleaned farm utensils on lowering the bacterial counts of raw milk frequently may be overemphasized. When farm utensils are properly cleaned and rinsed with water from a satisfactory supply, the numbers of bacteria remaining on the equipment will be very low. Terminal sanitization is consistent with other efforts to keep the entrance of bacteria into milk at a minimum. It should be emphasized, however, that proper cleaning is the more important step in the treatment of utensils, for it is in the cleaning that most of the bacteria are removed physically and that the utensils are freed from milk soil, which otherwise would provide nutrients for the growth of microorganisms.

### DETERGENT-SANITIZER TREATMENT OF UTENSILS

Within recent years detergent-sanitizers that permit the cleaning and sanitizing of utensils to be done in one operation have been developed. In cleaning with these agents the milk should be rinsed from utensils with tepid water, as in any other method. The dismantled equipment then is brushed in a hot solution of the detergent-sanitizer. It is not rinsed after the brushing. Next the utensils are placed on a rack to drain. This procedure is followed because the quaternary ammonium compound forms a film over the equipment; this film of sanitizer destroys microorganisms as long as any moisture is present. Furthermore, bacterial growth is prevented during the storage of the utensils. Just before it is used, the equipment is rinsed with water to remove the remaining detergent-sanitizer.

The performance of detergent-sanitizers is possible for several reasons. The small amount of milk remaining after the utensils are rinsed properly does not measurably interfere with the action of the quaternary ammonium compound, which is the sanitizer used in these products. The ability of detergent sanitizers to lower the surface tension of a solution enhances the wetting ability of the solution and aids in the contact of the germicide with the surfaces. The bactericidal film that quaternaries form on the utensils during storage is also a desirable characteristic. Since the quaternaries are essentially non-corrosive, their contact with the utensils during storage does not harm the metal.

Definite precautions are necessary in the compounding of detergent-sanitizers in order to obtain the desired results in their use. Quaternaries are cationic compounds, and therefore the detergent with which they are combined must be nonionic, for anionic detergents would neutralize their bactericidal property. As quaternaries are usually most active in alkaline solutions, their combination with certain alkaline detergents has been found to be quite compatible. High alkalinity may have an adverse effect, however, particularly if fat is present that may be saponified into a soap. Certain compounds present in hard water may lower the effectiveness of quaternaries and result in a lowered efficiency of the detergent-sanitizer in effecting sanitization. Detergent-sanitizers may be so compounded, however, that inorganic ions in hard water are chelated and hard water has no deleterious effects on the sanitizing properties of a quaternary ammonium compound.

There have been a number of field trials on the effectiveness of detergent-sanitizers as measured by the conditions of the utensils and by the total and thermoduric bacterial counts. Such studies have generally shown the detergent-sanitizer method to be equal to, or better than, the conventional alkaline detergent-chlorine procedure. Frequently the thermoduric counts particularly are lowered; quaternary ammonium compounds are recognized as being especially lethal to micrococci and thermoduric streptococci, which are the chief offenders in such counts (11). One of the main advantages afforded by detergent-sanitizers is the use of a single product for the cleaning and sanitizing. It is easier for the producer to integrate one product properly into an effective cleaning program than to integrate the several products used in conventional procedures.

The newer organic forms of chlorine and the iodophors have also been used as the sanitizers in detergent-sanitizer formulations. These appear to perform satisfactorily when measured by laboratory and field trial experiments.

### CLEANING AND SANITIZATION
### OF MILKING MACHINES

Milking machines frequently have been associated with high bacterial counts in milk. In such cases, poor cleaning and sanitizing of the machines have been the causes. Ample evidence exists to show that when milking machines are properly cared for they are not a significant source of contamination. It has been reported that the udder may be invaded by bacteria, particularly thermoduric types, through repeated use of improperly cleaned teat cups (6). In this instance, after the milking machine and utensils were satisfactorily cleaned and sanitized, the thermoduric microorganisms, which had been temporarily established in the udder, gradually were eliminated. After six months the counts were reduced to a very low level, as shown in Table 6.2.

The metal parts of milking machines should be cleaned in the same manner as other metal utensils. The rubber teat cups and tubes, however, cause the most trouble, owing to the porosity of rubber. The accumulations of milk solids in the pores of the rubber not only cause troublesome sources of bacterial contamination, but shorten the life of the rubber. The procedures used for cleaning metal surfaces are unsatisfactory for use on rubber. Soaking of the rubber parts between milkings in a solution of 0.4–0.5 per cent sodium hydroxide (lye) is commonly used in cleaning

**Table 6.2**      Bacterial counts of milk before and after milking
machine was satisfactorily cleaned and sanitized *

| Cow No. | MILK TAKEN ASEPTICALLY FROM COW | | MILK TAKEN FROM MILKER PAIL | |
|---|---|---|---|---|
|  | Raw | Lab. past. | Raw | Lab. past. |
| *SPC* during period of poor sanitation | | | | |
| 1 | 50,000 | 30,000 | 4,000,000 | 4,000,000 |
| 3 | 80,000 | 48,000 | 280,000 | 160,000 |
| 6 | 80,000 | 20,000 | 80,000 | 40,000 |
| 12 | 240,000 | 220,000 | 250,000 | 25,000 |
| *SPC* 6 months later after use of proper sanitation | | | | |
| 1 | 3,000 | 5 | 40,000 | 800 |
| 3 | 6,000 | 5 | 15,000 | 50 |
| 6 | 800 | 7 | 12,000 | 30 |
| 12 | 200 | 4 | 10,000 | 80 |

* Data from Bryan, Bryan, and Mason (6).

these parts for a number of reasons, viz.: (a) it effectively cleans the surface
and pores of the rubber by saponifying the fat and peptizing the casein;
(b) its high alkalinity acts as an effective bactericide; (c) it does not oxidize
the rubber; (d) it is unaffected by organic matter or salts in hard water;
(e) it is cheap and readily obtainable. The rubber inflations can be submerged in lye solution contained in an earthenware jar or placed on a wall
rack that provides for the filling of the tubes and teat cups. Except for
short-tube milkers, the latter method is preferred since it insures the flushing out of air when the lye is added; the failure to remove air can prevent
complete cleaning by keeping the solution from contacting all the surfaces
when the parts are submerged in the solution.

There are certain objections to the use of lye, such as irritation to the
hands and the possibility of misuse of the undiluted product. Detergent-
sanitizers have been studied as a replacement for lye. Different studies with
these agents have given somewhat variable results. The use of a mixture
containing primarily a nonionic wetting agent, polyphosphate, and a
quaternary ammonium compound has been found to provide satisfactory
cleaning and sanitizing (11). In one study the periodic disassembly and
soaking of the rubber parts removed accumulated solids that were not removed by the detergent-sanitizer. In a similar study in which detergent-
sanitizers were compared with lye, the storage of the rubber parts in lye
was found to give lower residual bacterial contamination. The addition of
trisodium phosphate, tetrasodium phosphate, and soda ash to the detergent-
sanitizer enhanced the effectiveness of the cleaner and sanitizer, although
the increased pH alone probably accounted for much of the improved re-

sults (9). The use of (a) an anionic synthetic detergent and near neutral polyphosphate for washing followed by rinsing or (b) rack storage in a solution of 0.5 per cent lye or 200 ppm cationic germicide was found to sanitize equally well, as determined by the numbers of bacteria that could be rinsed from rubber inflations and tubes.

There are certain points regarding the cleaning and sanitizing of rubber parts on which the various investigators generally have shown agreement. Regardless of the cleaning method to be used, milk should be thoroughly rinsed from the parts, with tepid water, immediately after use; this can be effectively done by raising and lowering the teat cups in a pail of water and allowing the entrapped air to provide a scrubbing action. Long tube milkers may be washed by flushing them with the cleaning solution; short tubes are brushwashed when disassembled. For some time it has been believed that the best cleaning and sanitization are obtained by soaking the parts with whatever solution is chosen; yet dry storage after cleaning and sanitizing is now gaining in use. Dry storage facilitates examination for deposits that are difficult to see when the rubber is wet. The use of quaternary ammonium compounds, either in combination with a detergent or as a sanitizing agent only, effectively combats the presence of thermoduric bacteria; gram-negative bacteria may not be so easily controlled by these compounds. Regardless of the cleaner used, once every week or two, inflations and tubes should be disassembled and boiled for 20 minutes in a 1–2 per cent lye solution, or soaked overnight in a balanced organic acid detergent containing a wetting agent. This is recommended so that any milk solids that have accumulated in the rubber will be removed, thus permitting better maintenance of the rubber. The provision of two sets of rubber parts for each milking machine, using each set on alternate weeks, maintains the rubber in good bacteriological and physical condition.

The use of hypochlorites for sanitizing rubber parts is usually avoided, for several reasons. Chlorine oxidizes rubber and accelerates its deterioration. Parts stored in chlorine solution are not effectively sanitized, probably as a result of the chlorine being unable to combat the bacteria contained in the pores of the rubber. Mineral deposits frequently form on rubber treated with chlorine, and these are troublesome in maintaining the parts in proper sanitary condition.

Heat also is used to sanitize rubber inflations and tubes, but it is not conducive to longevity of the rubber, particularly when steam or hot air is used. Heat treatments such as those used for metal utensils have also been used for the terminal disinfection of rubber parts of utensils. Proper sanitization by heat frequently is not obtained owing to the lack of water at a sufficiently high temperature or to the failure to expose at the proper temperature for a sufficient time. The general trend has been away from heat toward chemical sanitization, particularly for the rubber parts.

The importance of vacuum lines to the milkers as a source of contamination is a point of some controversy. It is well recognized that these lines can be highly contaminated by milk inadvertently drawn into them or by the formation of condensate. So long as the check valves on the milking machines are operating properly, there is little danger of contamination from this source. However, the check valves may default occasionally owing to particles drawn from the lines or to other reasons. Therefore, the lines should be maintained in a good sanitary condition. Periodic flushing of the lines with a regular dairy cleaner, 0.5 per cent lye, or a detergent-sanitizer is recommended.

The microbiological flora existing in the teat cups, hose, and pails of milking machines varies qualitatively as well as quantitatively, depending upon the thoroughness of cleaning and the kind of sanitizing. The micrococci, particularly the thermoduric species, have been isolated in larger numbers than other types. Coliform bacteria and streptococci (*Streptococcus lactis* and *Streptococcus bovis*) usually are present in lower numbers. Sporeformers constitute a very minor portion of the flora. In rubber parts, thermoduric bacteria are encountered less frequently when quaternary ammonium compounds are used as the sanitizing agent, but gram-negative rods, particularly species of the genus *Pseudomonas,* may be present in higher numbers. The reverse is the case when lye is used. Deterioration of the sanitizing solution, or the use of plain water (stationary or running) for storage of rubber parts, has favored the development of gram-negative rods of the types indigenous to water.

### PERMANENT PIPELINES

One of the most recent developments in milking procedures is the use of permanent pipelines to conduct the milk from the milking machine to refrigerated storage. These lines are not dismantled for cleaning and sanitizing, but are subjected to these operations while in place, as shown in Figure 6.3. This is the meaning of the term "cleaned-in-place" or CIP. There are numerous advantages in the use of such lines: milk is not exposed to air, dust, and insects during milking or while in transit to refrigeration; milk can be piped directly to the cooler, which provides for rapid cooling of the milk; the pipes can be cleaned as effectively in place as when dimantled and handwashed; because the lines are not dismantled, denting of the pipes, which could make cleaning more difficult, is held to a minimum; after cleaning, recontamination prior to sanitization is eliminated so that there is no over-taxing of the sanitizing agent; the need for pails, cans, and the customary strainer is eliminated; the cleaning operation is done with much less hand labor and thus reduces labor costs of the cleaning operation.

The satisfactory use of CIP lines can be accomplished by selection of correctly engineered equipment, by insistence upon proper installation, and by following recommended cleaning procedures. From an engineering standpoint, the pipes must be made of a non-corrosive material (e. g., stainless steel or resistant glass) with highly polished surfaces to allow thorough cleaning. The coupling of pipes once presented a possible cleaning problem, which equipment manufacturers have overcome with success. Gaskets of non-absorbent materials (synthetic rubber and plastics) that offer no impediment to cleaning have been made available. Furthermore, non-leaking metal-to-metal seals of very close tolerance are available; these minimize the gasketing area and keep the inner surface flush and smooth. During the installation of lines, a pitch of about 1 inch per 20 feet of pipe is provided to insure drainage of the product, and cleaning solutions, from the pipes. This not only avoids mixing the milk with solutions left in the lines, but allows the lines to drain dry between uses and prevents the growth of any remaining bacteria while the lines are not in use. Regulatory agencies usually recommend that the lines be assembled in such a way that they can be dismantled for inspection of the inner surfaces for cleanliness and sanitation.

**Figure 6.3**     A barn type combine two-unit milker. Milk is conveyed in a completely enclosed glass pipe directly from the cow, through a filter, and into cans. At the conclusion of milking the assembled units are placed on the manifold washer in the milk room; in the wash tank directly below, clear water is in one compartment, and detergent solution is in the other. The end of the milk hose is placed in the proper compartment, and the solution is circulated through the entire milk lines and milker units. Courtesy DeLaval Separator Co., Poughkeepsie, N. Y.

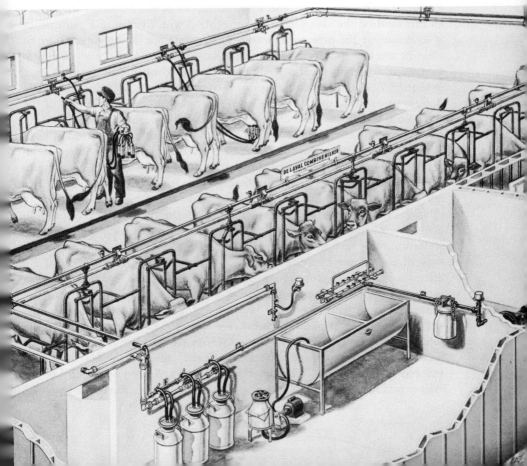

The use of CIP lines for milking can be adapted to various types of operations. The lines have been used in the regular stanchion type of milking barn to carry the milk directly from the milking machine to refrigerated storage. In the milking parlor or combine system, the milk usually is collected from the milker in a weighing jar and is then released into the CIP line for passage to refrigeration. In each system the milk may be drawn by vacuum to a surge jar, where the vacuum is broken; and then the milk flows by gravity to a refrigerated storage tank or to cans. In some systems the milk is drawn directly to cans held in a refrigerated tank of water. When the surge jar is used in the line, the vacuum line from the jar should not be in a vertical position, for the vapors from the warm milk can condense on the inner walls of the vacuum line and cause contamination. Instead, the line should be sloped away into a moisture trap so that the condensate will not return to the surge jar. The kind of coupling device on the CIP lines will determine the kind of cleaning that can be used. If the couplings depend on the vacuum in the system to maintain the seal, cleaning must be done using a vacuum method; in this case, no additional circulating pump is required. When the couplings can withstand pressure, a pressure circulation method can be used.

The pressure circulation method of cleaning is normally recommended for parlor CIP installations and for installations of the stanchion barn type. In this method the cleaning is accomplished with the aid of a pump that is used to rinse the pipes with water, to circulate hot detergent solution, to rinse again, and finally to circulate the sanitizing agent. For the recirculation steps, a second pipeline, which connects to one end of the milk line, is required. The other end empties into a solution tank from which the detergent or sanitizing agent is pumped back into the beginning of the milk line. When lines are cleaned by this method, the rinses are not recirculated, but are directed to a drain; and the rinsing is continued until the system has been rinsed free of milk or detergent. In order to clean properly, it generally is agreed, the pump must be of sufficient capacity to fill the pipes and to circulate the detergent at a flow rate of at least 5 feet per second. Factors such as the length and size of pipe, the number of elbows, and the height of pipes, which affect the pressure of the solution, are to be considered in selecting the pump required for any particular installation. The turbulent movement through the pipes, for about 30 minutes, of a good detergent having a temperature of about 71.3°C. (160°F.) effects a very satisfactory cleaning. As in cleaning other types of equipment, it is best to alternate the use of an alkaline detergent with the use of an acid detergent, the latter being employed about every fourth day.

In the parlor type of operation, the lines usually are shorter, and the solutions may be drawn through the lines by the vacuum pump. With this method, each solution is drawn into the system through the teat cups submerged in the solution. The detergent can be collected at the end of the system and allowed to flow in the opposite direction by gravity; the process is repeated a number of times. In another method, the teat cup assembly is dipped up and down in the detergent solution so as to trap air in the pipes and to obtain a brushing effect.

In any of the CIP cleaning methods, it is important that the proper detergents be selected. These are usually stronger than those used for hand-washing methods. Also a high temperature, such as 71.3°C. (160°F.), can be used, and this helps the detergent solution to perform its proper function. Regardless of the method used, valves, petcocks, and any equipment not connected to the circulating system must be dismantled and brushed by hand.

It is reasonable to expect a continued increase in the use of CIP lines by milk producers. Such factors as the trend toward larger milk producers seem to offer good opportunities for the advantageous application of labor-saving methods inherent in techniques like the use of CIP lines. Furthermore, the lessened opportunity for external contamination of the milk by the use of such equipment is consistent with the prevalent efforts of producers to better the sanitary quality of raw milk.

## BACTERIA FROM MISCELLANEOUS SOURCES

Microorganisms occur in air in varying numbers, those present obviously being in a dormant condition. They have survived the desiccation subsequent to being freed from their natural habitat. The number of bacteria occurring in this condition in the air is relatively low, and the types normally present are spore-formers (or the spores), micrococci, and mold spores. Dust particles originating from manure, soil, and feed may contain bacteria that were originally there, and possibly growing, while moisture was present. Conditions that increase the dust content in the air will increase the microbial population, usually in direct relation to the amount of dust present.

Although air is usually relatively unimportant as a source of bacteria in milk, practices that increase the dust content do increase the numbers present, especially when hand milking is used. Among such practices are the following: (a) sweeping a short time before milking; (b) handling hay and feeds just prior to milking; (c) brushing of cows immediately before milking; (d) having dusty bedding for the cows; (e) allowing the accumulation of dirt and dust on the walls and ceiling. In the absence of such conditions, studies have shown that air may be expected to add, during hand milking, 5–15 bacteria per milliliter of milk; on the other hand the continuous raising of dust can add hundreds of bacteria per milliliter (26).

Various means have been introduced to guard against the contamination of milk by external factors during farm milking operations. For instance, the use of the small-top milk pails for hand milking exposes less area for the entry of dirt and dust during milking. Milking machines will lessen air contamination, and the use of CIP lines in conjunction with milking machines can reduce air-borne contamination to a negligible level.

The milking barn or parlor can be kept in a clean condition only if the floors are free of manure and other soil. In order to facilitate cleaning, the floors are best constructed of smooth-surfaced concrete or other impervious material. Similarly, walls and ceilings can be kept clean more easily when made of a material having a smooth and moisture-resistant surface. Obviously adequate light, either natural or artificial, is needed in order to perform milking and cleaning operations in a satisfactorily sanitary manner. Proper ventilation is needed in the milk house in order to avoid condensation of moisture on the walls, for such condensation fosters mold development on equipment and walls and may help bring about deterioration of the walls.

There are numerous factors to be considered in the consistent production of milk with a high sanitary quality. Flies and other insects obviously must be kept out, since their presence on milking equipment contributes not only to the total bacteria entering milk, but also to the possibility that pathogens may be introduced. The milk house should have screened doors and windows, and the premises should be properly controlled to prevent breeding of flies. For such reasons the cow yard or loose-housing areas should be adequately drained, and manure should be removed frequently and disposed of properly.

Of considerable importance are the personnel handling the milk. These people should be in good health. Their hands must be free from any infections. Hands having infected wounds can add pathogenic streptococci or micrococci to milk, causing subsequent human infections, or may initiate mastitis infections in the cattle during milking. The practice of cleanliness by the milkers, both in appearance and action, is not only desirable on its own merits, but indicates an attitude that usually is reflected in the way the various procedures concerned with sanitary production of milk are carried out. Wet-hand milking is discouraged for the obvious reason that some of the material used as lubricant probably will enter the milk and add bacteria from the hands and teats.

Milk may serve as a carrier of human pathogens from one person to another. Typhoid and paratyphoid fever, dysentery, scarlet fever, septic sore throat, diphtheria, and cholera have been found to be milk-borne and to enter the milk from infected workers. Typhoid and paratyphoid fever have been milk-borne as a result of contamination of milk by carriers, i. e., persons who have recovered from the disease but who still shed the causative organisms in their excreta. Septic sore throat and scarlet fever have also been caused by the presence in milk of *Streptococcus pyogenes,* originating in certain active infections of mastitis in cows.

In order to minimize contamination from external sources, a given milk shed has certain requirements regarding cows, milking barn, milk house, toilet and water supply, utensils and equipment, and the milking operation. The various items are designated on a score card, such as that recommended in the United States Public Health Service Milk Ordinance and Code (24), and the producer must attain a certain score in order to qualify for the production of a given grade of milk. The scoring of the producer's facilities and procedures is done by milk sanitarians usually employed by city, county, or state health departments. The items stipulated do not guarantee that the producer's milk will meet a given grade requirement, but, selected on a basis consistent with good sanitation, they are intended to make easier the attainment of sanitary milk production.

## COOLING OF MILK

Refrigeration is the only acceptable means available to the producer for controlling the growth of bacteria in milk. The value of adequate refrigeration, as well as of proper sanitation, has become more important with less frequent deliveries to the processing plant and the customary 3-days-per-week delivery of milk from the plant to the consumer. The quality-deteriorating effects resulting from the growth of microorganisms during extended refrigerated storage of raw milk must be avoided in order to maintain high quality and flavor of market milk and milk products. The producer and processor have equal responsibilities in maintaining their products under adequate refrigeration, but obviously any harm done a product by the producer through the lack of such conditions can not be subsequently undone by the processor. The effectiveness of refrigeration in minimizing bacterial development in raw milk depends upon the types of microorganisms present. In lowering the temperature of milk, the primary purpose is to get as far as possible from favorable growth temperatures for the contained microorganisms. Some species are able to grow even at 0°C. (32°F.). For bacteria that are psychrophilic in nature, the growth rate also is decreased as temperatures decline so that, for reasonable periods of storage below 4.4°C. (40°F.), their growth does not constitute a problem in raw milk. The growth rate of those bacteria present in the milk as it leaves the udder is sufficiently diminished by temperatures below 10°C. (50°F.) that such bacteria seldom present a problem in milk held for reasonable periods at these temperatures unless contamination has been excessive. The contamination of milk by unclean utensils, rinse water, and manure with types such as coliforms, pseudomonads, and certain streptococci, however, limits the effectiveness of refrigeration, for many of such bacteria are relatively psychrophilic in nature. In order to impede sufficiently the growth of these types, temperatures closer to 1.7°C. (35°F.) are required, particularly when milk is to be stored for extended periods. The data in Table 6.3 illustrate the relative effectiveness of various storage temperatures on bacterial growth in milk having varying degrees of external contamination.

Various means of cooling milk on the producing farm have been used. The earlier practice of depending on spring or well water has, almost uni-

**Table 6.3** Effect of temperature on the growth of bacteria in milk that has been produced under various conditions *

| PRODUCTION CONDITIONS | STORAGE TEMPERATURE | STANDARD PLATE COUNT PER MILLILITER AFTER: | | | | |
|---|---|---|---|---|---|---|
| | | Fresh | 24 Hr. | 48 Hr. | 72 Hr. | 96 Hr. |
| 1. Clean cows, environment and utensils | 40°F. (4.4°C.) | 4,295 | 4,138 | 4,566 | 8,427 | 19,693 |
| | 50°F. (10°C.) | 4,295 | 13,961 | 127,727 | 5,725,277 | 39,490,625 |
| | 60°F. (15.5°C.) | 4,295 | 1,587,333 | 33,011,111 | 326,500,000 | 962,785,714 |
| 2. Clean cows, dirty environment and utensils | 40°F. (4.4°C.) | 39,082 | 88,028 | 121,864 | 186,245 | 1,056,922 |
| | 50°F. (10°C.) | 39,082 | 177,437 | 831,615 | 1,761,458 | 13,079,166 |
| | 60°F. (15.5°C.) | 39,082 | 4,461,111 | 99,120,000 | 633,375,000 | 1,355,650,000 |
| 3. Dirty cows, environment and utensils | 40°F. (4.4°C.) | 136,533 | 281,646 | 538,775 | 749,030 | 852,835 |
| | 50°F. (10°C.) | 136,533 | 1,170,546 | 13,662,115 | 25,687,541 | 41,207,272 |
| | 60°F. (15.5°C.) | 136,533 | 24,673,571 | 639,884,615 | 2,407,083,333 | 5,346,666,666 |

*Data from Ayers, Cook, and Clemmer (2).

versally, been replaced by more certain ways of insuring adequate refrigeration. Although well water below 10°C. (50°F.) is available in certain regions, an abundant supply is required for large volumes of milk, and the cost of pumping may keep this procedure from being economical. The use of ice to cool the water has largely been abandoned, since ice is not always readily available and since it usually is a comparatively expensive form of refrigeration. The extension of electric service to farms has made the use of mechanical refrigeration practicable and reasonable in cost.

Milk can be cooled much more efficiently when water rather than air is used as the coolant. When cans of milk are to be held in dry storage, the milk should be cooled first by running it over a surface cooler (aerator) that has a refrigerant circulating through the coils (Figure 6.4). The proper size cooler will cool the milk to a low level, and cold air storage can then maintain proper refrigeration. Many producers dislike this procedure; the cooler is one more piece of equipment to keep clean, and its undulating surface often is not cleaned properly.

Storage of cans in water refrigerated by mechanical means is usually recommended, and this is being used very widely. However, certain precautions are necessary to the successful use of these cold water cabinets (or "wet boxes"). There must be sufficient cold water to remove the heat from the milk, and the water level should be somewhat higher than the level of the milk in the cans. Allowing a bank of ice to form will provide better refrigeration for the heavy load placed on the system immediately after milking. Agitation of the water as well as of the milk will reduce the

**Figure 6.4**    Cooling of milk from a pipeline milker by a surface cooler before placing the milk in cans. Courtesy of DeLaval Separator Co., Poughkeepsie, N. Y.

**Figure 6.5**　　Cooling rates of milk in 10-gallon cans in water-cooled cabinets.

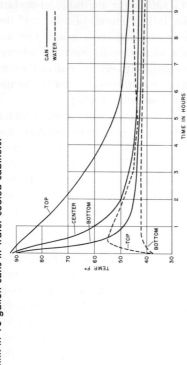

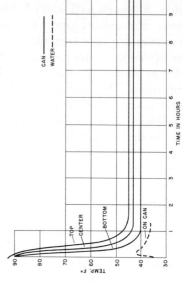

(a) Tank cooler, full load of cans, no ice bank reserve, water not agitated.

(b) Tank cooler, ½ load of 10-gallon cans, no ice bank reserve, no agitation.

(c) Tank cooler, full load of cans, heavy ice bank, water agitated 2.75 hours after cans were placed in cooler.

(d) Spray cooler, full load of cans, heavy ice bank, water sprayed on shoulders of cans for 1 hour after being placed in cooler.

cooling time and more effectively prevent the growth of bacteria during this period. Figure 6.5 illustrates the importance of some of these factors in lowering the temperature of the milk.

Coolers that spray refrigerated water over the outside of the can and recirculate the water through the cooling unit and back over the cans are also available (Figure 6.6). These coolers keep cold water constantly on the cans and aid in the efficient removal of heat from the milk. Note the cooling curves in Figure 6.5d for this type of cooling. For any method of cooling warm milk in cans, it must be remembered that the most time is required for removal of the heat from the top and the center of the cans. The rising of cream will cause most of the bacteria to be concentrated in the top portion of the milk where the temperature favorable for their growth persists the longest. Agitation of the milk overcomes this and aids in obtaining quicker cooling of the milk.

Care should be given to the sanitary condition of all cooling tanks. Even though cans are covered properly and the level of the water is ad-

**Figure 6.6**    Cooling cans of milk in a mechanical cooler by spraying refrigerated water on the outside shoulders of the cans. Courtesy of DeLaval Separator Co., Poughkeepsie, N. Y.

justed properly, the entrance into the milk of a small quantity of the water may occur. Psychrophilic organisms will grow in the water after an extended period of use, particularly since it is difficult to prevent the addition of some milk to the water from the outside of the cans. Growth of this type of bacteria usually produces a disagreeable odor, which not only is undesirable for aesthetic reasons, but also may be absorbed by the milk during refrigerated storage. This water may be so heavily contaminated that entry of only a few drops into the milk may introduce large numbers of undesirable microorganisms.

Mechanically refrigerated bulk storage tanks for producing farms have gained in popularity and use in recent years. Properly designed tanks will cool the milk rapidly to 4.4°C. (40°F.) or lower and will automatically maintain this temperature during the storage period. These tanks are particularly adaptable for use with pipeline milkers, since milk can be piped directly from the milker to the storage tank with no intermediate exposure to the environment. In the absence of pipelines, the milk can be poured directly from the milking machine pail into a tank and cooled very rapidly. These tanks have a large bottom area exposed to refrigeration coils or to water, which cools the milk rapidly as it first enters the tank. Subsequent

**Figure 6.7**     A farm bulk-milk tank for refrigeration and storage of raw milk, with milk flowing over a cold side wall before reaching the cold milk at the bottom of the tank. Courtesy of Cherry-Burrell Corp., Chicago, Ill.

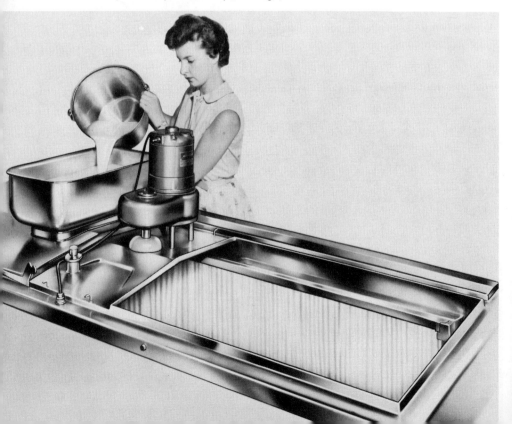

additions of milk are cooled by the cold milk present and by the added refrigeration afforded by the system. In some tanks one side wall is backed by an ice bank section that helps to cool the milk as it flows down the wall into the vat (Figure 6.7). In tanks of this type the milk flow is so directed that the wall precools the milk before it mixes with the milk already present. The refrigeration of the milk held in farm tanks is adequate to permit only every-other-day collection of the milk from the producer. An example of the bacterial count of milk held in a bulk tank under these conditions is shown in Table 6.4. For delivery to the plant, the milk can be drawn into cans or, preferably, pumped into a tank truck. Tank trucks to collect milk from farm storage tanks are now widely used, and their use can be expected to increase.

The effectiveness of proper milk refrigeration on the farm should not be offset by carelessness during transportation to the receiving station or processing plant. Cans of milk should be transported on carriers that are adequately insulated, protected from dust and dirt, and refrigerated for use on long routes. The use of refrigerated tank trucks for the collection and transportation of milk affords not only better refrigeration, but protection also from various deleterious environmental factors.

**Table 6.4**    The bacterial counts of milk held in a bulk tank under conditions of every-other-day pick-up *

| | STANDARD PLATE COUNT † | |
| TIME OF SAMPLING | *Trial 1* | *Trial 2* |
|---|---|---|
| After 1st milking | 7,600 | 3,300 |
| Before 2nd milking | 7,700 | 2,300 |
| After 2nd milking | 8,200 | 10,000 |
| Before 3rd milking | 6,700 | 9,600 |
| After 3rd milking | 6,700 | 7,300 |
| Before 4th milking | 7,100 | 7,300 |
| After 4th milking | 8,400 | 5,500 |

* Unpublished data of J. C. Olson, University of Minnesota.
† Plates incubated at 32°C.

## *References*

1. Ayers, S. H., and C. S. Mudge, The streptococci of the bovine udder, *J. Infectious Diseases,* 31 (1922): 40–50.

2. Ayers, S. H., L. B. Cook, and P. W. Clemmer, The four essential factors in the production of milk of low bacterial count, *USDA Bull. 642,* 1918.

3. Black, L. A., The probable identity of diphtheroids isolated from aseptically drawn milk with *Corynebacterium bovis* and *Bacterium lipolyticum, J. Bacteriol.,* 41 (1941): 99–100.

4. Breed, A. F., Micrococci present in the normal cow's udder, *N. Y. (Geneva) Agr. Exp. Sta. Tech. Bull. 132,* 1928.

5. Bryan, C. S., *Dairy Bacteriology and Public Health.* Minneapolis: Burgess, 1945.

6. Bryan, C. S., H. S. Bryan, and K. Mason, Heat resistant bacteria from an unclean milking machine invade the udder of the cow, *Milk Plant Monthly,* 35 (1946): (8) 30–32.

7. Bryan, J. S., An occurrence of udder infections caused by a thermoduric streptococcus, *Milk Plant Monthly* (March, 1947).

8. Dahlberg, A. C., H. S. Adams, and M. E. Held, Sanitary milk control and its relation to the sanitary, nutritive and other qualities of milk, *National Academy of Sciences—National Research Council, Publication 250,* 1953.

9. Dahlberg, A. C., F. V. Kosikowsky, H. W. Seeley, and A. A. Leventhal, The sanitizing of milk machines, *J. Milk and Food Technol.,* 13 (1950): 5–18, 24.

10. Dorner, W., The bacterial flora of aseptically drawn milk, *N. Y. (Geneva) Agr. Exp. Sta. Tech. Bull. 165,* 1930.

11. Elliker, P. R., J. W. Keesling, D. D. Miller, and G. H. Wilster, Cleaning and bactericidal values of detergent sanitizers, *J. Milk and Food Technol.,* 13 (1950): 215–224.

12. Enright, J. B., R. C. Thomas, and P. A. Mullett, Q fever and its relation to dairy products, *J. Milk and Food Technol.,* 16 (1953): 263–266.

13. Evans, A. C., The bacteria of milk freshly drawn from normal udders, *J. Infectious Diseases,* 18 (1916): 437–476.

14. ———, The large numbers of *Bact. abortus* var. *lipolyticus* which may be found in milk, *J. Bacteriol.,* 2 (1917): 185–186.

15. Faber, J. E., A study of the bacterial content of the fore milk of cows, *J. Dairy Sci.,* 13 (1930): 449–452.

16. Ferguson, L. C. and E. H. Bohl, The leptospiral diseases of animals. Proceeding Book of the 90th Annual Meeting of the American Vet. Med. Association (1953): 87–93.

17. Finnegan, J. K., P. S. Larson, R. B. Smith, H. B. Haag, J. D. Reid, M. L. Dreyfuss, Pharmacologic observations on two quaternary ammonium germicides, *J. Pharmacol. and Exp. Therap.,* 109 (1953): 422–430.

18. Harding, H. A., and J. K. Wilson, A study of the udder flora of cows, *N. Y. (Geneva) Agr. Exp. Sta. Tech. Bull. 27,* 1913.

19. Hird, E. W., T. Reiter, K. G. Weckel, and N. N. Allen, The effect of clipping the udders of cows on the quality of milk, *J. Dairy Sci.,* 31 (1948): 323–330.

20. Hucker, G. J., Mastitis V: The presence of mastitis streptococci in bovine mammary tissue, *N. Y. (Geneva) Agr. Exp. Sta. Tech. Bull. 241,* 1937.

21. Kesler, E. M., C. B. Knodt, and J. J. Reid, The effect of hypochlorite and quaternary ammonium compounds used in udder washes on the chemical composition and bacterial flora of the milk produced, *J. Milk and Food Technol.,* 13 (1950): 288–291.

22. Little, R. B. and J. A. Baker, Leptospirosis in cattle, *J. Amer. Vet. Med. Assoc.,* 116 (1950): 105–111.

23. Merchant, I. A., and R. A. Packer, *Handbook for the Etiology, Diagnosis and Control of Bovine Mastitis.* Minneapolis: Burgess, 1952.

24. *Milk Ordinance and Code: Public Health Bull. 229* (USPHS), 1953.

25. Petersen, W. E., *Dairy Science,* 2nd Ed. New York: Lippincott, 1950.

26. Ruehle, G. L. A. and U. L. Kulp, Germ content of stable air and its effect upon the germ content of milk, *N. Y. (Geneva) Agr. Exp. Sta. Bull. 409,* 1915.

27. Soike, K. F., D. D. Miller, and P. R. Elliker, Effect of pH of solution on germicidal activity of quaternary ammonium compounds, *J. Dairy Sci.,* 35 (1952): 764–771.

28. Turner, G. E., and F. R. Smith, Sources of hemolytic enterococci found in milk, *J. Milk Technol.,* 4 (1941): 183–186.

29. Waugh, R. K., P. R. Elliker, J. H. Hilton, and J. F. Bullard, The chlorine tolerance of certain mastitis bacteria, *J. Dairy Sci.,* 24 (1941): 506–507.

# 7

## The microbiology of market milk and related products

The term market milk means fluid whole milk that is sold to individuals for direct consumption. Examples of other products that are processed and distributed by the market milk industry are skimmilk, cream, chocolate milk, vitamin-fortified milks, and various fermented milks. For the most part, these products are pasteurized when sold, although large quantities of raw milk are still consumed by farm families and by residents of small towns and villages.

Of the total milk produced in the United States the largest percentage is used as market milk. Generally, milk of highest quality is selected. High quality in market milk products connotes the following: (a) that they contain no pathogenic bacteria and harmful or toxic substances; (b) that they are clean or free from extraneous material; (c) that they are normal in composition; (d) that they have good flavor; (e) that they are low in bacterial count; and (f) that they are adequate in keeping quality. With the exception of composition, each of the above factors may be influenced adversely by the presence or growth of microorganisms.

## GOVERNMENT CONTROL OF MILK SUPPLIES

Bacteriological standards and considerations comprise important parts of ordinances or regulations under which the market milk industry operates. Much of the bacteriological work that is done in industrial and in public health laboratories is related to the need for compliance with government regulations. Therefore, some discussion of government control over milk supplies may be helpful at this point.

In many countries of the world, the production, processing, and distribution of milk are subject to government control. In the United States, government control over the dairy industry is exercised at federal, state, and local levels. Strict control over the production, processing, and distribution of milk is desirable and necessary. Milk improperly handled provides a ready medium for the transmission of certain types of diseases. The pathogens so carried may result in disease outbreaks of epidemic proportions. A well-organized sanitary control program is essential to guard against such possibilities. High standards of cleanliness within the dairy industry and the distribution of wholesome products are in the best interests of the industry, as well as of milk consumers.

### PRINCIPLES OF EFFECTIVE CONTROL

In order to establish an effective milk control program, standards must be established; effective enforcement must be provided; and education must be extended to producers, distributors, and consumers.

*Standards.* Standards are primarily requirements pertaining to sanitation procedures that are to be followed in the production, processing, and distribution of milk and milk products. They relate to cows and to their care and treatment; to the use and construction of dairy barns, milk houses and milking equipment; and to milking methods. Standards have been developed for proper handling of milk in processing plants. These relate to types of equipment and to equipment use and cleanliness. Pasteurization is accepted by most people as essential to effective milk control. Standards for pasteurization that define the heat treatment necessary and that specify safeguards incident to effective pasteurization have been set forth.

*Enforcement.* Standards are meaningless without enforcement, which may be accomplished in several ways. Permits or licenses may be revoked or suspended for non-compliance with standards. Degrading, which prevents the sale of milk by a producer or which necessitates a change of label by the processor to that of lower grade, may be required if standards are not met. The consumer who is accustomed to buying milk of a certain grade may refuse milk bearing the label of a lower grade. This creates economic pressure and is an effective enforcement procedure. Prosecution under penalty clauses of ordinances is often resorted to in instances of non-compliance.

Sanitarians have been in general agreement that the bulk of enforcement work should be handled at the municipal or local level of government. This is based upon the premise that supervision and inspection then will be in the hands of people who have direct interest in quality milk for the community and who are in a position to provide close supervision of production and processing. Two developments that have taken place gradually over the years have somewhat modified the thinking of many in this regard. These developments are as follows:

(a) The growing tendency for wide distribution, in many instances over substantial areas of one or more states, of market milk products that have been processed in a large central plant. The economies so effected have eliminated many of the small or local milk distribution plants. This means that sources of milk supplies, raw and pasteurized, often are quite distant from the places of distribution and that there is not efficient and adequate direct control by the local enforcement agency where the product is sold.

(b) The extensive development of interstate milk shipments. This has necessitated close liaison among the various milk control agencies in matters of certification with regard to suitability of milk supplies.

Because of these developments, control efforts at the state level are being strengthened in an effort to bring about the elimination of overlapping jurisdictions and conflicting requirements. Uniform state-wide regulations and enforcement procedures should result in greater efficiency and effectiveness.

*Education.* Education of producer, processor, and consumer is the cornerstone upon which a successful quality milk program must be built. Consumers must be well enough informed so that their demands are in keeping with what can be supplied. Producers and processors should be given the reasons for the various requirements imposed upon them. Although the sanitarian has the primary responsibility for the safety of milk supplies, public health workers, state and federal agencies, public school authorities, county agents, and veterinarians are helpful in the dissemination of pertinent information.

## FEDERAL MILK CONTROL AGENCIES

The federal government has done a great deal to assist in milk control work. Through several of its agencies it provides inspection and educational assistance.

The United States Public Health Service controls milk supplies that are intended for consumption on interstate carriers. In areas involved in supplying milk for interstate shipment, the Service assists states and municipalities in making ratings of milk supplies, and it certifies laboratories of state agencies for the bacteriological examination of the milk. A particularly important activity of the Service is the preparation of a model milk ordinance and of a code of interpretation (22). In the interest of uniform regulations and effective milk control programs, this ordinance is recommended to states and municipalities for adoption.

The United States Department of Agriculture through the Animal Disease Eradication Branch regulates interstate shipments of dairy cattle, with special attention to the elimination of certain types of diseased or unhealthy cattle. The Dairy Research Branch has contributed to research efforts and to educational work on various standards for milk production, processing, and distribution.

The Food and Drug Administration formulates definitions for many dairy products and is on the watch for interstate shipments of unwholesome or adulterated milk products.

The Agricultural Extension Service, in cooperation with State Agricultural Experiment Stations, disseminates information about milk production and processing to farmers, to homemakers, and to the general public.

### STATE MILK CONTROL AGENCIES

Various state agencies contribute greatly to milk control work. At this level of government, the Department of Health or the Department of Agriculture is charged with the responsibility of promulgating and enforcing milk regulations as they apply to the milk supply of the state. The various states are about evenly divided with respect to which of the above agencies is charged with this responsibility. These state agencies cooperate with local governments or municipalities in initiating and maintaining milk control programs, and they often serve as liaisons between municipalities in matters of intrastate milk shipments. Usually state regulations are considered as minimum standards, and municipal ordinances can not be less strict. In the event that milk supplies in certain areas of a state are not governed by a municipal ordinance, the complete responsibility for control is assumed by the state agency. Obviously, effective milk control within a state requires the closest of cooperation between state and local governments.

### MUNICIPAL MILK CONTROL

In most states, municipalities are given authority to engage in milk control work. In some instances programs may be administered jointly by two or more municipalities. In many instances local governments have been far ahead of the state government agencies in the establishment of milk control programs. This has served to stimulate action on the part of state agencies; yet, at the same time, it often has resulted in the establishment of widely differing standards among municipalities within the same state. In view of the adoption of the *United States Public Health Service Milk Ordinance and Code* by various states, many municipalities have revised, or are in the process of revising, present ordinances. This is resulting in much more uniformity among milk regulations and is eliminating many inconsistencies.

### ORDINANCES

The establishment of milk ordinances in the United States began at about the turn of the century in several eastern cities. One of the major objectives of the early ordinances was to control adulteration of milk by adding water. Later, with an increase in knowledge about the role that milk plays in the spread of disease, came the promulgation of regulations designed to improve the sanitary conditions surrounding its production and handling. Unlike the situation that exists today, pasteurization was used but little; consequently, the early ordinances represented an attempt to provide the public with raw milk free from pathogens.

The scope of milk regulations by municipalities and state governments expanded rapidly. Many principal features of early ordinances were copied by other municipalities and states, but generally, each ordinance included special requirements applicable to the particular area for which it was promulgated. This resulted in the creation of a large number of laws and regulations governing the dairy industry and in requirements that differed from one jurisdiction to another. Certain clauses that appeared in ordinances were restrictive; they were effective trade barriers masquerading under the guise of public health safeguards. Thus, numerous standards for quality were established, some of which meant little, and some of which were often confusing and costly.

The seriousness of the lack of uniformity and the need for providing assistance to the states in the control of milk-borne disease were recognized by the United States Public Health Service. This agency, in 1924, published the first edition of its model milk ordinance, covering items of milk sanitation on farms and in pasteurizing plants. States and municipalities were urged to adopt this ordinance in the interests of a uniform system of effective milk control. In 1927 a code to be used in the interpretation of the various provisions of the ordinance was published. Since 1924, the ordinance, now known as the *Milk Ordinance and Code,* has been revised twelve times and has been widely adopted throughout the United States. The progress that has been made in standardizing milk regulations has done much toward establishing reciprocity between states in matters of inspection and certification of milk quality. Annual national conferences on interstate milk shipments, which were begun in 1950, have been particularly helpful in this regard (30).

### GRADE A MILK PRODUCTS

The grade A label on dairy products implies that high quality milk was used in these products. Most states and many municipalities have regulations defining grade A milk. Such regulations may or may not be the same as those contained in the United States Public Health Service grade A ordinance. However, widespread adoption of this ordinance has, for all practical purposes, served to establish grade A milk as milk that has been produced, processed, and distributed in conformance with the United States Public Health Service recommended ordinance or with ordinances substantially equivalent. Eighteen separate sections are included in the Health Service ordinance. Under these sections all of the various requirements for the grade are specified. Since Sections 5, 6, and 7 of the ordinance are of particular concern to laboratory and field service personnel, a brief discussion of each follows.

*Inspection of dairy farms and milk plants—Section 5, United States Public Health Service Milk Ordinance.* This section requires that, at least once every six months, all farms and milk plants must be inspected. If violation of any requirement (listed in Section 7) is discovered, a second inspection shall be made after a reasonable interval during which it may be expected that the infringement will be corrected. Violation of the same requirement on such reinspection shall call for immediate degrading, suspension of permit, or court action, depending upon which system of penalty is called for in the enforcement provision of the ordinance. The acceptance of industry inspection (inspection by fieldmen employed by industry) in lieu of official inspection is provided for; however, industry inspection, where authorized, must be subject to official checking at least once each year. This is done by checking a group of producers selected at random. The rating obtained by industry inspection personnel and that obtained by the official check must be in close agreement. Check-ratings are done in accordance with specified procedure.

*Examination of Milk and Milk Products—Section 6, United States Public Health Service Milk Ordinance.* This section requires that four samples of milk from every farm and that four samples of each finished product bearing the grade A label be submitted for laboratory examination during a period not to exceed six months. Examinations may include bacterial plate counts, direct microscopic counts, and temperature recordings on raw milk and coliform counts, the phosphatase test, and plate counts on pasteurized milk. Various chemical and physical determinations that may be deemed necessary by the control agency also may be made. The procedures used must conform to those given in the current edition of *Standard Methods for the Examination of Dairy Products* (36). Two systems for establishing compliance with bacterial standards are provided: (a) The logarithmic average of the last four standard plate counts or direct microscopic counts must be within the limit specified (see Table 7.1); or (b) three out of the four results must be within the limit specified. The first system is applicable only to standard

**Table 7.1**   Bacterial and coliform counts established by Section 7, United States Public Health Service Milk Ordinance *

| GRADE | RAW MILK AND CREAM FOR PASTEURIZATION AS DELIVERED FROM FARM | | PASTEURIZED PRODUCTS | | |
|---|---|---|---|---|---|
| | *Log. average plate count or direct microscopic clump count not to exceed:* | *Log. average plate count not to exceed:* | *Log. average plate count not to exceed:* | | *Not more than one of the last four coliform counts to exceed:* |
| | *For milk (per ml)* | *For cream (per ml)* | *For milk (per ml)* | *For cream (per ml)* | *Milk, cream and other products (per ml)* |
| A | 200,000 | 400,000 | 30,000 | 60,000 | 10 |
| B | 1,000,000 | 2,000,000 | 50,000 | 100,000 | 10 |
| C | no limit | no limit | no limit | no limit | no limit |

* From *Milk Ordinance and Code* (22).

plate counts and direct microscopic counts. The three-out-of-four system is applicable only to coliform counts.

Whenever the average bacterial count of the four samples is above the limit specified, a fifth sample may be taken and a new average obtained by using the last four consecutive samples. If the bacterial count limit then is exceeded and the last individual result exceeds the limit, immediate degrading, suspension of permit, or court action is required; however, if the last individual result is within the limit, the results are considered as being in compliance. When the three-out-of-four system is used, as in the case of coliform counts, and one of the four results is above the limit, an additional sample is taken. If three out of the four last consecutive samples are within the limit, or if the last sample is within the limit, regardless of the results of the preceding samples, the results are considered as being in compliance.

Provision is made for the acceptance by the official agency of results of examinations made by industry or other commercial laboratories in the case of raw milk for pasteurization. Such results are not accepted, however, unless official periodic checks indicate that the methods employed are in substantial conformance with the standard methods (36) recommended by the American Public Health Association. This is an important provision, for it represents a major concession on the part of government control agencies, and it indicates confidence in industry laboratory personnel. Furthermore, this provision is in harmony with the growing tendency to streamline government control in the interest of greater efficiency and effectiveness, for industry often is able to provide more frequent testing than would be possible by regulatory agencies.

*Grading Milk and Milk Products—Section 7, United States Public Health Service Milk Ordinance.* This section specifies the various standards on which grading shall be based. A summary of the bacterial standards is given in Table 7.1. Standards for production of raw milk for pasteurization and for processing and distribution of pasteurized milk also are specified. Standards which apply to grade A raw milk for pasteurization include:

1. Cows—health and cleanliness.
2. Milking barn—lighting, ventilation, cleanliness of barn and cow yard.
3. Manure disposal and toilet facilities.
4. Milk house—construction, equipment, and cleanliness.
5. Water supply.
6. Utensils—construction, cleaning, bactericidal treatment, storage, handling.
7. Milking—sanitary methods.
8. Cooling.

Standards which apply to grade A milk processing plants include:
1. Plant—floors, walls, ceilings, lighting and ventilation, cleanliness.

2. Equipment and supplies—construction, location, repair, cleaning, bactericidal treatment, and storage.
3. Sanitary piping.
4. Waste disposal.
5. Water supplies.
6. Pasteurization—specifications for temperature and time control.
7. Cooling, bottling, and packaging.

## INDUSTRY QUALITY CONTROL PROGRAMS

From the foregoing discussion it is evident that the milk industry is subject to extensive government control. Milk producers and processors must therefore engage in quality control programs in order to assure satisfactory compliance with regulations. Another objective of the programs, and fully as important, is the maintenance and improvement of the quality of raw and finished products.

The mechanics for the carrying out of such programs by industry are varied. In large organizations, the laboratory and field service departments usually are in charge. Field service personnel, or fieldmen, are largely responsible for producer relationships; they act as troubleshooters who seek to determine, by farm visits, the conditions responsible for unsatisfactory raw milk quality and to assist the producer in correcting the unsatisfactory conditions. In addition to these duties, they may perform methylene blue tests, sediment tests, and direct microscopic counts on individual shipments of milk from producers. The fieldmen are important links between plant and producer and much of the credit for improved raw milk supplies can be attributed to them.

The control laboratory is the heart of the large diversified milk processing plant. It is responsible for conducting routine bacteriological, chemical, and physical examinations of raw and finished products. Continuous checks on the efficiency of processes in maintaining satisfactory quality and on composition of various products are made through laboratory examinations of products taken at intermediate and final points during the manufacturing process. Since plant sanitation is such an important factor in assuring good keeping quality and wholesomeness of products, constant effort must be expended to maintain high standards of sanitation in plants where milk and milk products are processed. Laboratory personnel usually are assigned responsibility for determining the efficiency of this phase of plant operations. Methods employed include visual inspections and various physical and microbiological tests for determining the efficiency of cleaning and bactericidal treatment of equipment. Results and recommendations are reported to personnel responsible for directing the plant sanitation operations.

## THE PROCUREMENT OF MILK

The sequence of events that culminates in the purchase and eventual consumption of market milk by the consumer begins at the dairy farm. The influence of microorganisms on the product may be evident at each of the many stages involved in getting the milk to the consumer.

Milk may be delivered directly from the farm to the processing plant; however, in the case of large milk sheds, milk is brought to receiving stations from dairy farms in close proximity to the station. The principal function of receiving stations is to provide a central milk gathering place, with facilities for weighing, testing, cooling, and storage. Often, facilities are provided for the separation of milk and for the manufacture of butter, cheese, dried milks, and other products from surplus milk. From receiving stations, refrigerated milk is transported in large tank trucks or railroad cars to processing plants located in metropolitan areas. The receiving station system makes it possible to reduce the cost of transporting milk from the farm to the milk plant; furthermore, the system makes it easier to supply the processing plants with their needs, which often vary from day to day.

When milk arrives at the market milk plant, or at the receiving station, it will contain microorganisms that may or may not have affected its quality. In any event, subsequent effort must be directed toward the following objectives: (a) prevention of any further microbial contamination or growth prior to pasteurization; (b) efficient pasteurization; (c) prevention of recontamination after pasteurization; and (d) maintenance of finished products at low temperature to prevent growth of microorganisms that have survived pasteurization and those that may have entered milk adventitiously during post-pasteurization handling.

## PROCESSING MARKET MILK AND CREAM

The pasteurization of market milk and cream involves many operations that must be integrated to provide for adequate and economical processing. Each operation requires rigid sanitation measures, and after milk is pasteurized, particular care is needed to prevent its contamination. Much of the equipment used must comply with specific sanitary safeguards that are designed to prevent inadvertent mishandling of the milk. The success of other operations depends upon proper judgment of the worker.

An increasing volume of milk is being received at dairy plants in tank trucks, and a decreasing volume in cans. Transfer of milk from tank trucks is simple, and often the milk can be immediately processed without an intervening storage period in the plant. The use of cans requires a weigh vat for the determination of the amount of milk creditable to individual producers. Before being emptied, each can should be checked in order to detect and discard any milk that has an undesirable odor due to bacterial action or to feeds, or any that may have abnormal appearance. Care must be taken to avoid entrance into the milk of water or soil of any type from the exterior of the cans as they are inverted for emptying. The weigh vat assembly must be maintained in a sanitary condition, and must be kept covered. The milk may then be pumped through a clarifier to remove any solid foreign matter that may be present. Clarification has little effect on the bacterial count of milk, since some large clumps may be removed and others disintegrated. If the milk is not to be processed immediately, it should be passed through a cooler.

When raw milk is to be stored in the plant, the vats used should be provided with a refrigerating system to keep the milk at approximately 4.5°C. (40°F.) until it is processed. Vat covers should be in place, and ports should be properly covered to prevent any contamination.

In plants where vat pasteurization is used, the milk is piped to the pasteurizer and pasteurized at 61.7°C. (143°F.) for 30 minutes. In order to prevent inadequate pasteurization, timing must not begin until all of the given batch of milk is in the pasteurizer, and none must be taken out until the full 30-minute period has elapsed. For this reason, entrance and exit valves must be so constructed as to prevent leakage and to avoid entrapment of milk that may not be properly heated. Special heating units (space-heaters) should be provided to heat any foam that may form because of the agitation of the milk before or during pasteurization. Otherwise, many bacteria present in the foam would survive pasteurization since the air in the foam would prevent the transfer of heat from the pasteurizer to the entrapped bacteria. The cover of the vat must be kept down during pasteurization, and it must be constructed so that any liquid that may get on it is drained to the floor without entering the milk.

When high-temperature-short-time pasteurization is used, the milk is pumped through the unit by a positive-action type of pump; and the milk is heated to at least 71.6°C. (161°F.). It is held at this temperature for 15 seconds or longer in a holding tube, and then is cooled. A flow-diversion valve is located at the end of the holding tube; this valve automatically diverts milk below 71.6°C. (161°F.) back to the raw milk supply for re-pasteurization. The proper timing of the pasteurization is obtained by having the holding tube of such length and diameter that for a given rate of flow every particle of the milk requires at least 15 seconds to pass through it. For this reason the pump speed must frequently be checked by the sanitarian, who adjusts and seals it to provide the required rate of flow. The high-temperature-short-time plate pasteurizer is constructed to provide for economical use of heat and refrigeration; cold milk, as it enters, is partially heated by the hot milk leaving the pasteurizing section. This milk flows counter to the cold milk on the opposite sides of the plates of the unit. Leakage of the raw milk to the pasteurized must be guarded against by always maintaining a lower pressure on the raw milk. For this reason the raw milk is drawn into the unit by reduced pressure, and the pasteurized milk is forced out under slightly elevated pressure. (See Figure 7.1, p. 216.)

The homogenization of milk, when coupled with the low-temperature, holding system of pasteurization, is usually performed after preheating to approximately 60°C. (140°F.) and then is followed by heating to the desired pasteurization temperature and by holding for at least 30 minutes. When coupled with the high-temperature, short-time system, homogenization is usually performed as the milk leaves the regenerator section, just prior to its entering the heating section of the unit. The temperature at this point is about 57.2°C. (135°F.). In certain installations the homogenizer may be located between the heating section and the holding tube. In such an installation, the time involved in homogenization would constitute additional holding time. Homogenization before pasteurization is completed is more desirable from a sanitary standpoint. There is, however, a certain measure of risk of the development of hydrolytic rancidity resulting from the action of milk lipase on the increased surface of the milk fat globules unless additional heat treatment is applied promptly to inactivate completely the lipase. This may occur if delays in processing occur owing to such things as shutdowns.

The homogenizer must be maintained in a clean and sanitary condition. The sanitization method should insure the treatment of the packing around the pistons. The packing also should be replaced frequently enough to avoid leakage as a result of its being worn and incapable of forming a proper seal. After the homogenization process, milk may show a higher bacterial count owing to the dispersion of cells from clumps of bacteria that survive pasteurization.

The pasteurized milk is cooled by equipment that protects it against contamination from external sources. Leakage of refrigerating water to the milk must be avoided, and the flow of condensate on the cooler must be directed away from the milk.

The cold pasteurized milk should be stored in refrigerated surge vats prior to being bottled. These vats must be cleaned and sanitized before the pasteurized milk is put in them. Furthermore, covers and ports must be kept closed to prevent contamination.

The bottling of milk in glass containers is done by piping the milk to a filler. Condensate almost invariably forms on the outside of the cold filler bowl and becomes contaminated with bacteria present on the bowl. As the condensate flows off the filler, it flows to the lowest parts, which are the valves for filling bottles with milk. An integral part of the filler valve is the drip deflector, a stainless steel shield on which the condensate, first, collects and, then, is directed away from the bottles being filled. Improper installation or damage to this deflector usually results in its faulty performance and in the consequent post-pasteurization contamination of the milk.

The bottling of milk in paper cartons may involve special equipment in which pre-cut cartons are formed into the container, paraffined, cooled, filled with milk, and then sealed. For this type of equipment milk is drawn into cylinders and is forced into the containers by pistons.

The paper milk bottle is widely used in the market milk industry. Some plants utilize this type of container exclusively. Prior to general acceptance of paper bottles, exhaustive bacteriological studies were made of the raw materials and various processes used in their manufacture. Several steps in the conversion of wood pulp to paper have marked bactericidal effects. Among these are the bleaching process with chlorine; sizing, during which a low pH is attained; and the drying process, during which temperatures in the region of 121.1°C. (250°F.) are reached.

The types of microorganisms found in paper and paper board are typically resistant to heat or dryness. Generally about 90 per cent are aerobic spore-formers and micrococci; others that may be found are non-spore-forming rods, actinomyces, and mold spores (32). Total bacterial counts usually are quite low, as shown in Table 7.2.

Ample evidence is available to show that no public health problem is involved in the use of paper bottles (23) (32) (37). In fact, most such containers are sterile; for example, Mudge and Foord (23) found that approximately 95 per cent of all one-half pint containers studied were sterile. This indicates in part the effectiveness of the paraffining process, which usually is applied just prior to filling. Although this is not actually a sterilizing process, it does result in practical sterilization in that any bacteria surviving and present on the surfaces of the paper are locked in the paraffin coating. Actually the paraffining process may be considered as a final bactericidal treatment since the temperature of the bath is sufficiently high to destroy all but the most heat-resistant of the types of bacteria that may be acquired from miscellaneous sources during handling and shipment of the unparaffined stock.

**Table 7.2**   Bacterial counts from paperboard manufactured for use in making milk containers (samples obtained directly from mills, converters, and milk plants)*

| MILL | No. DISINTEGRATION TESTS | PERCENTAGE YIELDING COUNTS PER GRAM OF DISINTEGRATED PAPERBOARD [a] | | | | | MAXIMUM COUNT |
|---|---|---|---|---|---|---|---|
| | | 0–10 | 0–100 | 0–250 | 0–500 | Over 500 | |
| A | 495 | 46 | 91 | 97 | 99 | 1 | 1,085 |
| B | 452 | 23 | 84 | 98 | 100 | 0 | 440 |
| C | 1,279 | 17 | 86 | 97 | 99.9 | 0.1 | 587 |
| D | 163 | 61 | 100 | 100 | 100 | 0 | 84 |
| Total [b] | 2,877 | 26 | 87 | 94 | 98 | 2 | 10,300 |

* Taken from data of Sanborn (32).
[a] Medium Used: Standard Nutrient Agar and Tryptone-Glucose-Beef Extract Agar. Incubation Temperature: 37°C. for 48 hours.
[b] Summary of production from 13 mills. Includes results from mills A, B, C, and D.

Glass milk bottles must be cleaned and sanitized before milk is placed in them. The usual procedure is to place them, first, in an automatic washer, where they are soaked in a strong alkali solution. Then they are cleaned with fiber brushes or "air-brushed" by jets of solution and air under pressure, rinsed, and finally sanitized. The strong alkali used in the soaking and cleaning also destroys many bacteria. The final bactericidal treatment may be done with hot water, steam, chemical bactericide, or a combination of these.

There is, occasionally, danger of contamination due to improper operation of the bottle washer or even to the final rinse water itself. Although a water supply may be satisfactory from the public health standpoint, it may not be satisfactory for use in rinsing bottles or other equipment. This may be the case when the water contains psychrophilic bacteria or other types that may grow in milk and cause defects. Water supplies, therefore, should be checked carefully.

The bottles are led from the bottle washer to the filler on conveyor belts. The conveyor must have a shield on top that protects the bottles against contamination. Conveyors should not be too long, nor should they lead through areas of activity that would predispose the bottles to external contamination.

Glass bottles of milk are capped automatically, and almost always a hood is placed over the cap and lip of the bottle for added protection. Milk may expand and be forced above the plug type of cap, and precaution must be taken to prevent contamination from above the cap. This can be accomplished by not overfilling the bottles and by avoiding a rise in the temperature of the milk.

The bottled milk should be placed in refrigerated storage until delivery. The maintenance of pasteurized products at low temperature is essential to good keeping quality. Considerable fluid milk is consumed five or more days after pasteurization. Every-other-day delivery, increased store sales, and almost universal presence of mechanical refrigeration in the home are major factors tending to lengthen the time between processing and consumption. Although thermoduric bacteria generally will not grow rapidly enough in properly refrigerated milk [below 45°F. (7.2°C.)] to affect keeping quality, they may have a marked effect if milk is allowed to remain at temperatures above this level. The psychrophilic bacteria, which are post-pasteurization contaminants, if present, also will grow much more rapidly as temperatures of holding rise. Consequently, the temperatures at which milk is bottled and held during storage in the plant, as well as the temperatures of storage in store refrigerators and in the home, are of prime importance.

Experience has shown that the temperature of milk in bottles immediately after filling frequently is above 7.2°C. (45°F.) and at times may be at 10°C. to 12.7°C. (50°F. to 55°F.). This, coupled with plant storage room temperatures above 7.2°C. (45°F.), is not conducive to good keeping quality. Sufficient cooling capacity should be provided to permit milk in the bottle filler to be at 4.4°C. (40°F.) or lower. Some rise in temperature during bottling is almost inevitable due to warm bottles, delays occasioned by shutdowns, and failure to transport filled cases to the plant refrigerator room without delay. In addition, there are occasions when milk may stand unrefrigerated while awaiting loading or after having been unloaded at delivery points. When this happens to milk that has already been bottled or stored at high temperatures, its temperature is certain to be too high. It is a well known fact that milk in paper bottles is subject to less rapid temperature change than milk in glass bottles. This is an advantage in the instance of low bottling temperatures, but it is a decided disadvantage when milk is bottled at temperatures that are too high. In the latter instance the net effect is a longer period of exposure to high temperature, even though the storage room temperature may be sufficiently low.

The increased volume of milk sold through stores has drawn attention to the manner in which milk is handled in such outlets. In one study (2) it was found that in various types of cabinets the temperatures at the front-bottom or top-rear of the cabinets generally were satisfactory, averaging 6.1°C. (43°F.). This was not the case at the front-top of the cabinets where temperatures averaged 10°C. (50°F.) and occasionally were found as high as 13.3°C. (56°F.). These results were even more significant in view of the finding that the cabinet thermometer never was found to register a temperature above 4.4°C. (40°F.). The average temperatures of milk taken from the front and rear of cabinets were 9.7°C. and 7.4°C. (49.5°F. and 45.3°F.), respectively; the range was from 5°C. to 15.5°C. (41°F. to 61°F.) in the front and 2.2°C. to 11.1°C. (36°F. to 52°F.) in the rear.

In certain retail stores a common practice that contributes to elevated temperatures of milk is the piling of paper milk bottles in layers above those in the front part of the cabinet. Such milk receives little if any refrigeration from the cabinet and several hours may elapse before such milk may be sold. Storage conditions outside the cabinets, i. e., in vegetable rooms and in other areas of the store, contribute greatly to unsatisfactory milk temperatures. This frequently occurs in stores doing a large volume of business, but having inadequate refrigeration space.

These observations point up the fact that there are many opportunities for milk to be mishandled with regard to temperature control, and when such mishandling occurs, the careful control exercised at the plant loses much of its intended effectiveness.

### CREAM

In the processing of cream, milk must first be separated. Usually milk is separated while raw, after having been warmed to 32°C. to 38°C. (90°F. to 100°F.). Recently new equipment has made it possible to separate milk while it is cold. Although this is done primarily to obtain desired physical effects in the cream, it also aids in preventing the growth of bacteria during separation. Separation by centrifugal separators tends to remove some bacteria in the skimmilk and separator slime, although the breaking of bacterial clumps may result in no significant lowering of the bacterial count of the cream. Foreign matter and body cells are removed from the milk and are concentrated in the separator slime.

The high fat content in cream has no significant effect on the requirement for pasteurization, and exposures used for milk are considered adequate for cream. It has been shown that 20 and 40 per cent cream require only about a 0.7°F. higher temperature than whole milk for any given pasteurization time to inactivate milk phosphatase (31). Since increased viscosity is obtained when cream is homogenized at higher temperatures, the temperature usually is increased also in its pasteurization.

### CHOCOLATE MILK

Chocolate milk usually is prepared by adding about 1 per cent cocoa, 5 to 8 per cent cane sugar, and a small amount of stabilizer to milk containing 1 to 4 per cent butterfat. This is processed as is pasteurized homogenized milk, with the exception that a higher pasteurization exposure normally is used in order to solubilize the stabilizer and to prevent settling of the cocoa. Furthermore, the added cane sugar means that more heat is required to kill the bacteria present in the product. For pasteurization of chocolate milk, exposures of 61.7°C. (143°F.) for 49 minutes, or 62.8°C. (145°F.) for 30 minutes using the vat method, and 73.9°C. (165°F.) for 15 seconds using the high-temperature-short-time method have been recommended (35).

The numbers of bacteria in cocoa powders and in chocolate milk may be very few, or they may reach several thousand per milliliter. A survey of several commercial preparations by Fuller et al. (12) showed that neither gram-negative intestinal bacteria nor hemolytic cocci were present in the powders or syrups. Most of the organisms isolated were aerobic gram-positive spore-formers of the *Bacillus subtilis* type. Thus, it appears that there is little danger that the public health will be affected adversely by the use of such products. Added safety is assured by pasteurization of chocolate milk after the addition of the syrup or powder.

If considerable numbers of spore-forming bacteria are present in chocolate syrups or cocoa powders, it is conceivable that they may affect the keeping quality of the chocolate milks. Studies have shown (12), however, that chocolate milk made with cocoa powders and with cocoa-containing chocolate syrups did not increase in bacterial counts as rapidly as did the counts of milk. When syrup flavored with an extract of cocoa powder was used, no inhibition of bacterial growth occurred. It appears, therefore, that cocoa contains some growth inhibiting factor. Further studies utilizing pure cultures of common milk organisms showed that all but *Streptococcus lactis* were inhibited to some extent.

CLEANING AND SANITIZATION OF EQUIPMENT

Problems of maintaining dairy plant equipment in the proper state of cleanliness are essentially the same as those pertaining to the maintenance of producer equipment (Chapter 6). Equipment in which milk is heated usually needs particular care, since milk residues adhere to it tenaciously. Special care must be given to cleaning this kind of equipment in order to prevent the build-up of milk stone. The use of air-brushing (compressed air and detergent solution) is frequently more effective than the use of hand-brushing for certain equipment such as vats. Units such as high-temperature-short-time plate pasteurizers can be adequately cleaned by recirculation of hot detergent.

The bactericidal treatment can be effected with heat or chemical agents. Pipelines, pumps, fillers, and similar small volume equipment can be sanitized by being flushed with hot water at 85°C. (185°F.). Frequently a chemical bactericide is placed in a raw milk vat and pumped through the entire milk-handling system, a procedure that can provide very effective sanitization. Vats and tanks can be sanitized with a fogging device that applies the chemical in a fine mist, effectively covering all surfaces that may contact the milk.

After sanitization, equipment should not be opened or rehandled until after being used. If it is opened or rehandled, it should be sanitized again. At times, new gaskets and different lengths of pipe must be inserted into lines, for example, when changing from one product to another. Whenever this is required, the gasket and pipe should be sanitized before being placed in the line. Failure to observe this precaution is a common cause of contamination with coliform bacteria.

CLEANED-IN-PLACE PIPELINES

The installation of permanent sanitary pipelines in dairy plants and dairy barns or milking parlors has become commonplace. In contrast to the conventional sanitary pipeline system, the permanent lines remain in place during the cleaning and sanitizing procedures, hence the term "cleaned-in-place" (CIP).

There are numerous advantages to the CIP system. The lower labor cost for the cleaning operation is one of the most important of these. A major part of the total labor in the dairy plant is that necessary to disassemble, clean, and reassemble equipment. Cleaning CIP lines is relatively simple, since most cleaning is done by recirculation of a cleaning solution, with only such items as valves being cleaned by hand-brushing. Sanitizing is done similarly. Conventional sanitary pipelines, and particularly the fittings when taken down each day, frequently are damaged by being thrown together in wash tanks or by being placed in contact with the floor or other equipment. The use of CIP lines essentially eliminates such damage. A direct result of less damage to lines and fittings is less loss of product owing to poorly fitting connections. This also results in cleaner plants.

Numerous studies have shown that CIP lines can be maintained in a very satisfactory sanitary condition. Also, experience has shown that such lines, when contrasted with conventional take-down lines, are kept more uniformly in an excellent bacteriological condition day after day. This is due to the adaptability of the CIP system to a simple, standardized cleaning procedure, with the result that there is less chance for haphazard cleaning. Higher temperatures and stronger cleaning solutions can be used because there are no limitations based upon what the user's hands can stand.

CIP lines are made of stainless steel or glass. Although there are advantages and disadvantages to each, there is little or no difference between the two in over-all usefulness.

Many CIP lines have been in use for several years, never having been taken down except for an occasional joint or fitting that may have been opened for visual examination or for swab tests. Sterile rinse solutions passed through such lines, or swab tests of ends of lines or fittings, frequently indicate lower bacterial populations than are indicated by similar tests on conventional take-down lines. This does not mean that good bacterial counts can not be obtained with the take-down system, but only that opportunities for laxity in the cleaning and sanitizing of take-down lines are greater than with CIP lines.

If the CIP system is to be fully effective, certain precautions must be taken. Important factors in this regard are listed below:

a. Lines must be firmly supported so that fittings and gaskets remain in alignment. If this is not done, leakage behind gaskets may occur, resulting in ineffective cleaning.

b. Lines should be pitched for proper drainage; about one inch per 20 feet is commonly suggested.

c. Gaskets should form a substantially flush joint. This is necessary for efficient cleaning and drainage.

d. A recording thermometer should be installed in the return line to furnish a dependable record of temperature of solutions used in cleaning and sanitizing.

e. A solution tank equipped with a pump is necessary. The pump should be of sufficient size to force solutions through the lines at a high rate. A rate of 5 feet per second has been found to be satisfactory. This will cause the solutions to be forced through the lines in such a way that the entire line is completely filled, thus assuring contact of all surfaces.

f. A steam line direct to the solution tank has proven much more satisfactory than attempting to use the steam hose for maintaining temperatures of solutions.

g. A good cleaning compound must be used in preparing the cleaning solutions. This may be alkaline or acid in nature; usually the alkaline type is used more routinely with intermittent use of the acid type every third or fourth day.

The steps in the actual cleaning operation may vary in different plants. The following are essential steps which may or may not be supplemented, depending upon processing operations, design of installation and other factors:

a. Immediately after the day's processing operation, all connections between CIP lines and processing equipment (certain equipment such as plate coolers may be cleaned in place) should be disconnected and removed, the openings capped, the by-pass connections made, and the lines thoroughly rinsed with water at a temperature of 37.8°C. to 49°C. (100°F. to 120°F.).

b. The washing solution should be circulated at a temperature of 71°C. to 77°C. (160°F. to 170°F.) for approximately 30 minutes.

c. Drain lines and solution tank, and rinse thoroughly by pumping water at 51.7°C. to 60°C. (125°F. to 140°F.) through the lines. The water from the return line should not be recirculated.

d. Before operations begin again, necessary connections should be made; as many of the lines and individual pieces of equipment as possible should be assembled so as to allow circulation of either hot water or a chlorine solution for bactericidal treatment.

## BACTERIOLOGICAL PROBLEMS OF MARKET MILK PRODUCTS

In maintaining high quality milk and assuring compliance with the various regulatory requirements, the market milk operator is confronted with a number of bacteriological problems, any one of which may prevent the attainment of his goals. The bacteria involved may be considered under the following topics: (a) excessive total bacterial counts in the raw milk supply; (b) thermoduric bacteria; (c) thermophilic bacteria; (d) the coliform group; (e) psychrophilic bacteria; (f) certain bacterial defects; and (g) the spread of disease through milk. Since the dairy industry must assume the responsibility for providing the public with wholesome milk having good flavor and keeping quality, the control of the above problems is essential.

### EXCESSIVE BACTERIAL COUNTS IN RAW MILK

There are several considerations that have influenced the maximum number of bacteria allowable in market milk. These are the following: (a) the influence of bacterial numbers on organoleptic, physical, and chemical properties of raw milk per se, or their effect on predisposing the milk to changes during pasteurization; (b) the meaning of bacterial numbers with regard to the presence of pathogens; and (c) the relationship of aesthetic considerations and bacterial populations.

The number of microorganisms required to alter raw milk detectably is considerably greater than the maximum number allowed by present regulations. Generally, as shown by Hammer and Hix (14) and others, bacterial growth to a population of 5 million to 100 million per milliliter of milk, as measured by the plate count, is required to produce detectable changes in milk. For example, in a series of trials by Hammer and Hix using a pure culture of *Streptococcus lactis,* souring was not detected by taste until counts reached 30 to 90 million per milliliter. Slight ropiness caused by *Alcaligenes viscosus* was evident when counts reached 15 to 44 million per milliliter. However, slight coagulation by an organism producing a "sweet curdling" defect was observed when counts reached 1.25 to 4.9 million per milliliter. Results similar to those given have been obtained with certain other species capable of producing various defects.

The evidence available indicates that, when specific bacterial species are permitted to grow in milk to the extent that actively metabolizing cells reach a population of 5 to 20 million per milliliter, a detectable change in flavor or appearance may be evident or imminent. It is possible, however, for bacterial counts of milk to be considerably in excess of 5 or even 20 million per milliliter without causing any detectable change in milk. Usually the types of microorganisms and the activity level of those cells constituting the population are as important as the actual total numbers. Bacteriological changes in milk are brought about much more rapidly by actively growing populations than by those which are dormant. It is difficult, if not impossible, to know specifically whether a high bacterial count in raw milk is the result of growth originating from a few bacterial cells or the result of a massive inoculum from sources such as the unclean, highly contaminated surfaces of equipment used in handling the milk. In the first instance, it may be expected that, when defect-producing species grow to a level of a few million per milliliter, an undesirable change in the milk may soon occur; indeed, this change may have already occurred. In the case of a high initial contamination followed by proper cooling, such a population may remain dormant; and millions of undesirable bacteria may be present without a detectable change in flavor or appearance occurring, provided that low temperatures are maintained. Frequently, bacterial counts of several million per milliliter may be obtained on raw milk from individual farms without any off-flavor or other change being evident. In such instances bacterial activity may have been held in check by low temperature, or the predominant flora may have consisted of relatively inert species.

In view of the foregoing discussion, it might appear that present bacterial standards for raw milk are too stringent. Considering a maximum allowable raw milk count solely from the standpoint of the influence of bacteria on flavor or physical and chemical change in milk, it would seem that a standard of one million per milliliter would suffice. There is little, if any, evidence to indicate that finished products made from lower count milk would be superior in flavor and appearance insofar as these characteristics are affected by bacteria. Furthermore, these numbers of bacteria would not decrease the nutritional value of milk. There are, however, other factors that must be considered in establishing bacterial standards.

In considering the numbers of microorganisms required to effect changes in milk, the rapidity with which relatively low populations can multiply and cause defects must be considered. Several hours may suffice to permit such growth and metabolism to occur, depending on the types of bacteria present, on their level of population, and on the storage temperatures provided. The storage temperature alone may vary widely during the farm operations and the delivery to the processing plant. Furthermore, economic considerations have led to longer storage time of raw milk on the farm and to greater distances for its transportation to the pasteurizing plant. For such reasons, keeping the initial numbers of bacteria low aids in the prevention of defects in milk prior to processing and minimizes the load imposed on the pasteurization process.

The production of good quality raw milk is the responsibility of the producer. His responsibilities must be considered in relation to the maximum bacterial count standard which is established. There is ample evidence to show that no hardship whatever is experienced in producing raw milk having bacterial counts well under 1,000,000 per milliliter at the time of delivery to processing plants. In many market milk sheds over 50 per cent of the bacterial counts of milk received at processing plants from individual producers are considerably less than 50,000 per milliliter. Therefore, the present standard (see Table 7.1) of 200,000 bacteria per milliliter for grade A raw milk for pasteurization appears to be a reasonable one. There may be some justification for an even lower maximum allowable count. In establishing any lower standard, however, the economic demands imposed upon the producer must be considered in relation to the advantages gained for possibly increased milk quality and safety. Justification for requiring low bacterial counts for raw milk cannot be based upon the assumption that low count milk is necessarily safe milk. Likewise, reliance on environmental conditions designed to prevent all possible contamination of raw milk with pathogens as a means of providing safe milk is not economically feasible, even if possible. The only recognized positive means of assuring safe milk supplies is pasteurization to destroy any pathogens that are present, plus the application of rigid controls over the handling of milk after pasteurization. An outstanding example of the recognition of these facts is the application of the pasteurization process to certified raw milk.*

---

* Certified milk is the product of dairies operated in accordance with the methods and standards currently adopted by the American Association of Medical Milk Commissions, Inc. Certified milk had its origin in 1893, within the medical profession, through the desire of physicians to obtain clean, safe, and nutritious milk for infant feeding. Methods and standards for production have been revised from year to year. The belief that, regardless of what subsequent treatment may be given to milk, improvements of the product with regard to safety and nutritional factors can best be accomplished at the source of production has been the basis for much of the policy of this industry. Actually the sales volume of certified milk represents only a small fraction of milk sold for fluid consumption. For further discussion see reference (21).

It should be recognized that the certified milk industry played an important role in the development of high quality milk. Efforts of this branch of the industry have stimulated the dairy industry as a whole to establish better sanitary practices. The bacterial count limits for certified milks as given below indicate the high standards for this product.

> Certified milk, raw—Standard plate count not more than 10,000 per milliliter.
> Coliform count not more than 10 per milliliter.

> Certified milk, pasteurized—Standard plate count not more than 500 per milliliter.
> Coliform count not more than one per milliliter.

Aesthetic considerations undoubtedly have had a major impact on the establishment of bacterial limits for milk. Aesthetic values are intangible and vary with individuals. The standards of cleanliness practiced, and often self-imposed in the dairy industry, are reflected in the present high sanitary quality of milk. However, the extent to which aesthetic considerations may alter existing bacterial standards must also be controlled by requirements that are economically feasible for the producer, the processor, and ultimately the consumer. Since the majority of milk producers are able to comply with existing bacterial standards, it would appear that our present conception of acceptable sanitation is not unreasonable. It would seem, then, that the present bacterial count for raw milk of 200,000 per milliliter represents a median between a higher count that may adversely affect milk and an extremely low count that would be above reproach aesthetically but generally impractical of attainment. With time, continued improvement in methods and equipment undoubtedly will enable the industry to comply with more rigid standards. For example, the introduction of the bulk tank method of handling milk on the farm is likely to be a primary factor leading to the establishment of lower bacterial count standards. With this method of handling milk, poor cooling, one of the two major factors responsible for high bacterial counts in raw milk, is practically eliminated. Consequently, the occurrence of high counts will point even more directly than it has in the past to poor sanitary conditions of equipment.

### THE PROBLEM OF THERMODURIC BACTERIA

A great amount of effort is expended by the market milk industry to reduce the bacterial content of pasteurized milk. The thermoduric bacteria are especially troublesome in this regard. As generally understood by the dairy industry, the organisms that survive pasteurization in considerable numbers but that do not grow at pasteurization temperature are classed as thermoduric. This definition excludes the thermophilic bacteria, those which grow at pasteurization temperatures, although the literal meaning of the word thermoduric would include them. Thermophilic bacteria present a separate and distinct problem, which will be discussed later.

For the most part thermodurics are mesophilic bacteria that, remarkably, possess the characteristic of heat resistance, a peculiarity that is not shared by other species within the mesophilic group. These types do not grow at pasteurization temperature, but many cells of a culture of such organisms are capable of remaining viable throughout the process. When the temperature of milk is reduced again so that it is within their growth temperature range, they are able to resume growth.

Thermoduric bacteria should be held to low numbers in any milk supply. Excessive numbers in the raw supply make it difficult to meet bacterial count standards for pasteurized milk; furthermore, these bacteria are an undesirable group because their presence is closely allied with insanitary practices on the producing farm. Thermodurics also may affect the keeping quality of pasteurized milk stored above 45°F.; such temperatures, although not proper for the storage of pasteurized milk, are not uncommon in the routine handling of milk.

Two excellent reviews of the literature relative to thermoduric bacteria found in milk and on dairy equipment have been published (17, 38). The reader is referred to these reviews for additional discussion.

Thermoduric bacteria are detected routinely by means of the laboratory pasteurization test (see Chapter 5).

*Types of thermoduric organisms.* Thermoduric bacteria normally are limited to a few species of five groups of bacteria. These are micrococci, streptococci, aerobic spore-formers, microbacteria, and gram-negative rods, all of which have been described in Chapter 2.

1. MICROCOCCI. More work is necessary before a meaningful and precise taxonomic designation can be made of thermoduric micrococci found in milk. The confusion in this respect has been clarified somewhat by Abd-El-Malek and Gibson (1), who classified the micrococci into the following three main groups:

    a. Staphylococcus group—Sugar fermenters, relatively sensitive to heat. Mainly parasites of the animal body including the cow's udder.

    b. Intermediate group—Do not produce acid from sugars, obligate aerobes. Include some slightly thermoduric strains.

    c. The dairy micrococci—Thermoduric sugar fermenters that occur frequently on dairy equipment and in pasteurized milk.

These authors have questioned the use of certain differential characteristics used by others in classifying micrococci on the grounds that little significance can be attached to them. The result of the use of differential characteristics, which do not include heat resistance, in classifying micrococci is that the micrococci commonly found in the cow's udder are given the same species names as the thermoduric species. This has caused some misunderstanding; consequently, it has often been said that the udder is an important source of thermoduric micrococci. This now appears to be questionable in light of recent studies (1, 20, 25), which have shown that normally thermoduric micrococci are either absent or present in insignificant numbers in milk drawn aseptically from normal cows. Occasionally, however, a thermoduric flora may become established in the udder (see Chapter 6).

2. STREPTOCOCCI. *Streptococcus thermophilus* is a commonly occurring thermoduric streptococcus. *Streptococcus bovis, Streptococcus durans, Streptococcus zymogenes, Streptococcus liquefaciens,* and *Streptococcus faecalis* are other species that often may be found.

Occasionally the beta-hemolytic streptococci, *Streptococcus durans* and *Streptococcus zymogenes,* are found in pasteurized milk. These species, unlike the non-thermoduric *Streptococcus pyogenes,* are not regarded as pathogenic. *Streptococcus bovis* and closely related types are weakly hemolytic. Milk with high thermoduric counts thus may contain appreciable numbers of hemolytic streptococci (33).

3. AEROBIC SPORE-FORMERS. Spore-forming bacteria practically always are present in raw milk, although usually in low numbers. *Bacillus subtilis* and *Bacillus cereus,* including closely related strains or variants of the latter, generally are encountered most commonly. Other species that have been shown to contribute to the thermoduric flora of milk are *Bacillus pumilis, Bacillus circulans, Bacillus polymyxa,* and *Bacillus laterosporus.*

4. MICROBACTERIA. Frequently *Microbacterium lacticum* is found in pasteurized milk. This species probably is the most heat resistant among the non-spore-forming bacteria. However, these bacteria may be overlooked on plates, for their optimum temperature of growth is approximately 30°C. (86°F.), and the colonies produced at this temperature are small even after incubation for 48 hours. Growth is markedly reduced above this temperature, and consequently counts obtained from plates incubated above 30°C. (86°F.) may not include all of the microbacteria present in the milk.

5. GRAM-NEGATIVE RODS AND OTHER MISCELLANEOUS TYPES. Certain rather inert and ill-defined gram-negative species that eventually produce an alkaline reaction in litmus milk, a variety of anaerobic spore-formers, and certain lactobacilli represent this group.

It is questionable whether or not to include the coliforms. Generally coliform bacteria (*Escherichia coli* and *Aerobacter aerogenes*) do not survive pasteurization, but certain instances of their survival in fairly large numbers have been reported. Many reports which would indicate that survival of pasteurization is common among the coliform bacteria are based upon data obtained through faulty techniques used in determining heat resistance (see discussion of coliform problem).

An extensive study of the heat resistance of lactobacilli such as *Lactobacillus casei* has been reported by Slatter and Halvorson (34). On occasion these organisms might contribute significantly to the thermoduric flora.

*Sources and their control.* The control of thermoduric types starts at the pasteurizing plant. Heat-resistant bacteria may accumulate in plant equipment owing to faulty cleaning methods, but this is an exceptional cause for high thermoduric counts in milk pasteurized in well-operated plants. Sometimes the operator may make the unfortunate mistake of repasteurizing returned milk. This is a particularly undesirable practice because conditions that occur subsequent to the first pasteurization may allow prolific growth of bacteria that have survived. Milk returned from delivery routes may contain large numbers that would survive a second pasteurization. Repasteurization of return milk may serve to culture thermodurics selectively, and if this is done routinely, a processing plant will usually encounter an acute thermoduric problem. In the same way, the use of pasteurized skimmilk for standardizing milk and cream may lead to high thermoduric counts in finished products. Standardization should always be done with fresh skimmilk. In most instances these and other faulty practices in the plant lead to more difficulty with thermophilic or with high total counts due to organisms other than thermoduric types. Nevertheless, the plant operator should be certain that the difficulty does not have its origin within the plant before seeking elsewhere for the causes.

With the above in mind, the next logical step in locating the source of thermodurics is to turn to the raw milk supply. The major factor in high total counts on pasteurized milk has been shown to be the presence of excessive numbers of thermoduric bacteria in raw milk delivered from the dairy farm. These sources have been considered in Chapter 6.

*Effect of cooling.* Until recently there was very little factual information available about the effect that failure to cool milk on the farm has on thermoduric counts. Recent studies (24, 39) show rather conclusively that cooling of raw milk generally has little effect on the thermoduric counts. Although this fact may be helpful in interpreting results, it provides no justification for failure to cool milk properly. Other non-thermoduric types may grow rapidly and may seriously affect the flavor and appearance of milk. Both failure to cool milk and failure to clean utensils properly are often the result of carelessness; thus, high thermoduric counts frequently may be found on farms where cooling is inadequate, although the primary cause of the excessive thermoduric count in such instances generally is poor utensil sanitation.

*Seasonal effect on incidence of thermodurics.* High thermoduric counts occur more often in summer than in winter (19). This is due to a combination of poor cleaning of utensils and poor cooling. The data shown in Table 7.3 illustrate what has been found to be true in this regard. In warm weather organisms present on unclean utensils are able to develop larger populations than they are able to develop in cold weather, and this is reflected in higher thermoduric counts in the milk. High total counts that result from poor cooling of milk often are due to rapidly growing non-thermoduric types. Pasteurization of such milk usually will result in satisfactorily low counts.

*Thermodurics and keeping quality.* The keeping quality of properly refrigerated pasteurized milk (7.2°C.—45°F.—or below) generally is not adversely affected by thermoduric bacteria (3); however, many of these organisms do grow in milk held above 7.2°C. (45°F.). The keeping quality of milk held above this temperature, therefore, may be affected significantly by thermoduric bacteria. The importance of this is obvious since the storage temperatures in plants, in wholesale and retail outlets, and in the homes of consumers may not be sufficiently low to prevent the growth of these bacteria.

Thermoduric counts are of little use in predicting keeping quality. Such counts vary greatly among different milk supplies. Many factors determine whether or not any of the thermoduric bacteria present will grow. Since many organisms of this type are relatively inert biochemically, the population may reach considerable numbers without changing the product noticeably. Keeping quality will be discussed further in connection with psychrophilic bacteria.

The practical importance of the relative efficiency of the holder and HTST pasteurization processes in destroying bacteria is of some significance (see Chapter 4). In certain milk sheds, during periods when the thermoduric problem was particularly acute, raw milk supplies suspected of containing excessive numbers of thermoduric bacteria were diverted to plants employing the holder system. This served as a temporary measure until field and laboratory work resulted in elimination of the high numbers of thermoduric bacteria in the supplies.

**Table 7.3**     Comparison of results of laboratory pasteurization of milk during summer and winter months *

| BACTERIAL COUNT BEFORE PASTEURIZATION (per ml) | PER CENT DISTRIBUTION OF SAMPLES ACCORDING TO BACTERIAL COUNT AFTER PASTEURIZATION | | | | | | PER CENT DISTRIBUTION ACCORDING TO COUNT BEFORE PASTEURIZATION | |
|---|---|---|---|---|---|---|---|---|
| | Less than 5000 per ml | | 5000 to 25,000 per ml | | 25,000 or more per ml | | | |
| | summer | winter | summer | winter | summer | winter | summer | winter |
| Less than 25,000 | 59.6 | 93.4 | 32.1 | 5.8 | 8.3 | 0.7 | 39.3 | 47.8 |
| 25,000–99,000 | 37.7 | 77.3 | 51.9 | 17.3 | 10.4 | 5.1 | 31.0 | 37.3 |
| 100,000–249,000 | 23.8 | 50.0 | 59.0 | 32.2 | 17.1 | 17.8 | 10.8 | 8.6 |
| 250,000–999,000 | 19.5 | 35.0 | 64.6 | 26.1 | 15.7 | 38.8 | 10.4 | 4.9 |
| 1,000,000 or more | 7.8 | 38.5 | 63.3 | 25.6 | 28.9 | 35.9 | 8.5 | 1.4 |
| All samples | 40.5 | 80.1 | 47.1 | 13.7 | 12.4 | 6.2 | —— | —— |

* From data of Macy and Erekson (19).

## THE PROBLEM OF THERMOPHILIC BACTERIA

Problems with the thermophilic bacteria in the dairy industry center about the growth of organisms during the heat treatment of milk. Although thermophilic bacteria never have been shown to be pathogenic (16), they are objectionable in milk because their growth may cause off-flavors, high acidity, and a tendency for the milk to curdle upon heating. Furthermore, excessive numbers of these organisms, as in the case of thermoduric bacteria, may make the meeting of bacterial standards for pasteurized milk difficult.

*Definitions.* Thermophilic bacteria have been defined in a variety of ways. Perhaps the most useful definition (5) is that which limits use of the term "thermophilic" to those organisms that will grow readily at 55°C. (131°F.). This serves to separate thermophilic bacteria from a rather large group of mesophilic spore-forming and non-spore-forming bacteria that may grow rapidly up to 50°C. (122°F.) but that generally are markedly retarded in growth at higher temperatures. The term "facultative thermophilic" is useful in designating those types of thermophilic bacteria that also can grow readily at temperatures as low as 37°C. (98.6°F.)—sometimes lower—as well as at 55°C. (131°F.). The term "obligate thermophilic" (stenothermophilic) describes those that cannot grow at 37°C. (98.6°F.). Organisms of this latter type will not grow on the usual plates employed for enumeration. The upper limit for the growth of thermophilic types is about 70°C. (158°F.). The above definitions are somewhat arbitrary, since there is much overlapping of growth temperature ranges of bacteria. This makes it difficult to place all bacteria in precisely defined groups.

*Detection of thermophilic bacteria.* The agar plate method with incubation at 55°C. (131°F.) is the standard procedure for obtaining counts of thermophilic bacteria. The direct microscopic procedure also may be very useful both for semi-quantitative counts and for detecting the presence of thermophiles in milk suspected of containing excessive numbers of them (see Chapter 5).

*Types of organisms.* Thermophilic organisms encountered in milk consist primarily of certain species of aerobic or facultatively anaerobic spore-forming rods. For a detailed description of these species, the reader is referred to studies by Prickett (28). The only non-spore-forming thermophilic species of importance is *Lactobacillus thermophilus*. This organism was one of the first to be shown important in connection with the thermophilic problem in market milk plants and in the formation of pinpoint colonies on agar media used for routine plate counts of pasteurized milk (4). Actinomycetes and anaerobic spore-formers occasionally may be found.

*Sources, development, and control of thermophilic bacteria.*

1. RAW MILK. Thermophilic bacteria gain access to milk through soil, bedding, feeds, and other miscellaneous sources. Generally,

raw milk contains relatively few thermophilic bacteria; but sufficient numbers normally are present so that, if the milk is held long enough at high temperatures, large numbers will develop.

Occasionally water supplies, rural and municipal, may harbor thermophilic bacteria that develop to high populations in hot water storage tanks. Elevating the temperature of the water to 82.2°C. (180°F.) will prevent the multiplication of these bacteria in such instances. Contamination also may occur through the use of unclean pails when adding water to heaters of the type requiring the addition of water in order to draw hot water from the tank. Milk solids and other organic matter from the pail used may supply sufficient nutrients to support bacterial growth.

Extensive studies (15) have shown that thermophilic bacteria do not inhabit the cow's udder.

2. CONTINUOUS-FLOW PASTEURIZATION (LTH). When continuous-flow, low-temperature methods of pasteurization were used extensively (these now almost entirely replaced by HTST units), much difficulty occurred because of the growth of thermophilic bacteria in milk, and on equipment surfaces, during pasteurization. The pasteurization temperature of approximately 145°F. (62.8°C.) was well within the growth temperature range of thermophilic bacteria. Large numbers of thermophilic organisms often would begin to appear in the final product after 2 or 3 hours of operation. Table 7.4 shows examples of what may take place under such conditions. Inside surfaces of holder tubes become seeded with thermophilic bacteria, and as milk flows through, the organisms are continuously sloughed off in increasing numbers. Preheaters and filter cloths used in connection with this type of pasteurization are common places for growth of thermophilic bacteria.

3. VAT OR BATCH PASTEURIZATION (LTH). Before the advent of HTST units, this type of pasteurization was common in large plants, often in multiple installations that allowed practically continuous operation. The problem with thermophilic bacteria in such units is much the same as in

**Table 7.4**     Increase in direct microscopic count of milk leaving long-flow holders *

| DAY | BACTERIAL COUNTS AFTER SUCCESSIVE HOURS OF OPERATION | | | | | |
|---|---|---|---|---|---|---|
| | 0-1[a] | 1-2[a] | 2-3 | 3-4 | 4-5 | 5-6 |
| | | | Holder No. 1 | | | |
| 1 | 600,000 | 600,000 | 1,500,000 | 3,000,000 | 7,500,000 | ——— |
| 2 | <10,000 | <10,000 | 3,000,000 | 4,500,000 | 9,000,000 | ——— |
| | | | Holder No. 2 | | | |
| 1 | <10,000 | 1,500,000 | 300,000 | 4,500,000 | 6,000,000 | ——— |
| 2 | 600,000 | 1,500,000 | 6,000,000 | 7,500,000 | ——— | 30,000,000 |

* From Yale and Breed (43).
[a] Author did not consider counts obtained during the first two hours accurate.

continuous-flow tubular units. Films of milk remaining on the sides of vats that have been emptied may contain large numbers of bacteria that will serve to inoculate succeeding batches. Such a situation also would occur in non-multiple installations if the vats were used repeatedly and were not cleaned between runs.

Vat or batch pasteurization commonly is practiced in smaller plants not having sufficient volume to warrant use of HTST units. When high thermophile counts occur under these conditions, such counts commonly are associated with an increase in volume of milk handled. At such times the pasteurization, cooling, and bottling operations may not be well integrated. Consequently, hot or warm milk may be allowed to stand for excessive periods after pasteurization because of inadequate cooling capacity or because of a combination of inadequate cooling and inadequate bottling capacity.

The control of the growth of thermophiles during pasteurization requires the shutdown and flushing, or cleaning, of the unit after intervals of operation. The time between such clean-up periods may vary from 3 to 6 hours, depending upon the efficiency with which other sources of thermophiles are controlled.

4. REPASTEURIZATION OF RETURNED MILK. The addition of milk returned from routes and of drippings from bottle fillers and other points to the raw milk supply before pasteurization is very objectionable. This, in effect, increases the population of thermophilic bacteria in the raw supply and thus makes possible faster development of a large population during pasteurization. Then, too, use of returned milk and the practice of standardizing with skimmilk and cream separated from returned milk eventually may result in high counts of thermophilic bacteria due to selection (see discussion of thermodurics).

5. MISCELLANEOUS FACTORS. Milk foam left in vats after emptying may provide an excellent means of inoculating succeeding batches with thermophilic bacteria. If foam-heating devices are not used, or if they are improperly used, the temperature of the foam may be well below that of milk (42). Consequently, mesophilic organisms having rather high maximum growth temperatures, and facultative thermophilic organisms as well, may grow rapidly.

Dead ends or other places where hot milk is allowed to stand for any appreciable time have been found to be sources of difficulty. Shutdowns of pasteurizing units, when hot milk remains in the units, can result in growth of thermophilic bacteria.

6. HIGH-TEMPERATURE, SHORT-TIME PASTEURIZATION (HTST). The problem of thermophilic bacteria is not nearly so important in plants employing the HTST process. Figure 7.1 shows the progress of milk as it passes through a HTST pasteurizer. In this process milk passes successively through: (a) the regenerative section, where the raw milk is heated to approximately 57.2°C. to 60°C. (135°F. to 140°F.); (b) the heater section,

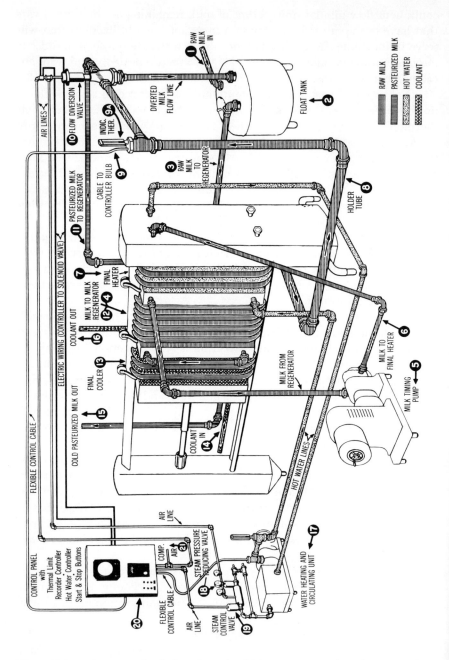

**Figure 7.1**    Diagram of milk flow through a high-temperature, short-time pasteurizer. Courtesy of the Creamery Package Manufacturing Company.

which raises the temperature to 71.7°C. (161°F.); (c) the holder section, which maintains the milk at 71.7°C. (161°F.) for not less than 15 seconds; and (d) once again the regenerative section, where it is partially cooled by the incoming raw milk to about 38°C. (100°F.). The pasteurized milk leaving the regenerative section flows through the cooling section, where it is cooled to at least 4.4°C. (40°F.) and on to a storage tank or directly to the bottle filler. In most units the interval elapsing from the time raw milk first enters the regenerative section until the pasteurized milk leaves it is approximately 70 to 80 seconds. This is much too short a period for there to be any appreciable growth of thermophilic bacteria. The regenerative section is the only place within the unit where the temperature would be favorable for growth. Some increases may occur in the cooked-on milk films, but this is dependent almost entirely upon the length of operation of the unit. In most plants this does not exceed 6 hours and little difficulty is encountered in this relatively short period. Allowing milk to remain in HTST pasteurizers during extended shutdowns will allow the growth of thermophilic organisms, if present, in the same manner as that described for the vat method.

Filter cloths, which are sometimes used between the regenerative and heating sections, have caused trouble because of the growth of thermophilic organisms in them. This source of contamination does not exist with the more commonly employed cold milk clarifiers, the use of which precludes the need for the filter cloths.

### THE PROBLEM OF COLIFORM BACTERIA

The presence of coliform bacteria (see Chapter 2) in pasteurized milk and related products is undesirable. Many milk ordinances contain a specification that limits the number of coliforms that may be tolerated in pasteurized milk; and in most areas, milk is examined for their presence as a matter of routine. The ordinances generally specify that the coliform count shall not be greater than 10 per milliliter, which is a very lenient standard. These organisms are very rarely pathogenic, and in interpreting the results of counts, one should keep this in mind.

*Significance of coliform bacteria in water supplies.* Through misunderstanding, the presence of coliform bacteria in milk often is interpreted as meaning the same thing as the presence of coliforms in water supplies. Because coliform bacteria are present in considerable numbers in fecal matter and commonly are present in soil and on plants and grains, their presence in water is almost universally interpreted as an index of undesirable contamination. Coliform organisms are not found in properly protected ground water supplies; natural filtration through soil layers removes them. These bacteria do not grow in water supplies suitable for human consumption or for the washing of food-handling equipment; therefore, the numbers found are indices of contamination and not of growth. Because the sources from which these organisms get into water may be contaminated with human fecal matter that also may contain human pathogens, such as *Salmonella typhosa,* water containing coliform organisms is looked upon as a potential source of bacteria pathogenic to humans.

*Significance of coliform bacteria in raw milk.* Coliform bacteria are almost universally present in raw milk. The extent of their presence at the time milk is received at the plant is dependent largely upon the sanitary conditions under which the milk has been produced and upon the extent of growth of these bacteria between the time of milking and delivery to pasteurization plants. Even under the best of conditions a few almost always can be found.

Coliforms rarely are found in milk drawn aseptically from normal udders. However, one of the most damaging types of mastitis may be caused by certain coliform types. Secretions from such infected udders may contain large numbers of coliforms and, of course, should be discarded. However, improperly cleaned utensils are the most common source. The exterior of the animal may contribute some of these bacteria, owing to contact with bovine fecal material. The coliforms may be considered, therefore, as one of the miscellaneous types of bacteria that typically comprise the flora of raw milk. Milk is an excellent medium for the growth of these organisms; so a small initial population may become a large population in the milk delivered to the plants for processing. Application of the same principles that have been advocated for the production of low-count milk will effectively control coliform populations.

*Significance of coliform bacteria in pasteurized milk.* Three basic reasons are commonly advanced for the presence of coliform bacteria in pasteurized milk products. These are the following: (a) heat resistance of certain strains, which allows them to survive pasteurization; (b) improper pasteurization; (c) recontamination after pasteurization owing to improper cleaning of equipment or to direct contamination from personnel.

In regard to the heat resistance of coliforms, there is sufficient evidence, based upon research and practical experience, to conclude that survival of pasteurization in numbers detectable by routine methods is rare. Although heat-resistant coliform bacteria may be isolated, the practical importance of these types in accounting for high coliform counts in pasteurized milk is minor indeed. There is the possibility of the survival of some coliforms during pasteurization because of the presence of excessively high numbers in the raw milk. Such a situation is unusual, especially in well-controlled supplies. For a critical review of the literature pertaining to the practical significance of heat-resistant coliform bacteria, the discussion by Buchbinder and Alff (6) will be helpful.

On the other hand, the presence of coliforms owing to improper pasteurization or to recontamination carries some obvious and serious implications. In this regard, the use of the coliform test to detect improper pasteurization is of little practical value. The phosphatase test is more accurate and simpler.

The real significance of coliform bacteria in pasteurized milk lies in the fact that their presence may be indicative of recontamination of milk after leaving the pasteurizer. If equipment through which properly pasteurized milk may pass has not been cleaned and sanitized adequately, coliform bacteria almost inevitably will be present in the final product. The coliform test, therefore, is the most generally useful test for detecting post-pasteurization contamination of pasteurized milk.

*Sources and control of coliform organisms in pasteurizing plants.* A list of sources and practices, which, singly or in various combinations, have been responsible for unsatisfactory coliform counts would include the following:

a. Unclean or improperly sanitized milk lines, pumps, bottle fillers, filling valves and related parts, bottles, and various gaskets.

b. Packing glands for agitator shafts and homogenizer pistons, which may be loose or functioning improperly, and which may be reached by milk.

c. Defective or worn equipment having pits or pockets, which favor the accumulation of milk solids. Such areas are difficult to clean, and they provide foci for coliform growth and for subsequent contamination of milk.

d. Condensate drippings, particularly from bottle fillers, filling valve assemblies (both glass and paper bottling machines), coolers, and pasteurizing or storage vats not having drip protector devices.

e. Unsanitary practices by personnel, such as assembling various pieces of equipment without properly washing and sanitizing the hands; holding gaskets and other miscellaneous small parts in the mouth or in pockets during the assembly of equipment; carelessness in handling and cleaning miscellaneous short pieces of pipe, elbows, valves, and those parts that may be inserted into previously cleaned and sanitized lines. The latter often occurs in connection with the processing of small volumes of various special products.

f. Failure to obtain samples of freshly pasteurized milk for analysis. High coliform counts of samples of milk and other fluid milk products obtained from delivery trucks and stores may be the result of the growth of organisms that were present in insignificant numbers when the product was fresh. Coliform counts from such samples are apt to be of limited use in assessing the extent of post-pasteurization contamination.

The coliform problem is essentially a plant problem. Furthermore, the initial effort in seeking the reasons for the appearance of coliforms in fresh pasteurized milk and related products should be directed toward the efficiency with which the cleaning, sanitizing, and other allied operations are performed in the plant. An example of what can be attained in regard to the control of coliforms in market milk plants is illustrated by Table 7.5. The first two sections of this table show routine coliform counts obtained over the same period from two plants that are essentially the same size, that have the same type of operation, and that have the same source of raw milk supply. In plant A much emphasis was placed upon proper cleaning and sanitizing of equipment and upon the following of good sanitary practices by employees. In plant B the attention given to these factors was haphazard. The third section of Table 7.5 shows the results obtained from plant B during a time after the correction of faulty sanitary practices.

The results in Table 7.5 also demonstrate that the greatest difficulty occurred with special products. This is true in many plants, largely because of the fact that these products are often, wholly or in part, processed

**Table 7.5**    Coliform counts (per 2 ml) of various products from two milk plants *

| DATE | TYPE OF PRODUCT | | | | |
|------|------------------------|-------|----------|-------|--------|
|      | Cream line milk | Cream | Skimmilk | HP[a] | VDHP[b] |
| Plant A (using good sanitary methods) | | | | | |
| 4/5   | 0  | 0  | 0  | 0    | 0     |
| 4/12  | 0  | 0  | 0  | 0    | 0     |
| 5/9   | 0  | 0  | 0  | 0    | 0     |
| 5/29  | 0  | 0  | 0  | 0    | 0     |
| 6/11  | 0  | 0  | 0  | 0    | 0     |
| 6/25  | 0  | 0  | 0  | 0    | 0     |
| 7/2   | 0  | 0  | 0  | 0    | 0     |
| 7/19  | 0  | 0  | 0  | 0    | 0     |
| Plant B (using poor sanitary methods) | | | | | |
| 4/12  | 35 | 5  | 2  | 14    | 25    |
| 4/23  | 92 | 1  | 24 | 1100  | 210   |
| 5/9   | 0  | 13 | 1  | 80    | 64    |
| 5/22  | 0  | 19 | 33 | >3000 | >3000 |
| 6/6   | 0  | 3  | 1  | 4     | 3     |
| 6/19  | 5  | 0  | 3  | 2     | 6     |
| 7/2   | 0  | 0  | 0  | 230   | 420   |
| 7/19  | 5  | 25 | 4  | 420   | 6     |
| Plant B (using good sanitary methods) | | | | | |
| 8/5   | 0  | 0  | 0  | 0     | 0     |
| 8/20  | 0  | 0  | 0  | 0     | 0     |
| 9/3   | 0  | 0  | 0  | 0     | 1     |
| 9/15  | 0  | 0  | 0  | 0     | 2     |
| 10/2  | 0  | 0  | 0  | 0     | 0     |
| 10/27 | 0  | 0  | 0  | 0     | 1     |
| 11/10 | 2  | 0  | 0  | 0     | 0     |
| 11/28 | 0  | 0  | 0  | 0     | 0     |

* Taken from data of Olson (26).
[a] HP = homogenized milk in paper carton.
[b] VDHP = vitamin D homogenized milk in paper carton.

in equipment other than that used for products of larger volume. The latter equipment in most plants receives a routine, standardized cleaning and sanitizing treatment. This routine treatment often is neglected in the case of equipment used for special products, and the result frequently is reflected in terms of high coliform counts.

*Effect of coliform bacteria on milk.* In addition to pointing up certain facts about the sanitary procedures employed in the handling of milk in which they are found, coliform bacteria are of significance because they may produce a variety of defects in almost any milk product. These defects include ropiness, gassiness, unclean and medicinal odors, and bitterness. Extensive growth of coliform organisms in raw milk may seriously impair the suitability of milk for processing; their growth in pasteurized milk may affect keeping quality (7), especially if the milk is stored at temperatures above 7.2°C. (45°F.) (see discussion of psychrophilic bacteria).

THE PROBLEM OF PSYCHROPHILIC BACTERIA

The term psychrophilic,* as commonly used in the dairy industry, refers to those bacterial species which are capable of relatively rapid growth at low temperatures, generally within the range of 1.7°C. to 10°C. (35°F. to 50°F.). Storage at low temperatures is a customary means of preserving milk products from deterioration by bacterial action; the existence of certain bacterial types that are able to grow rather well at low temperatures is a matter of concern in transportation, processing, and keeping quality of fluid milk products.

*Types of organisms.* The organisms belonging to this group are largely gram-negative, non-spore-forming rods. Members of the genera *Pseudomonas, Flavobacterium, Alcaligenes,* and *Achromobacter* are most commonly encountered (11, 18, 40). For selective culture of psychrophilic organisms, low temperature incubation is necessary (see later discussion in this chapter and also Chapter 5).

*Psychrophilic bacteria in raw milk.* Generally little difficulty is experienced because of the growth of psychrophilic bacteria in raw milk supplies for plants located close to the source of supply. This is not because these organisms are not found in the raw milk, but rather because the period elapsing from production to processing does not usually provide sufficient time for the organisms to reach excessive numbers. Raw milk and cream are being shipped in increasing volumes from the central and the upper midwestern areas of the United States to distant markets, particularly in the eastern and southern areas of the country. This shipping serves to extend considerably the time that such products are held before processing; thus, sufficient time may elapse during the receiving,

---

* "Psychrophilic" means cold loving. The term "cryophilic," now largely discarded, has often been used with identical meaning; however, the prefix "cryo" refers to a more intense cold, such as an icy or freezing one, and therefore is a less desirable term.

handling, and transporting of milk to allow very small numbers of psychrophilic organisms present initially to increase until they become
objectionable.

Psychrophilic bacteria invariably are present in all raw milk supplies.
Like the coliform, thermoduric, and thermophilic bacteria, they are a
part of the normal flora of raw milk, and, like the others, they constitute
a problem whenever milk is subjected to conditions that favor their growth.
Their numbers depend upon the sanitary conditions under which milk is
produced, the temperature of holding, and the time that elapses before
processing. Since growth of psychrophilic bacteria increases as temperature
increases, up to at least to 25°C. (77°F.), the temperature of holding will
influence their numbers appreciably. Initial contamination may be kept
to a minimum by using good sanitary methods in producing milk. In the
case of milk that is subsequently to be transported long distances, careful
attention should be given to the sanitary condition of tank trucks or cans.
These must be thoroughly cleaned and sanitized. It should be emphasized
that water supplies, otherwise satisfactory, may be a major source of
psychrophilic organisms (18); thus, rinsing tanks and cans prior to filling
may contribute sufficient numbers of these types so that subsequent growth
may become extensive. Even though the very nature of psychrophilic bacteria permits their development at low temperatures, these types are retarded markedly (although not as much so as other types) as the temperature approaches the freezing point.

*Psychrophilic bacteria in pasteurized milk.* The importance of
these bacteria in pasteurized fluid milk products is related primarily to
keeping quality. Numerous defects may be attributed to their activity.
Some of the more common flavor and aroma defects are unclean, putrid,
fruity, rancid, and sour odor and taste. A ropy or stringy condition or a
greenish-yellow coloration noticeable usually at the surface sometimes is
encountered. However, not all bacteria that can grow at refrigeration temperatures cause defects.

The influence of psychrophilic bacteria on the flavor of milk kept
under refrigeration does not usually manifest itself until after 3 or 4
days of storage and often not until a considerably longer period has elapsed
(see Table 7.6). Commercially pasteurized milk frequently keeps for 7 to
10 days of storage. Sooner or later nearly all commercially pasteurized,
bottled milk held at temperatures within a few degrees above freezing will
show defects due to psychrophilic growth. At a constant temperature of
storage, the rapidity with which deterioration takes place will depend
largely upon the initial number of organisms present, the rate at which
the organisms grow at that holding temperature, and the ability of the
organisms to cause an organoleptically detectable change in the product.
The latter is particularly evident from the data shown in Table 7.6 for
Plant F. In this instance, an excellent example of relatively inert bacterial

**Table 7.6**    Bacterial and flavor changes during storage of homogenized milk from various plants *

| PLANT | No. DAYS STORAGE | STANDARD PLATE COUNT 32°C. | 35°C. | COLIFORM COUNT | PSYCHROPHILIC[a] COUNT | FLAVOR SCORE AND COMMENTS[b] |
|---|---|---|---|---|---|---|
| C | 0 | 2,900 | 4,400 | 0 | 0 | 38 sl fe |
|   | 3 | 2,000 | 3,400 | 0 | 23 | 38 sl fe |
|   | 4 | 2,700 | 6,300 | 0 | 1,200 | 38 sl fe |
|   | 5 | 4,500 | 6,500 | 11 | 3,300 | 38 sl fe |
|   | 7 | 24,000 | 32,000 | 74 | 680,000 | 36 sl uc |
| D | 0 | 7,600 | 5,900 | 0 | 4 | 38 sl uc |
|   | 3 | 790 | 660 | 0 | 530 | 38 sl uc |
|   | 4 | 59,000 | 61,000 | 1 | 19,000 | 36 sl uc |
|   | 5 | 470,000 | 320,000 | 8 | 390,000 | 36 sl uc |
|   | 7 | 580,000 | 420,000 | 1,400 | 78,000,000 | 0 uc |
| E | 0 | 8,200 | 6,800 | 30 | 9,000 | 36 sl uc |
|   | 3 | 160,000 | 160,000 | 200 | 900,000 | 36 sl uc |
|   | 4 | 1,200,000 | 1,400,000 | 460 | 1,100,000 | 32 sl uc |
|   | 5 | 2,500,000 | 2,800,000 | 2,900 | 37,000,000 | 0 uc |
|   | 7 | 44,000,000 | 26,000,000 | 4,600,000 | 130,000,000 | 0 uc |
| F | 0 | 3,500 | 3,600 | 0 | 1 | 38 sl fe |
|   | 3 | 3,300 | 3,500 | 0 | —— | 38 sl fe |
|   | 4 | 60,000 | 44,000 | 0 | 5,200 | 38 sl fe |
|   | 5 | 87,000 | 89,000 | 0 | 280,000 | 38 sl fe |
|   | 7 | 240,000 | 430,000 | 0 | 26,000,000 | 38 sl fe |
| G | 0 | 24,000 | 21,000 | 0 | 0 | 38 sl fe |
|   | 3 | 17,000 | 17,000 | 0 | —— | 38 sl fe |
|   | 4 | 18,000 | 16,000 | 1 | 6 | 35 sl uc |
|   | 5 | 31,000 | 22,000 | 0 | 2,800 | 35 sl uc |
|   | 7 | 480,000 | 390,000 | 0 | 7,100,000 | 0 uc |

*Taken from data of Olson et al. (27). Storage was at 45°F.
[a] Incubation of plates at 45°F. for 10 days.
[b] sl = slight; fe = feed; uc = unclean.

activity, extensive growth occurred with no concurrent detectable flavor deterioration.

*Effect of pasteurization.* Most of the available information (27, 29, 41) indicates that proper pasteurization will destroy the psychrophilic bacteria present in raw milk, at least to the extent that any survivors would not be a factor in flavor deterioration over an extended storage period. This is illustrated by the data obtained after laboratory pasteurization and those obtained from samples drawn aseptically from the pasteurizer as shown in Tables 7.7 and 7.8, respectively. If the holding temperature rises above 45°F., such pasteurization-resistant bacteria as the enterococci may develop and cause defects.

**Table 7.7** Bacterial counts of mixed herd milk before and after laboratory pasteurization (143°F.—30 minutes) by sealed-tube, total-immersion technique *

| TRIAL | STANDARD PLATE COUNT AT 32° C. | 35° C. | COLIFORM COUNT | PSYCHROPHILE COUNT 7° C. |
|---|---|---|---|---|
| 1. Raw | 730,000 | 630,000 | 18,000 | 200,000 |
| 1. Pasteurized | —— | —— | —— | 0 |
| 2. Raw | 710,000 | 830,000 | 22,000 | 130,000 |
| 2. Pasteurized | 9,100 | —— | —— | 0 |
| 3. Raw | 3,000,000 | 370,000 | 8,000 | 150,000 |
| 3. Pasteurized | 30,000 | 30,000 | 0 | 0 |
| 4. Raw | 1,600,000 | 1,600,000 | 890,000 | 680,000 |
| 4. Pasteurized | 8,400 | 4,400 | —-- | 0 |
| 5. Raw | 360,000 | 480,000 | 5,400 | 62,000 |
| 5. Pasteurized | 330,000 | 110,000 | 0 | 0 |

* From data of Olson et al. (27).

**Table 7.8** Bacterial counts of pasteurized milk (a) drawn aseptically from HTST pasteurizer and (b) obtained as finished bottled product *

| BACTERIAL COUNTS AFTER STORAGE AT 45°F. FOR TIME INDICATED | FROM HTST PASTEURIZER Sample 1 | Sample 2 | BOTTLE OF FINISHED PRODUCT Bottle 1 | Bottle 2 |
|---|---|---|---|---|
| 0 days—fresh sample | | | | |
| SPC[a] (32°C.) | 11,000 | 12,000 | 10,000 | 11,000 |
| Coliform count | 0 | 0 | 2 | 8 |
| Psychrophile count (7°C.) | 0 | 0 | 26 | 40 |
| 3 days | | | | |
| SPC (32°C.) | 11,000 | 11,000 | 9,200 | 13,000 |
| Coliform count | 0 | 0 | 2 | 3 |
| Psychrophile count (7°C.) | 1 | 1 | 45 | 90 |
| 4 days | | | | |
| SPC (32°C.) | 8,900 | 11,000 | 9,400 | 12,000 |
| Coliform count | 0 | 0 | 0 | 2 |
| Psychrophile count (7°C.) | 0 | 0 | 49 | 300 |
| 5 days | | | | |
| SPC (32°C.) | 9,200 | 12,000 | 140,000 | 6,100,000 |
| Coliform count | 0 | 0 | 0 | 2 |
| Psychrophile count (7°C.) | 2 | 1 | 2,800 | 2,400 |
| 7 days | | | | |
| SPC (32°C.) | 9,700 | 10,000 | 6,700,000 | 4,700,000 |
| Coliform count | 0 | 0 | 5 | 6 |
| Psychrophile count (7°C.) | 3 | 0 | 9,600,000 | 2,100,000 |

* From data of Olson et al. (27).    [a] SPC = Standard plate count.

*Post-pasteurization contamination.* This is the major factor contributing to the presence of psychrophilic bacteria in pasteurized fluid milk products. The effectiveness with which the cleaning and sanitizing procedures are carried out directly influences the number of psychrophilic organisms that may be present in the finished product. The data, obtained from bottles of finished products, as shown in Table 7.8, illustrate the fact that psychrophilic organisms may be introduced at one or more points during post-pasteurization handling of the product. Water supplies used for rinsing purposes have been shown to contribute to such contamination. However, available evidence points more directly to the lack of effective cleaning and bactericidal treatment of all equipment surfaces involved from the pasteurizer on through the bottling and capping operations.

*Effect of temperature of storage.* Close attention to the maintenance of low temperatures (40°F., preferably lower) during storage and transportation will assist greatly in retarding the growth of psychrophilic bacteria. The importance of this is illustrated in Figure 7.2 showing the effect of temperature on the speed of growth of a typical psychrophile, *Pseudomonas fluorescens.* The generation time decreases (speed of multiplication increases) as the temperature increases. The relationship, however, is not linear. For example, as the temperature is raised from 1°C. to 4°C. (33.8°F. to 39.2°F.), the generation time is reduced by 8 hours. On the other hand, a similar rise of three degrees, from 11°C. to 14°C. (51.8°F. to 57.2°F.) produces only a 2-hour change in generation time. Thus it can be seen that the temperature influence is most pronounced in the vicinity of the freezing point. A practical implication of this phenomonon is the

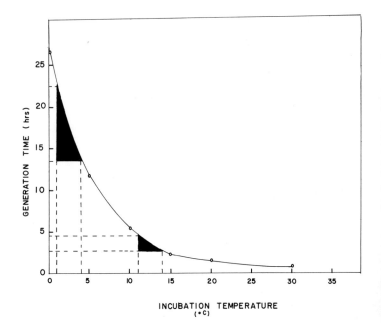

**Figure 7.2** Influence of incubation temperature on generation time of *Pseudomonas fluorescens.* Taken from data of Greene and Jezeski (13).

GENERATION TIME (hrs)

INCUBATION TEMPERATURE
(°C)

marked improvement in keeping quality of milk held near the freezing point. Milk inoculated with the above culture of *Pseudomonas* deteriorated in 4 days at 10°C. (50°F.), 16 days at 5°C. (41°F.), and 36 days at 0°C. (32°F.). This extension of keeping time is indicative of the importance of small temperature increments at low temperatures.

*Plate counts as indicators of keeping quality.* Since the presence of psychrophilic bacteria is related to keeping quality during low-temperature storage, the efficiency with which they may be detected is of importance. The temperature used in incubating plates is very important in this regard. The following summary is based upon available information, some of which is illustrated in Tables 7.6, 7.7, and 7.9:

1. Psychrophile counts at 7.2°C. (45°F.) on freshly pasteurized milk usually are very low. Counts obtained at 25°C., 32°C., and 35°C. (77°F., 89.6°F., and 95°F.) incubation are much higher, many pasteurization resistant bacteria that will not grow at the lower incubation temperature being capable of growth at these higher temperatures.

2. As storage progresses, counts at both 7.2°C. and 25°C. (45°F. and 77°F.) increase rapidly, gradually approaching each other; usually the counts at 35°C. increase slowly, but do not reach the levels attained at lower incubation temperatures; counts at 32°C. (89.6°F.) are somewhat intermediate. This is due to the fact that 25°C. (77°F.) is still within the growth temperature range for essentially all psychrophilic types of importance in milk supplies. Some may grow at higher temperatures, especially at 32°C. (89.6°F.), but a large proportion of them either do not grow or do not form countable colonies at 35°C. (95°F.). Also, 25°C. (77°F.) will allow growth of most non-psychrophilic types; hence, the close relationship between counts at 25°C. and 35°C. (77°F. and 95°F.) on fresh milk.

**Table 7.9** The effect of various plating procedures on total bacterial counts of commercially pasteurized milk after various storage periods (averages of 28 samples)*

| Days of storage at 5°C. | "Total" counts after plate incubation at | | | Coliform counts at 35°C. |
|:---:|:---:|:---:|:---:|:---:|
| | 35°C. | 25°C. | 5°C. | |
| | (per ml) | (per ml) | (per ml) | (per ml) |
| 0 | 2,800 | 8,800 | 2.5 | 0.6 |
| 3 | 2,400 | 15,000 | 160 | 2.2 |
| 6 | 12,000 | 150,000 | 28,000 | 8.2 |
| 9 | 68,000 | 1,400,000 | 810,000 | 41 |
| 12 | 130,000 | 3,800,000 | 2,700,000 | 360 |
| 15 | 280,000 | 11,000,000 | 8,400,000 | 440 |

* From data of Watrous et al. (41).

3. Coliform bacteria do not commonly increase in pasteurized milk maintained at 7.2°C. (45°F.) or below, although there are exceptions to this generality. Reference should be made to the extensive studies by Dahlberg (8) for further discussion of this point. The presence of coliform bacteria, even in small numbers, in freshly pasteurized milk usually is associated with poor keeping quality; however, a negative coliform count on a finished product does not always mean that such a product will have a long storage life free from deterioration due to growth of psychrophilic organisms. Contaminations with psychrophilic and coliform groups of bacteria are not always parallel.

4. The value of the psychrophilic count on freshly pasteurized milk is limited. Mere absence in 1 or 2 milliliters of product (the amount usually examined) is not necessarily a good indicator of satisfactory keeping quality; however, poor keeping quality may result if psychrophilic bacteria are present in detectable numbers in the product. However, since psychrophilic bacteria are destroyed by pasteurization, the presence of even a few in fresh products, or of large numbers after 3 or 4 days of storage, would indicate a lack of proper sanitization of post-pasteurization equipment.

5. When pasteurized milk products are held under refrigerated storage, the longer the storage period, the less the reliance that can be placed on counts obtained from plates incubated above 25°C. to 28°C. (77°F. to 82.4°F.) and especially above 32°C. (89.6°F.).

## THE SPREAD OF DISEASE THROUGH MILK

According to the annual reports of state and local health authorities, the number of disease outbreaks that are attributed to the consumption of infected milk and milk products is decreasing steadily. During the period of 1938–1950, 401 outbreaks involving 16,232 persons were reported. Beginning with the year 1946, a decided drop in the number of reported outbreaks and cases occurred. During that year, 19 outbreaks involving 795 persons occurred as compared to 29 outbreaks involving 2,161 persons in 1945, and 41 outbreaks involving 1,449 in 1944. A summary of reported outbreaks and cases that occurred in recent years is given below:

| Year | Number of outbreaks | Number of cases |
|------|---------------------|-----------------|
| 1951 | 12 | 90 |
| 1952 | 6 | 833 |
| 1953 | 4 | 97 |
| 1954 | 9 | 200 |

Of these 31 outbreaks, 9 were attributed to milk and 22 to milk products including ice cream, buttermilk, fruit cottage cheese, processed cheese, canned milk, egg nog, and cream cheese. In these outbreaks either raw or improperly pasteurized milk, raw or improperly pasteurized milk products, or recontaminated milk products were involved. The types of infections that occurred were varied. Among those outbreaks involving milk where the causative organism was determined, enteric infections caused by *Salmonella* and staphylococci were most common; one outbreak of brucellosis involved four members of one family that had consumed raw milk from a cow that had recently aborted. In 1953 no outbreaks were reported involving milk.

In spite of the relatively few cases of disease that occur through the consumption of infected milk and milk products, the preventive measures against the possibility of such disease still must be given great attention. Milk is consumed by the young and the old; in many countries it may be classed as a universal beverage, as is water. In larger cities, milk from a single milk plant may be consumed by hundreds, even thousands, of persons. In small towns and villages a single dairy or milk plant may serve most of the people. The opportunity, therefore, for dissemination of pathogens through an infected milk supply is great.

The diseases that may be spread by milk are numerous. They are often classed in two groups: (a) those diseases that are caused primarily by pathogens that infect the cow and gain entrance to milk directly from the animal, either by being present in the milk when it is drawn from the udder or from the immediate environment of the animal; and (b) those diseases that are caused primarily by pathogens that gain entrance to milk directly from humans. The two outstanding examples of the former group are tuberculosis and brucellosis. Also, septic sore throat and scarlet fever may be transmitted to persons through milk from cows having mastitis caused by *Streptococcus pyogenes*. Similarly, *Micrococcus pyogenes* var. *aureus*, a cause of mastitis in cows and of food poisoning in humans, may gain access to milk in large numbers as a result of udder infections by this organism. Other diseases of this group such as foot and mouth disease, anthrax, and Johne's disease are of much greater importance in the spread of disease from animal to animal, or from herd to herd, than in the spread of disease among human beings.

Recently considerable interest has been shown in the role of milk in the transmission of the disease known as Q fever (9). This is a rickettsial disease of man, which may be acute or chronic and which may induce a mild or severe illness. For further discussion of this and other diseases which may be spread by milk see Chapter 6.

Direct or indirect contamination of milk and milk products by persons who harbor some pathogen and who are involved in some way in handling milk and milk products probably is the most common method of infecting milk. Infection by *Salmonella*, other than that causing typhoid fever, and food poisoning caused by staphylococci (micrococci) are the types of disease outbreaks that have been reported as occurring most frequently in recent years. Epidemics of milk-borne typhoid fever have declined from an average of 12 per year in 1938–1940 to about one epidemic annually in the period of 1941–1951, and no cases of typhoid fever were reported for the years 1952 and 1953. In 1954 four cases of typhoid were reported to occur in a family that used raw milk, but definite proof that the milk was the vehicle of infection was not obtained.

Pasteurization plus extreme care in preventing post-pasteurization contamination is the major safeguard in the prevention of milk-borne diseases. Other measures involving the sanitary production and handling of raw milk prior to pasteurization are helpful. But in the final analysis only pasteurization can be depended upon to make the general supply of milk products safe to consume. Continued emphasis upon the sanitary aspects of handling milk and milk products and upon obtaining proper pasteurization of all milk and milk products consumed in the fluid state, as well as milk and cream used in the preparation of other dairy foods, is necessary to decrease further the outbreaks of disease from milk and milk products.

# References

1. Abd-El-Malek, Y., and T. Gibson, Studies in the bacteriology of milk, II: the staphylococci and micrococci of milk, *J. Dairy Research*, 15 (1948): 249–260.

2. Atherton, H. V., F. J. Doan, and G. H. Watrous, Jr., What happens to your milk, *Milk Plant Monthly*, 42 (1953): (9) 15–17, 66–67.

3. Atherton H. V., F. J. Doan, and G. H. Watrous, Jr., Changes in bacterial populations and characteristics of bottled milk during refrigerated holding, *Pa. Agr. Exp. Sta. Bull. 575*, 1954.

4. Ayers, S. H. and W. T. Johnson, Jr., Studies on Pasteurization, XII: cause and significance of pin-point colonies from pasteurized milk, *J. Bacteriol.*, 9 (1924): 285–300.

5. Breed, R. S., Thermophilic bacteria in milk pasteurized by the holder process, *N. Y. Agr. Exp. Sta. (Geneva) Tech. Bull. 191*, 1932.

6. Buchbinder, P., and E. C. Alff, Studies on coliform organisms in dairy products. The practical significance of so-called heat resistant coliform organisms in the coliform testing of pasteurized milk, *J. Milk and Food Technol.*, 10 (1947): 137–148.

7. Burgwald, L. H., and D. V. Josephson, The effect of refrigerated storage on the keeping qualities of pasteurized milk, *J. Dairy Sci.*, 30 (1947): 371–383.

8. Dahlberg, A. C., The keeping quality of pasteurized milk, *Cornell Agr. Exp. Sta. Bull. 838*, 1946.

9. Enright, J. B., R. C. Thomas, and P. A. Mullett, Q fever and its relation to dairy products, *J. Milk and Food Technol.*, 16 (1953): 263–266.

10. Erdman, I. E., and H. R. Thornton, Psychrophilic bacteria in Edmonton milk and cream, I: numbers, *Can. J. Technol.*, 29 (1951): 232–237.

11. ———, Psychrophilic bacteria in Edmonton milk and cream, II: kinds, *Can. J. Technol.*, 29 (1951): 238–242.

12. Fuller, J. E., W. S. Mueller, and R. W. Swanson, Bacteriological study of chocolate milk, *J. Dairy Sci.,* 25 (1942): 883–894.

13. Greene, V. W., and J. J. Jezeski, The influence of temperature on the development of several psychrophilic bacteria of dairy origin, *Appl. Microbiol.,* 2 (1954): 110–117.

14. Hammer, B. W., and R. H. Hix, Studies on the numbers of bacteria present in milk which has undergone various changes, *Iowa Agr. Exp. Sta. Research Bull. 29,* 1916.

15. Hansen, P. A., The udder as a possible source of thermophilic bacteria, *N. Y. Agr. Exp. Sta. (Geneva) Tech. Bull. 158,* 1929.

16. ———, The public health significance of the growth of thermophilic bacteria in pasteurized milk, *N. Y. Agr. Exp. Sta. (Geneva) Tech. Bull. 196,* 1932.

17. Hileman, J. L., Thermoduric bacteria in pasteurized milk. A review of literature, *J. Dairy Sci.,* 23 (1940): 1143–1160.

18. Jezeski, J. J., and H. Macy, Cryophilic organisms in water and butter, *J. Dairy Sci.,* 29 (1946): 439–452.

19. Macy, H., and J. A. Erekson, Seasonal variations in thermoduric organisms and methods of control, *Assoc. Bull. Intern. Assoc. Milk Dealers,* 6 (1941): 127–135.

20. Mallmann, W. L., and C. S. Bryan, Use of thermoduric bacteria test with special reference to a new rapid method, *Assoc. Bull. Intern. Assoc. Milk Dealers,* 35 (1943): 78.

21. *Methods and Standards for the Production of Certified Milk.* New York: American Association Medical Milk Commissions, 1954–55.

22. *Milk Ordinance and Code: Public Health Bull. 220,* (USPHS), 1953.

23. Mudge, C. S., and D. C. Foord, Needle puncture method for determination of the bacterial contamination of paraffined milk containers, *Am. J. Public Health,* 30 (1940): 273–277.

24. Murray, J. G., The speed of build-up of thermoduric organisms on farm equipment. *Proceedings of the Society for Applied Bacteriology, Part 2* (1949): 20–25.

25. Myhr, A. N., and J. C. Olson, Jr., Preliminary studies on the thermal resistance of micrococci in milk, *J. Dairy Sci.,* 35 (1952): 484.

26. Olson, J. C., Jr., Unpublished data, Minn. Agr. Exp. Sta., 1950.

27. Olson, J. C., Jr., D. S. Willoughby, E. L. Thomas, and H. A. Morris, The Keeping quality of pasteurized milk as influenced by the growth of psychrophilic bacteria and the addition of aureomycin, *J. Milk and Food Technol.,* 16 (1953): 213–219.

28. Prickett, P. S., Thermophilic and thermoduric microorganisms with special reference to species isolated from milk, V: description of sporeforming types, *N. Y. Agr. Exp. Sta. (Geneva) Tech. Bull. 147,* 1928.

29. Rogick, F. A., and L. H. Burgwald, Some factors which contribute to the psychrophilic bacterial count in market milk, *J. Milk and Food Technol.,* 15 (1952): 181–185.

30. Rowland, J. L., National conference on interstate milk shipments, 1952, *J. Milk and Food Technol.,* 16 (1953): 89–101.

31. Sanders, G. P., and G. S. Sager, Heat inactivation of milk phosphatase in dairy products, *J. Dairy Sci.,* 31 (1948): 845–857.

32. Sanborn, J. R., Microbiological content of paper-board used in the packaging of foods, *Am. J. Public Health,* 30 (1940): 247–255.

33. Slanetz. L. W., Prevalence and classification of hemolytic streptococci in pasteurized milk, *N. H. Agr. Exp. Sta. Tech. Bull. 70,* 1938.

34. Slatter, W. L., and H. O. Halvorson, The heat resistance of lactobacilli found in American Cheddar cheese, *J. Dairy Sci.,* 30 (1947): 231–243.

35. Speck, M. L., and H. L. Lucas, Some observations on the high-temperature-short time pasteurization of chocolate milk, *J. Dairy Sci.,* 34 (1951): 333–341.

36. *Standard Methods for the Examination of Dairy Products,* 10th Ed. New York: American Public Health Association, 1953.

37. Tanner, F. W., E. Wheaton, and C. O. Ball, Microbiology of paper and paperboard for use in the food industry, *Am. J. Public Health.,* 30 (1940): 256–266.

38. Thomas, S. B., J. W. Egdell, L. F. L. Clegg, and W. A. Cuthbert, Thermoduric organisms in milk: Part I, a review of the literature, *Proceedings of the Society for Applied Bacteriology,* 13 (1950): (1) 27–64.

39. Thomas, S. B., D. Griffiths, E. Davies, J. A. Charlton, and R. G. Jones, Heat resistant bacteria in raw milk, part V: influence of milk cooling, *J. Soc. Dairy Technol.,* 4 (1951): 245–250.

40. Thomas, S. B., and C. V. C. Sekhar, Psychrophilic bacteria in raw and commercially pasteurized milk, *Proceedings of the Society for Applied Bacteriology,* (1946): 47.

41. Watrous, G. H., F. J. Doan, and D. V. Josephson, Some bacteriological studies on refrigerated milk and cream, *Pa. Agr. Exp. Sta. Bull. 551,* 1952.

42. Whittaker, H. A., R. W. Archibald, C. S. Leete, and L. F. Miller, A comparison of the temperature and bacterial count of milk and foam during certain stages of the pasteurization process, *USDA Tech. Bull. 18,* 1927.

43. Yale, M. W., and R. S. Breed, The control of thermophilic bacteria in pasteurizing plants, *Am. J. Public Health,* 20 (1930): 1192–1198.

# 8

## *Microbiology of evaporated and concentrated dairy products*

Milk is often processed to make products with considerably reduced moisture content, because of desirable savings in transportation and in merchandising costs or because of a need for products with concentrations of milk solids above those found in normal fluid milk. In some instances desirable special properties are conferred by one or more of the processing operations. Dried milks and sweetened condensed milks are discussed in Chapter 9. This chapter will be concerned with the microbiology of the product commonly sold in cans as evaporated milk, with bulk condensed whole milk and skimmilk, with concentrated milk in both fluid and frozen forms, and with concentrated whey, buttermilk, and sour milk. Several of the products of this group keep well because large quantities of lactic acid prevent development of bacteria and of some yeasts. The other products are excellent substrata for development of microorganisms unless they are either frozen or heated to high temperatures and held in satisfactory containers, as is the case with evaporated milk. Many of the bacteriological considerations of Chapter 7 apply to these products.

### BULK CONDENSED MILK

This product may be made from either whole milk or skimmed milk, but the latter is manufactured in much greater quantity. Bulk condensed skim-milk is used extensively as a source of milk solids. Candy makers, bakers, and ice cream manufacturers are only a few of the outlets. Concentration usually is in a ratio of from 2.5:1 to 4:1, depending upon the desires of the consumer. The product is not sterilized during processing and does not contain a sufficient concentration of solids to cause any significant inhibition of microorganism growth. Therefore, microorganisms invariably will be present in the product, and these will be able to grow if other conditions are satisfactory. The rate of growth will depend upon many factors; the most important of these undoubtedly is temperature, although the type of contamination also is important.

232

## THE MILK SUPPLY

Bulk condensed milk ordinarily is prepared from manufacturing grade milk for which there are no rigid bacteriological standards. Where regulations require that all ingredients satisfy requirements for fluid milk supplies, grade A raw milk may be required as the starting material. Platform grading to reject milk that is obviously off in flavor and in aroma should be employed, even where no specific standards on the raw material are required. Rejection of all milk that has a methylene blue reduction test time of less than 2.5 hours is recommended. Other tests of comparable severity may be substituted for the methylene blue test where local circumstances warrant (see Chapter 5). Results of the sediment test usually bear no direct relationship to the bacteriological quality of the product. However, a sediment test also should be run on the milk as a means of preventing the use of raw material that is aesthetically unacceptable.

## PROCESSING

Following receipt, the milk is cooled to 4.6°C. (40°F.) or below if it is to be held, preheated for separation, separated, heated to 65.6°C. to 76.7°C. (150°F. to 170°F.) in a continuous heater or in a hot well, condensed to the desired degree in a vacuum pan in either a continuous or a batch process, cooled, standardized for solids content, and then placed in the final container. Hunziker's book (5) should be consulted for details of processing. In making concentrated whole milk, the separation step is not included, and the product usually is homogenized. Standardization for the desired fat: solids ratio may precede condensing or may be done at the time the product is standardized for solids content following condensing. For some purposes condensed skimmilk is superheated to 82.2°C. to 93.3°C. (180°F. to 200°F.) for about 15 minutes to increase viscosity and to impart other desirable characteristics to the product for use in specialized applications. The superheating usually is accomplished by the injection of live steam into the product, either in the pan after the condensing operation is completed or in a vat after the product has been drawn from the pan. When superheated condensed milk is being made, the forewarming temperature may be increased nearly to the boiling point, particularly where there may be some question as to the heat stability of the product during superheating.

Cooling of the milk as received usually is important to minimize bacterial development before the actual processing begins; where no time lag is encountered, cooling may be omitted. Forewarming preceding separation usually introduces few microbiological problems, for the process customarily is continuous and the product is not held at the forewarming temperature for any significant period. The separation process does not influence the microbiological content of the milk to any significant degree unless the separator has not been sanitized properly. The forewarmer, which may precede the hot wells, usually operates for long periods at a temperature range at which thermophilic bacteria can develop rapidly. These bacteria may cause acid and unclean flavors. However, difficulty ordinarily is not encountered unless the milk is contaminated excessively with thermophilic bacteria. The hot wells, which may serve only as surge tanks for preheaters or may be used for both heating and holding of the milk, may serve as incubators for thermophilic bacteria, particularly if operated at the lower end of the usual temperature range, i.e., near 65.6°C. (150°F.). Alternate use of two wells with one pan permits the hosing out of the wells at intervals during a day's run and thus minimizes the build-up of thermophilic bacteria. During the condensing operation the product usually is at 54.5°C. to 57.2°C. (130°F. to 135°F.), a temperature range very suitable for growth of thermophilic bacteria. When a pan or evaporator is operating continuously in either a batch or a continuous process, there is opportunity for build-up of a considerable thermophilic population; thus the need is great for proper sanitation and control in the preceding stages of the process.

### KEEPING QUALITY

Unless high preheating temperatures are used, the heat treatments to which the product is exposed are less severe than those for pasteurization of market milk. The final product, unless given additional heat treatment, will contain a considerable number of bacteria and will have a keeping quality no better than that of pasteurized milk and possibly less. As is true of all dairy products, the heat treatment leaves no residual anti-bacterial effect to act upon subsequent contaminants. These contaminants may grow better because prior heat treatment has eliminated, to some degree, inhibitory substances and certain forms of competing bacteria. Bulk condensed milk must not be considered equivalent to having been pasteurized in the public health sense, for heating has not been controlled as it should be for pasteurization.

During subsequent cooling, standardizing, and packaging, opportunities exist for contamination, particularly from improperly cleaned and sanitized equipment. The 10-gallon can often used as container for this product is one of the most important sources of contamination in many plants. The materials added for standardization must be of good bacteriological quality, or they will constitute a source of undesirable microorganisms.

Bulk condensed milk is not sterile and may contain appreciable numbers of bacteria that have survived the processing or that have gained entrance subsequent to heat treatment. Therefore, storage at low temperatures and for only limited periods of time is essential if spoilage due to microorganisms is to be avoided. The composition of the product does not confer any special keeping quality, so only prior heat treatment, protection from contamination, and time and temperature of holding are factors of importance in determining satisfactory storage life. As data of Table 8.1 show, increasing the storage temperature reduces markedly the storage life of this product. Bulk condensed milk that has been protected adequately from contamination keeps better under refrigeration than does a product that has been contaminated appreciably or that has not had most of the bacteria originally present destroyed by the heat treatments to which the product has been exposed. Certainly the subsequent keeping quality of the product is one of the factors that should be considered in determining the heating conditions used for the milk prior to condensing.

## CONCENTRATED MILKS

This is a generic name commonly applied to a condensed milk prepared for human consumption as fluid milk after dilution, but without further processing. The product differs from bulk condensed milk in that it usually is prepared from grade A market milk. The whole milk often is pasteurized or at least heated to a degree approximating pasteurization before condensing. The condensing operation is carried out at minimum temperatures

**Table 8.1**   Changes in counts of two representative samples of bulk condensed milk held at different refrigeration temperatures [a]

| TIME (days) | 38°F. TOTAL[b] | 38°F. COLIFORM[c] | 44°F. TOTAL | 44°F. COLIFORM | 55°F. TOTAL | 55°F. COLIFORM |
|---|---|---|---|---|---|---|
| | | | *SAMPLE A[d]* | | | |
| 0 | 13,000 | 14 | | | | |
| 2 | | | 15,000 | 16 | 3,700,000 | 400 |
| 5 | 8,000 | 7 | 20,000 | 19 | 15,000,000 | 100,000 |
| 9 | | | 40,000 | 40 | | |
| 12 | 34,000 | 10 | | | | |
| 21 | 2,900,000 | 22,000 | | | | |
| | | | *SAMPLE B[e]* | | | |
| 0 | 75,000 | 2,000 | | | | |
| 2 | 220,000 | 6,300 | 480,000 | 10,000 | 230,000,000 | 300,000 |
| 4 | 260,000 | 7,000 | 1,900,000 | 11,000 | | |
| 6 | 1,800,000 | 11,000 | 30,000,000 | 26,000 | | |
| 10 | 28,000,000 | 270,000 | | | | |

[a] Iowa State College data.
[b] TGEM agar, 30°C. incubation for 2 days.
[c] VRB agar, 37°C. incubation for 18–24 hours.
[d] Sample tasted all right at time of last count at each temperature.
[e] Sample off in flavor at time of last count at each temperature.

to preserve the character of the product, temperatures below 52.8°C. (127°F.) commonly being used. The product is standardized following condensing, forewarmed, homogenized, pasteurized, and bottled. A somewhat elevated pasteurization exposure frequently is used with the final product, an exposure of 79.4°C. (175°F.) for 25 seconds being recommended by some. The subsequent bottling and handling are much the same as for pasteurized fluid milk, except that the product may be diluted to normal concentrations before use as fluid milk in the home. The concentrated milk on the market at present usually is a 3:1 concentrate, the original milk having been reduced to one-third initial volume. In other words, the percentage of solids has been increased to three times the original level. Higher levels of concentration lead to problems of sandiness and to other technical difficulties. Lower levels give a product that is insufficiently concentrated to possess at a desirable level the advantage of ease of transportation and storage. Volatile flavors, such as those contributed by many types of feed, are removed in the condensing process, leaving a product that tastes better in the opinion of many people.

Grosche et al. (4) found that 3:1 concentrate required very little more heat than did plain milk for adequate pasteurization. A heat-resistant *Micrococcus* species (MS18s) was used as the test organism. Pasteurization by holding the product for 30 minutes at 62.5°C. (144.3°F.) or 15 seconds at 73.5°C. (164.1°F.) was tentatively recommended as giving an adequate margin of safety. This was based on comparisons of the per cent destruction of the test culture in concentrated and in whole milk. Processors of concentrated milk commonly have used the above-minimum pasteurization temperatures often employed with homogenized milk; the data of Grosche et al. indicate that such processing is bacteriologically adequate.

The good quality of the original milk required for this product, the double pasteurization (frequently with at least the second at an elevated temperature), the care employed in sanitizing all equipment with which the product comes in contact, and the rapid cooling and low storage temperatures employed—all help to confer upon this product unusually good keeping quality. Studies by Rosenberger et al. (8) on concentrate prepared in a slightly different manner from that employed in some plants indicate that recombined milk keeps equally as well as the concentrate. A 4:1 concentrate had no better keeping quality than a 3:1 concentrate. The data of Olson et al. (7) on a limited number of samples indicate that the concentrated milk keeps better at refrigeration temperatures than does milk diluted to 12 per cent solids with sterile distilled water. Although the results of these investigations do not agree completely, both do demonstrate that concentrated milk does not have unlimited keeping quality, even at low refrigeration temperatures. Therefore, concentrated milk must be protected most carefully from contamination during processing and bottling; it must be consumed without excessive delay, even when good refrigeration is employed. The same considerations with respect to psychrophilic bacteria apply here as apply to pasteurized milk.

Some experiments on holding concentrate in the frozen condition have been carried out. Although freezing completely stops the development of microorganisms and may even cause the death of some, chemical changes such as protein destabilization occur in the product. The chemical changes are relatively slow at low temperatures, but they may cause the milk to become unacceptable sooner than is desirable. When the frozen product is thawed, the microbiological keeping quality is much the same as it would have been if the original unfrozen product had been held under the same conditions.

The microbial changes that concentrated milk may undergo usually are those that would be anticipated in the spoilage of pasteurized, homogenized milk (see Chapter 7). Types and numbers of contaminating organisms and temperature and time of storage are among the most important factors that determine type of spoilage. Rancid, unclean, putrid, and cheesy conditions may be encountered almost as often as sour under usual holding conditions; this is because the organisms usually responsible for souring are unable to grow well below 10°C. (50°F.), although those soil and water types frequently responsible for serious trouble can grow and cause extensive biochemical change at refrigeration temperatures.

## EVAPORATED MILK

During the manufacturing operations, this product has much in common with bulk condensed and concentrated milks. However, it is placed in a closed final container and is treated with heat to destroy microorganisms that might reduce the keeping quality of the product held at room temperature. Most of the product is made from whole milk, but some is made from skimmilk. A similar product now available in some areas is made from "filled" milk, skimmilk to which a substitute fat has been added to replace the butterfat. According to the Federal Standards (3), evaporated milk must contain at least 7.9 per cent milk fat and 25.9 per cent total milk solids. Addition of limited amounts of stabilizer salts is permitted. A few states have local standards permitting slightly less fat and solids in the final product. The process of manufacture is outlined in the diagram, page 238.

### RAW MILK SUPPLY

The Evaporated Milk Association, a trade group of evaporated milk manufacturers, has established a sanitary standards code for the manufacture of this product (2). This code covers the quality of the milk supply, and some aspects of processing, plant design, and operation as well. Sediment tests are to be run at least twice each month on one or more cans of each producer's product. An off-bottom sediment test on one pint of milk is specified. Provisions for rejection and for retest are included for use where the product fails to test either Class 1 or Class 2 by the sediment standards of the Sanitary Standards Committee of the Evaporated Milk Association. The mixed milk of each producer is to be examined at least once each month by the methylene blue reduction test or by an approved equivalent procedure.

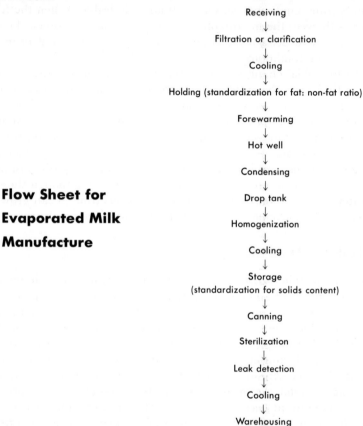

**Flow Sheet for**

**Evaporated Milk**

**Manufacture**

Receiving
↓
Filtration or clarification
↓
Cooling
↓
Holding (standardization for fat: non-fat ratio)
↓
Forewarming
↓
Hot well
↓
Condensing
↓
Drop tank
↓
Homogenization
↓
Cooling
↓
Storage
(standardization for solids content)
↓
Canning
↓
Sterilization
↓
Leak detection
↓
Cooling
↓
Warehousing

The methods used are to be those of the latest edition of *Standard Methods for the Examination of Dairy Products*. To be acceptable the milk must not have a methylene blue reduction time of less than 2.5 hours. Provisions for rejection and retest are included. Procedures for inspection of producing farms, use of acceptable procedures on producing farms, and transportation to the plant are included. In general, the standards are somewhat more lenient than those for fluid milk. The same is true of the standards for plant equipment and plant operation. Undoubtedly the feeling of the industry has been that the heat treatment given the final product permits the use of somewhat less rigorous standards during production and processing.

In practice, resazurin reduction tests and direct microscopic counts sometimes are used on producer's milk in place of the methylene blue reduction test. The plate count and counts for special groups of bacteria usually are not employed on the raw product.

### INFLUENCE OF MANUFACTURING PROCESSES
### UPON MICROORGANISMS

In order to retard bacterial development, the raw product usually is cooled as soon as possible after receipt, unless it is to be used almost immediately in processing. The industry standards only require cooling to 21.1°C. (70°F.) or below by the producer and do not require cooling of milk that is being delivered to the plant within 2 hours after milking; milk handled in this manner might develop very undesirable levels of bacteria if allowed to remain uncooled for more than a few minutes after receipt. The temperature of raw milk held in the plant should be below 4.4°C. (40°F.), and holding for more than 24 hours should be discouraged.

The milk frequently is clarified. As pointed out in Chapter 4, the clarification process does remove some bacteria and many body cells, but the change in the bacteriological quality of the product is not significant.

Common practice is to standardize the solids: fat ratio before the actual condensing operations begin. The products used in standardization, whether they be skimmilk or cream, should be at the time of use of a quality at least equal to that of the milk. This means that proper provisions must be made in the plant for the handling of standardization materials or that these materials must be obtained from a source that is in a position to furnish material of the proper quality.

Because the milk must be stable to the sterilizing temperatures used later on the canned product, the milk proteins usually are stabilized against subsequent coagulation by preheating to temperatures above 93.4°C. (200°F.) and by holding at this temperature for as long as 20 or 25 minutes. This heating may be accomplished in a circulating heater, or in a hot well when the temperature used is not above 100°C. (212°F.). In the latter case the longer holding times may be used. Particularly in continuous operations, the temperatures used may reach almost 121°C. (250°F.) and may be maintained for a few minutes in an enclosed preheater system. Any of these processes is sufficient to destroy all non-sporulating microorganisms and also many of the less resistant types of spore-forming organisms. Milk treated in this manner would be freed of any bacteria that might cause infectious disease. The temperatures employed are too high to make thermophilic growth a problem. However, the high temperatures used often cause a deposit of milk solids during the day's operations. This deposit may harbor heat-resistant bacteria and also may reduce heating efficiency. Thorough cleaning at the end of each run is essential, and special procedures and effort are necessary to accomplish this.

The condensing operation normally is done at about 54.5°C. (130°F.) in a single stage evaporator of the usual vacuum-pan type. In certain special evaporators, the temperatures employed may be somewhat lower, particularly in the final stage of a multiple-effect evaporator. These temperatures will be essentially without destructive effect upon those microorganisms that survive preheating. However, these temperatures are almost ideal for development of thermophilic bacteria, which may become a problem after prolonged operation. Under some conditions growth of thermophilic bacteria may become the limiting factor in determining how long the evaporator may be run before a shutdown for cleaning becomes necessary. Accumulation of solids on the condensing equipment also will impede heat transfer and will make adequate cleaning much more difficult. Unless cleaning is thorough, the residual soil may serve as a protection to undesirable microorganisms that might develop later.

Following condensing, the milk is homogenized. The precautions on homogenizer care as outlined in Chapter 10 must be observed to minimize microbial contamination from this source. The product then is cooled, placed in storage tanks, and standardized to the desired final concentrations of fat and total milk solids. The standardization materials, whether they be water, cream, or milk solids-not-fat, should be of a quality equal to that of the product being standardized. The product must be kept cold until canning and sterilization occur, for the product is not sterile and thus is subject to microbial spoilage.

The cans used ordinarily are made in an adjacent plant and are so treated with heat during the fabrication that they contribute few, if any, microorganisms to the canned product. Because the milk is cold when placed in the can, adequate head space for expansion during the sterilization process is essential, or the cans may become leakers and permit entry of bacteria. The canning machinery is relatively complex, and special care must be given to the many parts to insure adequate sanitation. The procedure outlined in the *Evaporated Milk Industry Sanitary Standards Code* (2) calls for essentially complete disassembly of the canner and for careful cleaning of each of the component parts. Because the cans are sealed automatically at a relatively high speed, they must be checked carefully for leaks. This usually is done by a device that discards any cans for which the dimensions before and after heat processing are beyond a range that has been established as normal. The dimension used is based upon the desired contours of the ends of a can that has been filled and processed properly. Automatic weighing also is used to determine the desired fill of the cans and to discover whether any material has been lost through spillage before, during, or after closure, or through leaks during processing and cooling. Detection of leaks is extremely important because leaks may provide a portal of entry for spoilage organisms. Since leakers constitute only a small and variable proportion of all the cans, their detection by incubation and subsequent examination becomes exceedingly laborious and impractical.

The heat processing of the milk in cans may be done by either the batch or the continuous processing procedure, the latter being the more widely used today. The time and temperature combination chosen is one that will give "practical" sterility. This is a level of heat destruction of microorganisms that will adequately protect the milk against spoilage under normal merchandising conditions. Even though absolute sterility may be attained in most of the cans, an occasional organism, which is extremely resistant but which will not grow and cause a defect in the milk under normal conditions, may survive in some of the cans. Absolute sterility could be attained quite easily, but only at the expense of increasing the cooked flavor of the product and probably affecting the body adversely. The common exposures are in the range from 114.5°C. to 118.4°C. (238°F. to 245°F.) for periods of 14 to 18 minutes. The exposures used provide a slight margin over those determined experimentally to be satisfactory for a given plant. When the spore load is high (the number of bacterial spores to be killed is above average), the exposure must be greater than normal. Presence of an unusually resistant spore type also increases the exposure needed. The temperature at which an organism has grown influences its heat resistance, since growth at optimum temperature yields spores of greater resistance than does growth at lower or higher temperatures (10). The sub-lethal heating during forewarming apparently serves as a sensitizing treatment, making the spores more sensitive to destruction by the final heating (1). The usual treatment is 116.7°C. (242°F.) for 15 minutes, which has been found to give adequate bacterial destruction under most conditions. This figure is for the actual time in the sterilizing chamber of the continuous sterilizer of the Anderson-Barngrover type, where heating-up time is regulated carefully in the preceding sections of the sterilizer and rapid cooling with cold water is provided. Approximately 115.5°C. (240°F.) for a minimum of 20 minutes often is recommended for batch sterilizers where the time required to reach the temperature is 15 to 20 minutes. According to Hunziker (5), common practice when using the gallon cans is to raise the temperature 0.55°C. (1°F.) above the values for the usual 14.5 ounce tall can and to reduce the temperature 0.55°C. (1°F.) for processing baby-size cans.

Cooling after sterilization should introduce no microbiological problems, but as cooling is started, external pressure must be maintained, usually with compressed air, to avoid bulging of the cans and possible weakening of the seams. The weakened seams may permit entry of defect-producing microorganisms. The water used in cooling could easily be the source of defect-producing organisms under these conditions, for the decreasing internal pressure associated with final stages of cooling would draw the bacteria into the imperfectly sealed container.

Experiments to reduce the temperature needed for sterilization of evaporated milk are being conducted in several laboratories at present. One of the most promising possibilities is use of a continuous high-temperature, short-time procedure, followed by aseptic canning in previously sterilized containers. Some evaporated milk processed in this manner is available commercially, but details of the processing procedures are not released. Experiments also are being conducted using higher temperatures and shorter heating times in the can.

Normal evaporated milk usually shows no organisms when examined bacteriologically. Even prolonged holding under usual storage conditions ordinarily does not permit development of microorganisms. Milk shipped to the tropics may develop more defects than that marketed in this country; thermophilic organisms probably are responsible. Physico-chemical changes are responsible for most of any deterioration encountered during prolonged storage. Many of the defects reported in the literature do not occur at the present time because of the improvements in processing and laboratory control that have taken place over a period of years in the industry. No longer is it considered necessary, or even desirable, to store the product in a warehouse for a time under warm conditions to detect those lots and occasional cans that might deteriorate in commercial channels and in the home. This results in considerable savings to an industry operating on a narrow profit margin, as is the case with the evaporated milk industry.

SPOILAGE

Microbial spoilage of evaporated milk can conveniently be divided into two categories. Spoilage of one type is due to bacteria of unusual or at least high heat resistance; these are the bacteria that may survive a marginal or slightly deficient heat treatment. The other type of microbial spoilage is due to organisms gaining entry to the product because of an imperfect seal or because of subsequent damage to the container; these organisms have no high or unusual ability to survive the level of heat treatment.

Curd formation due to microorganisms may be caused by any one of several species of the genus *Bacillus. Bacillus coagulans* appears to be responsible for most outbreaks, but *Bacillus calidolactis, Bacillus cereus, Bacillus simplex, Bacillus vulgatus (subtilis)* and *Bacillus megatherium,* the latter three in atypical form, also have been implicated in one or more cases. All of these organisms are relatively heat resistant. They usually have been cultured from milk that may have undergone a slightly sub-normal heat treatment. Occasionally, very resistant forms appear in the product and require some increase in the processing temperature if adequate destruction of the bacteria is to be attained. Similar changes must be made if the numbers of contaminating bacteria reach abnormal levels. *Bacillus coagulans* produces an increase in acidity as it grows, but ordinarily it causes no other definite change except for a slightly cheesy flavor. The organism grows best at 37°C. (98.6°F.) and above, but otherwise requires no special conditions for its cultivation. The characteristic defect is produced quite easily by inoculation of material from affected cans into fresh cans of milk. Three strains of the organisms Hussong and Hammer (6) described as *Bacillus calidolactis* have been reclassified as *Bacillus coagulans,* and two as *Bacillus stearothermophilus,* by Smith et al. (9). The latter authors found that only the *Bacillus stearothermophilus* strains grow at truly thermophilic temperatures. These organisms all produce a slight cheesy odor and flavor and considerable acidity in evaporated milk. High temperatures of storage and improper cooling predispose milk to spoilage by these organisms.

*Bacillus cereus* usually produces only a slight soft clot at the surface of milk in a can. Apparently this organism is highly aerobic. The more head space is left in a can, the greater the probability that a typical defect will appear; test tube cultures do much better than can cultures, presumably because of air supply. Coagulation by *Bacillus megatherium* is accompanied by some gas and by a cheesy odor. *Bacillus vulgatus* (*subtilis*) produces a non-acid coagulation.

Bulged cans of evaporated milk may be due to gas production associated with chemical action on the metal and to overfilling of cans with cold milk. However, gas-producing, anaerobic, spore-forming bacteria of unusual heat resistance may be responsible. Hunziker (5) found *Plectridium* (*Clostridium*) *foetidum* responsible not only for gas production, but also for an intense putrefactive defect with which hydrogen sulfide production was associated. The organism survived 118.3°C. (245°F.) for 15 minutes in the laboratory, so that care on the farm to avoid contamination from cow manure and crop and soil residues appears to be a factor of importance in the prevention of the defect. Fortunately, the defect is not common under present conditions.

Bitter flavor may be caused by *Bacillus amarus* and *Bacillus panis,* the latter closely related to, if not identical with, *Bacillus subtilis.* These organisms are facultative spore-forming bacteria of high heat resistance; the spores apparently survive marginal sterilization and are able to grow satisfactorily at room temperature. The defect seems to be due to partial breakdown products of proteins and is very objectionable to most people.

In numerous cases, milk with defects considered to be due to bacteria has not yielded organisms on culturing. This may have been due to the defects' being caused by non-microbial factors that resemble microbial activity. In other instances, the bacteria may have produced the change and then may have died off before the product was examined. The possibility also exists that the procedures employed for isolation may not have been adequate for the organism involved, particularly when some time had elapsed since the organism was actively growing in the milk. When organisms have been exposed to adverse conditions for a time, they are much more difficult to cultivate than when they are growing actively.

When cans do not remain sealed tightly, either because of improper sealing at first or because of subsequent corrosion or mechanical injury, the entry of a wide variety of bacteria is possible. If the product contains bacteria that are not heat resistant, this may be interpreted as being the result of contamination after heating. Gas production caused by coliform bacteria or *Streptococcus distendens,* coagulation by dairy streptococci, and fishiness caused by *Proteus ichthyosmius* (more properly called *Pseudomonas ichthyosmia*) are some of the defects of this type which have been reported.

The consumer must be better informed regarding the keeping quality of opened cans of evaporated milk. The heat treatment destroys only those microorganisms present in the product at the time of heating and has no killing effect upon subsequent contaminants. The can usually is opened in the home under conditions that permit entry of bacteria and possibly yeasts and molds. Only by the use of techniques such as those employed in the laboratory can such contamination be avoided. Careful cleaning of the top and possibly immersion in boiling water for several minutes will minimize contamination from the can. Immersion of the opener in boiling water is the best treatment for that instrument. Milk in a can opened carefully and properly protected from contamination may be kept for several days under adequate refrigeration, but the product usually will spoil rather quickly if held at room temperature.

## CONCENTRATED SOUR MILK AND WHEY

These products are made to utilize materials that might otherwise be wasted or that might present a disposal problem at certain dairy plants. The concentrates depend primarily on high acidity to prevent bacteria and some yeasts from growing, and on absence of air to inhibit development of molds and aerobic yeasts.

Concentrated sour skimmilk usually is made by first pasteurizing the milk at 76.7°C. to 82.2°C. (170°F. to 180°F.) in a continuous pasteurizer or by vat pasteurization at 65.4°C. to 71.1°C. (150°F. or 160°F.) for 30 minutes. This heating destroys many of the microorganisms that otherwise might compete with the culture of *Lactobacillus bulgaricus* plus mycoderm (see Chapter 2), commonly used in this product. The mycoderm is used primarily to help keep the lactobacillus in a highly active form prior to use in the vat. A high pasteurization temperature also tends to promote a smoother body in the finished product. The pasteurized milk should be cooled to 40.4°C. to 46.1°C. (105°F. to 115°F.) and then inoculated with 2 per cent of the mixed culture of *Lactobacillus bulgaricus* plus mycoderm. The product should be kept within 5.5°C. (10°F.) of the 46.1°C. (115°F.) incubation temperature for about 18 hours or until the acidity of the milk has reached 1.7 to 2.0 per cent, calculated as lactic acid. Before concentrating, the curd should be broken up as completely as possible, and the material should then be drawn into the pan at the same temperature used for incubation; forewarming of the highly acid product tends to harden curd lumps and be the cause of a rough-textured product. The product usually is condensed to give 6 per cent acid in the final product, 5 per cent being considered the lower limit for good keeping quality. To attain this level the total solids of the final product should be about 28 per cent.

Whey may be treated in essentially the same manner, except that the mixture should be concentrated to a ratio of approximately 3.9 to 1 because of the low solids content of the starting material. Whey may be concentrated without acidification, but such a product must be kept under refrigeration. Only if the pH is below 4.5 will the product keep reasonably well, and then only in the absence of air.

Condensed or semi-solid buttermilk may be prepared from buttermilk in much the same way as concentrated sour milk is handled. The acidity before condensing must exceed 1.6 per cent if good keeping quality is to be achieved. When the product is to be used for stock feed, an organic acid may be used to bring the acidity to the desired level, eliminating the need for ripening. Also, sour buttermilk should be forewarmed before condensing, temperatures up to 71.1°C. (160°F.) being used; live steam both raises the temperature adequately and breaks up the curd by agitation. The product usually is condensed to about one-third its initial weight.

These condensed sour products will keep almost indefinitely if they are stored in air-tight containers to prevent mold growth, since the acid level prevents growth of bacteria and some yeasts. The containers must be resistant to the action of acid. Wooden barrels coated with paraffin or sodium silicate are most satisfactory. Metal containers usually will rust through from the acid rather readily, and they are useful only for short-period storage of small lots. If leaks permit an air space to develop above the product, molds nearly always will cause spoilage of the product.

## References

1. Curran, H. R., and F. R. Evans, Heat inactivation inducing germination in the spores of the thermotolerant and thermophilic aerobic bacteria, *J. Bacteriol.*, 39 (1945): 335–346.

2. *Evaporated Milk Industry Sanitary Standards Code.* Chicago: Evaporated Milk Association, 1951.

3. Federal and state standards for the composition of milk and milk products, *USDA Agriculture Handbook No. 51*, 1953.

4. Grosche, C. A., H. L. Lucas, and M. L. Speck, Pasteurization requirements for concentrated whole milk, *J. Dairy Sci.*, 35 (1952): 793–799.

5. Hunziker, O. F., *Condensed Milk and Milk Powder,* 7th Ed. La Grange, Ill.: Published by the author, 1949.

6. Hussong, R. V., and B. W. Hammer, Observations on *Bacillus calidolactis. Iowa State Coll. J. Sci.,* 6 (1931): 89–93.

7. Olson, J. C., Jr., A. J. Nielsen, E. L. Thomas, and H. A. Morris, Changes in bacterial counts and flavor of concentrated and recombined milks during storage at low temperatures. *J. Dairy Sci.,* 36 (1953): 817–824.

8. Rosenberger, W. S., F. E. Nelson, and R. W. Baughman, New approach to fresh concentrated (milk), *American Milk Rev.,* 14(3) (1952): 16, 82, 83, 94, 95.

9. Smith, N. R., Ruth E. Gordon, and F. E. Clark, Aerobic sporeforming bacteria. *USDA Agriculture Monograph No. 16,* 1952.

10. Theophilus, D. R., and B. W. Hammer, Influence of growth temperature on the thermal resistance of some bacteria from evaporated milk, *Iowa Agr. Exp. Sta. Research Bull. 244,* 1938.

# 9

# Microbiology of sweetened condensed and dry milk products

## SWEETENED CONDENSED MILKS

Sweetened condensed whole milk is a dairy product prepared by addition of sucrose or dextrose (about 18 to 20 pounds per 100 pounds of whole milk) to whole milk and by subsequent evaporation of the water under vacuum at a ratio of approximately 2½ to 1. Federal standards require 8.5 per cent fat and 28 per cent total milk solids, but some state standards allow as low as 7.7 per cent fat and 25 per cent total milk solids. Sweetened condensed skimmilk usually must contain 20 per cent total milk solids, although certain state standards specify as little as 18 per cent (4).

Sweetened condensed milk is packaged in sealed cans for retail sale, and in milk cans, barrels, steel drums, and bulk tanks for industrial purposes. This product is widely used by bakers, confectioners, ice cream manufacturers, and in the prepared-food industries. More sweetened condensed whole milk is sold as case goods than as bulk; on the other hand, much more sweetened condensed skimmilk is sold as bulk than as case goods.

The principle upon which preservation of these products is based is well known. The addition of sugar increases the osmotic pressure to a point inhibitory to most microorganisms. The added carbohydrate also "binds" water, making it unavailable for metabolic functions, and this "binding" may be thought of as a type of drying process. The increased concentration of milk solids also is effective in raising osmotic pressure and in binding water. The concentration of sugar-in-water of sweetened condensed milk is known as the "sugar ratio." It is calculated as follows:

$$\text{Sugar ratio} = \frac{\text{per cent sugar in condensed milk}}{100 - \text{total milk solids in condensed milk}} \times 100$$

In case goods the ratio varies from 62.5 to 64.5 per cent; in bulk goods a ratio of 42 per cent is considered sufficient for sweetened condensed whole milk. The difference in sugar ratios is due to the fact that bulk sweetened condensed, for various reasons, is used quickly and is not stored for long periods, whereas case goods may be stored on shelves for long periods of time depending upon customer demand (12).

The addition of sugar to the condensed milk should not be considered as a substitute for good sanitation, good quality raw milk, or adequate processing practices. Since sterilization processes are not used, sweetened condensed milks contain a varied microbial flora. These microorganisms usually are inhibited, even though storage temperatures are favorable for their growth, and this is advantageous, since refrigeration is not required for preservation.

### INSPECTION OF THE RAW MILK SUPPLY

If a quality product is to be obtained, raw milk for condensing purposes should be inspected. Usually, inspection consists of one or more rapid platform tests for odor and flavor, acidity, physical character, and sediment, and of a methylene blue or resazurin reduction time or a direct microscopic count. Selection of raw milk to be used for condensing purposes is difficult because the flora remaining after heat processing can not be related to plate counts or to dye reduction times of the raw milk. It has been suggested that counts be made on milk samples heated to 80°C. (176°F.) for 15 minutes in order to overcome this difficulty (3).

A number of desirable standards are applicable to these tests. Flavor and odor should be that of natural milk except, possibly, for a slight feed odor, which volatilizes during the condensing. There should be no odors associated with acid formation detectable by smell. Titratable acidity, when calculated as lactic acid, should not exceed 0.03 per cent of apparent acidity when this has been established for an area. There should be no apparent flakes, clots, blood, insect parts, or curdling. "Off-bottom" sediment should not exceed 0.30 mg (United States Department of Agriculture standards for milk and milk products). Methylene blue should not be decolorized in 3.5 hours, and resazurin should be graded no less than PBP 7/5.5 (Munsell) in the 1-hour test. The direct microscopic clump count should not exceed 1,000,000 per milliliter. In some areas these suggested standards have yet to be met, but it is obvious that improvement in handling and sanitation, in control of bacterial growth, and in elimination of the use of mastitis milk can only be realized by following them.

### PROCESSING

Figures 9.1 and 9.2 may be helpful in illustrating the path and heat treatment of the milk from the weigh tank to the final container. The effects of each of these stages in the manufacture of sweetened con-

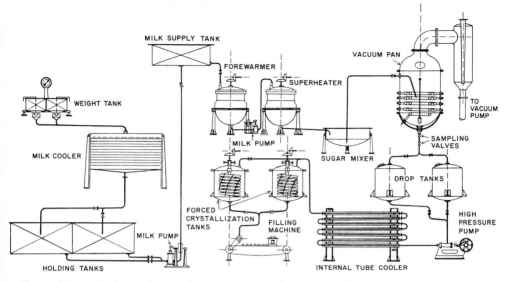

**Figure 9.1** Equipment for manufacturing sweetened condensed milk. Courtesy of A. W. Baumann and reprinted from *Condensed Milk and Milk Powder* by permission of O. F. Hunziker. Copyright, 1949, by O. F. Hunziker.

densed milk on the microbial flora will be considered in the subsequent sections.

*Forewarming.* Handling of the milk previous to this point results in the addition of some microbial contaminants. The total number present depends upon the sanitary condition of the milk, the temperature of storage, and the general state of sanitation of utensils and plant equipment. In the forewarming process a temperature range of 62.6°C. to 120°C. (145°F. to 248°F.) has been employed with the most common temperatures and times being 82°C. to 100°C. (180°F. to 212°F.) for 10 to 30 minutes. The forewarming temperatures may be attained by heating the milk to 76.6°C. (170°F.) in a steam-jacketed closed kettle and by then injecting live steam to heat to the desired temperature. A variety of other forewarming devices have come into use, among them multi-velocity type single-pass and recirculating high-pass velocity preheaters. Units like the Mallory heat exchanger and the Ste-Vac have been used for continuous-flow heating of milk above the boiling point. The temperature and time used are sufficient to destroy all pathogenic microorganisms and all other living forms except the most heat-resistant. In addition, forewarming inactivates the natural enzymes of milk, and it is necessary for satisfactory vacuum pan operation. The forewarming step is the only means by which sweetened condensed milk is freed of the possible presence of disease organisms, and it is, of course, instrumental in destroying spoilage organisms. Special attention should be given to possible spoilage problems and to high counts in the finished product arising from improper piping lay-out. Valves located at some distance from the forewarmer, or leakage from these valves,

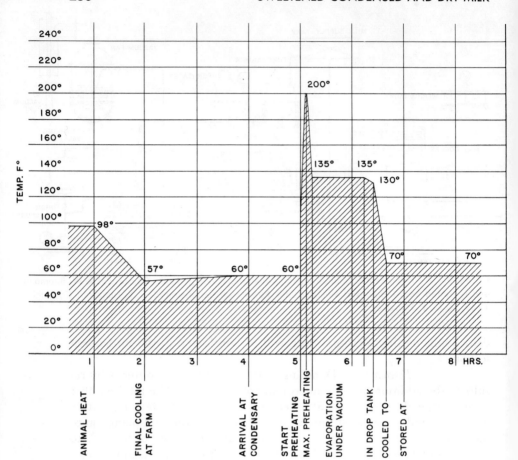

**Figure 9.2**    Processing temperatures for sweetened condensed milk. Courtesy of A. W. Baumann and reprinted from *Condensed Milk and Milk Powder* by permission of O. F. Hunziker. Copyright, 1949, by O. F. Hunziker.

may allow microorganisms to survive the forewarming process or to build-up in contaminated sections. For this reason, time and temperature of fore-warming should be rigidly controlled.

*Addition of sugar.* The addition of sucrose to milk before fore-warming would increase the thermal resistance of the microorganisms in the milk. For this, and for other reasons, the sugar is usually dissolved in hot—87.8°C. (190°F.)—water as a 65 per cent syrup, which is drawn into the vacuum pan near the end of the run. In practice, the sugar is dissolved in the hot, forewarmed milk for bulk supplies and separately as a syrup for case goods. The addition of sugar results in plasmolysis of some surviving organisms, and hot milk plus sugar, when drawn from the fore-warmer to the vacuum pan, usually has a very low count.

Although sugar is a relatively unimportant source of contamination (usually less than 100 bacteria per gram), the quality used is important if spoilage problems in the finished product are to be avoided. Sugar contaminated with mold spores, osmophilic yeasts, and bacteria producing acid and gas should not be used. Sugar stock must be stored in a clean, dry place free from dust, insect, and rodent contamination. In addition, sugar should always be handled in a sanitary manner, and unused stock must not be exposed to high humidity. Sugar may become moldy, fermented, or acid if left exposed to high humidity in an unsanitary storage room. Plant sanitation programs certainly ought not to overlook sugar handling as an important phase in the production of high quality sweetened condensed milk.

*Condensing.* The water from the forewarmed, sugared milk is removed by evaporation in a vacuum pan, where it boils at approximately 57.2°C. (135°F.) in a 25-inch vacuum, but toward the end of the operation the temperature is decreased to 48.9°C. (120°F.). The total number of organisms at this point is very low (usually around 500 or less per gram). This step in itself probably further reduces the numbers of organisms; however, this is dependent on the temperature employed and the rate of evaporation. The vacuum pan must be adequately sanitized in order to prevent it from becoming a serious source of contamination. A possible source of contamination may be the vacuum pan heads. Improper cleaning and sanitization at this point might lead to subsequent high counts or to spoilage of the finished product, and the sticky nature of sweetened condensed milk makes the cleaning operation difficult. Heating milk results in deposits of material that are quite difficult to remove, and these may become sources of contamination if not completely eliminated. Coils must be carefully cleaned of any "cooked on" material. Vapor traps used for the recovery of entrained condensed milk must be given careful attention, since these are potential sources of trouble. A suggested cleaning treatment involves the use of an alkaline detergent, which is preheated in the forewarmer to 82°C. (180°F.) and then is brought into the pan at a 14-inch vacuum in sufficient amounts to cover the top coil of the pan. After 30 minutes of "working," during which intake balances evaporation, the pan is emptied and flushed with hot—82°C. (180°F.)—water. Acid cleaners should then be used to prevent milk stone formation, and the same procedure is followed as with the alkaline detergent. The pan may be steamed for 30 minutes and then allowed to dry with the manhole cover off, but a rinse with a 600 ppm solution of chlorine is more effective in keeping this piece of equipment in a satisfactory sanitary condition (3).

*Forced crystallization.* After evaporation the milk is routed to drop tanks, where a temperature of 30°C. (86°F.) is desired. The milk is then seeded with lactose crystals (incorporated in some of the condensed milk) and is vigorously agitated for 1 hour. In this step the lactose is forced to form tiny crystals in the milk. The added lactose seed crystals usually are not heavily contaminated, but if their sterilization is desired, they should first be heated to 93.3°C. (200°F.) under vacuum so that they are converted to the alpha-anhydride form. The lactose then is ground to dust, transferred to cans, sealed, and sterilized at 130°C. (266°F.) for 1 to 2 hours. Approximately 8 ounces of seed powder are used per 1,000 pounds of original fluid milk. After forced crystallization, the milk intended for case goods is cooled to around 15.6°C. (60°F.) and for bulk goods around 21°C. (70°F.).

*Packaging.* Sweetened condensed milk for industry (bulk) is packaged in new, paraffin-lined white oak barrels, steel drums, and 10-gallon milk cans. Filling operations should take place in a separate sanitary room in an atmosphere of filtered air at around 16°C. (60°F.). Barrels can be filled directly from an internal tubular cooler or from the crystallizing tank discharge. Pipelines handling the product must be sterilized and frothing should be avoided. Case goods are packaged in 6- and 14-ounce and 1-gallon cans. The 6- and 14-ounce cans are filled and the top end is then crimped on, whereas the 1-gallon container is filled through a ¾-inch hole in the center of one end. Cans may be sterilized by being passed over gas jets, but no really good system has yet been suggested. Dust and insect contamination of stored cans and ends must be avoided. The 6- and 14-ounce cans are filled by adjustable multiple piston pump machines equipped with cut-offs to prevent dripping. Hand fillers usually are used for the 1-gallon cans. Filling machines should be dismantled, and the parts should be washed, steamed, and dried at the end of each day's run. Heavy contamination of these machines might result in disastrous spoilage outbreaks in the packaged product.

The filling operation may be a major source of micrococci, yeasts, and molds in sweetened condensed milk. Filling machines are intricate pieces of equipment, and measuring pistons, plungers, filler bowls, and nozzles may be contaminated by contact with workers or by soiled "drip cloths." This phase of the operation must be carefully supervised.

### INSPECTION OF THE FINISHED PRODUCTS

A number of methods are available for examining sweetened condensed milks bacteriologically (16). Special care must be exercised when opening cans of these products. Usually they are held at 45°C. (113°F.) for not more than 15 minutes to reduce the viscosity and then are washed with a detergent and are dried. One end of the can is sponged with a solution of 100 to 200 ppm chlorine or other sterilizing agent. The can is agitated thoroughly to mix the contents, and the sterilized end is punctured with a sterile instrument. If desired, the can may be moistened with alcohol and flamed; then a punch treated in the same manner may be used to make a hole in the can so that a sample can be drawn into a sterile container. In determining total numbers, the first dilution is made gravimetrically by weighing 11 g into a dilution blank. Further dilutions are made volumetrically. The same procedure is followed for coliform and yeast and mold determinations. These are especially important, since spoilage outbreaks frequently involve them. In examining sweetened condensed milks microscopically, a 1 to 5 dilution with sterile distilled water should be made before preparing smears for staining, for crystallization of sugar in the undiluted material would interfere with the operation. Application of the above determinations to a large number of samples has resulted in much information relative to the qualitative and quantitative aspects of the flora of normal samples of sweetened condensed milk. It has already been noted that this product is not sterile, and that total counts range from a few hundred to over 100,000 per gram. The microorganisms found in the product may include micrococci, yeasts and molds, spore-forming aerobes, and coliforms. These organisms probably enter as utensil and air contaminants after the forewarming step. Micrococci seem always to be present and sometimes in high numbers. The reason for this probably is their marked resistance to adverse conditions of osmotic pressure. Occasionally, aerobic spore-formers of the *Bacillus subtilis* type and thermophilic bacteria are recovered, probably because the spores of these organisms survive the forewarming process.

## DEFECTS CAUSED BY MICROORGANISMS

In addition to improper processing as a cause of spoilage problems, there is the possibility that improper can manufacture or can damage may be involved. Can and closure technique should be carefully inspected. Canned foods may be subjected to rough treatment, and occasionally a can is found with pinpoint holes through which spoilage organisms may enter. Severely dented and crushed cans should, of course, be removed from sale.

Microorganisms involved in the spoilage of sweetened condensed milks are of several distinct types. The formation of "buttons" is due to the growth of various species of molds. Buttons are composed of mold mycelia and coagulated casein, usually colored white to brown. They may be found on the surface or in the sub-surface layers of the product. The molds grow until the available oxygen in the head space is exhausted. The most abundant button formation is found in under-filled cans, because, here, considerable oxygen is available to the mold. Since mold spores are easily destroyed during the forewarming operation, buttons can be formed only if recontamination occurs subsequent to this point. *Aspergillus repens* and species of *Penicillium* have been identified as causes of buttons, although in some cases nothing remains besides mycelial debris and curd. Preventive measures against button formation include filling containers fully, vacuum packing, storing below 16°C. (60°F.), and improving plant sanitation with emphasis on prevention of contamination after forewarming. Inversion of stored cans at regular intervals is also helpful in reducing deterioration by molds.

Gassiness, or "bloat," is produced by organisms fermenting lactose and sucrose. Yeasts of the genus *Torulopsis* have been isolated from bulged and blown cans of sweetened condensed milk. Coliform organisms also have been identified in connection with this defect. The gases are carbon dioxide or mixtures of carbon dioxide and hydrogen. The defect is more prevalent in warm months, and since these organisms are not resistant to forewarming temperatures, contamination must occur after this process. Improvement of plant sanitation, as well as care in packaging, again is indicated.

Thickening of sweetened condensed milks may be due to physical or biological agencies. In the latter instance, the thickening usually is accompanied by acid flavors and cheesy odors. In some cases micrococci have been isolated, and in others yeasts are predominant. Thickening may be due to a rennet-like enzyme of microbial origin. Plant sanitation improvements and lower storage temperatures may be helpful in reducing the incidence of this defect.

In areas where sanitary control is poor, much gassiness and thickening are encountered in cases of spoilage. Where sanitary control is good, defects are limited mainly to off-flavors such as rancidity and cheesiness. Perhaps this is because of the activity of microbial enzymes following cessation of growth of the contaminating organisms. It has been found that from 10 to 30 per cent of the organisms present in samples of sweetened condensed milk may be lipolytic (3).

## DRY MILKS

Dry milks are dairy products in which nearly all of the water has been removed by evaporation. The various products have been defined by the American Dry Milk Institute (5, 6) and the United States Department of Agriculture (4, 17, 18, 19, 20).

Non-fat dry milk contains not more than 5 per cent moisture or 1.5 per cent fat (6). USDA standards (17) vary from 1.25 to 1.5 per cent fat and 4 to 5 per cent moisture, depending upon the grade. Dry whole milk is a dairy product prepared by removing the water from whole milk so that it contains not more than 4 per cent moisture nor less than 26 per cent fat (5). USDA standards (20) for moisture vary from 2.25 to 3 per cent, depending upon the grade. Dry buttermilk is obtained by removing the water from the liquid buttermilk that results from the manufacture of sweet cream butter. To meet USDA standards, the solids must not contain less than 4.5 per cent fat nor more than 5 per cent moisture (19). Malted milk contains not more than 3.5 per cent moisture nor less than 7.5 per cent fat. It is made by combining with whole milk the liquor of a mash, composed of ground barley malt and wheat flour, in which complete enzymatic action on the latter has been secured. This mixture is dried in a special vacuum pan, on a drum drier, or in a spray drier. Malted milk may contain added salt and sodium or potassium bicarbonate (11). Dry whey, although not a dry milk product in the strict sense, may be included here. It is made by spray drying pasteurized sweet, fresh cheese whey, and it must contain not more than 1.25 per cent fat or more than 5 per cent moisture to meet USDA standards (18).

Dried milks (whole and non-fat) are used in manufacturing ice cream, infant foods, bakery goods, confections, and sausage, and they are utilized by flour millers and cheese processors (1). Malted milk is used primarily in milk drinks at confectioneries. Dried buttermilk is used in small amounts in prepared-food industries and by bakeries, but the bulk of it is used as an animal feed. Non-fat dry milk makes up the greatest part of dried milk production each year. Most dry whole milk and about 75 per cent of non-fat dry milk are made by the spray process, but dry skimmilk for feed and dry buttermilk are made by the roller process.

Dried milk products are widely used because of the ease with which they are preserved and because of the conservation of transportation facilities and storage space that is obtained. Evaporation of the water is brought about by momentary high temperature heating in, or on, special drying devices. The keeping quality of dried milks depends primarily upon their low moisture content, for without adequate water there can be no microbial metabolism and, therefore, no microbial spoilage.

### INSPECTION OF THE RAW MILK SUPPLY

In order that the best possible milk obtainable will be used and that the finished product will meet standards acceptable to the industry, a number of tests are available for determining the quality of raw milk to be used for drying. Raw milk for drying purposes is examined for physical appearance, sediment, acidity, and bacterial quality. Standards of the American Dry Milk Institute stipulate that milk for drying be of good physical appearance; that is, flakes, clots, or blood must be absent, and there must be no objectionable flavors or odors. Sediment tests made by the "off-the-bottom" method should yield a disc equivalent to the American Dry Milk Institute Standard Discs No. 1 or 2. Acidity, when calculated as lactic acid, should not be greater than 0.03 per cent above the normal titratable acidity for the milk of a given locality. Methylene blue should not be decolorized in less than 3.5 hours (5, 6).

*Clarification.* This step is optional. The influence of clarification on the bacterial content of milk is well known, and although large numbers of bacteria are trapped in clarifier slime, no noticeable effect of their removal has been observed on microbial content. The number of microorganisms removed is dependent to some extent upon the number initially present. Usually the plate count is higher in clarified milk owing to the disintegration of bacterial clumps. The clarifier should be kept as free as possible from contamination by adequate cleaning and sanitization. After use it should be flushed with warm—48.9°C. (120°F.)—water, and the discs should be removed. The clarifier slime must then be brushed off with the aid of a good detergent, and after cleaning, the discs should be rinsed and allowed to dry. The bowl should be brushed with detergent to remove all slime and then rinsed in the same manner as the discs. Periodically, an acid cleaner should be used to prevent milk stone formation.

*Separation.* In the manufacture of non-fat dry milk, a centrifugal separator must be used; the resulting skimmilk contains fewer organisms than the whole milk from which it was derived, because many bacteria are thrown into the separator slime. However, the total bacterial count of cream plus skimmilk is higher because of the breaking up of clumps of cells. Here again, no effect on keeping quality is noted, but the separator must be kept clean and sanitized in the same manner as described for the clarifier.

*Homogenization.* If this step is employed in the manufacture of dry whole milk, increases in total counts may be expected owing to the disintegration of bacterial clumps and to the possible addition of contaminants from an inadequately cleaned homogenizer (see Chapter 10). It is doubtful that the disintegration of bacterial clumps noticeably affects the count of the finished powder.

### PROCESSING

Three methods of drying milk by the application of heat are used. The milk may be spray dried (Figures 9.3 and 9.4) by spraying a mist of concentrated milk under high pressure into a current of hot air in a drying chamber. It may be roller dried (Figure 9.3) by applying the milk to the surface of internally heated, revolving metal drums. The rolls evaporate the water from the thin film of milk adhering to them. After about one-half revolution the dried milk is scraped from the roll with a knife blade. In the vacuum drying process (Figure 9.3) the revolving metal drums are enclosed in a vacuum chamber in order that lower temperatures may be used. The "flow-sheet" (Figure 9.4) may be useful as a guide to the various steps involved in spray-drying.

*Preheating.* In the manufacture of spray dried milk, preheating from 61.1°C. to 93.3°C. (142°F. to 200°F.) is used, 85°C. (185°F.) for 10 to 30 minutes being the most common temperature and time. With roller dried milk, preheating to 65.6°C. to 85°C. (150°F. to 185°F.) is employed (12). High temperature preheating is a valuable aid in inactivating

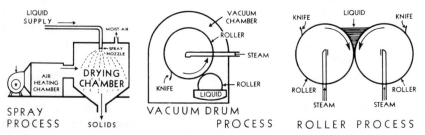

**Figure 9.3**    Major milk drying processes. Courtesy American Dry Milk Institute and reprinted from *The Dry Milk Industry* by permission of H. L. Cook and G. H. Day.

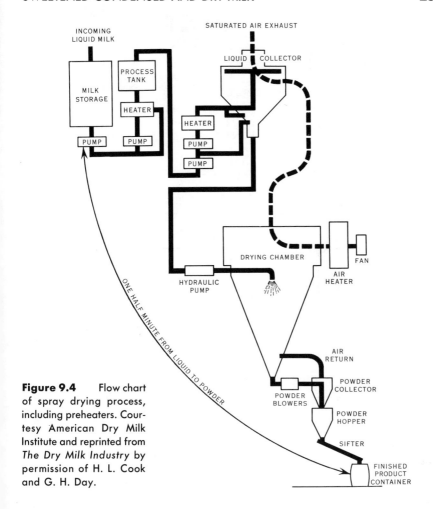

**Figure 9.4**    Flow chart of spray drying process, including preheaters. Courtesy American Dry Milk Institute and reprinted from *The Dry Milk Industry* by permission of H. L. Cook and G. H. Day.

milk enzymes and in reducing the number of thermoduric bacteria. When preheating is done at lower temperatures, microbacteria and micrococci may predominate in the finished product, whereas at higher temperatures streptococci and aerobic spore-formers predominate (2). Preheating destroys the majority of microbes, except the most heat-resistant. Disease-producing organisms are destroyed completely. In producing dry milks with a low total count, good plant sanitation practices and a good milk supply are more effective than raising the preheating temperature.

*Concentration.* Where spray drying is employed, the milk is passed from the heater to a vacuum pan, and from there it is sprayed into a current of spent air—71.1°C. (160°F.)—leaving the dryer. In this stage the milk is concentrated 2 to 1 or 3 to 1. A particularly good lay-out is illustrated in Figure 9.5. There seems to be little chance of air contamination, since the air enters the drying chamber at 121.1°C. to 204.4°C.

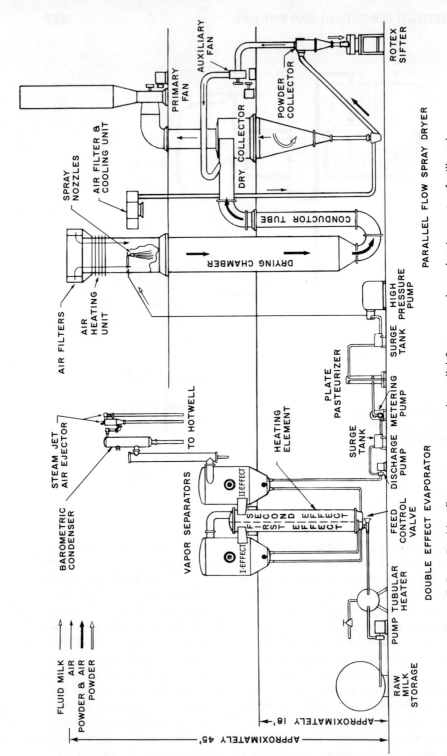

**Figure 9.5** Double effect evaporator and parallel flow spray dryer showing route of milk and powder. Courtesy Cherry-Burrell Corporation, Cedar Rapids, Iowa.

(250°F. to 400°F.). Ordinarily, further decreases in the total microbial population are to be expected in this operation; however, poorly cleaned condensers may cause outbreaks of thermoduric or thermophilic bacteria. In roller dried milk some concentration may take place in the roller troughs if two drums are used. If one drum is used, the milk must be pre-condensed before being applied to the drum.

*Drying.* In each of the methods of drying, the milk is introduced to the drying apparatus by the feed tank. In order to minimize contamination, the total volume of milk held in the feed tank should be kept as low as possible at all times. In the atmospheric roller process, milk is held at 65.6°C. to 85°C. (150°F. to 185°F.) and it is applied to the drums usually as a 3 or 5 to 1 concentrate. In roller drying, vacuum or atmospheric drying may be carried out. Vacuum drums are operated at less than 100°C. (212°F.), whereas atmospheric drums are run as high as 148.9°C. (300°F.). Most non-fat dry milk solids and dry buttermilk for animal feed are made by the atmospheric roller process and only relatively small amounts by the vacuum roller process. In spray drying, the milk is introduced into the drying chamber as a fine mist, produced by means of compressed air, pressure spray, or centrifugal spray atomizers. The milk is dried almost instantaneously by contact with hot, dry, incoming air. A protective layer of dried milk solids remains around the bacteria and prevents their complete desiccation. Since drying is evaporation, and therefore is cooling, the bacteria are further protected from the high air temperatures. In addition, dry air is not as effective a bactericidal agent as is moist air. There are two distinct effects of drying. First, the heat causes the death of most microorganisms; and second, the dry cells remaining viable die slowly as a result of oxidative changes (15). When milk is dried by the roller process, about one vegetative cell in every 10,000 survives, but the survival rate is much higher when it is spray dried. Dried milks prepared by the latter method, therefore, usually have much greater total bacterial counts than milk dried by the roller method (7, 13).

*Packaging and Storage.* Spray dried and vacuum dried milks are hygroscopic, and they must be protected from moisture during packaging and storage. However, dried bacteria have been found to die at a greater rate in air, in the presence of increased moisture, and at higher temperatures. They die at a slower rate in atmospheres of carbon dioxide, hydrogen, or nitrogen, or *in vacuo.* Therefore, packing processes that protect dried milk from chemical changes and deterioration generally prevent the dried bacteria from dying at a rapid rate. Non-fat dry milk is packed in barrels with moisture-proof double liners, in metal and fiber drums, and in square-base metal containers (1, 12). Dry whole milk for export or for use in infant formulas is packed in tin containers in which the atmosphere has been replaced by an inert gas, in order to minimize the oxidative changes mentioned above. Some increases may occur in total bacterial numbers during filling operations owing to careless handling.

During storage the total bacterial count of roller dried milk decreases rapidly at first and then becomes relatively constant after 2 to 4 months. With spray dried milk the tendency for decreases in total bacterial numbers upon storage is less marked (7). Spore-formers and micrococci appear to survive the longest.

### INSPECTION OF THE FINISHED PRODUCTS

The dairy microbiologist is interested in the numbers and the kinds of microorganisms found in dry milks even though these organisms do not grow in the products. Dry milks, when marketed as such, are subject to pure food laws, but when reconstituted for resale, they must comply with state and local regulations. In addition, dry milks are combined with many foods sold in restaurants or hotels, and therefore they must be wholesome and free from objectionable microorganisms. As a basis for quality control, bacterial standards have been set up by both the American Dry Milk Institute, an industry trade group, and by the USDA. Dried milks are commonly examined by plating methods, and determinations of yeasts and molds, coliform bacteria, staphylococci (micrococci), and beta-hemolytic streptococci have been suggested (16).

Considerable research has been done to discover the factors influencing the growth of bacteria from dried milk when the plate method is used. The method of reconstitution will be considered first (8, 10, 21). The dilution blanks may be buffered water, N/10 lithium hydroxide, 1 per cent sodium citrate, or Ringer's solution. The last three are used if the powder is difficult to dissolve in water alone. Dispersing is done manually or by shaking machine with or without glass beads in the dilution bottle. The solubility of milk powder is greatest around 50°C. (122°F.). In addition, a good emulsion is obtained at this temperature, and the bacteria from the dried milk possibly are affected favorably in some way. Total bacterial counts are higher when reconstitution is done at around 50°C. (122°F.) than at room temperature. The total count also is higher when the milk is added to dilution blanks at 50°C. (122°F.) than when it is added to cold blanks and then warmed to 50°C. (122°F.). Ringer's solution and 1 per cent sodium citrate are less toxic to the bacteria than N/10 lithium hydroxide. The latter is toxic principally because of the rather extreme rise it causes in the pH of the reconstituted solution (21).

Another factor influencing the total counts is the temperature of incubation of the plates. Studies on spray dried milk show that the greatest differences in total counts occur between 35°C. and 37°C., (95°F. and 98.6°F.), but the highest counts are usually obtained at 30°C. (86°F.). The fact that many of the bacteria of milk have optimum temperatures lower than 35°C. (95°F.) would explain the higher counts at 30°C. (86°F.)— (8). Qualitative differences also have been noted. At 30°C. (86°F.) large numbers of microbacteria, and occasionally aerobic spore-formers, are found. This is most often true when the powders were made from milk preheated at around 73.9°C. (165°F.) and below. The microbacteria not only survive this preheating temperature, but they also grow well on plates incubated at 30°C. (86°F.) because this is their optimum temperature. With high preheating temperatures—88°C. (190°F.)—microbacteria are not found, regardless of the temperature of incubation of plates. Obviously, they do not withstand the more drastic treatment. If plates are routinely incubated at 37°C. (98.6°F.), the flora consists mainly of micrococci, aerobic spore-formers, and heat-resistant streptococci. The qualitative differences are usually less marked when high temperature preheated milk is examined. It has been suggested that plates be incubated at 30°C. (86°F.) for 5 days and a second set at 37°C. (98.6°F.) for 3 days (8) in order to obtain an accurate determination of the numbers and types of organisms present.

The types of organisms found in dried milks are also found as contaminants from utensils, air, and soil. They are capable of greater resistance to heating and drying and are thus selected out of the mixed population present before the preheating treatment. Occasionally, contamination of the feed tank may seed the products with large numbers of thermoduric or thermophilic bacteria. Low count milk powders result when good quality milk is used and when excellent plant sanitation conditions are maintained. In addition, lower total counts will be obtained on milk preheated to high temperatures (2). Total numbers range from a few hundred to a few thousand per gram for most powders. Since the microorganisms of dried milks are continually dying during storage, the products should be examined bacteriologically as soon after manufacturing as possible.

The presence of coliform bacteria in dried milks has the same significance as does their presence in other pasteurized products. The American Dry Milk Institute and USDA standards for premium grade dry whole milk require that the coliform estimate not exceed 90 per gram (5, 20). Beta-hemolytic streptococci may be pathogenic, but more likely such organisms would be harmless enterococci (Group D rather than Group A streptococci). These organisms may be tested for toxigenicity before potentially alarming reports are made. The same may be said for staphylococci (micrococci). Molds may be indicative either of excessive air contamination or of poor handling of the dried product.

Microorganisms found in dried milks may cause defects in products made from them. In the baking industry bread sometimes becomes ropy. The cut surfaces of ropy bread have a strong odor similar to overripe or decomposed melons. The center is soft and has a brownish discoloration. Softened portions of the bread can be drawn out in threads 4 to 6 inches in length. *Bacillus subtilis* has been found in such defects, and dried milks may be a source of the organisms. A total spore count might be useful to apply to dried milks destined for use by the baking industry. This may be done by reconstituting the sample and placing it in a boiling water bath for 5 minutes. The sample is plated and then incubated at both 35°C. and 55°C. (95°F. and 131°F.), and the aerobic spore-formers are enumerated.

In the manufacture of process cheese a gassy defect accompanied by a penetrating putrefactive odor has been described. Some batches of non-fat dry milk may contain spores of *Clostridium sporogenes,* a causative agent of this defect. Some cases of process cheese spoilage have been reported in which this organism has been implicated.

### RECONSTITUTED DRY MILK

Reconstituted non-fat dry milk has been used for propagation of starter cultures and for the manufacture of cultured milks, and some problems have arisen from this practice. If the non-fat dry milk is made from poor quality raw milk, inhibitory substances such as residual antibiotics may be present that prevent starter cultures from exhibiting maximum activity. Certain inhibitory substances produced as a result of bacterial growth in the milk prior to drying also may be present. Total plate counts on reconstituted milk powders generally are low. Yeasts usually are not found, but mold spores, presumably entering after processing and during packaging, may be present. As stated above, coliform bacteria, beta-hemolytic streptococci, staphylococci (micrococci), microbacteria, and aerobic spore-formers may be present in various samples. High temperature treated powders may yield a reconstituted product that shows a tendency toward proteolysis and off-flavors instead of souring. This is due to the almost complete removal of the lactic acid producing flora and of the proteolytic characteristics of the remaining flora, particularly the aerobic spore-formers

It has been reported that reconstituted spray dried milk showed little increase in total numbers when held at 15.5°C. (59.9°F.) for 24 hours, but holding at 22°C. (71.6°F.) resulted in a two thousand-fold increase in total numbers and holding at 37°C. (98.6°F.) caused the milk to clot. In each case *Streptococcus fecalis* was among the predominant organisms as were pigmented micrococci and aerobic spore-formers (9).

Among the factors affecting the bacterial count and flavor of reconstituted dry milks are the temperature of recombination, type of water (chlorinated or not), sanitary condition of the utensils, and consumer practice. It has been found (14) that water at a temperature of 23.9°C. (75°F.) when used for recombination had little effect on the bacterial count or flavor of dry whole milk held at 1.67°C. (35°F.) or 10°C. (50°F.) for 48 hours. Water supplies may contain spoilage organisms even though coliform bacteria are absent, and in any event, chlorinated supplies should be used for reconstitution. When non-fat dry milk was reconstituted and held at 10°C. (50°F.) for 48 to 72 hours, total counts of several million per milliliter were commonly found. There seems to be little or no relationship between keeping quality and numbers of bacteria in reconstituted milk, since many of the surviving species of microorganisms are physiologically inert in milk or develop only slowly. There is no close correlation between the flavor of the original milk and that of the milk reconstituted from the powder, and in general, the processing treatment has a greater effect on the flavor than does the flavor of the original milk.

### BACTERIAL STANDARDS

The American Dry Milk Institute (5, 6) has recommended standards for dry milks. There are two grades of non-fat dry milk, "Extra" and "Standard." If the product is to receive a grade of "Extra," the total bacterial count must not exceed 50,000 per gram regardless of whether drying is done by the spray, or vacuum, or atmospheric roller methods. If the product is to receive a grade of "Standard," the total bacterial count must not exceed 100,000 per gram. The total plate count must be performed as recommended by the American Public Health Association (16). It should be pointed out that in addition to bacterial standards the American Dry Milk Institute has requirements for titratable acidity, solubility, and scorched particles on the reconstituted sample.

There are standards for each of three types of processing of dry whole milk. Gas packed, spray process must have a total bacterial count not exceeding 30,000 per gram and a coliform count not exceeding 90 per gram to be graded "Premium," or 50,000 per gram to be graded "Extra." Bulk spray process dry whole milk must have a total bacterial count not exceeding 50,000 per gram to be graded "Extra," or 100,000 per gram to be graded "Standard." Finally, bulk roller process dry whole milk must have a total bacterial count not exceeding 50,000 per gram to be graded "Extra" or 100,000 per gram to be graded "Standard." In addition various chemical and physical requirements must be met with regard to such things as the copper and iron content, color, titratable acidity, solubility index, and the flavor and odor of the reconstituted sample.

Dry whole milk or non-fat dry milk not meeting the requirements for the "Standard" grade are ungraded unless they have flavors or odors indicative of decomposition or neutralization, or if they fail to meet the general requirements for these products. In such instances they are termed "unfit for human consumption."

The USDA standards for "U. S. Extra" grade spray or roller dried non-fat dry milk (17) require a total bacterial count of not more than 50,000 per gram or 100,000 per gram if the product is to be graded "U. S. Standard." Neither the USDA nor the American Dry Milk Institute has proposed coliform standards for non-fat dry milk.

The USDA standards for "U. S. Premium" grade spray dried whole milk (20) require a total bacterial count of not more than 30,000 per gram and a coliform count of not more than 90 per gram. If the product is to be graded "U. S. Extra," the total bacterial count must not exceed 50,000 per gram. If it is to be graded "U. S. Standard," the total count must not be more than 100,000 per gram. For the latter two grades there are no coliform standards.

Spray or roller dried buttermilk (19) must have a total bacterial count not exceeding 50,000 per gram to receive a grade of "U. S. Extra" or not exceeding 200,000 per gram to be graded "U. S. Standard." The USDA standards for spray dried whey require a total bacterial count not exceeding 50,000 per gram for grading as "U. S. Extra" (18). Like the American Dry Milk Institute, the USDA has a number of chemical and physical requirements for each grade.

# References

1. Cook, H. L., and G. H. Day, *The Dry Milk Industry.* Chicago: American Dry Milk Institute, 1947.

2. Crossley, E. L., Spray-dried milk powder. Commercial observations over two years of the effect of high temperature pre-heating, *J. Dairy Research,* 14 (1945): 160–164.

3. ———, The microbiology of sweetened condensed milk. *XIIth International Dairy Congress, Papers and Communications,* 2, II (1949): 438–444.

4. Federal and state standards for the composition of milk products, *USDA Agriculture Handbook No. 51,* 1953.

5. The grading of dry whole milk and sanitary and quality standards including standard methods of analysis, *Bull. 913,* Revised. Chicago: American Dry Milk Institute, 1955.

6. The grading of non-fat dry milk solids and sanitary and quality standards including methods of analysis, *Bull. 911,* Revised. Chicago: American Dry Milk Institute, 1954.

7. Higginbottom, C., Bacteriological studies of roller-dried milk powders, roller-dried buttermilk and of roller- and spray-dried whey, *J. Dairy Research,* 13 (1944): 308–323.

8. ———, The technique of the bacteriological examination of dried milks, *J. Dairy Research,* 14 (1945): 184–194.

9. ———, Bacterial growth in reconstituted spray-dried milk, *J. Dairy Research,* 15 (1948): 285–291.

10. Hiscox, E. R., The effect of the method of reconstitution and of the temperature of incubation on the plate count of dried milk powder, *J. Dairy Research,* 14 (1945): 175–183.

11. Holm, G. E., Dried milks, USDA, BDIM-Inf-25, Washington, D. C., 1949.

12. Hunziker, O. F., *Condensed Milk and Milk Powder,* 7th Ed. LaGrange, Ill.: Published by the author, 1949.

13. Nichols, A. A., Bacteriological studies of spray-dried milk powder, *J. Dairy Research,* 10 (1939): 202–230.

14. Olson, J. C., Jr., and A. J. Nielsen, Changes in bacterial counts and flavor of dry milks after recombination by various means and storage at low temperatures, *J. Dairy Sci.*, 38 (1955): 361–370.

15. Rahn, O., Physical methods of sterilization of microorganisms, *Bacteriol. Revs.*, 9 (1945): 1–47.

16. *Standard Methods for the Examination of Dairy Products*, 10th Ed. New York: American Public Health Association, 1953.

17. United States standards for grades of non-fat dry milk solids. *Federal Register*, 18 (1953): 2663–2665.

18. United States standards for dry whey. *Federal Register*, 19 (1954): 3349–3351.

19. United States standards for grades of dry buttermilk. *Federal Register*, 19 (1954): 3955–3957.

20. United States standards for grades of dry whole milk. *Federal Register*, 19 (1954): 4899–4902.

21. White, A. H., Dilution procedures for plate counts on dry milks, *Sci. Agr.*, 32 (1952): 19–25.

# 10

## Microbiology of ice cream and related frozen products

These products are among the few foods consumed in the frozen state, and certainly they are among the most popular foods in the American diet. Ice cream generally means a pure, clean, frozen product made from various milk products, dry or liquid forms of glucose, sucrose or corn sugar, and water. It generally contains an edible flavoring; and it may, or may not, include an edible coloring, some egg products, and an added stabilizer composed of wholesome edible material (23). Quantitatively, ice cream contains from 8 to 14 per cent fat; 8 to 12 per cent milk solids-not-fat; 12 to 17 per cent sugar; and small but varying amounts of stabilizer, egg yolks, fruits, nuts, candy, colors, and flavors. State standards for ice cream vary considerably (12).

Ice cream and related frozen products have been classified on the basis of composition into the following categories: plain, nut, fruit, mousse, bisque, puddings, custards, ices, sherbets, specials, and novelties. Ice milk is an ice cream-like product (not legal in some states) that contains about 4 per cent fat, 12 to 14 per cent milk solids-not-fat, and approximately the same amount of sugar and stabilizer as ice cream. Frozen custards are products (including parfait, French ice cream, French custard ice cream, ice custard, and New York ice cream) that contain a large amount of whole eggs or egg yolk. Sherbets are composed of milk or ice cream mix, fruit juices, sugar, color, fruit flavoring, stabilizer, and citric or other edible acids. Sherbet made using starter cultures is known as lacto, and when egg yolks are added, it is known as a soufflé (23). Most of the statements made about ice cream in this chapter also will apply to the various frozen dairy foods as well. It can be seen that ice cream is a complex food prepared from several derived dairy products, that is, products that have been manufactured from whole milk. Among these are cream, sweetened condensed skimmilk, non-fat dry milk, butter oil, and 80 per cent or "plastic" cream. Ice cream has a number of microbiological aspects peculiar to itself, and a study of some of these will provide an insight into the wide range of problems encountered by the dairy microbiologist.

## MICROBIOLOGY OF ICE CREAM INGREDIENTS

*Cream.* Many cities and states have no bacterial standards for raw or pasteurized cream. Where standards do exist, they are generally twice as high as those for whole milk. States and cities having bacterial standards for pasteurized cream show ranges of variation from 5,000 to over 100,000 per milliliter for the maximum allowable total bacterial count (8).

Some ice cream still is made from cream with high total bacterial counts, and such cream may be the chief dairy product source of bacteria in ice cream. A lenient standard would not allow the use of pasteurized cream as an ice cream ingredient if the total plate count exceeded 100,000 per gram (14). The best ice cream is made only from sweet and unneutralized cream, since this has obviously not been subjected to bacterial action. If this cream has off-flavors from feeds or from chemical or microbial activity, these off-flavors often will be reflected in the finished product. Frozen cream, plastic cream, and reconstituted cream also have been used in ice cream manufacture. Plastic cream is cream with a fat content of 79 to 81 per cent obtained by separating milk, at pasteurizing temperature, in a special separator. Methods used for determining the bacteriological quality of milk also are used for fluid cream (27).

*Condensed and dry milk products.* These ingredients are used to give ice cream the required amount of milk solids. Microbiological examination of these products has been considered in Chapter 9. A lenient standard would limit the maximum bacterial count on these products, if they are to be used in ice cream manufacture, to less than 50,000 per gram as determined by total plate count (14). Thermoduric or thermophilic organisms may be the undesirable contaminants introduced when these products are used. Condensed products should be protected from contamination, and they should be adequately covered and stored in the ice cream plant in a manner that will prevent entrance of insects, bacteria, and mold spores. Dry milk products must be stored in rooms of low humidity that are free from insect and dust contamination, and during storage, the products should be tightly covered.

*Sugar and sweetening agents.* A number of substances are used as sweetening agents in the manufacture of ice cream. Among them are sucrose, invert syrup, corn and cane sugars, and honey. There is a rapidly growing trend toward the use of corn and cane liquid sweeteners in ice cream manufacture. Solutions of 65 per cent sugar solids can be delivered by tank car or truck to the processor and can then be stored in stainless steel tanks. The use of liquid sweeteners facilitates the handling of mix in continuous HTST units. In addition, a liquid can be more easily and exactly measured in quantity. Liquid sugar and blends of liquid and corn syrup now available to processors have good physical properties and keeping qualities. Precautions must be taken to prevent contamination of these sweeteners with molds and osmophilic yeasts. If liquid sugar is stored in tanks where condensation is prevented and where a positive air pressure is maintained, it will keep for months. If condensation forms as a thin film of dilute liquid sugar, any yeasts that are present may grow. Sweetening agents usually are not highly contaminated, but the degree of contamination is dependent upon the methods of production and upon storage conditions. Sweeteners should have low total counts when examined by the agar plate method. Most samples of sucrose have total bacterial counts of less than 20 per gram and should not exceed 200 per gram (28). The flora of sugar and sweetening agents reflects to some degree the care used in manufacture and, subsequently, the amount of protection from contamination accorded the finished product. Since the addition of certain groups of organisms to ice cream mix is unfavorable from the point of view of both the manufacturer and the public health official, a number of tests have been devised to detect undesirable organisms in sweetening agents. Among these undesirable organisms are aerobic, mesophilic, and thermophilic non-acid producers, anaerobic thermophilic hydrogen sulfide and non-hydrogen sulfide producers (1), yeasts and molds, and coliform bacteria. Most of these determinations are of interest primarily to canners, but the results give an indication of the sanitary quality of the sugar.

The standards of the National Canners Association (1) require that 5 samples of 10 g each be examined from a lot of sugar. To be acceptable, no sample can have a total thermophilic spore count in excess of 150 and the average for all 5 samples can be no more than 125 per 10 g; no sample can contain more than 75 flat sour spores and the average cannot exceed 50 per 10 g; not more than 3 (60 per cent) of the 5 samples can contain thermophilic anaerobes, and in any one sample not more than 4 (65 per cent) of the tubes can be positive; and not more than 2 (40 per cent) of the 5 samples can contain spores of sulphide spoilage organisms, and from any 10 g sample there can be no more than 5 colonies. Tentative standards for "bottler's" sugar require not more than 200 mesophilic bacteria, 10 yeasts, and 10 molds per 10 g of sugar (28).

*Stabilizers.* The purpose of stabilizers is to maintain a smooth body and texture in the finished ice cream by preventing the appearance of large ice crystals and to avoid churning of the fat during freezing. Sodium alginate, ground Irish moss, cellulose gum, locust bean gum, karaya gum, gelatin, and mono- and di-glycerides are examples of substances that have been used as stabilizers. Usually they are ground to fine powders that dissolve when added to the mix, or at least before the mix is pasteurized. Gelatin has been found to have bacterial counts varying from 10 to 100,000 per gram. Most samples have low total bacterial counts, which in any event should not exceed 10,000 per gram, and the yeast and mold count should not exceed 100 per gram (14). Most of the organisms are destroyed by proper pasteurization or by the heating required to dissolve the stabilizer. Many of the organisms in gelatin are aerobic spore-formers. Counts of bacteria, coliform bacteria, and yeasts and molds are the usual determinations made on stabilizers (27). These tests reveal the degree of unsanitary handling given to both the raw and the manufactured products and may be used as an index of general sanitation. There are no official standards for these determinations at the present time.

*Fruits and nuts.* These constituents may be important con-taminants of ice cream, especially since they are added after the mix has been pasteurized and therefore are not subject to heat treatment as is the rest of the mix. Fresh fruits are likely to increase the total bacterial counts, the extent of increase depending upon the nature of the fruit and the con-ditions of handling. In some cases fruits are given a bactericidal treatment before being added to the mix. Fruits used are of many different kinds—fresh, ripe, unripe, frozen, preserved, dried, candied, cold and hot packed, sterilized—and standards for each style and for each kind of fruit would be difficult to prepare (7). Microbiological grading would increase the num-ber of grades already in existence for fruits. In addition to increasing cost, there is the question of when the fruits would be graded, that is, on the vine or in the can. Finally, there would have to be enforcement agencies established, and this would give rise to even further problems of training and techniques. It should be remembered that many fruits are fragile and difficult to process or to free from microorganisms without destroying their delicate flavors. Contamination from pickers, handlers, soil, insects, and water is unavoidable. Despite this, the processor ought to take all precau-tions possible to ensure the use of wholesome raw materials and to see that these are prepared with careful handling. When frozen fruits are thawed, it is important to prevent contamination and subsequent growth of micro-organisms in the defrosted product. Fruit dealers supplying canned products (viz., pineapple) rely on sugar packing or on boiling in sugar solu-tions to preserve the products. Some fruits are treated with sulfur dioxide or with methyl bromide.

Nuts may be sterilized in cans that are not hermetically sealed through use of a mixture (1 to 9 or 2 to 8) of ethylene oxide and carbon dioxide (16). The cans are kept in special chambers for several hours, after which the gas mixture is flushed out. Insects, yeasts, molds, and bacteria are killed by this treatment, and the nuts should then be stored in sealed containers in the cold until used. They can also be dipped in boiling sugar solutions (50 per cent) and dried in an oven at 250°C. (482°F.) for a few minutes before use (29).

In addition to the total plate counts, fruits and nuts may be examined for the presence of coliform bacteria, beta-hemolytic streptococci, and yeasts and molds (27). The presence of coliforms is used as an indication of human, soil, utensil, or water contamination. Beta-hemolytic streptococci may be present as a result of contamination from human sources. Yeasts and molds to some extent indicate the degree of ripeness in fruits and nuts. Standards have not been adopted for these determinations as yet.

*Colors and flavors.* Aqueous solutions of colors sometimes add large numbers of microorganisms to ice cream (29). As with fruit and nuts, colors and flavors are added after pasteurization of the mix and therefore cause difficulty if they are heavily contaminated. Colors may be especially bad in this regard, for they are occasionally allowed to remain for some time at room temperature, as diluted and unused solutions, in contaminated containers. Only enough color for immediate needs should be prepared, and in addition, many colors may be dissolved in boiling water or sugar solutions or they may be pasteurized. Alcoholic solutions have low total counts, and dry colors have lower total counts than liquid colors (29). Flavors usually have low total bacterial counts owing to the presence of alcohol in many of them. Colors and flavors may be examined microbiologically by means of the agar plate count, coliform determination, beta-hemolytic streptococcus determination, and yeast and mold count (27). Standards for these determinations have not yet been adopted.

*Egg products.* These may be important sources of bacteria in ice cream. Egg yolks are obtained in fresh, frozen, or powdered forms. Total bacterial counts should not exceed 10,000 per gram by the agar plate method (14). They may be examined for total count, coliform bacteria, fungi, putrefactive anaerobes, beta-hemolytic streptococci, and species of *Salmonella* (27). Standards for these determinations have not yet been adopted.

PROCESSING ICE CREAM MIX

The flow-sheet in Figure 10.1 shows the route of ice cream mix from mixing tank to consumer, and it should be studied in connection with the following discussion.

*Mixing.* Materials used in ice cream mix are placed in a mixing vat or pasteurizer. Usually the order of addition is as follows: (a) cream, (b) milk, (c) concentrated milk, and (d) solid ingredients. Sugar is added when the liquid reaches about 43.3°C. (110°F.). Stabilizers may be added with the sugar, although some kinds cannot be added until a temperature of 65.6°C. (150°F.) is attained. Plastic cream, butter, frozen cream, and similar products should be comminuted before being placed in the vat. Complete thawing and dispersion must be obtained before the pasteurization temperature is reached. The microorganisms carried in each ingredient plus those of the equipment will now be in the mix. Additional contamination from careless handling by operators may increase the "load" on the pasteurization process.

*Pasteurizing.* The primary purpose of pasteurization is to destroy all pathogenic microorganisms that might be present in the mix. Heating results in a reduction of the total numbers of bacteria, thorough

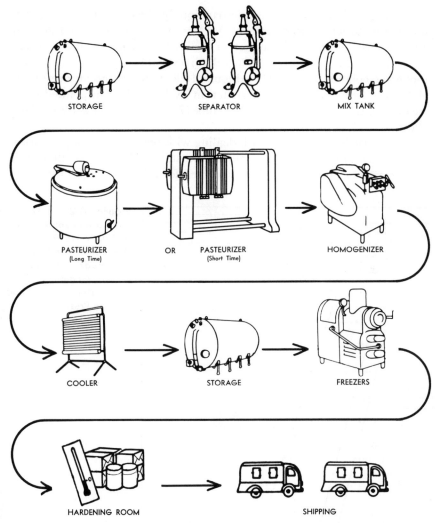

STORAGE                    SEPARATOR                    MIX TANK

PASTEURIZER          OR          PASTEURIZER                    HOMOGENIZER
(Long Time)                      (Short Time)

COOLER                    STORAGE                    FREEZERS

HARDENING ROOM                              SHIPPING

**Figure 10.1**    Flow sheet for ice cream manufacture. Courtesy Dairy Industries Supply Association, Inc., Washington, D. C.

mixing of the ingredients, dispersion of stabilizers, and in physico-chemical effects on the milk solids that are related to whipping ability and to body and texture of the ice cream. Heating is mandatory prior to homogeniza-tion. It is obvious from this that, even if raw mix were sterile, some heat treatment would be necessary to produce satisfactory ice cream. Higher pasteurization temperatures than for milk are required because of the pro-tection afforded the microorganisms by the sugar and the increased milk solids present in ice cream mix. Hypertonic solutions of glucose and sucrose made up in broth, milk, water, or ice cream mix have been found to afford protection to bacteria against destruction by heat when compared to survival in aqueous suspensions (11). Generally, a concentrated medium interferes with heat penetration, other factors being equal. It has been suggested that sugar probably prevents the irreversible agglomeration of protoplasmic colloids by heat (11). Figure 10.2 shows the greater resistance of *Micrococcus freudenreichii* to destruction by heat when suspended in ice cream mix than when suspended in milk (24). Other species are similarly affected.

Until 1930, most of the work dealing with the adequacy of pasteurization was confined to milk. Pasteurization standards for other fluid milk products generally followed those specified for milk, although in some in-

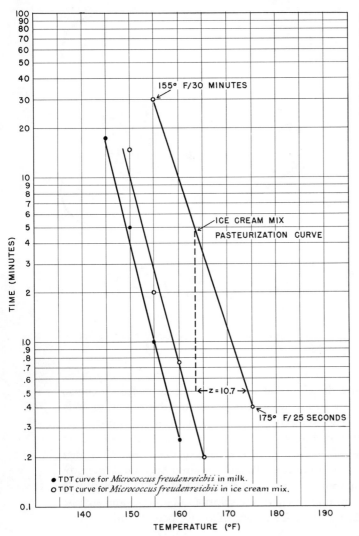

**Figure 10.2** Ice cream mix pasteurization curve, and TDT curve (99 per cent destruction) for *Micrococcus freudenreichii* in milk and ice cream mix. Courtesy *J. Dairy Science* and Science Press.

stances, as in the case of ice cream mix and cream, somewhat higher heat treatments were specified because of the greater solids content. Oldenbusch et al. (21) apparently were the first to determine the effect of heat on the destruction of pathogens in ice cream mix. Their studies, which also included cream, showed that *Mycobacterium tuberculosis* suspended in ice cream mix was destroyed in 6 minutes at 62.6°C. (145°F.). Less severe heat treatment was required for the destruction of *Salmonella typhosa, Corynebacterium diphtheriae,* and 2 cultures of pathogenic beta-hemolytic streptococci. Similar results were obtained for these same organisms when suspended in cream, although their heat resistance did not appear to be as great in cream as in ice cream mix. On the basis of this work, the Committee on Dairy Products and Eggs of the American Public Health Association concluded that an ample margin of safety was afforded by pasteurization of cream and ice cream mix at 62°C. (143.5°F.) for 30 minutes. Previously, it had been a common practice for ice cream manufacturers to use heat treatments much more severe than those used for the pasteurization of milk, although very few laws or ordinances existed at the time that stated specific pasteurization requirements for ice cream mix. This tendency toward the use of greater heat treatment has continued, and, at present, the standard of 68.3°C. (155°F.) for 30 minutes is quite common in various regulations and ordinances (8). The difficulty in meeting maximum bacterial count standards when lower heat treatments are used and the better quality ice cream that results are the primary reasons for use of these higher heat treatments.

The commercial use of HTST pasteurization of ice cream mix was reported in 1943 (9). Experimental work actually was begun about 1941 at the University of Connecticut. Certain engineering problems and lack of information with respect to the efficiency of bacterial destruction in ice cream mix when subjected for short intervals of time to temperatures above 73.9°C. (165°F.) were the principal reasons for the delay in the application of this process to ice cream mix. The desire of many ice cream manufacturers to use an HTST method presented public health officials with the problem of establishing proper temperature and time standards for use in such a process. Such standards should not only insure the destruction of any pathogenic bacteria that might be present, but should also provide for the destruction of other bacteria present to an extent comparable to that of the LTLT method, 68.3°C. (155°F.) for 30 minutes. A number of studies have been made to determine the temperature-time relationships that would result in bacterial destruction equivalent to that obtained at 68.3°C. (155°F.) for 30 minutes. Reviews of several of these studies (3, 25) are available.

In 1950 the temperature-time relationship of 79.3°C. (175°F.) for 25 seconds was provisionally established by the United States Public Health Service for HTST pasteurization of ice cream mix. In 1953 this standard was announced as an amendment to the definition of "pasteurization" contained in the *Frozen Desserts Ordinance and Code* (14). The final adoption of this standard was based on a number of studies by different investigators. Table 10.1 shows results of one study (26), results that are typical of those on which the adoption of the HTST standard was based. From the standpoint of public health significance, the data shown in Table 10.1 pertaining to *Micrococcus* sp. (No. MS–102) are of particular interest. This culture had been shown to possess much greater heat resistance than *Mycobacterium tuberculosis* or *Brucella abortus,* the two most heat-resistant bacterial pathogens likely to be present in milk. Since the heat destruction of the test micrococcus after approximately 20 seconds at 79.3°C. (175°F.) was essentially that which occurred at 68.3°C (155°F.) for 30 minutes, it is obvious that 79.3°C. (175°F.) for 25 seconds provides an adequate margin of safety insofar as the destruction of bacterial pathogens is concerned. Since *Mycobacterium tuberculosis* also is killed in 5 minutes at 68.3°C. (155°F.), it can be seen that a sixfold margin of safety is provided by pasteurizing at this temperature for 30 minutes. Since pasteurization at 79.3°C. (175°F.) for 25 seconds is at least equivalent to 68.3°C. (155°F.) for 30 minutes, a similar margin of safety is obtained in this process.

Considerable interest has been shown in the pasteurization of ice cream mix at temperatures well above 79.3°C. (175°F.). In addition to the above work, other studies (2, 30, 31) have shown that bacterial destruction in ice cream mix after exposure at 88°C. (190°F.) and above for short intervals of time (less than 2 seconds) is equivalent or superior to that obtained at 68.3°C. (155°F.) for 30 minutes. It should be mentioned at this point that errors inherent in the measurement of such short intervals of time make it extremely difficult to determine holding time accurately. An error that would be insignificant in the determination of a relatively long exposure time at a low temperature might be quite significant in the de-

**Table 10.1** Pasteurization times required at various temperatures to obtain the same bacterial destruction in ice cream mix as is obtained at 155°F. for 30 minutes *

| TEMPERATURE | *MICROBACTERIUM* Sp. (No. 342–S–1) | | *MICROCOCCUS* Sp. (No. MS–102) | |
|---|---|---|---|---|
| (°F.) | OBSERVED ** (*sec.*) | RECOMMENDED † (*sec.*) | OBSERVED ** (*sec.*) | RECOMMENDED † (*sec.*) |
| 175 | 16.0±0.3 | 16.5 | 19.9±0.7 | 21.2 |
| 180 | 11.0±0.2 | 11.4 | 11.4±0.2 | 11.8 |
| 185 | 6.4±0.05 | 6.5 | 7.1±0.05 | 7.2 |
| 190 | .25±0.01 | .27 | .94±0.03 | .99 |

* Data taken from Speck et al. (26). Courtesy *J. Dairy Sci.* and the Garrard Press.
** Mean observed in seconds with standard error of the mean.
† Mean plus standard error of mean x Student's one-tailed t taken at the 5 per cent level.

termination of exposure time at a high temperature. For example, assuming a bacterial TDT curve having a $z$ value of 10.7 (see Chapter 4 for definitions of TDT and $z$), an error of $\pm 0.5$ second would be insignificant in a TDT stated as 60 minutes at 68.3°C. (155°F.); however, if this same error of 0.5 second was made in the determination of a TDT stated to be 2 seconds at 87.8°C. (190°F.), it would be quite significant, for the equivalent of such an error at 68.3°C. (155°F.) would be approximately $\pm 15$ minutes. Because of the difficulties involved in accurately measuring exposure times at high temperature in commercial equipment, it is justifiable to require, by regulation, exposure times somewhat in excess of those actually necessary as determined experimentally.

Figure 10.2 shows a logarithmic curve drawn through the points represented by 68.3°C. (155°F.) for 30 minutes and 79.3°C. (175°F.) for 25 seconds. The slope of this curve expressed as $z$ value is 10.7. The experimental data that are available on the temperature-time relationships for heat killing above 79.3°C. (175°F.) for 25 seconds indicate that bacterial destruction equivalent to 68.3°C. (155°F.) for 30 minutes is obtained. This is in accord with the values indicated by the curve in Figure 10.2.

Among the various pieces of equipment used for HTST pasteurization of ice cream mix, the Vacreator and the Ste-Vac heater are common. The mix is heated in a forewarmer to 65.8°C. (150°F.) and is then homogenized at 2,500 pounds per square inch. It is then pumped to the Vacreator. This consists of 3 connected vacuum chambers and an ejector-condensor. Steam is introduced with the mix in the first chamber at a 6½ to 11 inch vacuum. The mix is then passed to 2 more chambers in which increasingly higher vacua and lower temperatures (20 inches in the second and 28 inches vaccum in the third) are applied. For example, the first chamber may heat the mix to 92.2°C. (198°F.), the second cools it to 71.1°C. (160°F.), and the third to 37.8°C. (100°F.). The progressive increase in vacuum results in the two-stage temperature drop, and the excess heat is dissipated in a process of differential distillation. Very low total counts on the pasteurized mix are obtained. Pasteurization after homogenization leads to even lower final counts and negates the effect of any contamination from the homogenizer.

The Ste-Vac heater is a continuous flow device of the tubular type designed to heat milk or mix in two stages, with a period of holding between them. The mix is taken from the balance tank and is pumped through a filter and through the first tubes of the heater where the temperature is raised to 71.1°C. (160°F.). It is then homogenized (see next section) and is returned to the heater where a temperature of 80°C. (176°F.) is attained in the last tubes of the heater. From here the mix goes to a holding tube where it is exposed to the pasteurizing temperature for the required time.

Mix that is pasteurized properly usually will give total bacterial counts of 10,000 or less per gram. Table 10.2 shows the effect of various pasteurization temperatures on a highly contaminated mix (32). The total

**Table 10.2** Effect of high-temperature-short-time (175°F.—25 sec.) pasteurization on the natural flora of ice cream mix *

STANDARD PLATE COUNT

| Time and Temperature | Batch 1 | | Batch 2 | | Batch 3 | | Batch 4 | |
|---|---|---|---|---|---|---|---|---|
| | Raw Count** | Pasteurized Count | Raw Count** | Pasteurized Count | Raw Count** | Pasteurized Count | Raw Count** | Pasteurized Count |
| 175°F., 25 sec. | 1,060,000 | 25,000 | 94,000 | 3,750 | 1,550,000 | 20,800 | 35,900,000 | 43,500 |
| 155°F., 30 min. | 1,060,000 | 27,000 | 94,000 | 3,250 | 1,550,000 | 9,800 | 35,900,000 | 25,500 |
| 160°F., 30 min. | 1,060,000 | 6,000 | 94,000 | 1,730 | 1,550,000 | 9,100 | 35,900,000 | 25,000 |
| | | | COLIFORM COUNT † | | | | | |
| 175°F., 25 sec. | 2,350 | 0 | — | — | 0 | 0 | 99,000 | 0 |
| 155°F., 30 min. | 2,350 | 0 | — | — | 0 | 0 | 99,000 | 0 |
| 160°F., 30 min. | 2,350 | 0 | — | — | 0 | 0 | 99,000 | 0 |

* Data taken from Tracy (32). Courtesy International Association of Ice Cream Manufacturers and P. H. Tracy.

** The raw count represents the count after preheating to 140°F. and homogenization.

† Violet Red Bile Agar.

count is lowest at the completion of this operation. Condensates, pumps used for mix after pasteurization, coolers, and pipelines from pasteurizing equipment may be important sources of post-pasteurization contamination. Many times coliform bacteria are introduced into the ice cream from these sources. Vat covers and hinges must be so constructed that nothing on them will drop into the vat regardless of whether they are open or closed. If covers are not made to prevent dust or condensates from entering the mix, contamination will take place, possibly with disease organisms. In addition, closed vat covers prevent the entrance of flies, dust, droplets, drip, and splash into the mix.

*Homogenizing.* Homogenizers pump liquids such as milk and ice cream mix through narrow slits, known as valves, at pressures up to 5,000 pounds per square inch. Usually three cylinders are used on homogenizers to insure an even pressure and flow of liquid. This process serves a number of purposes in the manufacture of ice cream. Among these are prevention of churning of butterfat during freezing, improvement of body and texture, and reduction of aging time. Homogenization is carried out at about 66°C. (150°F.) and at 2,000 to 2,500 pounds per square inch pressure, and the milk fat globules are broken down to spheres not over $2\mu$ in diameter. The pressure has little effect on microorganisms. Since the mix is forced through small apertures at high pressure, bacterial clumps are broken up, and an increase in total count may be observed. The homogenizer must be kept clean and sanitized, or it may contribute to post-pasteurization contamination of the mix. After being used, the homogenizer should be rinsed throughout with tepid water. All valves, pistons, cylinders, parts, and pipes should be scrubbed with a hot solution of washing powder, and then rinsed, and allowed to dry. Packing nuts on certain older types of homogenizer must be removed so that the packing glands around pistons may be thoroughly washed and rinsed of residual mix. If it is carelessly cleaned, the homogenizer may be a very important source of coliform and other bacterial contamination.

*Cooling.* After it passes through the homogenizer, the mix flows over a surface cooler or through a tubular or plate cooler and cools rapidly to 4.4°C. (40°F.) or below. Small increases in total count may result from contaminants on the cooler. The sudden decrease in temperature has little effect on the bacteria in the mix.

*Aging.* This step formerly required 1 to 3 days but now, depending on the stabilizer used, only a few hours are needed. The aging of ice cream mix affords an opportunity for the adsorption of protein on fat globules. The actual physical and chemical changes brought about by aging are unknown, but hydration of proteins and stabilizer may be involved. The effects of aging on body, texture, and "whippability" of ice cream mix also are poorly understood. There is little change in total count unless additional contaminants are introduced from the vats used for aging. Sixteen to 24 hours at 4.4°C. (40°F.) has little effect on the total bacterial count of ice cream mix. It has been found (19) that the bacterial count of ice cream mix stored at 4.4°C. (40°F.) or above increases with storage time and may reach considerable magnitude (millions per milliliter) as the storage temperature increases. Coliform bacteria also may increase in numbers in ice cream mix held at 8°C. (46.4°F.) or above. This increase may give rise to false conclusions relative to post-pasteurization contamination. It is better to store frozen ice cream rather than unfrozen mix in order to avoid such complications.

*Freezing.* Freezing of the mix generally occurs at −6.11°C. to −3.89°C. (21°F. to 25°F.). The mix is frozen in 20- to 160-quart batch freezers or in continuous freezers. The mix is frozen to the proper stiffness and whipped to the desired overrun by incorporation of air. During the latter phases of the freezing process colors, flavors, fruits, and nuts are introduced. The frozen, whipped mix then is withdrawn for packaging. The total bacterial count of the ice cream may be increased by contaminants introduced from the equipment and especially from the disintegration of bacteria clumps during the operation. Probably few organisms are killed by the freezing process itself. When operations are completed, freezers should be filled with cold water, and the blades should be rotated several times. This operation should be repeated several times, using increasingly warm water to 62.6°C. (145°F.). Washing powder in water at 62.6°C. (145°F.) should then be added, and the freezer blades should again be rotated momentarily. Next, the exterior of the freezer, hopper, and strainer should be cleaned with washing powder solution and a brush. Finally, the freezer itself should be drained, and the head and dasher assembly should be removed and brushed in the washing solution. The freezer is then reassembled, and water at 82.2°C. (180°F.) is added and is allowed to remain for 2 minutes.

A solution containing a 200 ppm hypochlorite, or a quaternary compound, may be used instead of the hot water, but hot water is helpful in that it facilitates the drying of the freezer after draining. After the freezer is drained, the gate should be allowed to remain open. Before being used again, the hopper and freezer should be rinsed with 200 ppm of a germicidal solution. CIP procedures lend themselves well to sanitization of ice cream plant equipment. In the case of continuous freezers, rotary seals, and rotors are removed from mix and ice cream pumps, together with the gauges and air valve assembly. All openings are closed with neoprene stoppers. The principle is to remove all dead ends in order to provide a continuous closed circuit to the solution tank. The system is first rinsed with water at 43.3°C. to 48.9°C. (110°F. to 120°F.), which is discharged into a drain. After the rinse water runs clear, the system is drained, and all valves and valve seats are washed manually and positioned. Pumps, freezer parts, valves, homogenizer parts, sanitary piping, and similar apparatus are placed in stainless steel baskets in the solution tank. Cleaning solution containing one pound of general purpose cleaner, 4 ounces of sodium hypochlorite, and 50 gallons of water at 51.7°C. (125°F.) is circulated through the system for 20 minutes. Chlorinated cleansers are also available for use in this operation. During the circulation period the outsides of pipelines and equipment are washed. After the circulation period the system is rinsed with water at 46.1°C. to 48.9°C. (115°F. to 120°F.) until traces of chlorine are removed. The system is then drained at the low points, the freezer heads being opened to allow complete drainage. Each day a different section is inspected, and once a week the entire system is dismantled for inspection and regasketing. The equipment is rinsed with 200 ppm germicidal solution prior to use. Further details of CIP procedure may be found in the work of Skelton (22). Standards proposed for batch freezers in satisfactory sanitary condition allow not more than one organism per ml capacity (i. e., no more than 10,000 total plate count for a 10-quart capacity freezer, 20,000 for a 20-quart, 100,000 for 100-quart) and less than 5,000 for continuous freezers (27).

*Packaging.* Packaging, molding, and cutting of ice cream must be carefully done to prevent contamination of the ice cream, otherwise the effects of pasteurization would be negated. The hands of the workers should be thoroughly washed, and their clothing should be fresh and clean. The finished ice cream may be brought directly from the freezer to an insulated or refrigerated hopper, and the hopper may be drained to filling mechanisms or to packaging machines. Additional contamination from these devices, as well as from the cans, cartons, caps, or containers into which the ice cream is packaged, must be expected, but in general it is low. Small molds used for specialty ice cream are often a serious source of contamination because of their frequent re-use without adequate cleaning and sanitization. They should be washed and sanitized after each use.

*Hardening and storage.* Hardening is carried out in a room at −17.8°C. to −28.9°C. (0°F. to −20°F). At least 12 hours are allowed for 5-gallon cans. Usually there is forced air circulation for rapid cooling. Ice cream is kept in the hardening room before being brought to cabinets for dispensing. There is a gradual, but not rapid, decrease in total bacterial numbers during storage. Frozen products are somewhat similar to dried products in that water, which in this case is in the crystalline state, is not available for microbial metabolism. Cold is not a sterilizing agent and can not be relied upon to free unpasteurized ice cream of pathogenic bacteria, if these should be present.

INSPECTION OF THE FINISHED PRODUCT

Ice cream may be sampled in the frozen state, or in the melted state. The former is convenient if carried out rapidly, for it avoids use of supplementary apparatus. In the latter case sterile sample bottles and a tempering bath must be available. Regardless of whether it is frozen or melted, the sample being used is weighed into a dilution blank. The remainder of the examination for total bacteria is similar to tests used for milk. Results of the determination are useful in giving an over-all indication of the sanitary conditions under which the ice cream was produced. High total counts usually mean neglect and unsanitary conditions. Among the reasons for high total counts in ice cream are poor quality ingredients, improper pasteurization, post-pasteurization contamination, improper aging, unsanitary equipment, and slovenly or uninformed personnel. The resazurin test, the end-point being either the time required for the color to become completely pink or the color of the indicator after 3 hours, has been used to detect ice cream samples with high counts (20). The 1-hour resazurin test or the methylene blue test did not seem practical for this purpose. On the other hand, the direct microscopic count of individual bacteria seemed useful for detecting bacteriologically poor samples of ice cream.

A great deal has been written on the significance of coliform bacteria in ice cream (5, 13). Certain precautions may be taken to prevent the entrance and growth of these bacteria in pasteurized ice cream mix. (a) Equipment used for handling mix should meet 3A (United States Public Health Service, International Association of Milk and Food Sanitarians, and the Dairy Industry Committee) standards. This will help eliminate difficulties caused by leakage of raw mix into pasteurized because of leaky valves and so forth. Readily dismantled, easily cleaned, correctly designed equipment that is amenable to inspection by operators and regulatory officials is assured when the equipment meets 3A standards. (b) Pasteurized mix should be stored at 4.4°C. (40°F.) or lower to prevent growth of coliform bacteria. Psychrophilic or cold-tolerant bacteria may grow in mix stored at this temperature, but coliform bacteria will not multiply in mix stored as long as 24 hours at 4.4°C. (40°F.). At 10°C. (50°F.) there will be a rapid increase in coliform numbers. (c) Pasteurized mix should be stored for as brief a time as possible beyond the aging period (4 hours). (d) Only coliform-free ingredients should be used. In this regard it has been observed that manufacturers who are able to make a satisfactory vanilla ice cream often have trouble with other types containing fruits, nuts, colors, and flavors, presumably because of coliform contamination. (e) A rigid sanitization program should be strictly and continuously followed. (f) All personnel involved in processing mix should be informed with regard to the problems involved and to the significance of sanitary practices.

A number of commercial ice cream samples have been found to contain coliform bacteria. In many instances rigorous plant inspections have revealed a high order of sanitation and apparently little opportunity for post-pasteurization contamination. It must be remembered that the unequal distribution of bacteria in ice cream and the amount of sample taken for analysis have great bearing on whether coliform bacteria will be found or not. Obviously, a large amount of sample will give more definite evidence than a small one. For example, if 1 coliform organism is present in 10 ml of mix and a 1 ml sample is assayed, the chances of detection are theoretically 1 in 10. If a 10 ml sample is taken, the chances for detection are correspondingly increased. In both cases the assumption is that the bacteria are uniformly distributed in the ice cream, and this is rarely the case. For reliable results, attention must be given the technique employed in detecting coliform organisms in ice cream. It has been suggested that the determination be made on 2 g amounts of unmelted sample, with desoxycholate lactose agar (6).

Interpretation of results of coliform determinations on ice cream should be made with reserve. One source of difficulty in freeing mix of coliform bacteria is the foam formation encountered in vat pasteurization. At times the foam in the vat at the end of the run may be 6 inches high. Even with space heaters, it is not easy to heat all of the foam to pasteurization temperature, because the air in the foam is a good insulator. According to Bartsch (5) materials should be added to vats in a manner conducive to the least foam formation. Liquids should be run down the walls of the vat rather than poured in. Solid materials ought to be flaked and allowed to fall only a minimum distance into the liquid ingredients. Materials that foam should be added last, and agitators that minimize air incorporation must be used.

More work must be done on the fluid dynamics of mix in an agitated vat in an effort to uncover the factors that influence the survival of coliform bacteria in under-heated areas. There is no doubt that the proper time and temperature will destroy the coliform bacteria, but these may not be uniformly achieved, and this has serious implications. HTST pasteurization eliminates a large amount of foaming, and higher pasteurization temperatures may be employed without cooked flavors resulting. These are advantages that cannot be ignored.

Recently it was demonstrated (4) that high coliform counts on strawberry, peach, and banana ice cream may be due to organisms other than coliforms that give positive tests on desoxycholate lactose agar. These organisms are mainly gram-negative short rods, and apparently they are able to ferment the sucrose present in ice cream mix and thereby give false positive tests. They can be isolated from the raw fruit of strawberries, peaches, and bananas and from the frozen packed fruit. Since positive tests for coliforms in this instance do not indicate faulty pasteurization, or improper cleaning or sanitization of equipment, or contaminated ingredients, it is obvious that careful interpretation of the tests must be made.

An examination of finished ice cream suggests standards for total count (18). In this connection a count of 50,000 per gram is considered satisfactory for factory-packaged ice cream. Most states specify maximum total counts not greater than 50,000 to 100,000 per gram. Legislation regarding ice cream standards has lagged noticeably behind that for fluid milk. Sixty-four of 87 cities in 30 states do not have a pasteurization standard for ice cream mix. Only 4 states and 12 cities have laws concerning ice cream ingredients, and only 20 cities in the United States have bacterial standards for ice cream (8). Requirements for total bacterial count on plain ice cream range from limits of 50,000 to 150,000 per gram and 50,000 to 500,000 per cubic centimeter or per milliliter. Only 3 states, two of which require "no coli" in ice cream, have coliform requirements.

Results of many determinations have shown that a variety of microorganisms may be found in ice cream; among these are micrococci, streptococci, coliform bacteria, spore-formers, and yeasts and molds. Some of these organisms are of dairy origin; others are from ingredients like fruits or colors; and still others come from equipment and operators. No specific source of contamination is ordinarily indicated by their presence.

### RECONTAMINATION BY DISPENSING

The greatest opportunities for general contamination of finished ice cream are afforded by the dispensing operation. A few careless dips by an unwitting or ignorant vendor may undermine all that the manufacturer and the equipment designers have done to produce a high quality product. There is little difference in principle between dipping pasteurized milk, which is not allowed, and dipping ice cream, which for some reason is allowed. Illustrative of the damage done to ice cream by dipping are the results (15) presented in Table 10.3.

Ice cream scoops and dippers usually are kept in containers of water. This water should be kept continually flowing, for total counts made on non-flowing dipper waters have been found to be as high as 6,000,000 per milliliter (17). There is little doubt that, from the point of view of sanitation, dispensing of hand-packaged ice cream is an extremely poor practice. Single service portions, protected by sanitary wrappers, are available, but their use is by no means general. Mixed ice cream drinks are subjected to dipper contamination plus additional microorganisms from syrups, fruits, mixers, spoons, and containers. Several surveys have shown that fountain sanitation is of a low order in many cases. The total bacterial counts on the finished drinks are frequently high.

### DISEASE TRANSMISSION BY ICE CREAM

Ice cream has been incriminated as a transmitter of pathogenic bacteria, but outbreaks of disease due to commercially manufactured ice cream are rare. Most cases have involved raw ingredients made into ice cream under "home" conditions. At various times ice cream has been found to harbor typhoid fever, paratyphoid fever, diphtheria, and scarlet fever organisms (10). Studies of pure cultures of pathogens inoculated into ice cream have shown that *Salmonella typhosa* may survive for 28 months at a temperature of $-20°$C. ($-4°$F.). Ice cream stored at $-23°$C. ($-10°$F.) has been found to contain viable paratyphoid and *Brucella* organisms that where inoculated into it 4 years previously (33). It is clear from these studies that cold in itself is not sufficient to kill pathogenic bacteria. Once ice cream mix has been pasteurized, it must not be exposed again to the possibility of contamination by disease bacteria. All ice cream mix should be made from clean, fresh, and wholesome ingredients that have normal flavor, odor, and appearance; and the mix must be free of pathogenic bacteria. Although some infectious agents are transmitted by flies, rodents, and similar vermin, perhaps the most frequent source of infection is the dispenser or vendor of ice cream. For this reason all persons employed in the dispensing of finished ice cream—and, indeed, those employed in ice cream plants—should be free from tuberculosis, diphtheria, typhoid, paratyphoid fevers, septic sore throat, and other communicable diseases. Obviously, persons having active cases of these diseases might contaminate ice cream by direct contact, and faulty pasteurization, or post-pasteurization contamination, could cause an epidemic. However, most cases of disease transmission ascribed to ice cream recently concern food poisoning outbreaks due to the production of gastro-intestinal irritants elaborated by certain micrococci. For such cases to occur the disease organism must not only be introduced into the mix, but it must

**Table 10.3**　　Relationship between sanitary rating of retailer and total and coliform counts of hand-packed and factory-packed ice cream *

| SAMPLE | RATING OF STORE (over-all appearance) | HAND-PACKED Total count (per g) | Coliform count (per g) | FACTORY-PACKED Total count (per g) | Coliform count (per g) |
|---|---|---|---|---|---|
| 1 | Good | 4,000 | 5 | <3,000 | 4 |
| 2 | Good | 3,500 | 0 | 3,000 | 0 |
| 3 | Good | <3,000 | 10 | <3,000 | 12 |
| 4 | Good | <3,000 | 2 | <3,000 | 0 |
| 5 | Good | 4,000 | 0 | <3,000 | 0 |
| 6 | Good | <3,000 | 1 | <3,000 | 0 |
| 7 | Fair | 4,000 | 0 | <3,000 | 0 |
| 8 | Fair | 5,000 | 71 | 4,000 | 2 |
| 9 | Fair | <3,000 | 0 | <3,000 | 0 |
| 10 | Fair | 5,000 | 50 | 4,500 | 0 |
| 11 | Fair | 5,000 | 5 | 3,000 | 4 |
| 12 | Fair | 10,000 | 195 | — | — |
| 13 | Fair | 8,000 | 163 | — | — |
| 14 | Fair | <3,000 | 20 | — | — |
| 15 | Poor | 230,000 | 27 | <3,000 | 8 |
| 16 | Poor | 70,000 | TNTC† | 5,000 | 88 |
| 17 | Poor | >300,000 | 25 | 75,000 | 3 |
| 18 | Poor | >300,000 | TNTC† | — | — |
| 19 | Poor | 50,000 | 28 | — | — |
| 20 | Poor | 120,000 | TNTC† | — | — |

\* Data taken from Gould et al. (15). Courtesy *Ice Cream Field*.
† TNTC—too numerous to count on plate containing 1 g of melted ice cream.

also have opportunity for growth. Usually this growth would take place if the mix were not properly cooled or aged before freezing; the micro-organisms may also have grown in one of the products used in making the mix.

The number of counter freezer installations in this country has risen very sharply during the past several years. Milk drinks, ice cream cones, frozen custard, milk shakes, and packaged goods are the items usually handled. Many of the installations are located at resorts and recreation spots and at various places along travelled highways. Until recently equipment in these installations was poorly sanitized, and in some instances it could not be properly sanitized because of faulty design. Washing of equipment, freezing of the mix, and vending were all done in one small room. Obviously, with such conditions high bacterial counts were found in many of the products sold. However, an increasing number of areas are establishing regulations for these installations, particularly with regard to mix storage, utensil san-itization, protection against insects, sewage disposal, separate rooms for processing, general construction of buildings, and health of employees. In short, regulations as stringent as those enforced at plants manufacturing ice cream and frozen desserts are being put into effect. It may be difficult to regard these establishments as manufacturing units because of their small size; nevertheless, a number of precautions must be taken to prevent contamination of the products dispensed. Hoppers should be refrigerated, and the front of the freezer should be insulated to prevent condensation of moisture that might then fall into the product. Any product that drips from the outlet should be discarded rather than refrozen, and the outlet should be protected as far as possible from droplet infection, flies, and other vermin. The air used for overrun should be filtered. The cans of mix should be around 4.4°C. (40°F.) when received, and should be kept refrigerated. It is well to note that warm cans of mix will not cool rapidly in dry storage refrigerators. Cans of mix ought not be held too long, and they never should be left open. The cans must be in good physical and sanitary condi-tion. Ice cream mix is viscous, and if the cans are not washed immediately after emptying, they are difficult to clean. Facilities for washing and san-itizing should be available, and should not be cramped. The public must not have access to the area around the freezer, and perhaps it would be best to have the freezer completely enclosed with an opening only on the side farthest from the public. The cones and containers should be stored in closed or self-closing units, and finger contact should be avoided as much as possible. Finally, there should be adequate and convenient hand-washing facilities, including warm water, soap, and clean toweling.

# References

1. Bacterial standards for sugar. Mimeographed sheets. Washington, D.C.: National Canners Association, 1949.
2. Barber, F. W., and H. P. Hodes, Bacterial studies of the high-temperature, short-time pasteurization of ice cream mix (Abstract), *J. Dairy Sci.*, 33 (1950): 402.
3. Barber, F. W., Bacteriological aspects of the evaluation of adequacy of pasteurization, *J. Milk and Food Technol.*, 14 (1951): 170–172.
4. Barber, F. W., and H. Fram, The problem of false coliform counts on fruit ice cream, *J. Milk and Food Technol.*, 18 (1955): 88–90.
5. Bartsch, W. C., Coliforms in ice cream require cautious interpretation. Proceedings of the 48th Annual Convention of the International Association of Ice Cream Manufacturers, Production and Laboratory Council, 2 (1952): 9–15.
6. Buchbinder, L., W. C. Bartsch, W. A. Cordes, and L. Habel, A survey of coliform organisms in ice cream, *18th Yearbook, Am. J. Public Health*, 43 (1953): 76–83.
7. Committee on frozen food sanitation, Sanitary control of frozen foods, *J. Milk and Food Technol.*, 15 (1952): 260–263.
8. Dahlberg, A. C., and H. S. Adams, Sanitary milk and ice cream legislation in the United States, *Nat'l Research Council Bull. 121*, 1950.
9. Dowd, L. R., and E. O. Anderson, Study of short-time, high-temperature pasteurization of ice cream mix, *J. Dairy Sci.*, 26 (1943): 37–46.
10. Fabian, F. W., Ice cream as a cause of epidemics, *Am. J. Public Health*, 16 (1926): 873–879.
11. Fay, A. C., The effect of hypertonic sugar solutions on the thermal resistance of bacteria, *J. Agr. Research*, 48 (1934): 453–468.
12. Federal and state standards for the composition of milk products, *USDA Agriculture Handbook No. 51*, 1953.
13. Fournelle, H. J., and H. Macy, A study of the coliform group in ice cream, *J. Dairy Sci.*, 25 (1942): 475–487.
14. *Frozen Desserts Ordinance and Code Recommended by the United States Public Health Service* (USPHS), 1940.
15. Gould, I. A., P. B. Larsen, R. N. Doetsch, and F. E. Potter, Maintaining quality in ice cream, *Ice Cream Field*, 52 (1948): 80, 84–86.
16. Jones, G. W., and R. E. Kennedy, Extinction of ethylene oxide fumes with carbon dioxide, *Ind. Eng. Chem.*, 22 (1930): 146–147.
17. Krog, A. J., and D. S. Dougherty, Scoops as a source of contamination of ice cream in retail stores, *Am. J. Public Health*, 27 (1937): 1007–1009.
18. Macy, H., Problems in meeting bacterial standards for ice cream, *Ice Cream Rev.*, 21 (1938): 27, 53–56.
19. Nelson, F. E., Changes in bacterial counts of stored ice cream mix, *J. Dairy Sci.*, 27 (1944): 459–462.

20. ———, Bacteriological evaluation of ice cream, *J. Dairy Sci.*, 27 (1944): 993–1005.

21. Oldenbusch, C., M. Frobisher, Jr., and J. H. Shrader, Thermal death points of pathogenic bacteria in cream and ice cream, *Am. J. Public Health*, 20 (1930): 615–618.

22. Skelton, F. M., Cleaned-in-place pipe lines, Proceedings of the 48th Annual Convention of the International Association of Ice Cream Manufacturers, Production and Laboratory Council, 2 (1952): 78–86.

23. Sommer, H., *The Theory and Practice of Ice Cream Making*, 5th Ed. Madison, Wisc.: Published by the author, 1946.

24. Speck, M. L., The resistance of *Micrococcus freudenreichii* in laboratory high-temperature, short-time pasteurization of milk and ice cream mix, *J. Dairy Sci.* 30 (1947): 975–981.

25. ———, High-temperature, short-time pasteurization of ice cream mix, *J. Milk and Food Technol.*, 13 (1950): 275–278.

26. Speck, M. L., C. A. Grosche, H. L. Lucas, and L. Hankin, Bacteriological aspects of high-temperature, short-time pasteurization of ice cream mix, *J. Dairy Sci.*, 37 (1954): 37–44.

27. *Standard Methods for the Examination of Dairy Products*, 10th Ed. New York: American Public Health Association, 1953.

28. Tentative standards for "bottler's" sugar (granulated). Mimeographed sheets. Washington, D. C.: American Bottlers of Carbonated Beverages, 1953.

29. Tracy, P. H., and W. H. Brown, A study of methods used to improve the sanitary quality of nut meats, flavoring, and coloring in ice cream. Proceedings of the 36th Annual Convention of the International Association of Ice Cream Manufacturers, Production and Laboratory Council, 2 (1936): 52–67.

30. Tracy, P. H., R. Pedrick, and H. C. Lingle, Pasteurization efficiency of the Vacreator when used on ice cream mix, *J. Dairy Sci.*, 33 (1950): 820–831.

31. Tracy, P. H., J. Tobias, and E. O. Herried, Application of the Vacreator and Mallorizer for high-temperature, short-time heating of ice cream mixes. Proceedings of the 46th Annual Convention of the International Association of Ice Cream Manufacturers, Production and Laboratory Council, 2 (1950): 21–30.

32. Tracy, P. H., High-temperature, short-time pasteurization of ice cream mix. Proceedings of the 47th Annual Convention of the International Association of Ice Cream Manufacturers, Production and Laboratory Council, 2 (1951): 38–45.

33. Wallace, G. I., The survival of pathogenic microorganisms in ice cream, *J. Dairy Sci.*, 21 (1938): 35–36.

# 11

# *Microbiology of lactic cultures*

For many years before microbiology as a science was applied to foods, those dairy products that depend upon lactic fermentation for their desired characteristics were prepared either by letting natural fermentation take place or by "seeding" milk with a portion of a previous lot of the desired product. In some cases a derivative, such as whey from a preceding lot of cheese, was used as inoculum. By 1890, Storch in Denmark and Conn in the United States were demonstrating the use of "natural" cultures for adding flavor and aroma to butter. These natural cultures were derived from ripened cream or buttermilk that had shown unusual development of flavor and aroma, in addition to the customary acidity. A combination of good culture and pasteurization of cream prior to addition of the culture was responsible for much of the fine reputation of Danish butter. The pasteurization not only destroyed those bacteria that might cause defects but also destroyed the bacteria that might cause natural souring. Addition of a good culture permitted controlled ripening of the cream and development of flavor prior to churning.

Both Conn and Storch found that pure cultures of bacteria usually do not give the desired development of flavor and aroma. Not until 1919 did practically simultaneous reports from Hammer and Bailey in the United States, Storch in Denmark, and Boekhout and Ott de Vries in The Netherlands establish that lactic cultures with good flavor and aroma contain a mixture of two types of bacteria. One of these types produces most of the lactic acid, while the other produces the volatile acids associated with flavor and aroma. Hammer established that citric acid is the primary source of the volatile acids. In 1929, van Niel and his co-workers and Schmalfuss and Barthmeyer demonstrated that biacetyl (known as diacetyl in much of the earlier literature and known as 2, 3-butanedione in current chemical terminology) is important as a flavor and aroma constituent of a good culture. Since these announcements, numerous other workers have established many of the factors concerned in the microbiology of a good lactic culture. The early history of lactic cultures, as well as the literature up to

1943, was reviewed by Hammer and Babel (10). This review should be consulted for more detailed information on the early phases of the understanding of lactic cultures.

Lactic acid and flavor and aroma compounds of several types are produced by a variety of cultures used in dairy products. The discussion in this chapter will be limited primarily to those cultures in which lactic acid is produced by *Streptococcus lactis* or *Streptococcus cremoris,* sometimes referred to as the lactic streptococci. *Streptococcus cremoris* is found much more commonly in commercial cultures. Where flavor and aroma production due to the presence of volatile acids and biacetyl is concerned, the citric-acid-fermenting cocci, *Leuconostoc citrovorum* and *Leuconostoc dextranicum* (or only one of these), usually are growing in association with the lactic streptococci. The major characteristics of these organisms are described in Chapter 2.

The lactic streptococci ordinarily make up more than 90 per cent of the population of a culture. In the manufacture of Cheddar cheese and most other types of ripened cheese, the acid production by *Streptococcus lactis* and *Streptococcus cremoris* is the important factor; flavor and aroma production by *Leuconostoc citrovorum* or *Leuconostoc dextranicum* usually is not considered essential. Carbon dioxide and other fermentation end-products produced by these last two organisms may actually be detrimental, under some circumstances, in cheese making; a pure culture of lactic streptococcus may be used. In the manufacture of butter, of cultured milk, of buttermilk of the usual type, and of the unripened varieties of cheese such as cottage, cream, and Neufchâtel, flavor and aroma compounds are fully as important as lactic acid production. Cultures used in these products are selected both for acid producing ability and for the fine flavor and aroma associated with biacetyl and other products of the citric acid fermentation. Specialized cultures for some of the less common fermented milks and for the types of cheese that require specific different organisms for proper manufacture and ripening will be discussed in Chapters 12 and 13.

### LACTIC ACID PRODUCTION

The formula for lactic acid is

$$H-\overset{\displaystyle H}{\underset{\displaystyle H}{\overset{\displaystyle |}{\underset{\displaystyle |}{C}}}}-\overset{\displaystyle OH}{\underset{\displaystyle H}{\overset{\displaystyle |}{\underset{\displaystyle |}{C^*}}}}-\overset{\displaystyle OH}{\underset{\displaystyle O}{C{<}}}$$

The starred carbon atom has each of its four valences satisfied by a different group; thus the compound has optical activity and may exist as L(+)-lactic acid (dextrorotatory), D(−)-lactic (levorotatory), or as DL-lactic acid (a mixture of the two forms having no optical activity), depending upon the organism responsible for the fermentation. The primary source of lactic acid in the cultures under consideration is the fermentation of lactose by *Streptococcus lactis* or *Streptococcus cremoris.* The characteristics of these organisms and the type of fermentation for which they are responsible have been discussed in some detail in Chapter 2. Over 90 per cent of the lactose fermented is usually converted to L( + )-lactic acid. The titratable acidity of the milk increases to 0.80 to 1.0 per cent, calculated as lactic acid, and the pH is dropped to 4.5 to 4.3, well below the level necessary to coagulate milk. Traces of acetic and propionic acids commonly are formed from lactose by these organisms, but the amounts are not sufficient to produce much flavor and aroma. Under usual conditions, no detectable quantity of biacetyl or related compounds is formed. Lactic acid is responsible for an acid taste, attributable to the presence of hydrogen ions; lactic acid, being non-volatile, does not contribute directly to the aroma.

The lactic streptococcus in the culture must be able to produce lactic acid at such a rate, and in such quantities, that the fermentation process may be carried out at a normal and predictable rate to fit in with the usual factory schedules. Some strains are too slow under even the most favorable conditions. Strains that are normally very satisfactory may become slow because of prolonged exposure to high acidities, particularly at temperatures above 21.1°C. (70°F.). The lactic streptococcus chosen must be able to continue acid production over the entire temperature range at which it will be used. In the manufacture of Cheddar cheese, this means production of acid at 38.9°C. to 40.0°C. (102°F. to 104°F.). When manufacturing Swiss cheese by the usual procedure or when making Brick cheese by cooking at temperatures of 45.6°C. (114°F.) and above, organisms other than *Streptococcus lactis* or *Streptococcus cremoris* must be used, because these two organisms can not produce acid at such elevated temperatures. The lactic streptococci used in the usual lactic culture should be as resistant as possible to antibiotics and to attack by bacteriophage, and they should be as active as possible in the presence of traces of chemical sanitizers. In addition, the cultures should not produce nisin or any of the other antibiotic-type substances that are produced by some lactic streptococci and that may be responsible for inhibition of other strains in the mixed culture. The organism must be free from any tendency to produce undesirable body characteristics or undesirable flavor and aroma. Ropy body, malty flavor, or similar defects usually can not be tolerated. In addition to these characteristics, the lactic streptococcus to be used in a mixed-strain culture in association with citric-acid-fermentng cocci (leuconostocs or associates) must be able to combine with these associates to give maximum flavor and aroma production without inhibition of acid production. The association must be stable and give a consistently good culture, even after many transfers.

### CITRATE FERMENTATION

Citrate is fermented by *Leuconostoc dextranicum* or *Leuconostoc citrovorum* to give biacetyl (2,3-butanedione), acetylmethylcarbinol (acetoin or 3-hydroxy-2-butanone), 2,3-butylene glycol (2,3-butanediol), carbon dioxide, acetic acid, and propionic acid as the principal products. Traces of alcohols, aldehydes, and similar compounds are formed. Fermentation of the citrate usually is so complete that all of the 0.13 to 0.18 per cent (expressed as citric acid) present in normal mixed milk is utilized. One way of increasing the amounts of flavor and aroma compounds formed is to increase the available citric acid by adding 0.15 to 0.20 per cent of citric acid or sodium citrate to the milk before the fermentation begins.

Of the products formed in the fermentation of citrate, biacetyl undoubtedly contributes most to the flavor and aroma. Acetic and propionic acids also are important in this respect. Acetylmethylcarbinol and 2,3-butylene glycol do not contribute directly to flavor and aroma. Carbon dioxide, because it is in solution as carbonic acid, may contribute to some degree to the acid taste of the final product. Some strains of associates, particularly those such as *Leuconostoc dextranicum*, will ferment lactose to the extent that milk will be coagulated; other strains may cause little or no fermentation of lactose and may show little or no change in litmus milk. All strains of these organisms ferment glucose and fructose with the production of considerable lactic acid, as well as of acetic acid, ethyl alcohol and carbon dioxide. These organisms produce primarily the D($-$)-lactic acid although small amounts of L($+$)-lactic acid may be produced by some cultures.

Biacetyl, acetylmethylcarbinol; and 2,3-butylene glycol are related chemically and also are related in the fermentation of the citrate. The formulae are as follows:

$$H\text{—}\overset{\overset{\displaystyle H}{|}}{\underset{\underset{\displaystyle H}{|}}{C}}\text{—}\overset{\overset{\displaystyle O}{\|}}{C}\text{—}\overset{\overset{\displaystyle O}{\|}}{C}\text{—}\overset{\overset{\displaystyle H}{|}}{\underset{\underset{\displaystyle H}{|}}{C}}\text{—}H \qquad \text{Biacetyl}$$

$$H\text{—}\overset{\overset{\displaystyle H}{|}}{\underset{\underset{\displaystyle H}{|}}{C}}\text{—}\overset{\overset{\displaystyle OH}{|}}{\underset{\underset{\displaystyle H}{|}}{C}}\text{—}\overset{\overset{\displaystyle O}{\|}}{C}\text{—}\overset{\overset{\displaystyle H}{|}}{\underset{\underset{\displaystyle H}{|}}{C}}\text{—}H \qquad \text{Acetylmethylcarbinol}$$

$$H\text{—}\overset{\overset{\displaystyle H}{|}}{\underset{\underset{\displaystyle H}{|}}{C}}\text{—}\overset{\overset{\displaystyle OH}{|}}{\underset{\underset{\displaystyle H}{|}}{C}}\text{—}\overset{\overset{\displaystyle OH}{|}}{\underset{\underset{\displaystyle H}{|}}{C}}\text{—}\overset{\overset{\displaystyle H}{|}}{\underset{\underset{\displaystyle H}{|}}{C}}\text{—}H \qquad \text{2,3-butylene glycol}$$

These three compounds represent three levels of oxidation of the same 4-carbon basic structure. Interconvertibility of these compounds occurs to some degree within the culture. However, there is considerable evidence to indicate that biacetyl arises primarily from intermediates in the citrate fermentation, rather than from the biological oxidation of acetylmethylcarbinol.

*Mechanism of citrate fermentation.* Pette (23) has presented evidence that the production of the 4-carbon compounds proceeds according to the following scheme: Citric acid ———→ pyruvic acid ———→ intermediate X $\xrightarrow{+ O_2}$ probiacetyl ———→ biacetyl. Under anaerobic conditions all of the intermediate X is considered to be changed to acetylmethylcarbinol; under aerobic conditions, as shown above, some of intermediate X is oxidized to probiacetyl. Pette considers that this oxidation is chemical, counteracting to some degree the biological reduction tendency of the bacteria. Without this oxidation the citric-acid-fermenting leuconostocs would direct the fermentation toward reduction to 2,3-butylene glycol. Yeasts and other forms of microorganisms may reduce the amount of biacetyl by also bringing about its biological reduction. Evenhuis (5) has demonstrated that the leuconostocs must be present to bring about the necessary oxidative changes required for biacetyl production from pyruvic acid or from citric acid. Thus the oxidative change necessary is not a purely chemical reaction. Evenhuis (6) also has demonstrated that a compound, presumably methylglyoxal, is formed in equimolar concentration when pyruvic acid is changed into biacetyl. The change apparently is as follows:

$$3CH_3COCOOH \longrightarrow CH_3COCOCH_3 + CH_3COCHO + 2\ CO_2 + H_2O.$$
pyruvic acid      biacetyl     methylglyoxal

The methylglyoxal can not be converted into additional 4-carbon compound by the culture organisms or components of the culture. Some of these conclusions have been reached on the basis of deduction, rather than of direct experimental evidence. Studies of a more definitive nature are essential for final proof of the mechanisms involved.

## SYMBIOTIC RELATIONSHIPS

*Influence of acid production on citrate fermentation.* One of the most important reasons for the production of smaller amounts of volatile acids, biacetyl, and acetylmethylcarbinol in pure cultures of leuconostocs than in cultures containing both lactic streptococci and the associates is the dependence of the fermentation pattern upon the pH of the culture. Since many strains of leuconostocs produce comparatively little lactic acid from lactose, they fail to lower the pH in the culture to a level conducive to production of maximum amounts of the flavor and aroma compounds. Studies by Michaelian et al. (16) on pure cultures of leuconostocs indicated maximum biacetyl formation in the range from pH 4.1 to 4.4, when lactic acid was the acidifying agent. Maximum biacetyl production occurred at somewhat lower pH levels when sulfuric or citric acid was the acidifying agent. Other studies have demonstrated greater production of volatile acids at pH levels somewhat below those of normal unfermented milk.

The leuconostocs must be permitted to reach a high population before the pH drops to a low level; otherwise the number of cells present will not be adequate to cause the desired change when conditions are favorable for production of biacetyl. The bacteria will not continue to grow at the low pH levels necessary for good flavor production.

*Stimulatory effect of lactic organisms upon leuconostocs.* Many cultures of lactic streptococci are mildly proteolytic. The stimulatory action that the lactic streptococci seem to have upon growth of the associates has been ascribed to the greater availability of nitrogen fractions as a result of proteolytic activity of the lactic streptococci. However, direct experimental proof of this hypothesis is lacking. Unpublished preliminary studies indicate that possibly the lactic streptococci produce one or more growth factors that can replace certain liver extract fractions that are necessary for the growth of associates on otherwise chemically defined media. The nature of the specific compound or compounds involved has not been determined. Nurmiko (20) has shown more recently that *Streptococcus lactis* changes folic acid to folinic acid, the "citrovorum factor" that promotes the growth of at least some strains of *Leuconostoc*.

*Reducing capacity of lactic organisms.* The lactic streptococci are able to cause strongly reducing conditions in media in which they grow. Biacetyl is the most oxidized of the three 4-carbon compounds produced in good cultures. Reducing conditions, particularly at less acid reactions, tend to shift the equilibrium of the reaction toward 2,3-butylene glycol, rather than toward biacetyl. This is particularly true in older cultures in which much of the total amount of the 4-carbon compounds is apt to occur in the reduced form that contributes nothing to flavor and aroma (27).

*Influence of temperature of incubation and other factors in the handling of the culture.* Because commercial cultures are mixtures of two or more types of organisms, any factor that affects only a portion of the culture will influence the numerical relationship between the types. The usual temperature at which a mixed culture is incubated is 22.2°C. (72°F.) or a few degrees above. Mixtures usually are chosen so they will maintain a desirable balance of the two organism types at this temperature. At incubation temperatures of 32.2°C. (90°F.), or above, the growth rate of the leuconostocs usually will be depressed far below normal. Under these conditions the leuconostocs either will be reduced to an unworkably low level or will be eliminated entirely. The higher incubation temperatures have an added disadvantage in that unwanted bacteria that may have survived the heat treatment given the milk, or that may have contaminated either milk or culture, commonly can grow at a greater rate. These bacteria may be more troublesome in the culture than they would be if incubation were at 22.2°C. (72°F.) or slightly above.

Prolonged holding of the culture, particularly at room temperature or slightly above, usually will result in an increase in the relative number of leuconostocs. These organisms are appreciably more tolerant to acid and to other adverse factors found in a ripened culture than are lactic streptococci; and thus they will live in greater numbers under these adverse conditions. For these reasons a culture low in associates sometimes can be brought back to normal by moderate overripening.

*Establishment of symbiosis between strains.* If one takes a series of lactic streptococci and a series of leuconostocs and attempts to make combinations of the different species, only a small number of the combinations can be expected to prove satisfactory. Present knowledge of the factors that influence establishment of the desired balance does not permit advance determination of whether a satisfactory combined culture may be expected. Obviously the cultures combined should not have any definitely undesirable characteristics such as ropiness, off-flavor, slow development, abnormally slow acid production, unusual sensitivity to bacteriophage, or great susceptibility to antibiotics, chemical sanitizers, or other potentially inhibitory compounds.

The associate strain normally is grown in sterile milk at 22.2°C. to 26.7°C. (72°F. to 80°F.) for approximately 24 hours before the lactic streptococcus is added. Incubation is continued somewhat beyond the time when coagulation occurs. Several transfers then are made in sterile milk, a normal incubation period of 14 to 16 hours at 22.2°C. (72°F.) usually being used. The culture then is transferred several times in larger quantities of milk (sometimes only heat treated as for usual cultures, rather than sterile) and finally is judged for the desired characteristics. The combination must be carried through a number of additional transfers to establish its stability. The combination usually is further tested by being used in the manufacture of the products for which the culture is intended. Recombination is a procedure to be carried out in the specialized laboratory. If a culture is not behaving satisfactorily in the plant, a new transfer should be obtained from an organization that has the proper facilities and personnel to do the manipulation and testing necessary to the preparation of desirable combinations.

### CARRYING OF CULTURES

*Selection of milk.* The choice of a proper milk supply is exceedingly important in carrying satisfactory cultures. Not only does a good milk supply contribute to consistent, satisfactory development of the cultures, but it also permits proper judging of the cultures at each transfer. The milk chosen must be from normal healthy cows that are secreting a product of normal physico-chemical character. Occasionally milk from cows suffering from mastitis appears normal, but the development of a culture inoculated into such milk is retarded. This retardation fortunately is not common—if it were, the widespread incidence of mastitis would make culture carrying very difficult. Milk from animals being treated with antibiotics, sulfonamides, or other therapeutic agents that may be inhibitory to culture organisms certainly should be avoided. Milk with unusually high lipolytic activity should not be used, for the lower fatty acids freed by lipase activity are inhibitory to culture organisms. Milk containing excessive numbers of bacteria should not be used. These bacteria might produce antibiotic substances that would resist the heat treatment and hinder normal culture development. Excessive numbers of bacteria in the milk used also increase the possibility that some of the bacteria may survive the heat treatment and develop in the culture.

Other things being equal, the milk used for carrying cultures should have an average or above-average solids content. Milk low in solids, because of secretion of this type by the cow or because of dilution, yields a culture soft in body and difficult to judge properly. Whether the milk is skimmed or whole usually makes no difference except that the presence of butterfat increases the apparent richness of the culture and thus adds to the pleasure of judging the product. Homogenization is desirable, if whole milk is used, since the formation of a cream line is avoided and the culture thus is somewhat easier to handle and to judge.

Many laboratories have been carrying their cultures on reconstituted milk solids-not-fat with good results, provided they use pretested spray process powder. This has the advantage of helping to maintain the conditions for propagation as uniform as possible; also fluctuations in the character of the cultures can be observed and evaluated more readily. The powder should be reconstituted to give between 10 and 11 per cent solids. Each new lot of powder should be examined by one of the activity tests to be certain that normal growth and acid production will be supported. Occasionally, a lot of presumably satisfactory powder will not give the desired results; therefore, it is good to have a new lot on hand for testing well before the lot in use is exhausted.

*Treatment of the milk.* Heat treatment of the milk is essential to inactivate the normal germicidal effect of the milk and to destroy the majority, or all, of the microorganisms present so that a fresh start may be made on the fermentation. As pointed out in Chapter 3, a minimum of about 30 minutes at 71.1°C. (160°F.) is necessary to inactivate the germicidal component of milk; the use of higher temperatures is based primarily on the need for greater bactericidal action than would be achieved by this minimum exposure. Some people feel that only sterile milk should be used for propagating mother cultures. Exposures of 15 or 20 minutes at 15 pounds pressure may be employed. Such a treatment removes the possibility that an organism that survives heat treatment may develop in the culture and cause difficulty later. Some strains of lactic streptococci grow better in moderately autoclaved milk, apparently because of an increase in available nitrogen (7). More drastic heating results in inhibition of the cultures. However, the curd formed by a culture grown in sterile milk is soft and sloppy, and the scorched flavor hinders the accurate judging of flavor and aroma development. For these reasons, somewhat less drastic heat treatments often are used to prepare milk for culture propagation, even though such treatments are known to permit the survival of some bacteria. The rapid acid production by the lactic streptococci and the relatively low temperatures used for incubating the culture usually can be relied upon to prevent significant development of the surviving organisms. When exposure of the milk to steam or boiling water for 30 to 60 minutes is employed, some reduction in curd strength occurs, and some cooked flavor results; however, neither of these defects is as prominent as in sterile milk. The equipment required for steam or boiling water for 30 to 60 minutes is much less expensive and is simpler and safer to use than that employed for sterilization. Milk exposed to such a heat treatment has been used successfully by some laboratories in carrying mother cultures for years. Temperatures as low as 85°C. (185°F.) for 30 minutes have been used in some laboratories for treating milk for mother cultures, and no apparent difficulties from bacteria surviving the heat treatment have been encountered. However, use of such low temperatures is not recommended.

Following heat treatment, the milk should be cooled to inoculation temperature as rapidly as practical. Rapid cooling minimizes the physicochemical changes occurring in the milk as the result of prolonged exposure to high temperatures. It also reduces the possibility of growth of surviving thermophilic bacteria. Immersion in flowing cold water probably is the best procedure to use for cooling. A control container in which water and a thermometer have been placed permits one to stop cooling when the desired temperature is reached.

*Containers for carrying cultures.* Containers for mother cultures may be made from a variety of materials. Glass containers offer the advantage of easy examination for cleanliness and for character of the culture curd, but they do break easily, and they withstand little thermal shock unless made of one of the more expensive resistant glasses. Pottery containers are heavy, easily broken, and do not permit good observation of curd characteristics. Metal containers offer the advantage of resistance to breakage and thermal shock, and they transfer heat most rapidly, but they are attacked readily by the culture acids unless some of the more expensive resistant alloys are used. Metal containers do not allow easy examination of the curd.

The container closure should prevent entry of undesirable organisms and should also protect the container lip so as to minimize chances for contamination during transfer. Ordinary plug-type glass stoppers are not desirable as closures unless supplemented by a parchment or foil hood, in which case the hood alone would suffice. Cotton wool batting stoppers are messy and do not protect the lip well. Foil or parchment hoods held on by rubber bands or string are quite satisfactory, if they extend down well below the sides of the opening. Small beakers inverted over the tops of the containers also have been used. Large glass medicinal ovals with plastic screw-on caps are very satisfactory containers and closures for carrying cultures. The plastic tops need to be replaced periodically since most types will not stand repeated heating indefinitely, but the replacement cost is small. Milk bottles closed with parchment caps provide another container-closure combination. A number of containers with desirable features are available from certain supply houses.

*Amount of inoculum.* The amount of inoculum to use for each culture depends upon the time and temperature of incubation employed, the individual characteristics of the culture, and the condition of the culture at time of inoculation. The usual range is from 0.5 to 2.0 per cent of the amount of the milk to be inoculated. Lesser or greater quantities may be required under unusual circumstances. Temperature of incubation ordinarily is fixed, and no adjustments in amount of inoculum are necessary because of this factor; this fixed temperature is the desirable situation toward which each person carrying cultures should strive. Naturally, shorter incubation times call for heavier inoculum, and longer incubation times for less inoculum. The period of incubation usually is adjusted to plant operations, and the inoculum must be adjusted accordingly.

Some cultures must be inoculated at higher levels than are others if desirable characteristics are to be maintained in succeeding transfers. Such a requirement is a characteristic of the individual culture. The optimum amount of inoculum for the individual culture under the propagation conditions routinely employed must be determined by observing the effects of variations in inoculum. The amount once determined ordinarily will remain fairly uniform over a period of time. However, the amount of inoculum may need to be changed, either temporarily or permanently, to compensate for changes in the culture. As an example, a heavier inoculum, with other conditions remaining constant, may be used to increase the proportion of leuconostocs in the culture and may thus increase the flavor and aroma production.

*Inoculation procedures.* A special area should be set aside for the inoculation of cultures. This area may simply be a small shelf in the plant, where the materials can be arranged conveniently and the transfer made with the minimum possibility of contamination. Preferably it should be a special culture room in which provisions are made for effective isolation from contaminants. Under any circumstances the transfer should be carried out aseptically and with as little chance for aerial contamination with bacteriophage, molds, and other undesirable microorganisms as is possible. The table should be wiped off thoroughly, immediately before use, preferably with a cloth moistened in chlorine water of a strength of 200 parts per million. A number of other bactericidal agents may be used. Plain water is better than nothing because it assists in the removal of particulate material such as dust and microorganisms that otherwise might gain entrance to the culture.

Inoculation should not be made by pouring the culture over the lip of the container. Ideally a pipette or a glass tube should be used for removing an appropriate amount of material from the previous transfer and depositing it in the fresh lot of milk. Pipettes are expensive, but sections of glass tubing with properly smoothed and flamed ends can be made easily and economically. A glass tubing of essentially uniform bore permits ready estimation of the relative amount of material being transferred, an important factor in assuring uniformity of handling procedures.

Spoons or small dippers also may be used in making transfers, although they are considered less convenient and less desirable than are pipettes or tubes.

The transfer implement must be properly treated before use to destroy potential contaminating microorganisms; it also must be properly protected between treatment and use. Pipettes, tubes, and even spoons and dippers may be wrapped individually or in small groups in heavy kraft wrapping paper or metallic foil, heat treated, and stored in the wrapper. They also may be placed in metal cans or glass jars or large glass tubes for treatment and storage. Whatever type of enclosure is used, it must be sufficiently tight to prevent entry of microorganisms after treatment.

The ideal treatment for transfer equipment undoubtedly is sterilization in a dry air sterilizer at 170°C. (338°F.) for 1 hour, but this is not a convenient procedure for most plants. Autoclaving at 15 pounds pressure for 20 minutes is equally as effective as dry air sterilization, if the steam can actually reach all portions of the container. However, many autoclaves do not yield a dry package, and moist heat also is considerably more corrosive than dry heat. Placing the implements in flowing steam for half an hour, or slightly longer, also has been used, as has immersion in boiling water for several minutes, followed by storage in a container similarly treated in which the implements can drain before use. Direct heating immediately before use by immersion in boiling water, direct steaming, or direct heating over an open flame such as that of a gas or alcohol lamp also might be employed, but less conveniently.

*Incubation.* Incubation has components of time and of temperature. Temperatures of 21.1°C. to 22.2°C. (70°F. to 72°F.) usually are recommended. This temperature range permits good growth of the culture organisms, but it usually is not as satisfactory for development of potential contaminants or of those bacteria that may survive heat treatment. Temperatures up to 23.9°C. (75°F.) or even 26.7°C. (80°F.) have been used under some circumstances, apparently with reasonably satisfactory results. However, as temperatures increase, the possibilities of undesirable changes in the balance between the lactic streptococci and the leuconostocs increase, and the culture also becomes more susceptible to other undesirable changes.

The time of incubation is closely related not only to the temperature of incubation but also to the amount of inoculum used and to the individual character of the culture(s) employed. Usually a time of incubation that works in well with other routines is selected, and then the amount of inoculum is adjusted to this time, taking into consideration the individual character of the culture. An incubation time of 14 to 16 hours at 22.2°C. (72°F.) with an inoculum of approximately 1 per cent normally is satisfactory.

The need for careful control of incubation temperature is great, for variations in this factor make proper management of cultures much more difficult. Only when all factors are closely controlled can one be reasonably certain that a culture's deviation from the normal is due to some external influence such as bacteriophage or antibiotics. A culture cabinet with provisions for both raising and lowering temperatures in relation to the room temperature is desirable. An insulated refrigerator-type box with thermostatic control of mechanical refrigeration and electric heating is the ideal solution, but such an arrangement is expensive. Human ingenuity is about the only limitation on how closely cheaper systems can be made to approximate the results obtained with the ideal equipment. Where tap water is cold and plentiful, a water-cooled coil may be used for cooling the incubator. The rate of water circulation can be controlled by a manual valve to adjust to external temperature conditions. Some incubators available use ice in place of mechanical refrigeration. An incubator with only thermostatic control of electric heating may be placed in a large refrigerator or in a cold room, and it may provide good control of temperature. A large volume of water in a well-insulated tank provides reasonably good temperature control for cultures placed in a smaller water-tight container immersed in it. During warm weather the water needs to be slightly cooler than the desired incubation temperature at the start to compensate for the warming tendency. The water should be slightly warmer at first if external temperatures are, or are expected to become, somewhat lower than the desired level. The most primitive procedure for temperature control is the placement of the cultures in an area where the temperature is expected to be about that desired for incubation. Frequently this involves guessing about what the temperature changes in any given location will be during the incubation period. At best such a procedure is a questionable stop-gap to be used only until more positive temperature control can be established.

*Cooling.* Once a culture has reached the level of development most satisfactory for the conditions under which it is being handled, it should be cooled to stop further development and to keep it in good condition for the next transfer. Although recent studies indicate that moderate overripening is not as harmful as has commonly been supposed in the past, unlimited development still is not desirable. In addition, most people, possibly because they are accustomed to such a procedure, find a cold culture easier to judge than a warm one.

Small mother cultures usually can be cooled satisfactorily merely by being placed in a refrigerator until the next transfer. Larger cultures benefit by immersion in ice water. Stirring or shaking of the mother cultures to hasten cooling usually is not advocated because the body and texture of the cooled culture would be made more difficult to judge and because there is danger of contamination during such an operation.

## JUDGING CULTURE QUALITY

Cultures are examined by organoleptic tests to determine whether body, texture, flavor, and aroma are at desirable levels. Chemical tests may be used to determine whether the levels of acidity, biacetyl, acetylmethyl-carbinol, and volatile acids are within the ranges accepted as normal for a good culture. "Activity" tests give an index of the biological activities of the organisms in the culture, particularly those producing acidity. Bacteriological tests are used primarily to determine the presence of con-taminating microorganisms, but they also may be used for enumeration and characterization of the desirable bacteria.

*Organoleptic tests.* The body of a good culture should resemble that of a firm custard. The coagulum should be firm enough to hold its shape during gentle tapping of the container against hand or table, but not so firm that it will not break away from the side of the container with a more pronounced blow. The curd should break cleanly and smoothly. Evidence of lumpiness or of whey pockets is undesirable. When the culture has been agitated thoroughly, it should have a body that is smooth and somewhat viscous, with a complete absence of lumpiness.

The proper taste of the culture is one of clean acidity with no sugges-tion of bitterness, saltiness, or other undesirable tastes. (Taste is used here in the sense of the basic tastes, such as acidity, bitterness, and saltiness, rather than in terms of volatile characteristics, which properly belong in the area of aroma and flavor.) To describe the flavor and aroma of a good culture in definitive terminology is almost impossible, at least at our pre-sent level of understanding of this difficult area, where an almost infinite range of possibilities of both quantitative and qualitative nature may be encountered. The outstanding aroma is that of a weak solution of biacetyl associated with the aroma of dilute acetic and propionic acids. However, other substances undoubtedly contribute in some degree to the typical flavor and aroma. Blends of two or more aromas unquestionably affect the senses differently than do single aromas. One is almost reduced to defining a good culture as one that tastes and smells as if it were a good culture. Such definition leaves one in the position of depending almost completely on past experience of a very subjective nature. This is a type of experience that does not provide an adequate background for quantitative definition. Also a culture must be free of foreign flavors and aromas, for these would make a negative contribution. Malty, bitter, rancid, unclean, yeasty, fruity, and putrid are only a few of the adjectives used to describe unde-sirable flavors and aromas that have been encountered in cultures.

*Chemical tests.* Titratable acidity often is determined on cultures, either during incubation to note the rate of acid development, or, more commonly, on the final culture to establish definitely that proper acid development has occurred. This test may be made on a pipetted sample, provided that the pipette has been rinsed properly to remove most of the sample to the titration vessel, but a more accurate procedure is to weigh out the culture. This avoids the errors inherent in any volumetric procedure involving a product of high viscosity. Because dilution influences the salt balance, the greatest accuracy in titration results if the sample is not diluted with water unless the milk used has been fortified with added milk solids; in this case the amount of warm water added should be such as to bring the solids-not-fat content to approximately that of normal milk, e. g., about 8.5 per cent. Otherwise, normal procedures are used for titration and for expression of results in terms of lactic acid.

Several procedures have been used for determining the volatile acidity of lactic cultures. The procedure of Hammer and Bailey (11) has the advantage of relative simplicity, and it gives results that are satisfactory for comparative purposes. After 250 g of culture is weighed out in the distillation flask, sulfuric acid is added to give pH 2, and the culture then is steam distilled. The first liter of distillate is collected, and an aliquot is titrated with $0.1N$ hydroxide; the results are expressed in terms of the milliliters of $0.1N$ alkali required to neutralize the volatile acids in the first liter of distillate.

Determination of biacetyl involves steam distilling this compound from the culture under an inert atmosphere to minimize chemical oxidation. The distilled compound may be converted to nickel dimethylglyoximate and determined gravimetrically (15) or to ammono-ferrous dimethylglyoximate and determined colorimetrically (24). Other similar procedures also have been employed.

Determination of acetylmethylcarbinol involves the chemical oxidation of this compound to biacetyl, commonly by addition of ferric chloride to the culture before distillation begins. The conversion of acetylmethylcarbinol to biacetyl is almost quantitative. The biacetyl in the culture after the chemical oxidation is the sum of that originally present and that originating from conversion of acetylmethylcarbinol. If the original biacetyl content alone is obtained by a separate determination, the acetylmethylcarbinol content is obtained by figuring the difference between the value for acetylmethylcarbinol plus biacetyl and that for original biacetyl.

A rapid test for acetylmethylcarbinol plus biacetyl was devised by Hammer (9), who modified the O'Meara test for acetylmethylcarbinol. The intensity of the red color that develops in the surface layer after mixing 2 ml of culture plus an equal volume of 40 per cent sodium hydroxide and a small amount of creatine is a rough index of the content of acetylmethylcarbinol plus biacetyl in the culture.

*Bacteriological tests.* Because acidity tests are so much quicker and simpler to run than plate counts or other enumerations of bacteria and because they give results that ordinarily can be used equally as well, counts are not made routinely on cultures. Differential procedures for enumeration of the leuconostocs also have not proven applicable to more than an occasional culture combination and thus find only very limited usage.

Some of the organisms that may contaminate a culture are morphologically quite distinct from the culture organisms. Direct microscopic observation of stained smears may be used to detect many types of contaminants, providing that these are present in considerable numbers. Some dilution of the culture usually will be necessary before preparation of the smear, for otherwise the bacteria will be so numerous, and the milk film so thick, that both staining and examination will prove difficult.

Because the microscopic procedures are not suited to detection of low-level contamination, selective plating procedures are used in some laboratories. Plating on acidified potato dextrose agar permits detection of yeasts and molds at low levels of contamination. Any of the usual procedures for the detection of coliform bacteria may be used on cultures. Plating or streaking on a minimum medium, such as beef extract-peptone agar, usually will permit some of the common contaminants, such as spore-formers, to develop easily distinguishable colonies. Under these conditions the normal culture organisms either produce no colonies or such small ones that they do not interfere significantly with the detection of other colony types. Tests for yeasts and molds have been used most extensively, but a number of laboratories have found coliform tests of value in the detection of culture contamination. Complete freedom from these organisms in 1 ml quantities of culture is the desirable goal.

*Activity tests.* Most of the activity tests that have been proposed depend upon determining the increase in titratable acidity during a specified interval of time. In order to reduce the time interval to a minimum, heavy inocula usually are employed, and the incubation temperature is raised considerably above that ordinarily used for culture propagation. The exact conditions chosen for the test should be determined to some degree by conditions under which the culture is to be used. When the use is to be in Cheddar cheese, activity must be maintained at temperatures of 37.8°C. (100°F.) and slightly above. Accordingly, the activity tests for cheese cultures often are run at 37.8°C. (100°F.). A number of procedures for running activity tests have been suggested. Horrall and Elliker (12) used a 3 per cent inoculum in autoclaved, reconstituted nonfat dry milk, and titrated the acidity after incubation for 3.5 hours at 37.8°C. (100°F.). The results are recorded as per cent lactic acid. Development to 0.40 per cent titratable acidity usually indicates a culture that gives good activity in the cheese vat. All conditions must be standardized carefully if the test is to have value.

When the culture is to be used in cottage cheese or cultured milk, the activity test, whether that of Horrall and Elliker or one of the others, may be run at about 30°C. (86°F.), although many use 36.7°C. (98°F.) or 37.8°C. (100°F.) in order to make the test more rapid.

Another type of activity test, one based on resazurin reduction rate, was introduced by Leber (14). Spray-process powder is reconstituted at 26.3°C. (80°F.) in distilled water, and 9 ml is used as the substratum. To the milk, are added 1 ml of culture and 1 ml of 0.005 per cent resazurin solution. Incubation is at 36.7°C. (98°F.) with examination at 30 minutes and every 5 minutes thereafter. The end-point is a pale pink that just precedes complete decolorization. An excellent culture will reduce in less than 35 minutes, but a fair culture will require 50 to 60 minutes. Control milk without culture should not reduce in 4 hours. This procedure also has been used to detect milk grossly contaminated with antibiotics or otherwise definitely abnormal, the culture being the constant factor whenever this use is made of the test.

The activity tests frequently will not detect bacteriophage or antibiotics at levels that still may be great enough to retard acid development under plant conditions. The heavy inocula and high incubation temperatures used in the tests minimize the chances that bacteriophage or antibiotics will prevent or reduce normal development of acidity.

## CULTURE DEFECTS

### INSUFFICIENT DEVELOPMENT OF ACIDITY

This is one of the most common defects of lactic cultures. In some instances the cause is as obvious as insufficient inoculum or too low incubation temperature; the former usually is an error on the part of the person transferring the cultures; the latter may be due to inadequate control over incubation temperature, failure of the source of heat on a cool night, or improper adjustment of temperature controls. The literature on many of the causes of insufficient or slow acid development has been reviewed by Babel (2).

*Contaminating microorganisms.* These have been shown to be a cause of reduced acid production under some circumstances. Workers at the National Institute for Research in Dairying in England have shown that some strains of *Streptococcus lactis* produce the antibiotic nisin, which is inhibitory to growth and to acid production by some strains of *Streptococcus cremoris.* Thus, extensive growth of *Streptococcus lactis* in milk prior to pasteurization may result in the production of sufficient nisin to inhibit subsequent growth of a lactic culture. However, in a somewhat similar situation the milk needed to be heated before the inhibitory principle produced by organism growth was active against the lactic culture; possibly another type of inhibitory substance was involved. Spore-forming aerobic bacteria and also coliform bacteria growing as contaminants have been suspected of causing reduced acid production, but the experimental evidence for such beliefs has not been conclusive.

*Abnormal milk.* Milk, as secreted by the cow, may be inhibitory to the growth of lactic cultures. The so-called germicidal activity of milk is somewhat effective against lactic cultures; inactivation requires heating to 71.7°C. (160°F.) for 30 minutes. The activity may be a cause of reduced acid production in milk for cheese making, but not in milk heated to the temperature ordinarily used in treatment of milk for culture propagation. Milk from cows suffering from mastitis may be sufficiently abnormal that lactic organisms fail to develop normally. Fortunately this is not a common property of milk from quarters infected with mastitis; otherwise the wide incidence of mastitis in dairy herds would make the carrying of lactic cultures almost an impossibility.

Milk in which an abnormal amount of lipolysis has occurred as the result of action of normal milk lipase is not a satisfactory medium for lactic cultures because the lower free fatty acids produced are inhibitory to lactic streptococci. The remedy is either the use of milk normal in lipase activity, or the pasteurization of the milk very soon after production to inactivate the lipase before it can produce any detrimental quantity of fatty acids.

*Quaternary ammonium compounds.* If these substances are present in the milk at levels of approximately 5 parts per million or above, acid production is apt to be below normal. Some plants that have been having trouble with poor acid development have minimized their difficulties by having the producers discontinue use of these compounds. This is not to be construed as an indication that quaternary ammonium compounds are unsatisfactory for sanitizing utensils in which milk to be used for cultures or cultured products is to be handled. It is, however, necessary to rinse the equipment thoroughly after sanitizing with these compounds in order to prevent their occurrence in milk in inhibitory concentrations. Some evidence indicates that the quaternary ammonium compounds are more important in retarding the production of flavor and aroma compounds than in reducing production of acid.

*Chlorine compounds.* Chlorine compounds of the types commonly employed for the sanitization of food-handling utensils usually react so completely with milk that any reasonable level of residues will be destroyed and will not cause any significant retardation of acid production. However, chlorine does have an inhibitory action on culture organisms when certain levels are present in the milk. The addition to milk of 5 ppm as hypochlorite has been found to inhibit lactic cultures slightly, and 25 ppm is very inhibitory (1). Caution therefore must be taken to prevent the addition of chlorine sanitizers to milk to be used for culture making.

*Antibiotics.* Antibiotics in milk are the cause of much concern to those who use lactic cultures (21). Acid production by even the more resistant strains of *Streptococcus lactis* usually is inhibited demonstrably by

0.25 units of penicillin per milliliter of milk and at comparable levels by other antibiotics now used in mastitis therapy. *Streptococcus cremoris,* which is the more common lactic streptococcus component of commercial cultures, usually is even more sensitive. A culture inhibited by antibiotics characteristically is very slow in beginning to form acid. The time required for the inoculum to initiate rapid growth may be such that undesirable organisms have developed in numbers detrimental to the quality of the product, or that the desirable changes have been so retarded that the quality of the final product is subnormal. In other instances, acid production may start and then slow down markedly, much as if bacteriophage were acting upon the culture. Sometimes manufacturing schedules are disrupted to a most undesirable degree.

The use of the enzyme penicillinase has been suggested for destruction of penicillin in milk when the antibiotic may be inhibitory to acid production. Aside from the cost and the question of adulteration, there are no suitable enzymes for selective inactivation of other antibiotics commonly used in mastitis control. With many preparations now containing aureomycin (chlortetracycline), other antibiotics, and combinations of several antibiotics, routine use of an enzyme active against only one antibiotic would not solve the problem at all.

The processor should follow acid development in his product. If acid development is below the normal rate and if antibiotics are suspected of being responsible, additional culture sometimes may be used to permit acidity to develop more rapidly. Considerable adsorption of antibiotic onto the initial inoculum will occur, leaving a much lower level to act on the added culture. Under some circumstances, a second addition of culture may provide enough cells practically free from antibiotic to permit resumption of essentially normal production of acidity. This procedure has been used with large quantities of cultured milk. Abnormally large amounts of inoculum have been used to combat antibiotics, but this practice can cause complications if antibiotic is not present and the acid develops too rapidly. Selection of cultures with increased resistance to antibiotics has not provided an adequate answer to the problem.

The activity tests ordinarily employed for cultures usually do not detect amounts of antibiotic that, although small, still may cause trouble in making fermented products. The most sensitive test apparently is observation of growth of the culture under the same conditions employed for the product for which the milk would be used. This usually means that the milk would need to be tested one day, and that the fermented product would be prepared the next day if the milk were satisfactory. Most plants do not have storage facilities that would permit this.

*Bacteriophage.* Some of the characteristics of this virus active against lactic streptococci are described in Chapter 2. Whitehead (25) and Babel (2) have reviewed much of the literature relating bacteriophage to slow acid production in fermented products and cheese. Bacteriophage apparently is one of the most important causes of slow acid production by lactic cultures. Bacteriophage must build up in a culture or cultured product, usually from an initially quite low level, to a particle population equal to, or exceeding, that of the bacteria present before marked retardation of acid production becomes apparent. When this population level is reached, essentially all of the sensitive bacterial cells are infected, and these usually will lyse or disrupt within about 40 to 60 minutes under favorable conditions. When lysis occurs, acid production by the affected cells stops (Figure 11.1). Thus a culture infected with bacteriophage usually develops acidity, normally during the early stages of culture development. As the sensitive bacteria are lysed, acid development comes to a stop unless nonsensitive bacteria are present to carry on fermentation.

The relatively high level of strain specificity of bacteriophage against host bacteria (17, 28) means that, in many mixed cultures, resistant strains of bacteria are present to carry on the fermentation after the sensitive strain or strains have been lysed. The extent to which lysis of sensitive strains reduces acid production depends upon the relative numbers of sensitive and non-sensitive organisms in the culture.

Bacteriophage activity in cultures may be combatted in a variety of ways, none of which insures complete freedom from attack. By using combinations of proper procedures such as sanitation, culture selection, and culture rotation, a plant definitely can minimize the probabilities of trouble with bacteriophage. Substitution of a new culture for the old one often will give at least temporary relief from an outbreak of bacteriophage

**Figure 11.1**    Changes in count and pH of a *Streptococcus lactis* culture in the presence and the absence of bacteriophage active against that culture. Data of Turner and Nelson, Iowa State College.

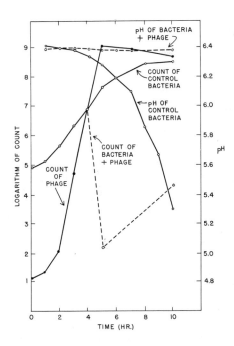

activity. The new culture should be chosen to contain lactic streptococci resistant to the bacteriophage strain or strains that attacked the first culture. However, this is not always possible on the basis of information available to the plant. Also, if conditions of culture preparation and of handling of products in the plant are conducive to trouble with bacteriophage in one culture, eventual difficulties may be anticipated with any culture introduced into the plant; no cultures known at the present time are completely resistant to bacteriophage attack. In New Zealand, where single-strain lactic cultures (one strain of *Streptococcus lactis* or *Streptococcus cremoris,* without any citric acid-fermenting associates) often are used, the practice of rotating a series of these cultures in a cycle 6 days or more in length has been employed (25). The cultures are selected for different bacteriophage sensitivities, in order that a bacteriophage that might begin to build up against one culture will not find a suitable sensitive culture to attack on any one of several subsequent days and thus will not increase to a dangerous level in the culture room or plant. This rotation procedure has been used successfully in a limited way in other cheese-producing countries, even where the usual multiple-strain cultures are employed.

In England some success has been obtained by combining culture rotation with use of a mixture of two cultures of different bacteriophage sensitivities on each day. Usually the cultures are carried separately and are inoculated simultaneously into the final product. In such a procedure care must be taken to see that the two cultures are compatible, e. g., that they develop at much the same rate and that neither produces nisin or any other agent that might be inhibitory to growth of, and to acid production by, the other strain. This procedure also has been used to a considerable extent in the United States.

Cultures must be protected against bacteriophage contamination during inoculation and incubation. Bacteriophage has been shown to be blown around in the air under certain conditions. Since only one bacteriophage particle may increase in numbers proportionately much more rapidly than the culture in which it is found, an initial infection with one particle may, under favorable circumstances, cause lysis of an entire culture. Thus bacteriophage contamination usually is much more serious than contamination with a single cell of a bacterium; the latter quite probably will be overgrown by the culture organisms and never become apparent, but the former may destroy the culture. The declining pH and the less favorable physiological condition of the host bacteria may retard or stop the increase in bacteriophage numbers soon enough so that the culture gives no indication of extensive bacteriophage contamination (22). On the following transfer into fresh milk, both the pH and the physiological state of the host cells will be favorable for resumption of bacteriophage increase. Under these circumstances lysis of the culture may occur rather quickly. Reasonably heavy contamination with bacteriophage may be necessary for lysis to occur in a single transfer of the culture. Unless some bacteriophage reproduction has occurred in the preceding transfer of the culture or the level of contamination is high, cessation, or even appreciable reduction, of acid formation in the cheese vat or cultured milk is not probable.

Although experiences vary somewhat, bacteriophage contamination of mother cultures evidently is not common under the conditions of careful handling employed in good laboratories. It is true that some cultures apparently are carriers of bacteriophage (8). The carrier condition usually is not directly responsible for an outbreak of slow culture in the succeeding transfer, for the carrier culture often is normal in acid production through a whole series of transfers. The carrier culture may serve as a source of bacteriophage for other cultures or even as a source of bacteriophage that may mutate to attack some of the previously unattacked strains in the carrier culture. So long as multiple-strain cultures are used, it is difficult to determine by any procedure other than detailed laboratory study whether a culture is a carrier; even laboratory study may not reveal the carrier state unless the proper "indicator" strains are available to detect the particular strain of bacteriophage that is present, sometimes in quite small numbers.

The conditions under which intermediate and bulk cultures are handled may permit more bacteriophage contamination than occurs with mother cultures. The containers used for the larger volume cultures are difficult to inoculate without exposing considerable surface to aerial contamination, and they are difficult to seal adequately. The conditions in the room frequently are less conducive to complete sanitation of the surroundings. These considerations have led to the design of special culture containers, some of which are inoculated through comparatively small and more easily protected openings. Some have special seals, including water seals, and others have special provisions for heat treatment of the milk and of the container in which the milk is heated. In New Zealand certain factories have special culture rooms that are removed some distance from the cheese making operations and placed on the windward side of the main buildings in order that bacteriophage will not be carried by the prevailing winds from the plant and its surroundings to the culture room. Some central culture laboratories have been established quite apart from the cheese plants, to supply to a number of cheese plants in the area culture in quantity for inoculating the final product. Frequently these special rooms are designed particularly for ease of cleaning and for fogging with a chlorine aerosol (19) to destroy any airborne bacteriophage before inoculations take place. The interchange of personnel between laboratory and plant must be avoided for best bacteriophage control. One who has been working at the cheese vat or cheese press may easily carry bacteriophage, on his clothes or person, to infect the cultures. Ultraviolet light has been suggested for control of airborne bacteriophage (4). The ultraviolet light would be of little value for destruction of phage particles protected by milk, moisture, or soil.

Certain plant practices contribute to the dissemination of bacteriophage particles. The levels of contamination of cheese milk may be sufficiently high under some circumstances to retard acid development significantly, even though the culture, when added to the vat, contained no bacteriophage. Whey separators often produce a fine whey mist in which many bacteriophage particles may be suspended. Whey that is permitted to run on the floors may spread bacteriophage, for it may be splashed into milk or onto surfaces from which the milk may be contaminated. Some of the bacteriophage particles are quite resistant to drying and apparently may remain viable for a considerable period of time on dry walls and equipment. The particles also remain active for long periods in Cheddar cheese; such cheese may form a reservoir for future contamination in the plant (18). Some plants return whey to the producers for animal feeding in the same cans used for handling milk. Work in New Zealand (26) has shown that, when this is the practice, the milk coming into the plant may contain considerable quantities of bacteriophage, because the usual farm sanitation procedures fail to destroy the bacteriophage. Chlorination of the whey has proved effective but expensive, and heating is troublesome because of coagulation of whey proteins. The only really satisfactory solution seems to be the banning of the use of milk cans for the returning of whey.

### INSUFFICIENT FLAVOR DEVELOPMENT

Since adequate production of lactic acid is essential for the lowering of the pH to a level where biacetyl and other compounds are formed in sufficient quantity for good flavor, any of the factors interfering with proper acid development will retard or prevent adequate flavor development.

The culture may be incapable of producing adequate amounts of flavor compounds because the leuconostocs either fail to develop properly or are unable to carry out the desired fermentation at an adequate level. Maintenance of proper balance between them and the lactic streptococci is not always easy because the two types of organisms do not react in the same degree to a change in the environment. For example, raising the incubation temperature to above 32°C. (89.6°F.) usually causes a dominance of the lactic streptococci, which are able to grow at a faster rate than the leuconostocs at these higher temperatures. On the other hand, continued ripening to low pH levels may result in a dominance of the leuconostocs because the latter are more tolerant of acid than are the lactic streptococci. Some of the antibiotic agents that find their way into milk may have a selective action upon one or the other type of organism, and thus may upset the balance of population. Quaternary ammonium compounds are reported to be more restrictive to flavor and aroma fermentation than to growth of either the lactic streptococci or the leuconostocs. Education of the producers to minimize the residues of sanitization rinses left in equipment is one answer to this problem. When the leuconostocs make up less than the desirable 5 to 10 per cent of the culture, flavor and aroma production may decrease. Such a situation may be corrected after several additional regular transfers. Also when the culture has been over-ripened, resulting in greater development of leuconostocs, several serial transfers usually restore the proper balance of the different species. In the manufacture of fermented milk products, a culture that does not re-establish balance fairly readily should be replaced by one that does.

Under unusual circumstances the milk used might be abnormally low in citrate ions and thus might not provide adequate substratum for the flavor and aroma fermentation. Changing the milk supply or supplementation with added citrate would be means of correcting this situation.

In cottage cheese some of the gram-negative contaminating bacteria have been shown to destroy biacetyl and to reduce the flavor level. Such an undesirable change might be possible in lactic culture under certain circumstances. However, experimental evidence for such a situation has not been presented.

Although holding a culture for a short time under refrigeration normally increases the level of flavor and aroma, presumably by gradual conversion of preformed compounds to the desirable end-products, prolonged holding usually results in decreased flavor and aroma. This decrease ordinarily is attributed to a reduction of biacetyl and acetylmethylcarbinol to 2,3-butylene glycol, a compound that makes no direct contribution to flavor and aroma. Neutralization of acidity with the resultant shift in pH toward neutrality increases the rate at which this conversion takes place. Overripening or failure to cool the culture promptly will result in some decrease in flavor and aroma because of biacetyl destruction, due to continued activity of the culture organisms.

### HARD AND LUMPY CURD

This defect usually is associated with overripening, particularly at higher temperatures when some of the whey tends to be expressed from the curd as the result of the elevated temperature. The defect has sometimes been ascribed to contaminating bacteria, but these are not believed to be a common cause.

### HIGH ACIDITY

This defect usually is associated with overripening due to high incubation temperature, incubation for too long a time, excessive inoculum, or combinations of these factors. In mother cultures this defect is not so important as it once was considered to be, for the resultant retarding effect upon the lactic acid streptococci does not seem to persist (13). If it is not excessive and is not repeated too frequently, the slight favoring of the leuconostocs that results may be advantageous to the culture.

### WHEYING OFF

Whey may collect on the surface or at the bottom of the culture or beneath a cream layer. The latter type of collection usually is difficult to eliminate when unhomogenized whole milk is used for carrying the culture. A low solids content in the milk, either natural or due to dilution, predisposes cultures carried therein to wheying off; the curd formed is not firm enough to avoid fracturing and the resultant freeing of whey. Overripening, with the resultant tendency for the curd to lose whey because of the higher acidity, also predisposes culture to wheying off. Agitation or vibration of the culture, particularly during the interval soon after the curd begins to form, may cause wheying off too. During this period the curd still is fragile; it is at approximately the isoelectric point of casein, at which point the casein is in a state of minimum hydration. Precautions should be taken to avoid any disturbance of the culture during this critical period in coagulation.

### ROPINESS

The ropiness usually encountered is not that of the extremely stringy type, such as is caused by *Alcaligenes viscosus;* rather it is a thickening of the product associated with only a moderate tendency to form rather heavy, short strings. Although ropiness will not interfere with the use of a lactic culture for furnishing flavor and aroma to butter, the defect often is undesirable in such cultures. Ropiness usually is undesirable in cultures used for cultured milk, for cultured buttermilk, and in the various types of cheese. In some localities, however, a ropy strain of lactic streptococcus is used in the mixed culture to provide a heavier body in cultured buttermilk.

Often ropiness in lactic cultures is due to a change in the character of the lactic streptococci. Some strains of these streptococci seem to have no tendency to become ropy, while other strains seem inclined to ropiness for reasons unknown at present. With a culture that has a tendency to be ropy, taking of inoculum from the surface portions has been reported to accentuate the tendency; taking of inoculum from the depths of the culture apparently minimizes the ropy tendency. The ropy condition may disappear after a few transfers, or it may persist more or less permanently.

Ropiness may be due to the dominance of a ropy strain of leuconostoc in the culture. All species of the genus *Leuconostoc* have a tendency toward ropiness. This tendency is very prominent in the species *Leuconostoc mesenteroides,* a common cause of slime formation in sugar refining. In the species used in lactic cultures the tendency toward ropiness is not so pronounced, and the factors controlling the tendency are not well understood.

Ropiness may not persist in the culture, but if it does, the culture may well be discarded.

Ropy strains of coliform bacteria have been encountered as contaminants of lactic cultures. Their presence has resulted in ropy conditions of various degrees. Usually elimination of these contaminants is not practical except in a specialized laboratory. The usual solution is to replace the culture with one having desirable characteristics.

### GASSINESS

This is not a common defect in cultures, but it may be troublesome occasionally. As indicated earlier, some carbon dioxide is produced by the leuconostocs during the fermentation of citric acid. Usually the amount produced and the rate of production are such that the gas does not become obvious because of its relatively high solubility in the water phase of the culture and its gradual escape into the atmosphere. Occasionally the rate and timing of gas production may be such that gas bubbles and even gas rips show in the curd of the culture. Some cultures are much more inclined to be this way than are others, but the situation usually is not serious enough to cause concern. In cottage cheese a culture containing unusually active leuconostocs may contribute to the floating of the curd; in Cheddar cheese, particularly that packed in cans, the gas formation may become quite troublesome because of eye formation or bulging of the cans. Selection of the proper associate for combination probably is one answer to this problem. Certain "wild" strains of *Leuconostoc* encountered in Cheddar cheese have been shown to be especially active producers of gas.

Even a culture quite normal in appearance under ordinary circumstances may show some gas evolution if it is taken from a refrigerator and placed at room temperature. This is due to the considerable reduction in the solubility of carbon dioxide in the water phase as the temperature rises; an amount of carbon dioxide which would remain dissolved at a low temperature may go off as gas at a higher temperature.

Coliform contaminants occasionally may reach such numbers that they will cause gassiness in a culture because of the breakdown of lactose to products that include carbon dioxide and hydrogen gasses. The lactic streptococci provide a coagulum in which these gaseous products may be trapped and in which they may become more apparent than they would be in a pure culture of coliform bacteria in milk. In a pure culture of coliform bacteria coagulation commonly occurs late in the fermentation cycle after most of the gaseous products already have been released. Lactose-fermenting yeasts also may reach sufficient numbers in a lactic culture to cause a definite gassiness. These yeasts can grow well in a lactic culture, for they actually are favored by the mildly acid condition of such an environment. In addition to the gassiness, yeasts may cause a yeasty or fruity flavor when they reach appreciable numbers.

### BITTERNESS

This defect is relatively uncommon. Most often it can be attributed to the presence of proteolytic bacteria in the culture. *Streptococcus liquefaciens* and some of the spore-formers that survive the usual heat treatment of the milk are the most usual causes. Spore-formers have been found to have been added to lactic cultures through the use of reconstituted dry milk as the culture medium; such a condition is the result of using dried milk that has not been prepared under proper sanitary precautions. Factors that may cause slow development of a lactic culture inoculated into such milk would generally permit the spore-formers to grow and to cause defects in the culture. Cheesy flavor and curdy body may be associated with bitterness, and they may be caused by the same organisms.

### MALTINESS

Growth of *Streptococcus lactis* var. *maltigenes* is the usual cause of this defect. A culture containing this organism should be discarded.

### METALLIC OR PUCKERY FLAVOR

Defects of this type may be due to metallic contamination of the cultures. The acidity produced during the ripening process is sufficient to attack to some degree all but the most resistant types of materials used in the construction of culture-handling equipment. Tinning is removed from copper and other base metals quite quickly, leaving them open to attack by the lactic acid of the culture. Certainly only the most acid-resistant materials should be used for fabrication of equipment for carrying cultures.

This type of flavor defect also may be due to overgrowth by the leuconostocs. The compound or compounds responsible for these undesirable characteristics are not known at the present time. The remedy for overgrowth by associates usually is the underripening of the culture through a series of transfers, the new transfer thus being made before the leuconostocs have reached their maximum population level.

### GREEN OR GREEN-APPLE FLAVOR

This defect generally is associated with underdevelopment of the leuconostocs, sometimes as the result of repeated transfer of the culture before adequate development. On occasion the trouble may be remedied by several transfers of the culture with some overripening at each transfer. In some cases the defect has disappeared on the addition of 0.2 per cent sodium citrate to the culture milk before inoculation. Whether this effect is due to increased buffering action or to an increase in the available substratum for the leuconostocs has not been determined.

## INTERMEDIATE CULTURES

The amounts of milk employed in carrying mother cultures impose a very definite limit on the amount of product that can be inoculated from one mother culture. Where thousands of pounds of milk are made into cheese or cultured milk, relatively large quantities of culture must be available for inoculum. Intermediate cultures of such size that the mother cultures may be used to inoculate them usually are prepared. When large quantities of inoculum are needed, the intermediate culture then is used to prepare the larger culture for the final inoculum. Much the same considerations apply in preparing the intermediate cultures as in handling the mother cultures. Because intermediate cultures are handled on a larger scale, the equipment and materials used for them cannot be chosen from as wide a selection and as high a quality as those used for the mother cultures. However, any differences should be kept to a minimum. The milk used must be of high quality; some plants prefer to use reconstituted non-fat dry milk solids, rather than fresh milk, because a day-to-day uniformity usually can be achieved more readily by this procedure. The milk almost never is autoclaved, heat treatments such as raising to 87.8°C. (190°F.) for 30 to 45 minutes usually being accepted as adequate.

Glass containers ordinarily are not of sufficient size and mechanical strength to handle the desired amount of culture; therefore 5- or 10-gallon metal containers usually are employed. When culture is prepared in this manner, insulated tanks are available wherein the cans of milk can be pasteurized, cooled, and incubated. Such apparatus must have connections for steam and cold water. Pasteurization is done by injecting steam into the water around the cans to attain and maintain pasteurization temperature. Cooling is effected by allowing cold water to enter the vat until the milk reaches the proper temperature. By adjusting the temperature of the water to that desired for incubation, the temperature will not vary over 1°F. to 2°F. (0.55°C. to 1.11°C.) during incubation, due to the insulation in the walls of the vat. Thermostatic control may be applied to the water, to help materially in maintaining the desired incubation temperature. Special stainless steel or glass-lined culture tanks frequently are used to prepare the larger culture. These have most of the features described for the tanks in which metal cans are used as containers, but the container for the milk is an integral part of the equipment.

Termination of the incubation period and the beginning of cooling usually take place when a definite titratable acidity has been reached. The exact acidity to employ is determined by the conditions prevailing in a particular operation. The culture used, the purpose for which it is to be used, the type of equipment in which the culture is carried, the nature of the cooling procedure, and other related factors must be considered in arriving at a specific figure. A desirable acidity value may be determined for a particular operation; this figure will be subject to change when any of the factors just mentioned is altered in any way. Some modification may be needed from day to day to compensate for small variables.

Some plants are following the procedure of preparing their intermediate cultures early enough so that an activity test may be run on each batch before being used as the final inoculum in a fermented product. Such a procedure may lead to a slight decrease in the activity of the culture when it finally is employed because the bacteria have been held for some hours at a stationary phase—without active growth. However, the advantages of knowing that the culture is in a good condition to provide the desired acidity, unless something is wrong with the milk supply, tend to outweigh this disadvantage. Unfortunately it often is not practical to receive the milk a day in advance so that it may be tested for suitability for use in cultured products.

## SOURCES AND TYPES OF COMMERCIAL CULTURES

The first cultures used in cultured products usually were inoculated from material saved from a good lot of product. The lactic cultures used today usually are the result of combinations of pure strains of the desired organisms that have been prepared in the laboratory. A number of commercial laboratories furnish lactic cultures especially suited for manufacture of each of the different products in which such bacteria are used. Many of the agricultural colleges and experiment stations also carry cultures and make them available to the industry.

Some years ago cultures prepared in broth, dried on filter paper, or formed into tablets were available. Today nearly all of the cultures on the market are in milk. The actual material purchased may be in the liquid form, or it may be dried. The liquid cultures frequently are shipped with a small amount of sterile calcium carbonate added to reduce the acidity to some degree; the calcium carbonate will prolong slightly the period over which viable cells will be present in quantity to develop in the succeeding transfer. Liquid preparations have the advantage of being easy to make up without special equipment and with minimum chance for contamination —they are ready to grow quickly on the first transfer if they have not been held too long, or at transit or storage temperatures that are too high. They do lose their vitality quickly, particularly if exposed to high temperatures. Usually they can be held only a few days, even under refrigeration, before they require several transfers to assume normal characteristics. After being held for some time they may be impossible to bring back to usefulness. A freshly prepared liquid culture may be frozen and then held for several months with only minor loss in vitality. This procedure is recommended for those who use liquid cultures and who wish to keep a culture on hand for emergency use without having to make daily transfers. Frozen culture in quantities sufficient to inoculate intermediate cultures of 10 gallons or more now is available from some laboratories. If this material is kept frozen, it will maintain its usefulness as an inoculum for a month or more.

Dried cultures may be prepared in different ways. One procedure involves mixing the liquid with some dry material, such as lactose or non-fat dry milk; the resulting moist mass can be dried in a warm air stream, or in a cabinet where moisture is removed under vacuum. Many organisms die as a result of this procedure, since the drying is slow and the cells are bathed in a very concentrated solution of ions and lactose for an appreciable period during the drying operation. In addition, the presence of warm air undoubtedly results in considerable oxidative action that will kill many cells. Such preparations do have the advantage of remaining viable for much longer periods of time than do liquid cultures; thus, they may be shipped further and held longer in the plant, particularly under refrigeration. They have the disadvantage that several transfers frequently are required before the culture returns to normal and may be used in the manufacture of fermented products. The so-called freeze-dried or lyophilized preparations result from freezing a culture as a thin shell in the bottle, and then drying it by subliming off the water while the culture remains frozen and under a high vacuum. Because the material remains frozen during drying and because oxygen is removed during the drying operation, the cells are not exposed to high salt, sugar, or oxygen concentrations, and the survival of the cells is at a very high level. Such cultures have good storage qualities, particularly under refrigeration, and they can be shipped considerable distances without serious deterioration. They usually develop almost normally on the first transfer, and thus they are available for use quickly. They have been used for direct inoculation of milk for cottage cheese or cultured buttermilk, although this is not the general practice. Such cultures may cost slightly more than those prepared by other means.

Many plants acquire new cultures at regular intervals, in order to minimize the consequences should the culture in use for some reason become unsuitable. Other plants take pride in carrying the same culture for years without having it show undesirable changes. In still other plants all of the culture for use in the final product is sent in from a central culture supply. Each of these routines has advantages and disadvantages. The system adopted will be affected by such factors as the internal organization of the plant and the larger group of which it may be a unit, the distances between source and plant, the personnel and equipment available for handling culture, the supervisory staff available, and the products for which the culture is required.

## References

1. Babel, F. J., Changes in bacterial population of milk due to the addition of some chemical bactericides (Abstract), *J. Dairy Sci.,* 37 (1954): 635–636.

2. ————, Slow acid production by lactic cultures: a review, *J. Dairy Sci.,* 38 (1955): 705–733.

3. Berridge, N. J., Testing for penicillin in milk, *Dairy Inds.,* 18 (1953): 586.

4. Czulak, J. Control of airborne bacteriophage by ultraviolet irradiations. *Proceedings of the XIIIth International Dairy Congress, Volume 3* (1953): 1094–1097.

5. Evenhuis, N., De vorming van diacetyl in zuursels, *Neth. Milk Dairy J.,* 5 (1951): 110–117.

6. ————, The manufacture of aromatic butter, *Neth. Milk Dairy J.,* 5 (1951): 201–228.

7. Foster, E. M., The effect of heat on milk as a culture medium for lactic acid bacteria, *J. Dairy Sci.,* 35 (1952): 988–997.

8. Graham, D. M., C. E. Parmelee, and F. E. Nelson, The carrier state of lactic streptococcus bacteriophage, *J. Dairy Sci.,* 35 (1952): 813–822.

9. Hammer, B. W., The creatine test for acetylmethylcarbinol plus diacetyl in butter cultures, *J. Dairy Sci.,* 18 (1935): 579–581.

10. Hammer, B. W., and F. J. Babel, Bacteriology of butter cultures: a review, *J. Dairy Sci.,* 26 (1943): 83–168.

11. Hammer, B. W., and D. E. Bailey, The volatile acid production of starters and organisms isolated from them, *Iowa, Agr. Exp. Sta. Research Bull. 55,* 1919.

12. Horrall, B. E., and P. R. Elliker, An activity test for Cheddar and cottage cheese starters, *J. Dairy Sci.,* 30 (1947): 523–524.

13. Johns, C. K., and H. L. Bérard, The effect of over-ripening upon the activity of Cheddar cheese starters, *J. Dairy Research,* 13 (1943): 127–135.

14. Leber, H., A resazurin starter activity test, *Milk Plant Monthly,* 39(9) (1950): 40–42.

15. Michaelian, M. B., and B. W. Hammer, Studies on acetylmethylcarbinol and diacetyl in dairy products, *Iowa Agr. Exp. Sta. Research Bull. 179,* 1935.

16. Michaelian, M. B., W. H. Hoecker, and B. W. Hammer, Effect of pH on the production of acetylmethylcarbinol plus diacetyl in milk by the citric acid fermenting streptococci, *J. Dairy Sci.,* 21 (1938): 213–218.

17. Nichols, Agnes A., and Margery Hoyle, Bacteriophage in typing lactic streptococci, *J. Dairy Research,* 16 (1949): 167–208.

18. Nichols, Agnes A., and J. Z. Wolf, The persistence and recovery of bacteriophage in cheese, *J. Dairy Research,* 13 (1944): 302–307.

19. ————, The destruction of air-borne phage by hypochlorite mists in the control of starter manufacture, *Dairy Ind.,* 11 (1946): 174.

20. Nurmiko, V., Phenylalanine as a precursor in the biosynthesis of folinic acid (citrovorum factor) in lactic acid bacteria, *Suomen Kemistilehti,* 28B (1955): 62–66.

21. Overby, A. J., Antibiotics in milk, *Dairy Sci. Abstr.*, 16 (1954): 2–23.

22. Overcast, W. W., F. E. Nelson, and C. E. Parmelee, Influence of pH on proliferation of lactic streptococcus bacteriophage, *J. Bacteriol.*, 61 (1951): 87–95.

23. Pette, J. W., Some aspects of the butter aroma problem. *Proceedings of the XIIth International Dairy Congress, Volume 2, Section 2* (1949): 572–578.

24. Prill, E. A., and B. W. Hammer, A colorimetric method for the microdetermination of diacetyl, *Iowa State Coll. J. Sci.*, 12 (1938): 385–395.

25. Whitehead, H. R., Bacteriophage in cheese manufacture, *Bacteriol. Rev.*, 17 (1953): 109–123.

26. Whitehead, H. R., and G. J. E. Hunter, Bacteriophage in cheese manufacture. Contamination from farm equipment, *J. Dairy Research*, 15 (1947): 112–120.

27. Wiley, W. J., G. A. Cox, and H. R. Whitehead, The formation of diacetyl by starter cultures, II: rate of diacetyl production by lactic streptococci, *J. Council Sci. Ind. Research*, 12 (1939): 239–249.

28. Wilkowske, H. H., F. E. Nelson, and C. E. Parmelee, Serological classification of bacteriophage active against lactic streptococci, *Applied Microbiol.*, 2 (1954): 243–249.

# 12

## Microbiology of fermented milks

Centuries ago man learned that milk became sour soon after it was drawn from the animal. He also learned that sour milk does not readily undergo proteolysis and other less desirable changes; therefore he handled the milk in a manner to encourage souring whereby it could be preserved for several days or longer. Methods of treating the milk differed from one tribe of people to another, and naturally the products differed too. Thus there originated a large number of fermented milks, which are known by different names. All of them are soured by lactic acid bacteria and, in addition, some undergo an alcoholic fermentation.

Microbiologists became interested in sour milks before 1890, while bacteriology was still in its infancy. They isolated and studied the organisms in the fermented milk and tried to determine which ones were important and what changes they caused. These early workers, especially von Freudenreich, contributed much information on the lactic acid bacteria and their role in the conversion of milk into fermented products. In the past half century knowledge of the bacteriology of fermented milk preparations has increased to the extent that now it is possible to produce some of them on a large scale and obtain consistently the desired physical and organoleptic properties.

Much of the interest in fermented milks has stemmed from the ideas and writings of Metchnikoff, who worked in France during the early part of the 20th century. Metchnikoff proposed the theory that the life span of man is shortened by the absorption of certain products of anaerobic protein degradation from the intestines. He knew that putrefaction was inhibited in an acid environment; therefore, he reasoned that autointoxication resulting from anaerobic decomposition could be prevented if an acid-producing microbial flora were established in the human intestine. He had observed that many Balkan peoples retained their vigor and lived unusually long lives. Metchnikoff attributed their longevity to the consumption of large quantities of sour milk and to the establishment in their intestines of an acid-producing microbial population.

Metchnikoff and his associates tried to prove that an acid reaction could be established in the intestine of an individual by feeding him milk cultures of *Lactobacillus bulgaricus*. Their claims of successful implantation of this organism have since been disputed by others, although *Lactobacillus acidophilus* can be established under certain conditions. Metchnikoff's theory on the prolongation of life has never been proved or disproved to the satisfaction of everyone, but his writings have greatly stimulated the public's interest in fermented milks.

Many claims have been made for the therapeutic or medicinal value of fermented milks in the diet of man. Ancient physicians prescribed sour milk for dysentery, tuberculosis, liver complaints, inflammation of the intestinal tract, and a host of other maladies. Persian women used acid milk as modern women use cosmetics. At one time some of the tuberculosis sanitoriums in Russia included in the patients' diets large quantities of kumiss, a fermented preparation made from mare's milk, in the belief that it had unusual curative powers. Even though most of the claims for the therapeutic value of fermented milks are grossly exaggerated, physicians today prescribe acidophilus milk in the diet of some persons afflicted with constipation or diarrhea. People who cannot consume ordinary milk because of an intestinal disturbance often can tolerate sour milk. The more friable curd of the acid product presumably makes it easier to digest. As far as is known, however, fermented milk has essentially the same food value as the original milk from which it was made.

The purpose of this chapter is to describe the essentials of what is known about the microbiology and preparation of certain fermented milks, with emphasis on those produced commercially in America. Many others are made in small quantities, usually in the home, but little is known about the microorganisms responsible for their characteristics. The same general procedure is used in making all commercial fermented milks, although details of the method vary from one product to another. Whole, skimmed, partly skimmed, or sometimes concentrated milk first is heated to destroy part or all of its microorganisms and to inactivate its labile enzymes. The severity of the heat treatment can range from ordinary pasteurization to autoclaving. After being cooled to incubation temperature, the milk is inoculated with a starter culture and incubated until the desired flavor and body are attained. The product then is chilled and is ready for distribution. The characteristics of the final product depend to a considerable degree on the kinds of organisms in the starter.

## CULTURED BUTTERMILK

True buttermilk is the fluid remaining after cream is churned into butter. If made from sweet cream, it has approximately the same composition as skimmilk. Cultured buttermilk is prepared by souring true buttermilk or, more commonly, skimmilk with a butter starter culture that produces a desirable flavor and aroma. The resulting product is not simply sour milk. It possesses the distinctive characteristics of a good butter starter and is relished by persons who like a cultured buttermilk of fine quality.

Many manufacturers add 1 or 2 per cent butterfat to cultured buttermilk to improve the flavor and appearance of the product. The fat may exist as granules or as flakes, which can be obtained in a variety of ways. Some manufacturers add the fat to the milk before inoculation. After souring, the product is churned until the fat particles are of the desired size. Other makers churn cream to obtain granules and either mix it directly with cultured milk or recover the granules, wash them in ice water, and add them directly to the sour milk. Flakes of fat can be obtained by chipping cold and hardened butter into small pieces or by adding droplets of hot butter oil onto the surface of cold buttermilk where they congeal immediately during agitation. If regulations permit, the fat is colored artificially to make the particles more conspicuous in the finished product. Small amounts of salt sometimes are added to cultured buttermilk to improve the flavor. Also, manufacturers may mix fruit juices with buttermilk to produce a drink preferred by some consumers.

Buttermilk manufacture, like any commercial fermentation, requires the preparation of a large quantity of culture from a small amount of stock or mother culture. If the final volume of culture is very large it is necessary to build up the inoculum in a series of propagations, each 50 to 100 times larger than the preceding one. Conditions during this process must be such that the characteristics of the original culture are maintained in the final product. Sometimes even minor variations in the procedure can have an undesirable effect on the starter organisms, especially if a mixed culture is used. Methods of carrying mother cultures and of preparing bulk starter were described in Chapter 11. Cultured buttermilk is prepared by extending this process through one additional step. The directions that follow contain the essential information necessary to make a good product.

1. Heat good quality skimmilk, whole milk, or reconstituted skimmilk to 82°C. to 88°C. (179.6°F. to 190.4°F.) for 30 minutes. If dry skimmilk is used, disperse 10 to 12 pounds of powder in each 100 pounds of water.

2. Cool the milk to 21°C. (69.8°F.) and inoculate with 0.5 to 2 per cent of bulk starter, the amount depending on the activity of the culture. Thoroughly mix the starter with the milk but avoid agitation later during incubation.

3. Continue incubation at 21°C. (69.8°F.) until the acidity reaches 0.80 to 0.90 per cent. Cool the buttermilk to 5°C. (41°F.) with minimum agitation, then bottle. With very large volumes of culture in certain types of equipment it may be necessary to start cooling when the acidity is considerably below 0.80 per cent to avoid overripening before cooling is completed. If desired, hold the chilled product in the vat for several hours to

increase the viscosity before bottling. Store the bottled milk at 5°C. to 10°C. (41°F. to 50°F.) until it is distributed.

With a good starter culture this procedure will yield a cultured buttermilk having excellent flavor and aroma. Certain conditions can be varied slightly to suit the requirements of an individual maker, but to avoid difficulties the variations should not greatly exceed the ranges indicated. The following paragraphs explain why it is important to adhere to the suggested procedure.

### ORGANISMS IN THE CULTURE

As was explained in Chapter 11, the starter used for cultured buttermilk consists of a mixture of lactic streptococci (*Streptococcus lactis* or *Streptococcus cremoris*) with aroma bacteria (*Leuconostoc citrovorum* or *Leuconostoc dextranicum*). In the usual culture the streptococci greatly outnumber the others, but both types are essential for the production of the characteristic flavor and aroma of the buttermilk. If the original culture contains the correct organisms and is carried by the methods described in Chapter 11, there should be a satisfactory balance between the two groups of organisms in the mixture. This balance must be maintained through the bulk starter propagation so that all of the important organisms are present and active in the preparation of the finished buttermilk.

The main function of lactic streptococci in the starter is to produce lactic acid, which is necessary to give the desired sour taste, to curdle the milk, and to lower the pH to the point where the aroma bacteria produce maximum amounts of volatile acids and neutral products. The species of *Leuconostoc* function chiefly by producing acetic acid, acetylmethylcarbinol, and biacetyl from citric acid (see Chapter 11).

### THE MILK AND ITS HEAT TREATMENT

It is especially important that the milk be free of flavors and odors that might be noticeable in the final product. It should not contain large numbers of extraneous microorganisms, some of which produce substances that interfere later with growth of the starter organisms. Although some dairy plant operators use heat-sterilized milk for carrying mother cultures (Chapter 11), the milk for bulk starter and especially that for the final buttermilk must not be heated this severely. Heating at temperatures below 82°C. (180°F.) or much above 88°C. (190°F.) causes a weak body that allows whey separation in the buttermilk. Furthermore, excessive heating discolors the milk and produces a cooked flavor. With most milks optimum viscosity and whey retention in the final product result from heating to 85°C. (185°F.) for 30 minutes.

### STAGE OF ACTIVITY OF BULK STARTER

To produce the desired flavor and aroma in the buttermilk, all of the organisms in the starter must grow actively and must be present in sufficient numbers to cause their respective changes in the time available. Practice has shown that starter cultures for buttermilk should be used when the acidity is between 0.80 and 0.85 per cent and, if a culture cannot be used immediately, it should be chilled to 10°C. (50°F.) or below to avoid overripening. Starter cultures ripened to higher acidities often are not sufficiently active in the final stage of buttermilk manufacture because the lactic streptococci have passed their peak of activity. Conversely, starter cultures that are ripened to acidities much below 0.80 per cent will not have sufficient numbers of aroma bacteria. The recommended amount of starter is chosen mainly because this quantity of active culture will produce the desired stage of ripeness in the buttermilk in 12 to 16 hours. This time period can be adjusted easily to the operations in most dairy plants.

### INCUBATION TEMPERATURE

There are several reasons for choosing 21°C. (69.8°F.) for incubating buttermilk cultures. At appreciably lower temperatures the starter organisms grow too slowly, and curdling is delayed excessively. At much higher temperatures the streptococci overgrow the aroma bacteria, and the product will lack flavor and aroma. Any departure of more than a degree or two above or below the optimum will cause imbalance in the bacterial mixture and will adversely affect the product. At higher incubation temperatures the curd forms at a lower acidity, and it tends to shrink, causing whey separation. Finally, the use of the lowest practicable incubation temperature inhibits growth of undesirable bacteria that survive the heat treatment given the milk.

### THE CORRECT STAGE OF ACID DEVELOPMENT IN THE BUTTERMILK

Most consumers prefer a buttermilk that is not too viscous, yet one which has a smooth consistency with no whey separation. At the curdling point, usually about 0.60 per cent acidity at 21°C. (69.8°F.), casein is in its minimum state of hydration. As the acidity increases into the range 0.75 to 0.80 per cent, hydration (and thus whey-retaining property) again increases, thereby improving the stability of the product. Additional acid formation causes increased viscosity but has little effect on the whey-retaining property of the curd (4).

Acid formation also markedly affects the formation of flavor and aroma substances by the leuconostocs. At 0.70 per cent acidity the volatile acids comprise only about 5 per cent of the total acid. At 0.90 per cent titratable acidity, however, the volatile acids account for about 15 per cent of the total acid. The neutral aromatic compounds increase similarly. With additional acid formation a harsh flavor develops, and frequently some of the biacetyl is lost. Practice has shown that an acid range of 0.80 to 0.90 per cent is about the best compromise to yield the optimum physical and organoleptic properties in the final buttermilk.

## CARE IN CHILLING AND BOTTLING

Excessive agitation decreases the stability of buttermilk and increases whey separation. This is especially critical during curdling of the milk when the gel is weakest. After the desired stage of ripening is reached, as indicated by the acidity, the curd must be cooled rapidly to avoid over-ripening. Mixing may be necessary to hasten cooling, but it should be done gently and in a manner that does not incorporate air. Stability is best if the buttermilk is held at a temperature near 5°C. (41°F.) until it is distributed. Wide variations in temperature favor separation of whey.

## DEFECTS

The most common defect of cultured buttermilk is poor stability, which results in whey separation. As a remedy, some makers add small amounts of gelatin to the milk to increase the viscosity, others may add about 10 per cent of a milk culture of *Lactobacillus bulgaricus* to the cultured buttermilk, and still others may add 1 to 2 per cent of fat to the milk before pasteurization. Cultured buttermilk with adequate stability usually can be made without these additions if care is taken to avoid the factors that predispose to a weak curd. For example, heating the milk to temperatures much below or above the range 82°C. to 88°C. (179.6°F. to 190.4°F.) for 30 minutes yields a curd that tends to be weak. Agitation or even excessive vibration during curdling causes poor stability, as does air incorporated during cooling, pumping, and bottling. Ripening to acidities much below 0.80 per cent and incubation at temperatures much above 21°C. (69.8°F.) often result in whey separation in the final product. Some milk samples yield curd that is inherently weak, regardless of the method of treatment. To prevent whey separation in buttermilk made from these, it may be necessary to add gelatin or some other stabilizing material if local regulations permit.

Another common defect of cultured buttermilk is insufficient flavor and aroma development. This occurs when the culture is handled in a manner that does not permit sufficient activity of the *Leuconostoc* organisms. Use of milk that is low in citric acid also may result in a product that lacks flavor and aroma. Milk usually contains about 0.18 per cent citric acid, but values from individual cows have been as low as 0.07 per cent. This low concentration is not enough to yield sufficient flavor and aroma products for a full flavored buttermilk. Where it is legally permitted, some makers improve the flavor and aroma of buttermilk by adding 0.1 to 0.2 per cent citric acid or its equivalent as sodium citrate to the milk before inoculation.

Control of the total acid development in buttermilk sometimes is difficult. Too much acid is caused by overripening and can be avoided by shortening the incubation time or by reducing the amount of starter. Too little acid may result from a variety of causes, one of the most common being use of an inactive starter. This condition usually results from over-ripening the mother starter during daily transfers. Another cause of poor acid development is "non-acid milk." This usually results from growth of bacteria in the milk before heating and production of heat-stable substances that inhibit growth of the starter organisms. Difficulties from this cause can be avoided by using better quality milk. Bacteriophage can inhibit or prevent acid development in buttermilk just as it can in other fermented products. The phage may be carried in the mother culture, or the bulk starter may become infected. Sometimes phage activity is not apparent until the final mass culture is prepared. Methods of prevention and control of bacteriophage in the plant were discussed in Chapter 11. During recent years the importance of antibiotics in milk has been recognized. The full extent of this problem is not known, but it is certain that milk drawn soon after antibiotic therapy for mastitis can interfere with growth of the organisms in cultured buttermilk and other fermented dairy products.

## CULTURED SOUR CREAM

Although not strictly a fermented milk, cultured sour cream is made in a manner similar to that of cultured buttermilk, and the problems of production are much the same. Sour cream is a heavy, viscous product with the flavor and aroma of cultured buttermilk. Ordinarily it is consumed as a dressing or topping on other foods such as fruits.

In the usual method of preparation, cream standardized to about 20 per cent fat is heated to at least 82°C. (179.6°F.) for 30 minutes. It is homogenized while hot at 2,000 pounds or more per square inch, then is cooled to about 21°C. (69.8°F.) and inoculated with 0.5 to 1 per cent of butter starter. Incubation is continued at 21°C. (69.8°F.) until the acidity reaches about 0.6 per cent.

Since a heavy body is desired in the final product, agitation of the ripened cream must be kept to a minimum. Some makers cool the product in the vat to 5°C. (41°F.) with gentle mixing, then package the cream, and age it at this temperature for several hours to increase the viscosity. Others package the cream directly after ripening and cool the cartons in a refrigerated room. Some dairies are equipped to fill retail containers with the inoculated cream, incubate them at 21°C. (69.8°F.), and move them to a cold room when the desired acidity is reached. This procedure avoids agitation entirely and yields a product with a stiffer body than usual. The addition of dry milk solids to the original cream also increases the consistency of the cultured product.

## BULGARIAN BUTTERMILK

Milk soured with *Lactobacillus bulgaricus* is marketed as Bulgarian buttermilk. Often it is more viscous and has a higher acidity than cultured buttermilk, and it lacks the aroma characteristic of a good buttermilk culture. The method of manufacture is essentially the same as that described for cultured buttermilk, but is modified to suit the growth requirements of *Lactobacillus bulgaricus*. The mother culture is carried in sterile milk and is incubated at about 37°C. (98.6°F.) for 10 to 14 hours, developing an acidity of 1 per cent or slightly more. The final bulk culture is handled in the same way except that the milk is heated as described for cultured buttermilk. Most consumers object to an acidity appreciably higher than 1 per cent. Because of the elevated incubation temperature, defects sometimes result from growth of contaminating bacteria that survive heating. Use of very high quality milk minimizes trouble from this source.

Some makers mix Bulgarian buttermilk with cultured buttermilk to improve the stability of the latter and to increase the acidity slightly. Attempts to grow the buttermilk culture with *Lactobacillus bulgaricus* and to maintain a correct balance between the organisms usually are unsuccessful because of the widely different temperature requirements of the organisms. Also, some cultures of *Streptococcus lactis* produce substances that inhibit growth of the lactobacillus.

## ACIDOPHILUS MILK

*Lactobacillus acidophilus* is found in large numbers in the intestinal contents of the human infant but is supplanted by other organisms when the child is fed a varied diet. Several decades ago it was learned that *Lactobacillus acidophilus* can be established in the intestines of an adult and that persons afflicted with constipation, diarrhea, and certain other alimentary disorders often are benefited thereby. Following this discovery, considerable amounts of *Lactobacillus acidophilus* were distributed in the United States, mostly in the form of a milk culture of the organism. At present, distribution is limited almost entirely to the larger cities, and most of the milk is consumed for relief of intestinal disorders on the advice of physicians.

Not all strains of *Lactobacillus acidophilus* can be established with equal success in the intestinal tract of man. If acidophilus therapy is to be of any value, therefore, large numbers of viable cells of a readily implantable strain of the organism must be consumed daily, along with a suitable carbohydrate such as lactose or dextrin. Presumably these carbohydrates are effective because they are absorbed from the tract fairly slowly, thus remaining available longer as food for the lactobacilli. The ability of *Lactobacillus acidophilus* to grow at a low surface tension may account for its implantation in the intestines when closely related species cannot grow there.

*Lactobacillus acidophilus* does not multiply rapidly in milk and is easily overgrown by contaminating bacteria; hence the milk must be sterilized, or nearly so, before inoculation. The flavor of the resulting product is not relished by most consumers. Many attempts have been made to distribute

*Lactobacillus acidophilus* in a form that is more palatable. For example, the organism has been incorporated in candies, jellies, sherbets, powders, tablets, and other materials. Most of these preparations are worthless when they reach the consumer because the organism dies readily. A palatable and effective preparation is the so-called sweet acidophilus milk. For its preparation, cells of *Lactobacillus acidophilus* are centrifuged out of a broth culture and dispersed in pasteurized whole milk. Under ordinary refrigeration this product remains sweet, and most of the cells remain viable for one to two weeks.

### PREPARATION OF ACIDOPHILUS MILK

*Mother culture.* Skimmilk is sterilized in covered flasks or bottles at 15 pounds for about 20 minutes. After the milk cools to 37°C. (98.6°F.) it is inoculated with about 1 per cent of an active culture of *Lactobacillus acidophilus* that is known to be implantable. Some makers add 5 per cent of tomato or carrot juice to the milk before sterilization to stimulate growth of the organism. Daily transfers of the mother culture are desirable to maintain the activity of the organism. Careful bacteriological technique must be followed to avoid contamination during handling. Gram-stained preparations of the culture should be examined at frequent intervals to check its purity. Micrococci, apparently from the air, are the usual though not invariable contaminants.

*Bulk starter.* If large batches of acidophilus milk are to be made, a bulk starter must be prepared to provide sufficient inoculum for the final batch. The bulk starter is handled in the same way as the mother culture except that ample volumes of milk are sterilized in large flasks or other suitable containers. If small quantities of the fermented milk are to be made, the mother culture will provide a sufficient volume of inoculum.

*Final culture.* The milk for the final product may be sterilized in flasks or bottles as described for the mother culture. Some makers also add 5 per cent tomato or carrot juice to this milk before sterilization. If the milk is of good bacteriological quality it may be given a less severe heat treatment than this. Some makers heat it almost to boiling for 1 hour, cool to 37°C. (98.6°F.), hold for 4 hours to allow spore germination, then reheat almost to boiling for 1 hour to destroy any new vegetative cells. Following this treatment the milk is cooled again to 37°C., inoculated with 1 to 2 per cent of active culture, and held until it coagulates. Then it is chilled, bottled, and distributed. Some makers use an even less severe heat treatment than this. They hold clean, pasteurized skimmilk at 37°C. for about 3 hours to permit spores to germinate, then heat the milk almost to boiling for 30 minutes. Thereafter it is cooled rapidly to the incubation temperature and handled as described above.

The two major problems in manufacturing acidophilus milk are to avoid contamination of the culture and to keep the cells of *Lactobacillus acidophilus* alive until they are consumed. Contamination can best be avoided by strict attention to sterilizing the milk and by following established bacteriological procedures in making transfers. The organisms can be kept alive with greatest success if the acidity is not allowed to become excessive and if the storage temperature is maintained near the optimum. Studies have shown that *Lactobacillus acidophilus* survives best if the acidity does not exceed 0.6 to 0.7 per cent and the temperature is between 5°C. and 20°C. (41°F. and 68°F.). Under these conditions milk cultures of *Lactobacillus acidophilus* can be kept satisfactorily for at least 1 week. For longer storage, Kulp (6) has suggested that foreign bacteria, if present, must be in negligible numbers, that the acidity of the culture should be about 0.65 per cent, and that the temperature of storage should be 16°C. (60.8°F.).

## YOGURT

Yogurt is one of the oldest fermented milks known. Since early times it has been an important food item of peoples in the Middle East, especially in those countries bordering the eastern Mediterranean coast. In contrast to the mildly acid, slightly alcoholic kefir and kumiss to be described later, yogurt is a quick-curdled, decidedly acid preparation with little or no alcohol. It is similar to fermented milks called "leben" in Egypt, "lebeny" in Syria, "dadhi" in India, and "mazun" in Armenia.

Commercial production of yogurt increased rapidly in Europe early in the 20th century after Metchnikoff's publications advocated consumption of sour milk to prolong life. Attempts to popularize yogurt in the United States and Canada were first successful in the 1940's.

Traditionally, yogurt was made from milk that had been boiled for a considerable time to evaporate off part of the water and thus concentrate the solids. Today a similar effect is achieved by removing ¼ to ⅓ of the water in a vacuum pan, by adding 4 to 5 per cent of dry skimmilk solids to whole milk, or by mixing appropriate quantities of whole or skimmilk with ordinary condensed milk. In some countries the product made from these concentrated milk preparations is called "Bulgarian yogurt" to distinguish it from the "milk yogurt" prepared from unconcentrated milk.

Most yogurt has a heavy consistency resembling custard. Ideally the curd is smooth and firm. In addition to being acid, yogurt is said to have a mildly nut-like flavor and a typical "yogurt" aroma.

### MANUFACTURE OF YOGURT

Methods of commercial preparation of yogurt vary considerably in certain details, but the basic process is essentially the same in all dairy plants. Good quality milk is heated both to reduce its microbial content and to improve it generally for growth of the yogurt organisms. For yogurt made in America from concentrated milk, the heat treatment usually falls within the range 82°C. (179.6°F.) for 30 minutes to 93°C.

(199.4°F.) for 60 to 90 minutes. This treatment is too severe for milk of normal solids content, however, causing a weak-bodied product. For this type of yogurt Pette recommends an exposure of 10 minutes at 80°C. to 90°C. (176°F. to 194°F.). Milk for yogurt can be whole or skimmed, although fat improves the flavor of the product. Frequently it is homogenized before inoculation.

After the heat treatment, the milk is cooled to about 48°C. (118.4°F.) and inoculated with 2 to 3 per cent of yogurt culture. The inoculum is mixed well with the milk, the mixture is dispensed in the final retail containers, usually jars or cartons, and these are incubated at 45°C. (113°F.). The final acidity desired in the yogurt depends on the tastes of the consumer, but most seem to prefer a product with a titratable acidity of 0.85 to 0.90 per cent. To achieve this range many makers remove the yogurt from the incubator when the acidity reaches 0.65 to 0.70 per cent. Further acid formation occurs while the product is being cooled. Under the conditions described here an active yogurt culture requires only 2.5 to 3.5 hours to produce the desired amount of acid.

The yogurt is cooled to about 5°C. (41°F.) and held at this temperature until distributed to the consumer. Under these conditions the product can be kept satisfactorily for 1 to 2 weeks.

### ORGANISMS IN YOGURT

The essential bacteria in a yogurt culture are *Streptococcus thermophilus* and *Lactobacillus bulgaricus*. Other organisms have been reported in this and similar fermented milks, but the two species named are the only ones essential for production of a good product. For best results these organisms should be in approximately equal numbers in the culture; otherwise the yogurt will lack the most desirable consistency, flavor, and odor. When the mixture is inoculated into milk, the cocci grow much more rapidly than do the rods, often outnumbering the latter by 3 or 4 to 1 at the end of the first hour of incubation at 45°C. (113°F.). Thus the initial acid production is due largely to the activity of *Streptococcus thermophilus*. Gradually the rods increase in numbers until at the end of the incubation period they again approximate the cocci in numbers. Acid production during the latter part of the incubation period is accomplished by *Lactobacillus bulgaricus* (8, 10).

In the yogurt culture, the function of *Streptococcus thermophilus* is not completely understood beyond the fact that it grows more rapidly than *Lactobacillus bulgaricus* and thus initiates acid production. Some workers claim that the coccus contributes to the flavor and aroma of the final product. Pette and Lolkema (10), on the other hand, attribute all of the yogurt aroma and most of the flavor development to *Lactobacillus bulgaricus*. *Streptococcus thermophilus* is said to improve the body of yogurt by reducing the viscosity characteristic of milk cultures of *Lactobacillus bulgaricus*. Whatever its specific role may be, *Streptococcus thermophilus* is necessary for production of good quality yogurt.

The function of *Lactobacillus bulgaricus* is better understood than is that of the coccus culture. Pette and Lolkema (9) have shown that the rods stimulate growth of *Streptococcus thermophilus* by liberating essential amino acids, especially valine, from the milk proteins. They have further shown that *Streptococcus thermophilus* grown in association with *Lactobacillus bulgaricus* produces considerably more acid per cell than does the same culture when grown alone. The rod culture produces enough acid to give the product its desired final characteristics and in addition liberates the volatile products responsible for the typical yogurt flavor and aroma. The identity of these products is not known with certainty, but Schulz and others (13) have shown a correlation between yogurt flavor and the presence of acetaldehyde.

### CARRYING THE MOTHER CULTURE

Some authorities suggest that yogurt makers obtain pure cultures of *Streptococcus thermophilus* and *Lactobacillus bulgaricus,* carry them separately, and then mix the two for preparation of the final yogurt. The cultures can be obtained either from stock culture collections or by isolating them from a good yogurt culture. If the latter is done, one must be certain that the individual strains selected are capable of producing good yogurt. Even if the organisms are carried separately, the results of Pette and Lolkema (9) suggest that they should be grown together for at least one transfer to activate the cocci prior to use in making yogurt.

Most commercial yogurt cultures are supplied as mixtures of the desired organisms. Distributors of these cultures usually advise yogurt makers to obtain new starters each week or two, rather than attempt to carry the cultures in the dairy plant and run the risk of changes in the characteristics of the starter. With sufficient attention to detail, however, the mixed culture can be carried for long periods without adverse effects on its desirable qualities.

Yogurt mother cultures should be carried in sterile skim or whole milk. To maintain the optimum 1:1 ratio between the two species, inoculation should be at the rate of 2 to 3 per cent, incubation should be at 45°C. (113°F.), and the final acidity should be 0.85 to 0.90 per cent. Preferably the culture should be transferred daily. Bulk starter is prepared in the same way, using larger quantities of milk.

Wide departure from these conditions will favor either the coccus or the rod and will result in imbalance between the two. The proportion of *Streptococcus thermophilus* in the mixed culture is increased by (a) ripening the culture to a low acidity, e. g., 0.60 per cent; (b) using a low incubation temperature, e. g., 37°C. (98.6°F.); (c) employing a small inoculum, e. g., 0.1 per cent. Conversely, *Lactobacillus bulgaricus* becomes predominant if

(a) the culture is ripened to high acidity; (b) the incubation temperature is too high; or (c) the inoculation rate is excessive. Yogurt cultures should be examined frequently not only for contamination but also for the ratio of rods and cocci in the mixture. If the organisms are not present in approximately equal numbers, balance can be restored by modification of the method of handling so as to favor the species in the minority (11).

### DEFECTS OF YOGURT

Flavor defects are common to yogurt just as they are to any milk product. Perhaps the most common fault is the absence of typical yogurt flavor and aroma. Assuming that the mother culture contains the desired balance of cocci and rods, insufficient flavor development in the final product usually results from inadequate acid formation. Optimum flavor development occurs only after the acidity reaches about 0.85 per cent, but ripening much beyond 0.95 per cent yields a product that is too sour. Aroma compounds are formed over a considerably wider range of acidity. Absence of typical yogurt flavor and aroma also can result from use of strains of *Lactobacillus bulgaricus* that produce little of the flavor and aroma substances.

Unclean and bitter flavors in yogurt sometimes result from using poor quality milk or contaminated starter. Certain strains of *Lactobacillus bulgaricus* can cause a bitter taste.

Slow acid production by yogurt cultures has been traced to bacteriophage attacking the cells of *Streptococcus thermophilus* (7). Phage resistant cultures have been obtained, but the body of yogurt made with these cultures is not as firm as is desired.

Weak curd formation is a serious problem with yogurt made from milk of normal solids content. According to the results of Pette and Lolkema (12), a weak curd is most likely to result if the solids content of the milk is low or if a significant amount of the milk is from cows early in the lactation cycle. Also, some cows give milk that inherently forms a weak curd. Firmness of the curd from "weak curd" milks can be increased by adding 1 to 2 per cent of dry milk solids or by homogenizing the milk at about 54°C. (129.2°F.) and a pressure of 3,000 pounds per square inch just before inoculation. Addition of a small amount of rennet also increases firmness, but it harms the flavor and texture of the yogurt. The temperature at which the milk is heated before inoculation also can influence the strength of the curd. Pette and Lolkema (12) advise a heat treatment of 80°C. to 90°C. (176°F. to 194°F.) for 10 minutes to obtain maximum firmness of body.

Sometimes, but not always, associated with weak curd formation is whey separation, which, according to Pette and Lolkema (12), is caused by an incorrect salt balance in the milk. These workers were able to minimize the defect by reducing the heat treatment as much as possible and by adding small amounts of calcium chloride to the milk.

## KEFIR

In contrast to the fermented milks previously described, kefir is a product of mixed lactic acid and alcoholic fermentations. The acid is produced by organisms resembling *Streptococcus lactis* and *Lactobacillus bulgaricus,* while the alcohol is formed by lactose-fermenting yeasts. Other organisms doubtless are present from time to time, but presumably they are not necessary to make kefir. This product usually contains up to 1 per cent of acid, 1 per cent or less of alcohol and, if prepared in a closed container, sufficient carbon dioxide to cause effervescence.

The organisms in kefir exist in convoluted masses somewhat resembling popcorn. Usually the masses range in size from ¼ to ¾ inch in diameter. During active fermentation these masses or grains are carried to the surface by the carbon dioxide produced. They can be strained out and used to inoculate other batches of milk. The grains can be washed, dried, and stored for long periods of time between uses. For reactivation they are transferred daily in pasteurized skimmilk. As they become more active they enlarge, become gelatinous, and tend to rise to the surface.

Kefir is native to the Caucasus Mountain area, where it is made from the milk of any of several animal species. Traditionally the fermentation takes place in a sealed leather bag made of the skin of a goat. The fermentation is more or less continuous in that fresh milk is added as kefir is removed for use. Ordinarily the bag is hung out of doors in the shade during the summer, but is kept indoors during the winter for warmth. It is hung near the door so that each person going past can kick or shake the bag to keep the contents mixed.

Kefir is not produced in significant commercial quantities in America, although some persons make it for home use. Directions for its preparation are found in references 1 and 3 at the end of this chapter.

## KUMISS

Another fermented milk containing both acid and alcohol is kumiss. This product is native to parts of Southern Russia, where it is made from mare's milk. The organisms responsible for the fermentation are similar in most respects to those described for kefir, but they do not develop masses or grains. A small amount of fermented kumiss is used to inoculate each batch of fresh milk.

Aside from the effects of contaminating organisms that undoubtedly grow during the preparation of kumiss, the characteristics of the final product vary considerably with age. Incubation for 12 to 24 hours usually yields a mildly acid milk with relatively little alcohol. On incubation for several days the acidity may reach 1 per cent and the alcohol content may rise as high as 2 per cent.

## TAETTE

In the Scandinavian countries considerable amounts of taette are produced, mainly in the home, by fermenting fresh milk with a strain of *Streptococcus lactis* resembling the *hollandicus* variety. Taette is mildly acid in flavor and is markedly viscous.

## SKYR

This product has been made in Iceland since the 10th century. In recent years it has been introduced into Denmark. For its preparation, skimmilk is fermented to a high acidity, and sufficient whey is removed to increase the solids content to 18 to 20 per cent. The resulting product is, in reality, a fairly firm curd. For consumption, milk and sugar are added to produce a smooth, creamy mass. It is eaten with a spoon.

The identities of the organisms responsible for the skyr fermentation are not known with certainty. Apparently the main ones are *Streptococcus thermophilus* and *Lactobacillus bulgaricus*. For commercial production skimmilk is heated to about 93°C. (199.4°F.) for a few minutes, cooled to 42°C. to 44°C. (107.6°F. to 111.2°F.), and inoculated with 0.1 to 0.5 per cent of the mixed starter. About 0.005 per cent of rennet is added with the starter. When incubated in this temperature range, the milk should coagulate in 3 to 4 hours. As soon as the acidity reaches 1.4 to 1.6 per cent (20 to 24 hours) the curd is dipped into cloth bags. Drainage proceeds until the solids content reaches 18 to 20 per cent and the titratable acidity is 2.5 to 3.0 per cent.

## FERMENTED MILKS AS CARRIERS OF PATHOGENIC MICROORGANISMS

Although it is too acid to permit growth of most pathogenic bacteria, sour milk has been incriminated in a few outbreaks of disease and thus has come to the attention of health authorities as a potential source of danger. Many workers have tested the survival times of various pathogens in naturally and artificially infected sour milk. From their results there is no doubt that pathogenic bacteria can survive for several days or more in buttermilk. Species of *Salmonella, Shigella,* and *Brucella,* the tubercle bacillus, and enterotoxin-producing micrococci are among the bacteria that can persist longest. Wilson and Tanner (14), for example, have reported the survival of species of *Salmonella* and *Shigella* for at least 63 days in cultured buttermilk stored at 8°C. (46.4°F.).

To eliminate the danger of disease transmission, fermented milks should be prepared only from high grade milk that has been adequately pasteurized. At all times after heating, the product must be protected from contamination with pathogenic microorganisms.

Coliform bacteria should not be present in commercial fermented milks because these products are prepared from adequately pasteurized milk. Therefore the coliform test (Chapter 5) can be used to determine the sanitary quality of cultured milks. As is true for other milk products, absence of coliform bacteria indicates probable freedom from contamination with pathogenic bacteria of intestinal origin. Presence of coliform bacteria suggests inadequate pasteurization or recontamination after heating, either of which might mean danger to the consumer.

## References

1. Burkey, L. A., Preparation of kefir fermented milks, *Milk Plant Monthly*, 37 (January, 1948): 48–49.

2. ———, Bulgarian and acidophilus cultured milks, *Am. Milk Rev.*, 10 (1948): 46–49.

3. Elliker, P. R., *Practical Dairy Bacteriology*. New York: McGraw-Hill, 1949.

4. Hales, M. W., *Cultures and Starters*, 2nd Ed. Milwaukee: Chr. Hansen's Laboratory, Inc., 1945.

5. Hammer, B. W., *Dairy Bacteriology*, 3rd Ed. New York: Wiley, 1948.

6. Kulp, W. L., Studies on the viability of *L. acidophilus* in acidophilus milk, *Am. J. Public Health*, 21 (1931): 873–883.

7. Pette, J. W., and J. S. Kooy, Bacteriophages in yogurt, *Neth. Milk Dairy J.*, 6 (1952): 233–241.

8. Pette, J. W., and H. Lolkema, Yogurt, I: symbiosis and antibiosis in mixed cultures of *Lb. bulgaricus* and *Sc. thermophilus*, *Neth. Milk Dairy J.*, 4 (1950): 197–208.

9. ———, Yogurt, II: growth stimulating factors for *Sc. thermophilus, Ibid.*, 4 (1950): 209–224.

10. ———, Yogurt, III: acid production and aroma formation in yogurt, *Ibid.*, 4 (1950): 261–273.

11. ———, Yogurt, IV: factors influencing the proportion of streptococci and lactobacilli in a yogurt culture, *Ibid.*, 5 (1951): 14–26.

12. ———, Yogurt, V: firmness and whey separation of milk yogurt, *Ibid.*, 5 (1951): 27–45.

13. Schulz, M. E., E. Voss, and W. Kley, Beiträge zur Chemie des Joghurts, II. Mitteilung. Untersuchungen über die Anwendbarkeit der Acetaldehyd-farbreaktion zur Beurteilung von Joghurt, *Milchwissenschaft*, 9 (1954): 361–365.

14. Wilson, F. L., and F. W. Tanner, Behavior of pathogenic bacteria in fermented milks, *Food Research*, 10 (1945): 122–134.

# 13

## Microbiology of cheese

A discussion of the preservation of milk by fermentation (Chapter 12) can be extended logically to a study of cheese. Both in fermented milk and in cheese a lactic acid fermentation occurs initially, but in making cheese a portion of the water and soluble constituents is removed. This is accomplished by precipitating the casein in the form of a curd, which holds most of the fat and other suspended materials while allowing water and dissolved constituents to drain away.

The origin of cheese making is lost in unrecorded history. Methods of making cheese were described by Greek and Roman writers several centuries before the birth of Christ, and it is known that cheese was made long before that. Primitive peoples learned that the curd of sour milk could be concentrated by pressing and partial drying and that the product could be preserved longer than could sour milk itself. Early cheese makers used milk of the goat, sheep, cow, buffalo, mare, donkey, and perhaps other animals. The milk was curdled in any of several ways—by natural souring, with rennet from the stomachs of nursing animals, with vinegar, or with the juices of certain plants. Spices and salt often were added to the curd, and some varieties of cheese were smoked. Many of these methods still are in use.

Few, if any, distinct varieties of cheese have been developed deliberately. The actual origins of all of the basic types are not known, but most of them doubtless arose through chance. Early cheese makers in a given locality made a cheese which, when ripened under the conditions available, acquired certain characteristics of its own. Cheese made in other localities and subjected to different manufacturing and ripening conditions acquired other characteristics. Thus specific varieties appeared. Those with desirable qualities became articles of commerce and usually were named after the village or district in which they were manufactured. When these were produced in still other localities, the resulting cheese often developed characteristics differing slightly from those of the original type. In this way new varieties and sub-varieties originated. As knowledge of the basic facts of cheese making has emerged during recent decades, it has been possible to develop a few new cheeses by modifying the making and ripening processes of established varieties. In all there are hundreds of cheeses bearing dif-

**334**

ferent names, but many of them differ only slightly, if at all, in their characteristics (57).

The characteristics of ripened cheeses vary widely. In consistency alone they range from cheeses that are so hard they must be grated for eating to cheeses so soft they can be spread like warm butter. Between these extremes lie all possible gradations. Certain fundamental factors determine the consistency of a cheese, and control of these factors is necessary if the product is to have the desired characteristics. Softness, for example, is favored by a high moisture content, extensive proteolysis, and high fat; hardness by the opposite of these. By regulating these factors the maker can produce a cheese with almost any consistency desired. At the same time he can regulate the flavor of the product by providing conditions that will bring about the necessary chemical changes.

For a better understanding of the discussion that is to follow, the reader should be familiar with the characteristics of the important groups of cheese. The following outline lists the main groups with typical varieties that belong in each.

### THE MAIN GROUPS OF CHEESE

I. Natural cheeses
  A. Unripened, soft
    1. Low fat—Cottage, Baker's cheese
    2. High fat—Cream, Neufchâtel
  B. Ripened
    1. Hard grating cheese—Romano, Parmesan, Asiago old
    2. Hard—Cheddar, Swiss, Gruyère, Provolone
    3. Semi-soft—Roquefort, Blue, Gorgonzola, Brick, Limburger
    4. Soft—Camembert, Brie, Liederkranz
II. Pasteurized process cheeses, cheese foods, and cheese spreads
III. Whey cheeses—Mysost, Ricotta

The natural cheeses in group I are consumed as prepared and ripened. Comminuting, blending, and heating one or more varieties of natural cheese yield the pasteurized process products designated as group II. The foods distributed commercially as whey cheeses (group III) are not cheese by strict definition, since they are made from whey rather than from milk.

All of the soft natural cheeses, whether ripened or not, contain large amounts of water; the hard grating cheeses contain little. Between these extremes the hard and semi-soft varieties occupy ill-defined positions into which the placement of certain varieties is largely a matter of opinion. The divisions of the ripened natural cheeses are chosen to conform with the classes designated by the Federal Security Agency (17) in its definitions and standards for food. The characteristics of representative cheeses within each of the above groups will be considered in more detail later in this chapter.

## THE ESSENTIAL STEPS IN CHEESE MAKING

The basic ingredients of cheese are milk, microorganisms, salt and, with few exceptions, the enzyme rennin. The main purpose of the latter is to help curdle the milk. It is available commercially as rennet extract, which is obtained by soaking the stomachs of young calves in a strong salt solution. The extract contains both rennin, the primary curdling enzyme, and pepsin. Rennin also is distributed as rennet paste, made by grinding the stomachs of young milk-fed calves and kids, or as an extract of the paste.

The conversion of milk into finished cheese can be divided into five distinct steps, although these do not necessarily occur in the order shown. The numerous variations within each of these general steps make possible the hundreds of varieties of cheese known.

1. Preparing and inoculating the milk with lactic acid bacteria.
2. Curdling the milk.
3. Shrinking the curd and pressing it into forms.
4. Salting.
5. Ripening.

### PREPARING AND INOCULATING THE MILK WITH LACTIC ACID BACTERIA

*Milk for cheese.* Cheese can be made from the milk of any mammal, but most of it is produced from cow's milk. The milk of sheep is used for a few varieties (e. g., Roquefort in France, Liptauer or Brinsen in Hungary), and small amounts of cheese are produced from the milk of goats and buffaloes in various parts of the world. The milk must be from healthy animals, and to avoid undesirable fermentations, it must be of good bacteriological quality. Of the tests for milk quality described in Chapter 5, the methylene blue and resazurin tests are most widely used in cheese factories because of their simplicity. In addition, many cheese makers, especially in Europe, perform some kind of fermentation test that supposedly shows the main types of organisms that may grow in the cheese. The test is performed simply by incubating a sample of the milk with or without added starter and rennet, and by then observing the types of changes that result. The test is most valuable for revealing gas-forming organisms. Since the milk must support active growth of acid-forming bacteria, it must be free of inhibitory substances such as residual antibiotics used in treating mastitis.

Milk may be subjected to any of several treatments before it is placed in the cheese vat. To provide the desired fat content in the final product, for example, the composition of the milk may be adjusted either by adding cream, by removing part or all of the fat, or by adding non-fat milk solids. For some types of cheese, e. g., the very hard varieties, a reduced fat content is necessary, whereas varieties such as cream cheese require a higher fat content than is normally present in milk. For many types of cheese the milk is run through a clarifier to remove extraneous matter. This treatment probably has little influence on the quality of most cheeses, but for Swiss it has a beneficial effect on eye formation. Some Cheddar makers also think clarification improves the quality of their product.

Pasteurization of milk has been practiced successfully with nearly all types of cheese made in the United States, and its use is increasing. This process destroys not only pathogenic microorganisms but also many potential spoilage types so that defects are less common in cheese made from pasteurized milk. Unfortunately such cheese ripens less rapidly than cheese made from raw milk, presumably because many of the bacteria originally present are destroyed, and some of the natural milk enzymes are inactivated. The federal requirement (16) that all cheese intended for consumption without processing be made from pasteurized milk or be ripened for at least 60 days has provided a strong stimulus to increased use of pasteurization of milk for cheese. The purpose of this order is to help insure the absence of disease-producing microorganisms, which, if present, should be destroyed during the aging process.

*Starter cultures.* Lactic acid formation by bacteria is necessary in the production of all kinds of cheese. Acid has several important functions: (a) it promotes curd formation by rennin; (b) it causes the curd to shrink and thus promotes drainage of whey; (c) it helps prevent growth of undesirable microorganisms during making and ripening; (d) it affects the elasticity of the finished curd and promotes fusion of the curd into a solid mass; (e) it affects the nature and extent of enzymatic changes during ripening and thus helps determine the characteristics of the cheese. The amount of acid formed and the time at which it is produced in the making operation help determine the kind of cheese that will result. These can be controlled by the kind and amount of starter used and the method of handling the curd.

At one time cheese makers depended on the bacteria normally present in milk to produce the necessary acid in the cheese. Because the desirable organisms usually are accompanied by undesirable ones, however, it is preferable to use milk with the lowest practicable microbial content and to add the desired kinds of organisms as actively growing starter cultures that can produce acid rapidly. This is essential, of course, if the milk is pasteurized.

The type of organism used in the starter is determined mainly by the heat treatment given the curd during manufacture. If the curd is not heated (cooked) or is heated only up to 38°C. (100°F.) or slightly higher, *Streptococcus lactis* or *Streptococcus cremoris* is used. The culture may consist of a single strain, but more often it contains several strains of one or the other species. For cheeses that are cooked to high temperature, such as 49°C. to 54°C. (120.2°F. to 129.2°F.), lactic organisms with high growth temperatures and resistance to heat are used. These starters almost always consist of a mixture of *Streptococcus thermophilus* with a lactobacillus, usually *Lactobacillus bulgaricus, Lactobacillus helveticus,* or *Lactobacillus lactis.* With cheeses cooked to intermediate temperatures, e. g., 42°C. to 46°C. (110°F. to 115°F.), some makers use a mixture of *Streptococcus thermophilus* and *Streptococcus lactis.* The former can produce acid while the curd is hot, and the latter becomes active after the temperature falls to about 38°C. (100°F.).

To some extent the cheese maker can control the rate of acid development in cheese by varying the amount of starter added. In the so-called short method of making cottage cheese, for example, he may add as much as 5 per cent of starter to achieve coagulation in a short time, whereas in the long method the amount of starter commonly is 0.3 to 1 per cent. For some types of cheese as little as 0.1 per cent starter is used so that acid production will not be too rapid.

Cheese makers often ripen the milk or hold it at a favorable temperature to allow the starter organisms to form a small amount of acid before rennet is added. With some types of cheese this is especially important to permit optimum drainage of the curd. The temperature of holding varies with the type of cheese and with the starter organism.

### CURDLING THE MILK

Curdling (or coagulation) is the term used to describe the change of milk from a liquid to a solid or gel state by precipitation of casein. The structure of the gel is such that most of the fat, the bacteria, the colloidal calcium phosphate, and other particulate constituents are trapped in the curd. Water and dissolved materials are present to the extent that whey is retained after the bulk of the curd is reduced by shrinkage. To understand the changes that occur during curd making it is desirable, therefore, to consider first the nature of the proteins in milk and the effect of the coagulating agencies on them.

Casein is the principal nitrogenous constituent of milk. It is classed as a phosphoprotein and in its natural state exists in combination with calcium. In milk the calcium caseinate complex is dispersed as a colloidal suspension of minute, gelatinous particles in the liquid phase. These particles vary considerably in size, although the larger ones are believed to represent multiples of a smaller basic unit. Calcium caseinate particles can be demonstrated with an ultra-microscope, and the larger ones, at least, can be removed by high speed centrifugation. The particles do not pass through a semi-permeable membrane, and they can be removed from milk by certain types of unglazed porcelain filters. The structure of the casein particle still is not understood exactly, but there are known to be at least three fractions, usually designated as $\alpha$, $\beta$, and $\gamma$. For purposes of this discussion, however, casein can be considered as a single entity. In making cheese, casein is precipitated with acid or with rennin.

When casein is removed from milk, the remaining clear liquid contains lactalbumin and globulin, the so-called whey proteins. These proteins are very finely dispersed as a colloidal solution of the hydrosol type. Because of their small particle size they can not be removed by ordinary high speed centrifugation, but they can be taken out with very fine membrane filters. As far as is known at present, lactalbumin is a single chemical entity, but the globulin fraction consists of at least three apparently distinct compounds called $\alpha$-, $\beta$-, and $\gamma$-globulin. Lactalbumin and the globulins are readily precipitated by heat but not by acid or rennin. They comprise the bulk of the protein in the so-called whey cheeses that are made by boiling whey.

Acid precipitation is employed in certain methods of making cottage cheese and a few other types. As acid is formed by the starter organisms, calcium is gradually removed from the calcium caseinate to form calcium lactate. When the calcium content of the protein is reduced to a low enough point, the casein precipitates. At its isoelectric point, pH 4.6 to 4.7 at 21°C. (69.8°F.), casein is in its purest form and at its lowest point of hydration, that is, its minimum solubility. Acid precipitation of casein can be reversed by restoration of the original pH and salt balance.

Acid curd is very fragile and must be handled carefully at first to avoid its dispersion as small particles, with consequent loss of yield of cheese. After the curd is cut into pieces and loses part of its whey, its firmness increases to the point where it can be stirred and manipulated without loss. The initial firmness of the curd can be increased by adding to the milk small amounts of rennet extract, as is done in some methods of making cottage cheese.

Milk for most cheese is coagulated by rennin. The mechanism of this process has been studied for many years and still is not completely understood. According to the most widely accepted theories, however, the clotting process occurs in two steps. First the calcium caseinate is acted on by rennin to form calcium paracaseinate, a compound with greater base-combining power than casein. Next the paracaseinate reacts with free calcium ions and becomes insoluble, thus precipitating to form the typical gel or curd. Coagulation is accelerated by heat and acid, part of the function of the latter being to increase the concentration of calcium ions by dissolving calcium phosphate. Certain milks are naturally low in calcium, and for this reason cheese makers may add small amounts of calcium chloride to improve the curdling properties.

At the normal pH of milk when curdled, the gel consists mainly of a compound called dicalcium paracaseinate (64). This curd is jelly-like and much less fragile than an acid curd. It will shrink more than an acid curd during subsequent operations. Cheese made by rennin or acid coagulation contains only that portion of the lactalbumin and globulin that is dispersed in the whey retained by the curd after draining.

In making cheese, rennet extract is diluted with several volumes of water and mixed with the milk after the desired stage of ripeness has been reached. Coagulation usually occurs in less than 30 minutes. The speed of coagulation and the firmness of the curd depend on a number of factors including the composition of the milk, its acidity, the amount and strength of rennet added, and the temperature, all of which are to some extent under the control of the cheese maker.

### SHRINKING THE CURD AND PRESSING IT INTO FORMS

For all types of cheese the coagulum formed as described in the foregoing section is caused to shrink, thus losing water and becoming more firm. The degree of shrinkage determines the moisture content of the curd and thereby affects to a considerable extent the final consistency of the cheese. Also it determines the lactose content and, since most of this sugar is rapidly fermented to lactic acid, the acidity of the fresh cheese is related directly to the moisture content of the curd.

Curd shrinkage is favored by heat, acid, and rennet. Escape of whey is promoted by cutting the curd into small pieces, stirring, and subjecting the mass to pressure. To produce a cheese with low moisture and relatively low acidity, therefore, the maker does one or more of the following: (a) heats the curd to a fairly high temperature; (b) cuts it into small pieces; (c) assures rapid acid development early in the making process; or (d) subjects the curd to high pressure. Conversely, for a high moisture cheese the curd is not heated; it is cut little, if at all; acid develops after most of the whey drainage has ceased; and the curd is not pressed.

Methods of handling the curd to adjust its moisture content to the desired level are many. The procedures listed below represent various possibilities, ranging from the method that results in least moisture loss to those that cause the most.

(a) The curdled milk is ladled directly from the vat into perforated molds or forms that retain the curd but allow whey to escape. No pressure is applied. This method yields curd with high moisture, high acidity, and a very soft consistency.

(b) The curd is cut into cubes, and part of the whey is allowed to separate, usually with stirring. The mixture is dipped into forms as in method (a). Light pressure may or may not be applied.

(c) The curd cut as in method (b) is heated or cooked before dipping into forms where pressure may or may not be applied. High cooking temperature and high pressure on the curd yield cheese with low moisture and relatively low acidity.

(d) The curd cut and cooked as in method (c) is left in the vat, and the whey is drained off. The curd particles may be kept distinct by frequent stirring, or they may be allowed to fuse into a solid piece. This may be cut into the sizes desired and the pieces may then be placed in molds;

or it may be chopped (milled) into small pieces, which are packed into forms and subjected to high pressure.

Methods (c) and (d) are used for cheese in which careful control of the final acidity is important. For most varieties this control is accomplished by reducing the moisture content to such a level that the lactose contained therein will, when completely fermented to acid, yield the desired pH. For a few varieties it is desirable to have a fairly high moisture content yet a relatively low acidity (e. g., Brick, soaked-curd cheese). This can be accomplished by immersing the curd in water, thus removing part of the lactose without reducing the moisture content. By regulating this treatment, cheese can be made with almost any acidity desired.

Throughout this discussion of curd making the importance of acidity has been mentioned repeatedly. Since acid is a product of the bacteria in the starter and since the amount of acid produced has a pronounced effect on subsequent microbial activity, it is desirable to consider here the effect of acid on the chemical and physical composition of the curd.

According to the views of Van Slyke (64), casein exists in rennet curd as dicalcium paracaseinate. When lactic acid is formed by the starter organisms, it reacts with the paracaseinate as follows:

(1) Dicalcium paracaseinate $+$ Lactic acid $\longrightarrow$ Monocalcium paracaseinate $+$ Calcium lactate

(2) Monocalcium paracaseinate $+$ Lactic acid $\longrightarrow$ Free paracasein $+$ Calcium lactate

These reactions are written separately because the compounds formed, free paracasein and its monocalcium salt, have widely different properties.

As soon as acid is produced in appreciable amounts, cheese curd begins to show elasticity. This property becomes more and more noticeable as the acidity increases until finally the curd can be stretched considerably or, if heated, it can be drawn out in long strings. For some types of cheese (e. g., Swiss, Provolone) elasticity is an essential characteristic of the curd. Van Slyke (64) attributes this "plastic and ductile" quality of cheese curd to the presence of monocalcium paracaseinate (reaction 1). He has shown that this substance comprises over 90 per cent of the nitrogenous material in Cheddar cheese a few hours after the curd is put in the press. Most likely it appears similarly in other cheese curds at some time.

If acid production continues far enough, however, the curd loses much of its elasticity, becoming hard and brittle. Referring again to Van Slyke's theory, this change probably results from the formation of free paracasein (reaction 2). This substance does not show the elastic properties of its monocalcium salt.

Thus the amount of acid formed in fresh cheese curd determines the form in which the casein exists, that is, as free paracasein or as the monocalcium salt. In cheeses that become very acid (e. g., Camembert, pH 4.6 to 4.8), all of the casein appears as free paracasein (Van Slyke, 64). In Cheddar, Swiss, Brick, and related types (pH 5.0 to 5.2), there is a mixture of the two, the proportion of each depending on the actual pH reached. Whether these two forms of casein are equally available to the ripening organisms or are equally reactive with proteolytic enzymes is not known. Regardless of this question, the form in which the protein exists affects the elasticity of the curd and therefore affects the characteristics of the ripened cheese.

### SALTING

Sodium chloride is added to practically all varieties of cheese at some stage in their manufacture. The most common methods of application are to float the fresh cheese in a strong salt brine or to rub the surface with dry salt. The amount of salt taken up by the cheese depends on the concentration of the brine, the time and temperature of exposure, the ratio of surface to volume of the cheese, and its moisture content. At first the salt is most concentrated near the surface, but in time it diffuses fairly uniformly throughout the cheese. With cheese made by method (d), as described in the preceding section, the salt is mixed with the drained curd particles shortly before they are pressed. In this way the salt rapidly becomes distributed uniformly throughout the mass.

Among its several functions in cheese, salt contributes to the flavor. In addition, it withdraws whey from the curd and thus helps control moisture and acidity. Of primary importance is the action of salt in controlling growth of undesirable microorganisms. Strongly proteolytic bacteria, for example, are sensitive to sodium chloride in the concentrations found in most cheeses.

### RIPENING

Fresh cheese curd consists mainly of protein and water, with variable quantities of fat, lactic acid, and sodium chloride, plus small amounts of lactose and salts. Even though the amounts of these constituents may vary widely, the curd always has a bland, slightly sour, and somewhat salty taste. When chewed it is fairly tough and, with some varieties, rubbery. To increase its palatability, most cheese curd is caused to undergo a ripening or curing process by which it acquires the desired flavor and physical characteristics. The chemical changes responsible for transforming the fresh curd into the final cheese are catalyzed by enzymes from three main sources: (a) rennet or other enzyme preparation of animal or vegetable origin; (b) microorganisms that grow within the cheese or on its surface; and (c) the milk itself. The composition of the fresh curd and the conditions under which it is held during ripening determine the nature and extent of the enzymatic changes and thereby determine the kind of cheese that results.

*Gross changes.* During ripening, cheese undergoes marked changes in body and flavor and, with certain varieties, texture. Body is the term used to refer to the consistency of the cheese. It includes such characteristics as elasticity, firmness, cohesiveness, and plasticity. Changes in these properties are associated largely with enzymatic hydrolysis of the protein, thus making more of the casein soluble. As a result the cheese loses its toughness and elasticity, becoming softer and, in low moisture cheese, more crumbly. If large amounts of acid are developed during manufacture, the fresh curd tends to be crumbly and brittle, and the body is described as "short," meaning that it will not stretch without breaking (Figure 13.1). With some varieties of cheese this condition is considered to be a defect; with others it is unimportant, or it may even be desirable (e. g., Roquefort). The careful control of acid development in making Cheddar, Swiss, Brick, and similar varieties is intended partly to avoid shortness of body and to retain the elasticity characteristic of these types of cheese.

**Figure 13.1**  Body of Cheddar cheese. (*Top*) Normal "long" body. (*Bottom*) "Short" body caused by excessive acidity. Photos courtesy of Kraft Foods Co.

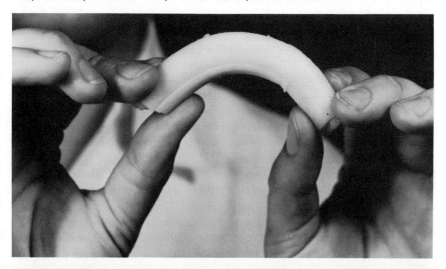

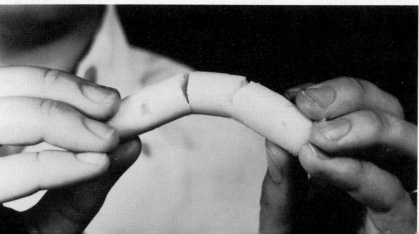

Any constituent that can be tasted or smelled contributes to flavor; hence the characteristic flavor of any cheese is a result of a balanced mixture of compounds, some present in the fresh curd, others resulting from enzymatic decomposition of one or more of the constituents of the cheese (47). Each variety of cheese is made and ripened in a way that will provide the required quantities of flavor compounds typical of that variety. Thus an insufficient or excessive amount of any essential flavoring constituent is undesirable, just as is the formation of atypical flavoring substances. Knowledge of the specific compounds responsible for the typical flavor of a cheese is difficult to obtain because of the complex mixture of compounds involved, some of which are present in extremely small amounts. No doubt the lactic acid and sodium chloride present initially in the curd contribute to the flavor of the cheese, but these serve mainly as background for more distinctive flavors caused by products of decomposition of lactic acid and lactates, citrates, proteins, and fats. For example, volatile acids such as acetic, propionic, butyric, caproic, caprylic, and capric, and their esters or ketones, may appear in varying amounts during ripening of many cheeses. In addition, some of the amino acids and other products of protein hydrolysis have characteristic tastes that are believed to influence the flavor of the cheese. Glutamic acid, for example, is found in considerable amounts in most types of ripened cheese (36, 37).

Texture refers to the amount of openness or gas space within the cheese. Cheese with no gas space is said to have a close texture; that with considerable space has an open texture (Figure 13.2). Openness can result from failure of curd particles to fuse during pressing or from subsequent gas production. With many types of cheese a close texture is desired, and any considerable amount of openness is considered to be a defect (e. g., Cheddar). With others (e. g., Roquefort) an open texture is necessary to permit vigorous growth of molds throughout the cheese. Moderate openness caused by gas formation is acceptable in some varieties (Brick, Limburger) and necessary in others (Swiss, Gruyère), but excessive or non-characteristic gas production is undesirable in all cheeses.

*Chemical changes in the main cheese constituents.* The bulk of the lactose disappears from most varieties of cheese within the first few days after manufacture. This time may be considerably longer, however, with the very soft, high-moisture cheeses. In Cheddar, and presumably in other varieties as well, the evidence indicates that the lactose is rapidly hydrolyzed to glucose and galactose. The glucose then quickly disappears, whereas galactose may be found for several weeks, especially in cheese made from pasteurized milk (15). Apparently galactose is less readily fermented by the normal Cheddar cheese organisms than is glucose.

Most of the sugar is fermented to lactic acid, but some of it is changed to volatile acids, alcohol, and small amounts of other products. Part of the lactic acid reacts with basic radicals in the cheese to form salts. In a few

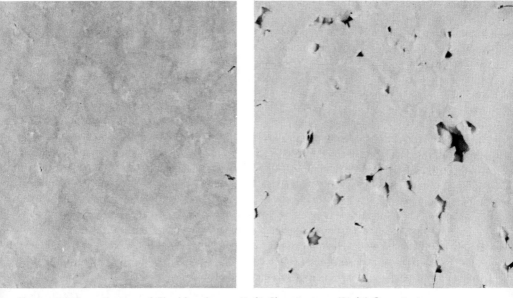

**Figure 13.2**    Texture of Cheddar cheese. (*Left*) Close texture. (*Right*) Open texture. These are mainly mechanical openings which result from incomplete fusion of the curd during pressing. Photos courtesy of The Borden Co.

varieties a portion of the lactic acid is converted to propionic and acetic acids, carbon dioxide, and other compounds.

Practically all of the nitrogenous constituents of young cheese exist as water-insoluble protein. As ripening progresses, part or all of the protein is hydrolyzed enzymatically to simpler compounds that are soluble in water. The general course of these changes may be illustrated as:

$$\underset{(insoluble)}{\text{protein}} \xrightarrow{+\,H_2O} \underset{(\ldots\ldots\ldots\ldots\ldots\ldots\ldots\ldots}{\text{proteoses}} \xrightarrow{+\,H_2O} \text{peptones} \xrightarrow{+\,H_2O} \underset{soluble\ldots\ldots\ldots\ldots\ldots\ldots\ldots)}{\text{peptides}} \xrightarrow{+\,H_2O} \text{amino acids}$$

Microorganisms may deaminate the amino acids to yield ammonia and fatty acids or, less commonly, may decarboxylate them to liberate carbon dioxide and amines.

The decomposition of protein in cheese can be followed in any of several ways. One of the most common methods is to determine the amount of nitrogen in water extracts of cheese at different ages. As protein is hydrolyzed to water-soluble compounds, the values thus obtained increase, showing the progress of ripening. Since most of the nitrogen initially present is in the form of protein, periodic measurements of non-protein nitrogen also reveal the progress of ripening. For this purpose the protein in a suspension of cheese is precipitated with acetic, trichloroacetic, or other acid, and the nitrogen remaining in solution is measured and expressed as non-protein nitrogen. Values for water-soluble nitrogen and non-protein nitrogen merely indicate the disappearance of protein; they do not show the extent or degree of decomposition. More specific information on the extent of protein degradation can be obtained from measurements of amino nitrogen. The resulting values increase markedly with the liberation of free amino groups by hydrolysis to amino acids or simple peptides. Measurement of ammonia indicates the extent of amino acid breakdown by microbial action. In recent years there has been considerable interest in the free amino acids that result from protein hydrolysis. These can be identified by microbiological assay procedures or by partition chromatography on paper or on suitable columns.

The extent of proteolytic action and the specific compounds resulting therefrom help to determine the characteristics of the final cheese. In some of the softer cheeses such as Camembert and Limburger, practically all of the protein is converted to water-soluble compounds, including appreciable amounts of simple peptides, amino acids, and ammonia. This extensive solubilization of the protein, along with the high water content, is responsible for the softness of these cheeses.

Hard cheeses, by contrast, undergo relatively much less protein decomposition. In Cheddar and Swiss, for example, rarely more than 25 to 35 per cent of the protein is made soluble even on extended ripening. Nevertheless, a relatively large proportion of the protein decomposition products is in the form of amino acids and simple peptides, especially in well-aged cheese.

The enzymes responsible for protein decomposition in cheese originate primarily from rennet, or other added natural enzyme preparation, and microorganisms. According to information now available, rennin can cause extensive conversion of casein to water-soluble compounds, but these are relatively complex in nature (i. e., mostly proteoses and peptones). Microbial enzymes, on the other hand, can carry the decomposition farther, yielding relatively large amounts of amino acids and even ammonia. In the hard cheeses the microorganisms involved are mainly lactic acid-forming cocci and rods that grow throughout the mass and produce only small amounts of extracellular proteinases. When they die and autolyze, they liberate intracellular enzymes. In the soft, quick-ripened cheeses, however, most of the proteolysis is attributed to extracellular proteinases liberated by a variety of microorganisms that grow on the surface. With certain of these cheeses, as well as with some of the semi-soft varieties, molds are important agents of proteolysis.

Although its decomposition is by no means as extensive as is that of protein, the fat in cheese also undergoes a certain amount of hydrolysis during ripening. Especially prominent and probably of greatest significance among the hydrolytic products are the volatile lower fatty acids, including butyric, caproic, caprylic, and capric. These acids can be separated from cheese by distillation or by ether extraction of an acidified cheese suspension. The individual acids then can be separated and identified by partition chromatography.

The enzymes responsible for lipolysis in cheese may be from the milk, from microorganisms, or from enzyme preparations added to the milk. Milk lipase is appreciably active only in cheeses made from raw milk. Of the normal cheese-ripening microorganisms, certain strains of lactobacilli, and possibly other bacteria, liberate upon autolysis intracellular lipases that are thought to account for most of the lipolytic activity in Cheddar and similar hard cheeses. Molds are important sources of lipases for cheeses in or on which they grow. Rennet extract has little lipolytic activity, but rennet paste and extracts of certain animal glands are actively lipolytic. These preparations are widely used in the so-called Italian varieties of hard and grating cheeses. Attempts to use purified or concentrated lipase preparations, such as steapsin, to hasten flavor development have been, on the whole, unsuccessful. The flavors thus produced usually are too strong or are undesirable in some other way.

*Methods of ripening.* Cheeses are ripened in either of two basically different ways. In one the cheese is held under conditions that discourage growth on the surface and limit activity to microorganisms and enzymes inside the mass. This procedure is followed with the hard grating cheeses and with practically all of the hard varieties. In the other procedure the cheese is held under conditions that favor growth of organisms on the surface, the so-called "smear" or "slime" development. The enzymes produced there diffuse into the cheese and contribute to the ripening changes. All soft cheeses are ripened in this way. Semi-soft cheeses are ripened by a combination of these methods. With Roquefort and Brick, for example, organisms and enzymes inside the cheese are responsible for most of the ripening changes, but surface organisms contribute to a greater or lesser extent to the flavor. Limburger, on the other hand, is ripened mainly by surface organisms.

Hard cheeses can be made in very large sizes if desired (e. g., Cheddar, Swiss). Salt can be added to the curd before pressing or the pressed cheese can be salted on the surface. Generally these varieties ripen slowly and keep for relatively long periods of time. The relative humidity of the air in the curing room is kept fairly low to discourage surface growth but high enough to prevent excessive evaporation. For some varieties loss of moisture is minimized by coating the surface with paraffin or a plastic film. Because of the long holding time possible, cheeses of widely different degrees of ripeness can be produced within any single variety.

Because surface growth is essential for their ripening, soft cheeses must be made in small pieces to provide the optimum amount of surface in relation to mass. These varieties always are salted on the outside, an important factor in determining the kinds of organisms that grow there. They must be held at a high relative humidity to permit the surface growth.

The development of microorganisms on soft and semi-soft cheeses follows a regular sequence. The only organisms capable of rapid initial growth on the surface with its high acid and salt content are film yeasts and certain molds, notably *Geotrichum candidum*. These organisms metabolize the lactic acid at the surface of the cheese, thus increasing the pH until salt-tolerant bacteria can grow. Also they release vitamins, which stimulate subsequent bacterial development. With some varieties of cheese the first bacteria to appear are micrococci. Whether or not these develop, however, the surface soon becomes reddish to orange in color from growth of *Bacterium linens* or *Bacterium erythrogenes*. With Camembert and Brie the characteristic surface ripening species of *Penicillium* develop after the initial growth of film yeasts. Later, however, the molds are supplanted by the species of *Bacterium*. Figure 13.3 illustrates the changes in microflora on the surface of Blue cheese during ripening.

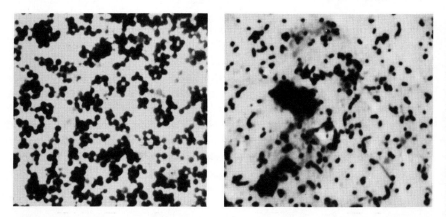

**Figure 13.3**    Photomicrographs from the smear of Blue cheese. (left) At 34 days. Note the predominance of yeasts. (right) At 118 days. The yeasts have been replaced by bacteria, mostly short rods. A similar succession of organisms occurs on all surface-ripened cheeses. Photos courtesy of Dr. H. A. Morris and Professor W. B. Combs, University of Minnesota.

The extent of development of the surface smear markedly affects the characteristics of the final cheese. Extensive growth of *Bacterium linens*, for example, is believed to be responsible for the typical "Limburger-like" flavor, and heavy surface growth is encouraged where this is desired. If a mild flavor is wanted, however, the smear can be washed off at intervals with salt brine to prevent excessive development of the surface organisms.

## PRESERVATION OF CHEESE

At least one reason for converting milk into cheese is to increase the keeping time of the milk constituents. In general, the keeping time increases as more and more water is removed. Cottage cheese with a moisture content of 70 to 80 per cent keeps only a week or two under normal conditions of refrigerated storage; the soft ripened cheeses keep for a few weeks; the semi-soft cheeses a few months; the hard cheeses up to a year or two; and the hard grating cheeses keep almost indefinitely. Aside from the differences in moisture content between milk and cheese, however, several other factors are responsible for the lesser likelihood of the latter to spoil.

The abundance of lactose is one reason why milk is a good culture medium for many microorganisms. In ripened cheese, however, no sugar remains to serve as a source of energy for spoilage organisms. This fact alone largely limits spoilage of properly made cheese to organisms that can oxidize lactate or protein decomposition products. Predominant among these are film yeasts, molds, and certain anaerobic spore-forming bacteria.

The interior of cheese, even small pieces, is essentially anaerobic. This limits the activity of film yeasts and molds to the surface where oxygen is available. With some types of cheese, growth of these organisms is minimized by frequent cleaning of the surface (Swiss); with others by drying the surface and by excluding oxygen with paraffin (Cheddar) or other coating. On surface-ripened cheeses the growth of undesirable molds is prevented by keeping spores of the unwanted organisms away from the curing room.

In practically all cheeses an acidity of at least pH 5.3 is developed, and with many the pH may go as low as 4.5. This acidity does not prevent the development of film yeasts and molds, but it inhibits spoilage bacteria inside the cheese. Fortunately the putrefactive, anaerobic types are among the most sensitive to acid of the potential spoilage bacteria.

The amount of salt added to cheese ranges from as little as 1 per cent or less in Swiss to 5 per cent or more in Roquefort and related types. In assessing the preservative effect of the salt, it should be remembered that all of the sodium chloride is dissolved in the water of the cheese; thus the effective concentration is actually the percentage of salt in water. Assuming 1.5 per cent sodium chloride in Cheddar cheese containing 38 per cent water, for example, the actual brine concentration is 4 per cent [(1.5 ÷ 38) × 100]. This is sufficient to inhibit many potential spoilage bacteria.

Most cheese is ripened at temperatures between 5°C. and 16°C. (41°F. and 61°F.). This is too cold for rapid growth of most spoilage bacteria, although some can grow slowly if the acid and salt concentrations are low.

In considering the reasons why cheese does not spoil readily it should be remembered that no one factor is responsible—rather preservation results from a combination of two or more of them. For example, a cheese at pH 5.3 may spoil readily if insufficient salt is present or if the ripening temperature is too high. Furthermore, the usual preservative factors are effective only with normal low levels of contamination with spoilage organisms. A cheese may show no evidence of spoilage during ripening if it is made from a good milk supply containing a minimum number of spore-forming bacteria. But if large numbers of these organisms are present, serious spoilage may result even though the acidity, salt concentration, and ripening temperature are normal.

## SPOILAGE OF CHEESE

### MOLD

Even though certain mold species are essential for ripening some varieties of cheese, mold growth on most cheeses is undesirable. This is true not only for aesthetic reasons but also because the growth imparts musty or other undesirable flavors to the cheese. Considerable loss is occasioned by the necessity of trimming away the moldy parts. Figure 13.4a shows mold development on Cheddar cheese.

Many species of molds find cheese an excellent medium and are able to develop in curing rooms. The ones most commonly found are in the genera *Penicillium, Cladosporium, Alternaria, Monilia, Mucor,* and *Aspergillus.* Species of *Geotrichum* often grow on high-moisture cheeses such as cottage and cream. Any of these molds can develop on the walls and shelves of curing rooms if there is sufficient moisture and can thus produce spores for infection of fresh lots of cheese.

Rigid sanitation is the first and principal step in controlling mold growth on cheese. Curing room shelves should be varnished to make cleaning easier. Between uses they should be washed with a warm detergent solution and treated with a fungicide. A solution containing 10 per cent formalin or at least 5,000 ppm of active chlorine or a quaternary ammonium compound is satisfactory for this purpose. If the walls and ceiling become infected with molds, it may be necessary to empty the room and disinfect all surfaces thoroughly, either by washing with a fungicide solution or by fumigating, for example with formaldehyde in a hot, moist atmosphere. Fungistatic paints have been used with fair success. Attempts to control molds with ultraviolet ray lamps installed in the curing room have had limited success because not all surfaces can be exposed to effective amounts of the germicidal rays. This problem is intensified by the fact that the molds that form black spores, e. g., *Aspergillus niger,* are very resistant to destruction by ultraviolet rays. Ozone generators sometimes are operated in cheese curing rooms to restrict mold growth, but again this method is not

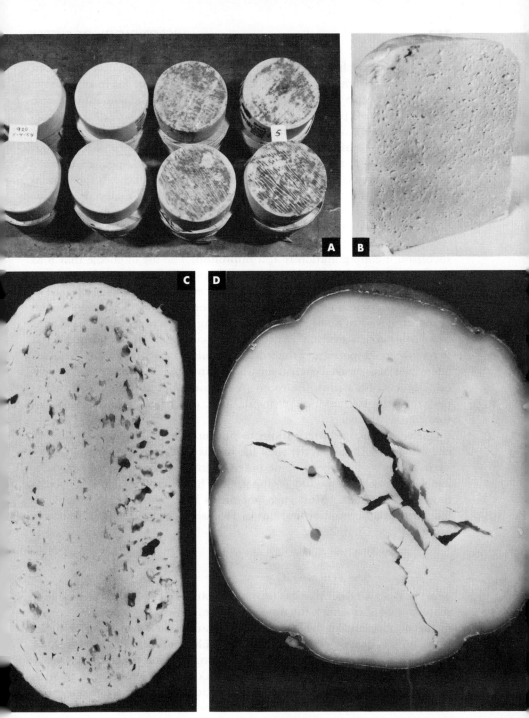

**Figure 13.4** Defects of Cheese. (a) Mold on Cheddar. (b) Early gas in Cheddar caused by *Aerobacter aerogenes*. (c) Early gas in Brick caused by a lactose-fermenting yeast. (d) Late gas in Provolone caused by *Clostridium* sp. Photos courtesy of (b) The Borden Co., and (c and d) Dr. W. V. Price, University of Wisconsin.

completely successful because of the low concentrations of ozone that can be tolerated without causing excessive oxidation of the fat in the cheese.

In recent years there has been a great increase in the amount of cheese prepared in small packages for the retail market. For this purpose the natural cheese is cut into convenient sizes, e. g., ½ to 1 pound, and each piece is sealed in a transparent plastic film. The resulting exposure of fresh cheese surface greatly increases the problem of mold spoilage because several weeks may be required for this cheese to pass through the normal trade channels to the consumer. Many of the wrapping materials used for pre-packaged cheese do not completely prevent the passage of oxygen, hence molds may grow slowly under them.

Control of mold growth on pre-packaged cheese is more likely to be successful if contamination is at a minimum. The use of cheese that is as free of mold as possible naturally is indicated. The surface of the cheese must be cleaned thoroughly, and this may even include slicing off part of the surface. Isolated mold spots must be trimmed away. Then the cleaned cheese is moved to another room for cutting and wrapping. Rigid sanitation in this area is essential. The air to the cutting room should be filtered to remove mold spores, and the workers should change their outer garments often. Surfaces must be cleaned and disinfected frequently to prevent growth of molds within the room. A certain amount of help can be expected from installation of germicidal ultraviolet ray lamps over surfaces that contact the cheese.

Even with rigid precautions to minimize contamination of the cut cheese with mold spores, the shelf life of this product is shorter than is desired. Attempts have been made to lengthen the keeping time by packaging the cheese in a plastic wrapper that has been impregnated with a fungistatic chemical. Most such chemicals have not been acceptable to federal regulatory authorities, but in 1953 sorbic acid was given tentative approval (see Chapter 3).

GAS FORMATION

Undesirable gas formation can occur at almost any stage of manufacture or ripening, the time it becomes noticeable depending largely on the numbers and kinds of gas-forming organisms in the milk. For example, if the milk is heavily contaminated with coliform bacteria and if it is not pasteurized, gas may become evident during cooking of the curd. It may even cause the curd to float rather than sink. Such vigorous gas formation during manufacture of most cheese varieties is likely to occur only with very poor milk supplies in the summer months. It is fairly common with cottage cheese, however, because of the long setting times employed. With this variety the leuconostocs in the starter probably contribute to the gassy condition.

More commonly gas is not noticed until the curd is removed from the press or sometimes two or three days after manufacture. Almost always this "early gas" is produced by coliform bacteria (Figure 13.4b). The time of appearance of the gas and the severity of the defect depend on such factors as the number of coliform bacteria in the milk, the kind of organism involved (species of *Aerobacter* are more active gas formers than species of *Escherichia*), the activity of the starter organisms, the amount of lactose available for fermentation, and, of course, the conditions of holding the curd during draining and for the first few days of ripening. It should be remembered that coliform bacteria, in contrast to some of the other gas producers, are especially difficult to inhibit by starter organisms. Coliform bacteria are fairly tolerant of acid, they ferment lactose readily, and they grow well at the temperatures used in making most kinds of cheese. Therefore, their growth can best be controlled by using good quality milk and, if possible, pasteurizing it.

Lactose-fermenting yeasts may cause early gas in cheese made from raw milk (Figure 13.4c). Also incriminated in a few outbreaks have been gas-producing, aerobic, spore-forming rods. The members of this group, *Bacillus polymyxa* and *Bacillus macerans,* ferment lactose to carbon dioxide and hydrogen plus acetic acid, ethyl alcohol, and small amounts of other substances.

Sometimes gas is not detected in cheese until a few weeks after manufacture. This "late gas" defect usually is caused by species of *Clostridium,* including *Clostridium sporogenes, Clostridium lentoputrescens, Clostridium pasteurianum, Clostridium butyricum* and many others (Figure 13.4d). The severity of the defect can vary from an occasional small hole to large nests of holes or even cracks and fissures, depending on the amount of gas, the rate of its formation, and the elasticity of the curd. Clostridia are present in small numbers in practically all samples of milk. As a group they are sensitive to acid and salt, and most of them have a fairly high optimum temperature as compared with that of the desirable organisms. Consequently they do not grow readily in cheese.

Anaerobic sporeformers are numerous in manure, soil, and defective silage. Their control in cheese is best assured by keeping them out of the milk, by insuring vigorous acid formation in the curd, and by adequate salting. Attempts to control them by using a nisin-producing strain of *Streptococcus lactis* (Chapter 2) in the starter have given hopeful results.

Excessive openness of cheese, usually Cheddar, has been attributed to carbon dioxide production by certain strains of *Leuconostoc citrovorum* and *Leuconostoc dextranicum*. This defect often is seasonal in occurrence and is most noticeable in cheese ripened at temperatures above 10°C. (50°F.). Unless the openness is too pronounced, the cheese is well accepted in American markets, but in other countries a very close texture is desired in Cheddar.

### RIND ROT

Accumulations of moisture on the surface of hard cheeses may allow film yeasts, molds, proteolytic bacteria, and various other types of microorganisms to grow and cause softening, discoloration, and undesirable odors. This condition is called rind rot. It is prevented by keeping the cheese surface dry.

### MISCELLANEOUS FLAVOR DEFECTS

Undesirable flavors in cheese can result from a variety of causes. "Feedy," "weedy," "cowy," "barny," and related flavors result from the use of milk that already has these defects. Flavors resulting from microbial growth are described by a variety of names, and many of them can have several causative agents. Among the defects that have been described, bitterness has been attributed to various acid-proteolytic bacteria as well as to several non-microbial agents; yeasty flavor is caused by growth of yeasts in the cheese; fruity or fermented flavors result from growth of any of a variety of organisms, including coliform bacteria and yeasts; rancidity is caused by activation of milk lipase or by lipolytic microorganisms. These are but a few of the terms that are used to describe flavor defects, many of which are not associated with any specific causative organism.

### COLOR DEFECTS

Atypical colors in cheese often are traceable to mechanical causes, but some of them are produced by microorganisms. Surface discoloration may result from mold growth. Colored spots inside cheese are uncommon but have been reported from time to time. For example, "rusty spots" caused by growth of pigmented strains of *Lactobacillus plantarum* and *Lactobacillus brevis* have been observed in Cheddar cheese. Similarly, pigmented species of propionibacteria sometimes cause spots in Swiss cheese.

## EXAMPLES OF THE IMPORTANT GROUPS OF CHEESE

A discussion of the microbiology of cheese is simplified by first assigning related varieties to groups within which all of the representatives have certain characteristics in common. No classification system prepared for this purpose is completely satisfactory, but the identification of specific varieties and types has been simplified and to some extent standardized by the publication of definitions and standards of identity of most of the important varieties of cheese made in or imported into the United States (16, 17). These regulations specify ingredients that may be used, the maximum moisture content, the minimum percentage of fat in dry matter, the minimum holding period, and any special requirements of specific varieties.

Class standards are provided to regulate the composition of ripened natural cheeses that are not specifically defined. The intent of the regulations is that undefined varieties shall be subject to the limits of the appropriate class standard. The composition limits and ripening requirements of most of the important commercial cheeses are listed in Table 13.1. Requirements for the various processed cheese products also are specified in the federal regulations.

The remainder of this section is devoted to a discussion of a few varieties of cheese chosen to represent the different major groups with emphasis on those important in American commerce and about which there is a fair amount of scientific knowledge. Sufficient information is given about the method of manufacture of each variety to enable the reader who is not familiar with cheese making to understand how the product is prepared and thus the manipulations that might affect microbial activity.

## UNRIPENED NATURAL CHEESES

The simplest of all cheeses to prepare are the soft, unripened varieties that are ready to eat as soon as they are made. They contain relatively large amounts of water, a fact which contributes to their softness and to their short keeping time. Their fat content may vary over a wide range, and they contain relatively small amounts of salt.

## COTTAGE CHEESE

Cottage or pot cheese exemplifies the soft, unripened varieties usually made from skimmilk. Fresh milk, reconstituted powdered skimmilk, or concentrated skimmilk can be used. The finished product may be marketed as such, or it may be mixed with cream, chives, pineapple or other fruit. Baker's cheese is a low-fat product made from skimmilk and widely used in the baking industry. Production of cottage and Baker's cheese in the United States exceeds 300,000,000 pounds per year.

### MANUFACTURE

Good quality pasteurized milk is inoculated with a mixed lactic starter culture containing lactic streptococci and the associated *Leuconostoc* species. This culture has essentially the same function and is carried in much the same way as was described for cultured buttermilk in Chapter 12. Rennet extract in small quantities may be added if desired.

The time allowed for curdling can be adjusted to suit the convenience of operations in the plant. Some makers use a short-setting period in which the curd is ready to cut within 4 to 6 hours after the starter is added. To achieve such rapid curdling the milk is held at 29°C. to 32°C. (84.2°F. to 89.6°F.) and inoculated with 4 to 5 per cent of starter. In some factories it

**Table 13.1**  Federal definitions and standards of identity for natural cheeses *

| Cheese | Maximum per cent moisture | Minumum per cent fat in dry matter | in total mass | Minimum ripening time (mos.) | Remarks |
|---|---|---|---|---|---|
| *Class Standards* | | | | | |
| Hard grating | 34 | 32 | | 6 | |
| Hard | 39 | 50 | | | |
| Semi-soft | 50 | 50 | | | |
| Soft | — | 50 | | | |
| *Individual Varieties* | | | | | |
| Unripened (*soft*) cheeses | | | | | |
| Cottage† | 80 | | — | | |
| Creamed cottage† | 80 | | 4 | | |
| Cream† | 55 | | 33 | | |
| Neufchâtel† | 65 | | 20 | | |
| *Ripened cheeses* | | | | | |
| Parmesan (Reggiano) | 32 | 32 | | 14 | ⎫ |
| Asiago old | 32 | 42 | | 12 | Primarily |
| Romano | 34 | 38 | | 5 | grating |
| Asiago medium | 35 | 45 | | 6 | cheeses |
| Sapsago | 38 | — | | 5 | ⎭ |
| Cheddar | 39 | 50 | | | |
| Granular (Stirred-curd) | 39 | 50 | | | ⎫ Similar |
| Colby | 40 | 50 | | | to |
| Washed-curd | 42 | 50 | | | ⎭ Cheddar |
| Caciocavallo siciliano | 40 | 42 | | 3 | |
| Provolone | 45 | 45 | | | |
| Edam | 45 | 40 | | | |
| Gouda | 45 | 46 | | | |
| Swiss | 41 | 43 | | 2 | ⎫ Contain |
| Gruyère | 39 | 45 | | 3 | ⎭ eyes |
| Gorgonzola | 42 | 50 | | 3 | ⎫ |
| Roquefort | 45 | 50 | | 2 | Mold |
| Blue | 46 | 50 | | 2 | ripened |
| Gammelost | 52 | — | | | ⎭ |
| Monterey† | 44 | 50 | | | |
| High moisture jack† | 49 | 50 | | | |
| Asiago fresh | 45 | 50 | | 2 | |
| Brick | 44 | 50 | | | ⎫ Smear |
| Muenster† | 46 | 50 | | | ripened |
| Limburger | 50 | 50 | | | ⎭ |

* (17).

† Pasteurization is specifically required for these varieties which normally are consumed within less than 2 months after manufacture. For all other varieties the cheese must either be: (a) made from pasteurized milk (or receive an equivalent heat treatment during manufacture); or (b) held after manufacture for at least 60 days at a temperature not less than 35°F. (1.67°C.).

is more convenient to use a long-setting process in which the milk is incubated overnight and curdling takes place in about 16 hours. For this purpose the temperature is held near 21°C. (69.8°F.) and 0.3 to 1 per cent of starter is added. Cheese made by the long-setting method is more likely to have a pleasing aroma because it provides better conditions for growth of the leuconostocs.

When the titratable acidity of the whey within the mass reaches 0.5 to 0.6 per cent, the curd is cut into cubes and heated to a temperature of 43°C. to 54°C. (110°F. to 129°F.). The whey is drained off, and the curd is washed 2 or 3 times with cold water to increase its firmness, remove the sour whey, and inhibit further acid formation. The wash water is drained off, and salt may be added at a rate of 0.5 to 1 per cent based on the estimated weight of the curd. Sometimes salt is not added, or it may be added later during creaming.

Usually cottage cheese is stored in bulk at about 2°C. (35.6°F.) until it is packaged and marketed. Under these conditions it can be kept for 1 to 2 weeks at most. Experiments have shown that uncreamed cottage cheese curd can be preserved under a 2 to 4 per cent salt brine at $-1.1°C.$ to 4.4°C. (30°F. to 40°F.) for times up to 3 months. Alternatively the curd can be frozen and stored for several weeks, but the thawed product has a less desirable consistency than that of the fresh curd.

DEFECTS

Like that of all other dairy products, the quality of cottage cheese is affected adversely by milk of poor bacteriological quality. Excessive growth of acid-forming bacteria, yeasts, coliform organisms, and others in the milk may give rise to undesirable flavors in the finished product, even though the organisms themselves are destroyed by pasteurization. Similarly, strong feed and weed flavors in the milk often can be detected in the cheese. Prevention of these defects obviously lies in the use of better quality milk, since it is impractical to remove the undesirable flavors during washing of the curd.

Improper manufacturing methods are responsible for certain defects, most of which are associated with the physical characteristics of the curd. Cutting a rennet-type curd before sufficient acid develops, for example, is likely to yield a tough, rubbery product. Insufficient cooking and consequently insufficient firming of the curd will yield a product that is too high in moisture and that may have a soft, sticky, or pasty consistency. Conversely, excessive cooking produces a curd that is dry and hard, possibly even grainy or gritty.

Defects attributable to abnormal starter activity are the most common of all in cottage cheese. A sour flavor may result if too much acid is allowed to develop before cutting the curd, if washing is inadequate, or if the curd is stored at a fairly high temperature, e. g., 10°C. (50°F.), where the starter organisms can continue to grow. A much more frequent trouble with starter cultures is insufficient acid development. Not only does this produce a defective curd and a "flat" flavor, but it also will allow more rapid bacterial spoilage. Causes of poor starter development are discussed in Chapter 11.

Lack of aroma is a common fault in cottage cheese just as it is in cultured buttermilk. Often this defect results from insufficient development of the citrate-fermenting species of *Leuconostoc* that produce the typical aroma of a mixed lactic starter culture. Methods of increasing the activity of these organisms have been discussed in Chapters 11 and 12. It has been shown that cultures of *Pseudomonas viscosa* and *Pseudomonas fragi* can destroy the aroma of cottage cheese during storage by converting the biacetyl to acetylmethylcarbinol (48).

Even though cottage cheese is made from pasteurized milk, it may develop defects during manufacture if the milk is inadequately heated or if it is handled in improperly cleaned and sterilized equipment after pasteurization. Most likely to compete with the starter bacteria during curdling are coliform bacteria (especially species of *Aerobacter*) and lactose-fermenting yeasts. If these organisms are present in sufficient numbers, they may produce gas in the curd, especially if the starter culture is not sufficiently active. Even if gassing is not apparent, growth of contaminating microorganisms during curdling may give rise to unclean, fermented, or yeasty flavors in the finished product. Gas formation sometimes becomes evident only after the curd has been stored for a few days.

As long as air is available, molds and film yeasts grow well on moist acid foods even at temperatures near freezing. Cottage cheese curd with its porous texture provides an ideal environment for these organisms. *Geotrichum candidum* almost always appears in time, and various species of *Penicillium, Mucor, Alternaria,* and other genera may be found. Growth of molds and film yeasts imparts stale, musty, moldy, and yeasty flavors to the product. Areas of discoloration appear if the growth is extensive. Spoilage by these organisms can be held to a minimum by careful plant sanitation, by avoiding excessive exposure of the cheese to air, and by storing at the lowest practicable temperature.

During storage, cottage cheese sometimes develops a gelatinous or slimy defect in which the curd particles become coated with a soft, slimy film (Figure 13.5). The slime may present a varied appearance—it may be white, yellow, brown, or greenish-brown; it may be watery; sometimes it is ropy. Often, but not always, it is accompanied by a rancid, putrid, or fruity odor (11, 49). As might be assumed from the diverse appearance of the defect, slimy curd can be caused by any of several organisms. Species of *Alcaligenes, Pseudomonas, Proteus, Aerobacter,* and *Achromobacter* have been implicated in outbreaks. All of the causative organisms can grow at the normal storage temperatures used for cottage cheese. Some of them are fairly sensitive to acid and will not grow below pH 5.0, but others will

**Figure 13.5** Slimy curd defect of cottage cheese caused by *Alcaligenes metalcaligenes*. (Uninoculated cheese on the left.) Photo courtesy of Dr. P. R. Elliker, Oregon State College.

grow down to at least pH 4.7. These organisms are destroyed by pasteurization. To be of significance, therefore, they must get into the milk or cheese at some time after heating. Many of them are typical water bacteria, and the water used to wash the curd and the equipment often is their primary source. Sometimes they build up in filters or water-holding tanks where they may be difficult to eliminate by the usual levels of chlorination. Also they may be found in milk stone deposits, deep abrasions, and other places where cleaning and sterilization are difficult.

Dairy plants sometimes have trouble with slimy curd defect in creamed cottage cheese but not in the uncreamed product. When this happens there is a natural tendency to associate the defect with the cream or the creaming equipment and to attempt to prevent the trouble by more careful handling of the cream, more rigorous pasteurization, and more thorough sanitization of the creaming equipment. Although the creaming operation may indeed be at fault, the organisms responsible for the defect often are present in the plain curd but are unable to grow appreciably until some of the acid is neutralized by adding sweet cream. This addition usually raises the pH of the cheese by 0.25 to 0.35 of a pH unit.

Development of the slimy curd defect is favored by low acidity, relatively high storage temperature, and heavy contamination with the causative organisms. It can be minimized or prevented, therefore, by making conditions as unfavorable for the bacteria as possible. The acidity can not be too high without damaging the quality of the cheese, but the pH should not be above 5.0 if slimy curd defect is a problem. Many of the slime organisms can grow slowly at 0°C. (32°F.), but their growth rate is markedly reduced at temperatures below 5°C. (41°F.); hence the cheese should be held at all times as near the freezing point as is practicable. Thorough cleaning and sanitization of equipment and containers, pasteurization of cream, and chlorination of the water used to wash the curd and the equipment usually will reduce the numbers of the causative organisms to negligible levels. For treating the water, sufficient chlorine must be added to provide a residual of a few parts per million and sufficient retention time (usually a few minutes) must be allowed to insure destruction of the undesirable bacteria. The chlorine concentration and the time required depend on the level of contamination and on other factors.

The source of the slimy curd organisms may be learned by performing plate counts on line samples taken during manufacture of the curd and during creaming. The plates should be incubated at about 10°C. (50°F.) and examined at intervals up to seven days. Samples should include the curd itself before washing, the water used for washing, the cream, rinsings from the equipment, and anything else that might contribute the responsible organisms.

## CREAM AND NEUFCHÂTEL CHEESES

Largely because of their high fat content, cream and Neufchâtel cheeses have a smooth, buttery consistency, and a rich, mildly acid taste. These varieties are made by similar procedures but differ in their final composition (Table 13.1, page 356). Stabilizers such as vegetable gums, gelatin, or algin can be added to either cheese up to a concentration of 0.5 per cent, provided the addition is stated on the label. The Neufchâtel cheese made in the United States differs from the product of the same name in Europe in that the latter is caused to undergo a short ripening process to enhance its flavor. Baker's cheese resembles cream and Neufchâtel in that it has a smooth body and is made by a similar process, but it contains practically no fat. Its moisture content usually is 65 to 75 per cent.

Most cream cheese is made by a cooked-curd process resembling the method used for cottage cheese. Cream containing 16 to 20 per cent fat (usually) is pasteurized and homogenized, then starter and rennet are added as was described for cottage cheese. Either a short or a long coagulation period can be used. When the acidity reaches 0.6 to 0.7 per cent (pH 4.6 to 4.7), the curd is stirred until it is smooth and homogeneous. Then it is heated to 46°C. to 54°C. (115°F. to 129°F.), either by admitting steam or hot water to the jacket of the vat or by mixing hot water directly with the curd. Cheese heated by the latter method is less acid than the other.

The hot curd is placed in muslin bags for draining. As soon as the moisture content is reduced to the desired level, the bags are emptied into a vat for mixing and blending to obtain the desired fat and moisture composition. Salt is added at a rate of 0.8 to 1.0 per cent of the weight of the curd. The curd can be filled into retail containers at this stage, or it may be chilled, sliced, and wrapped in small packages. Some manufacturers pasteurize and homogenize the drained and blended curd and dispense it directly into the final containers while it is still hot. When this is done, a stabilizer such as locust bean gum is added before homogenization. The hot-packed product is less likely to contain spoilage organisms, hence usually will keep better than one that is packed cold.

Cream, Neufchâtel, and Baker's cheeses are stored at 0°C. to 2°C. (32°F. to 35.6°F.). In this temperature range the first two varieties usually will keep for 10 to 14 days when made by the cold-pack process; up to 4 weeks when the hot-pack method is followed. Baker's cheese rarely keeps for more than a week unless it is frozen.

Cream cheese and related varieties are subject to most of the defects described for cottage cheese. Because of its lower moisture content, cream cheese is slightly less susceptible to microbial spoilage than Neufchâtel, and this in turn is more stable than Baker's cheese and cottage cheese, but these are merely differences of degree. Mold growth on cream cheese is the most common evidence of spoilage during storage. This defect can best be minimized by protecting the cheese from mold contamination.

## HARD GRATING CHEESES

As a group, the hard grating varieties are characterized by low moisture and fat contents, both of which contribute to the hardness of the cheese (Table 13.1, page 356). Most of these varieties are of Italian origin. They are made from partly skimmed milk and are ripened for long periods of time to achieve the required loss of moisture and to permit sufficient fat hydrolysis to give the sharp flavor typical of these cheeses.

The method of making and ripening most hard grating cheeses is basically similar to that to be described for hard cheeses. Parmesan, for example, is made by a procedure resembling that of Swiss. Rennet, rennet paste, or extract of rennet paste may be used for curdling the milk. Some makers add, in addition, special lipolytic enzyme preparations of animal origin. The curd is cut into small pieces and cooked to a fairly high temperature to promote whey removal. Information on the microorganisms in these cheeses is fragmentary. The starter cultures usually contain high-acid-producing lactobacilli. During ripening other organisms develop. In Parmesan, for example, Gorini has found acid-proteolytic cocci to be predominant (Weigmann, 67). Maskell et al. (44) reported the flora of Romano cheese made from raw milk to consist mainly of enterococci (such as *Streptococcus liquefaciens* and *Streptococcus zymogenes*). Micrococci and spore-forming rods also were isolated from most samples.

Sapsago is a variety of grating cheese made mostly in Switzerland from a mixture of skimmilk and buttermilk. This mixture is boiled, and sour whey is added to precipitate the casein. The resulting curd is collected and held under pressure for 5 or 6 weeks during which it drains and ferments. Following this the curd is mixed with salt and ground dry leaves of an aromatic clover plant, *Melilotus coerulea*. The cheese is held for at least 5 months during which it ripens further and becomes much drier.

## HARD CHEESES

The term hard cheese is applied to certain varieties that usually are sliced or cut for eating and that have a reasonably firm consistency. The dividing line between these and the semi-soft varieties is not sharp, and certain fairly high moisture cheeses logically might be placed in either class. For convenience, the hard cheeses may be divided into those with eyes and those without. The most important member of the latter group is Cheddar. Similar to Cheddar in many respects are the Italian varieties Provolone and Caciocavallo siciliano. In American commerce the most important of the varieties with eyes is Swiss. The cheeses of Dutch origin, Edam and Gouda, resemble in many respects the typical hard cheeses, although by virtue of their relatively high moisture content they might be considered semi-soft.

## CHEDDAR CHEESE

Like many other varieties, Cheddar is named after the village in which it was first made—Cheddar, Somersetshire, England. It is the most popular single variety produced in English-speaking countries. In the United States it is often called American cheese or American Cheddar. It is made in cylindrical, rectangular, or square pieces usually weighing between 10 and 78 pounds. Giant cheeses weighing several hundred pounds have been produced for special purposes.

To be shipped in interstate commerce in the United States,.Cheddar cheese must contain no more than 39 per cent moisture and no less than 50 per cent fat in the dry matter. Analyses of hundreds of lots of Cheddar cheese of satisfactory market quality have shown that the moisture content usually is 35 to 37 per cent; fat, 33 to 36 per cent (52 to 54 per cent in the dry matter); casein, 23 to 25 per cent; and salt, 1.4 to 1.8 per cent.

### MANUFACTURE

As is true with most kinds of cheese, the manufacturing process for Cheddar is subject to many relatively minor variations. The procedure outlined here is essentially that described by Van Slyke and Price. Figure 13.6 shows some of the main steps in Cheddar making.

In the United States most Cheddar cheese is made from pasteurized whole milk. Pasteurization results in better, more uniform quality and permits standardization of the making process, thus simplifying factory operation. The milk is warmed to about 30°C. (86°F.) and inoculated with 0.5

**Figure 13.6** Manufacture of Cheddar cheese. (a) Cutting the curd into cubes. (b) After most of the whey is removed, the curd is piled along the sides of the vat. (c) The curd particles fuse into a solid piece. This is cut into slabs, which are turned occasionally and stacked to promote whey removal. (d) The curd is milled or cut into small pieces, which are mixed with salt and pressed in molds. Photos courtesy of: a, b, c, The Borden Co.; d, Kraft Foods Co.

to 1.0 per cent of starter. As soon as an increase in acidity is detectable (usually about 45 minutes with pasteurized milk and an active starter), rennet extract is added. When the curd is firm enough to break cleanly, it is cut into ¼ to ⅜ inch cubes, and the temperature is increased slowly to about 39°C. (102.2°F.).

After the required degrees of acidity and firmness are reached, the curd is allowed to settle to the bottom of the vat, and the whey is drained off (dipped). During this operation half of the curd is pushed to each side of the vat to form a trench down the center along which the whey can escape. This operation is called packing. The curd in each of the two long piles thus formed rapidly mats together to form solid slabs, which then are cut into blocks. These are turned at intervals to facilitate drainage of the whey. Later they are piled 2 high and finally 3 high to increase the pressure and retain the heat. This entire operation is called cheddaring. The curd is ready for the next step, milling, when the acidity of the whey draining from it has increased 0.3 to 0.35 per cent above the acidity at dipping. Usually this amounts to a whey acidity of 0.4 to 0.45 per cent. At this time the curd is at approximately pH 5.4.

The slabs of curd are milled or cut into pieces about ⅝ x ⅝ x 2 inches and mixed with salt. The amount of salt desired in the final cheese is about 1.5 per cent, but this often varies between 1 and 2 per cent. The salt helps remove whey by hardening and shrinking the curd, it retards further acid formation, and it tends to suppress growth of undesirable microorganisms.

The curd is placed in forms or hoops and is subjected to pressure for several hours, usually overnight. During this operation the pieces knit together into a solid mass. For the traditional method of ripening, the cheese is removed from the hoops and held in a cool, dry atmosphere where the surface dries slightly, forming a rind. After 3 or 4 days the cheese is dipped in wax and moved to the curing room.

Considerable amounts of Cheddar cheese now are prepared without rind. For this purpose the curd is pressed in a rectangular block, then it is encased in plastic film and placed in a tight box for curing. After the desired degree of ripeness is reached, the block of cheese is cut into small squares or rectangular pieces that are individually wrapped and returned to the original box for further storage. The cutting and re-wrapping must be accomplished under the most sanitary conditions to avoid mold contamination. This method of ripening minimizes losses from evaporation and surface spoilage.

Most Cheddar cheese made in the United States is cold-cured in rooms maintained at 0°C. to 5°C. (32°F. to 41°F.) and 75 per cent relative humidity. The cheese is held for 3 to 12 months, the time depending on the temperature of curing and the degree of flavor development desired. Cheese of excellent quality sometimes is aged for as long as 2 or 3 years. Cold-cured Cheddar cheese is mild in flavor when compared with cheese of comparable age ripened at higher temperatures.

Warm-curing is widely practiced outside the United States and is becoming more popular in this country. In most curing rooms the temperature is 10°C. to 15°C. (50°F. to 59°F.), and the relative humidity is 85 to 90 per cent. The cheese is held under these conditions for 13 to 18 weeks or until the flavor is of the desired intensity; then it is moved to a colder room for continued mellowing. Sharper and more pronounced flavors can be developed by warm curing than are possible at very low temperatures.

Within limits, the rate of desirable flavor development increases as the temperature is raised. At the same time, however, the rate of development of defects also accelerates. The choice of a ripening temperature thus becomes a compromise—it must be high enough to develop the flavor as quickly as possible, yet low enough to minimize defects.

Cold-curing became widely accepted when most Cheddar cheese was made from raw milk whose quality varied widely. Balanced against the obvious disadvantage of long holding with its consequent higher cost and loss of moisture was the advantage of a product with better and more uniform quality. The mild flavor has been well accepted by the American public. Many consumers, especially outside the United States, demand a more highly flavored cheese, which can be obtained by cold-curing only after very long periods. Warm-curing will permit sufficient flavor development in a relatively short time, but it can be used only with cheese that will not develop internal defects at the temperatures used. This method has certain disadvantages which are unrelated to the quality of the cheese per se. Loss of moisture is rapid unless the humidity is maintained at a high value. When the humidity is high, mold growth, rind rot, cheese mites, and other pests are more difficult to control. Therefore, warm-cured cheese requires much more attention during ripening than does that cured at 5°C. (41°F.) or below.

Types of cheese closely resembling Cheddar are made by modifications of the above procedure. The stirred-curd or granular process, for example, yields a product that is practically identical to Cheddar in composition, flavor, and body, but it has a more open texture. In this process the cheddaring operation is omitted, the curd being stirred constantly during draining to prevent its matting together. It is salted and hooped in the usual way.

Washed-curd or soaked-curd cheese is made like Cheddar through the stage of milling. At this point the milled curd is covered with cold water for 5 to 30 minutes, then is drained and salted as for normal Cheddar. The water treatment removes some of the lactose and soluble salts while increasing the moisture content. As a result, less acid is formed, and the cheese has a softer body and more open texture than Cheddar. Washed-curd cheese is cured for only a month or two at 10°C. (50°F.) or below, hence it has a mild flavor. If held too long it develops flavor defects characteristic of excessive protein decomposition.

Colby cheese is made by a combination of the stirred-curd and washed-curd procedures. For this variety the curd is handled as it is for Cheddar up to the time of dipping. After most of the whey is drained off, enough cold water is added to reduce the temperature of the mixture to about 27°C. (80.6°F.). Then the curd is drained, salted, and put into hoops as described for Cheddar. Colby cheese has a fairly soft body, an open texture, and a mild flavor resembling that of young Cheddar.

## CHANGES DURING MANUFACTURE

With no other type of cheese are microbial activity and acid formation more important during manufacture than they are with Cheddar. The organisms responsible for acid production are lactic streptococci, either *Streptococcus lactis* or *Streptococcus cremoris*. Cheese makers in the United States usually employ a mixed culture consisting of one or more strains of *Streptococcus lactis* in association with the citrate-fermenting species of *Leuconostoc*. This type of starter is carried as described in Chapter 11. Cultures are ripened to 0.70 to 0.75 per cent acidity to maintain maximum activity of the lactic streptococci, and under these conditions the aroma bacteria do not thrive. Presumably this is of no consequence, however, because the leuconostocs have no known desirable function in Cheddar cheese. *Streptococcus faecalis* and *Streptococcus durans* have been used successfully in experimental Cheddar cheese. Cheddar makers in other countries usually employ pure cultures of *Streptococcus cremoris* as starters.

Little has been recorded about the actual changes in numbers of starter organisms during the manufacture of Cheddar cheese. Immediately after inoculation the milk contains a few million starter bacteria per milliliter. As can be judged from acidity measurements, these multiply only slightly during curdling and cooking, but growth accelerates rapidly after the whey is removed. By this time the organisms have been able to overcome the initial lag, and the curd begins to cool to a more favorable temperature. The rate of acid formation increases very rapidly because the majority of the organisms are concentrated in the curd rather than lost with the whey. Multiplication continues at a rapid rate during cheddaring and even while the cheese is in the press. By the next morning the cheese may contain one or two billion starter organisms per gram.

Because of its importance in bringing about the desired changes during Cheddar cheese manufacture, a great deal of attention has been paid to acid development and its measurement. In fact, it is routine procedure to adjust the timing of the various steps in making by results of acid determinations. The usual method is to titrate the milk or whey with alkali. Measurements of pH are helpful and have the advantage that they can be made on the curd, but they are not widely used in factory practice because of the special equipment required. The rennet test on the milk and the so-called hot iron test applied to the curd are essentially measurements of acid development.

Figure 13.7 illustrates the changes in acidity of Cheddar cheese during manufacture. The curves show that acid development is most rapid during the interval between dipping and milling the curd. This is the stage where slow acid production usually is most noticeable and where excessive delay can cause serious loss in quality of the cheese. Slow acid formation can result from use of an inactive starter, from the action of bacteriophage, or from any of the other causes discussed in Chapter 11.

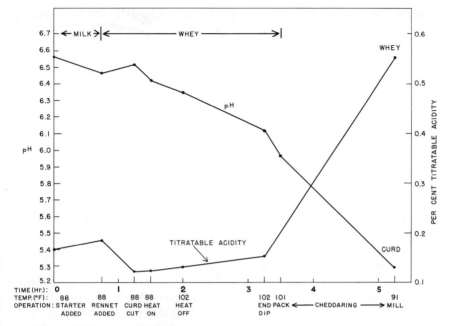

**Figure 13.7**     Acid production in Cheddar cheese. From Brown and Price (6).

The starter organisms continue to grow and produce acid until the lactose is completely used up. Normally this occurs within a few days after manufacture. It is apparent, then, that the final acidity reached in the cheese is determined by the amount of sugar left in the curd during making, and this is regulated in turn by the moisture content. Fresh curd with excessive moisture will contain too much lactose and will most likely become too sour. Conversely, curd that is too dry will not contain enough lactose to yield the correct amount of acid. Brown and Price (6) observed that acid defects did not develop in cheese in which the reaction at 3 days was in the range pH 5.05 to 5.20.

CHANGES DURING RIPENING

Freshly made Cheddar cheese has a firm, elastic, "curdy" body with a mildly acid flavor and slight aroma. Reduction in firmness and elasticity normally become apparent within 2 to 4 weeks in cheese ripened at 7°C. (44.6°F.). These changes in body are accompanied by conversion of part of the protein to water-soluble compounds, mainly proteoses and peptones. As ripening continues, more and more of the simpler nitrogenous compounds appear, while the conversion of protein to water-soluble materials proceeds at a slower rate. Table 13.2 illustrates these changes. In the study from which these results were taken, the decrease in protein and the corresponding increase in water-soluble derivatives were most rapid during the first 10 weeks. Further hydrolysis to amino acids

**Table 13.2**    Nitrogen compounds in Cheddar cheese during ripening at 10°C. (50°F.)*

| Age of cheese (weeks) | Per cent of total nitrogen in form of | | | |
|---|---|---|---|---|
| | Mono-calcium paracaseinate | Water-soluble compounds | Amino acids | Ammonia |
| 1 | 57.49 | 14.55 | 4.06 | 0 |
| 10 | 42.08 | 25.18 | 8.98 | 1.87 |
| 20 | 35.24 | 31.56 | 8.95 | 2.44 |
| 28 | 31.82 | 33.00 | 12.70 | 3.48 |

* From Van Slyke, Smith, and Hart (65).

occurred over the entire ripening period, accompanied by an increase in ammonia. The rate of these reactions depends on the usual factors that affect enzymatic and microbial activity. High ripening temperature, low salt content, high moisture, or extra rennet, for example, accelerates ripening; the opposite of these delays the changes.

The development of typical Cheddar cheese flavor occurs more slowly than do the changes in body. A considerable number of volatile and soluble compounds have been found in cheese at different stages of ripening, but knowledge of the specific contribution of each is fragmentary. Lactic acid, lactates, and sodium chloride doubtless account for much of the flavor of mild Cheddar. Appreciable quantities of acetic and n-butyric acids and traces of biacetyl also have been found in young cheese. As the cheese ages its odor becomes more noticeable, and flavors become sharper. Coincidentally there is an increase in volatile fatty acids, particularly acetic, n-butyric, caproic, caprylic, and capric. Small amounts of alcohol and esters of fatty acids have been found in highly-flavored Cheddar cheese.

The mode of origin of these compounds is not entirely clear. Lactose fermentation is the source of lactic acid and may give rise, in addition, to the biacetyl, acetic acid and n-butyric acid found in young cheese. The further increase in acetic acid may result from lactate decomposition or deamination of glycine, but the additional n-butyric, caproic, caprylic and capric acids most likely result from fat hydrolysis (55).

Some of the products of protein decomposition doubtless contribute to the flavor. Peptones in general are bitter, and they may account for part of the "background" flavor. Certain of the amino acids and the simple peptides have considerable taste. Several free amino acids have been identified in ripening Cheddar cheese, with glutamic acid and some of the basic amino acids occurring most often and in greatest amounts (36). Salts of ammonia, especially ammonium butyrate, are believed to be responsible for some of the sharpness of aged Cheddar.

The chemical reactions that occur during ripening of Cheddar cheese cause a slow but steady increase in the pH. Brown and Price (6) obtained the following average values for several lots of good quality:

| Age of cheese | pH |
|---|---|
| 3 days | 5.05 |
| 7 days | 5.06 |
| 49 days | 5.13 |
| 9 months | 5.32 |
| 24 months | 5.58 |

These figures are typical of the trend that is observed in normal cheese, but a product of atypical composition may show widely different values.

The sources of the enzymes responsible for protein breakdown in Cheddar cheese are not known with certainty. It is generally accepted that rennin is chiefly responsible for the initial conversion of protein to proteoses and peptones, whereas most of the further hydrolysis to amino acids and liberation of ammonia from these is attributed to microorganisms. The enzymes responsible for fat hydrolysis are mainly from bacteria. Natural milk lipase is inactive at the pH of cheese, and rennet has little lipolytic activity. The increase in lipase enzymes during ripening can be accounted for, therefore, only by assuming microbial origin (54).

The microorganisms in Cheddar cheese undergo a regular succession during ripening. The lactic streptococci from the starter reach maximum numbers, usually a few billion per gram, soon after making is finished. For the remainder of the ripening period their number decreases, fairly rapidly at first, then more slowly. At one month they may number a few hundred million per gram; later they may be reduced to a few million or less. The specific function of these organisms in ripening has never been determined.

At times varying from a few days to a few weeks after ripening begins, lactobacilli usually can be detected in Cheddar cheese. They increase gradually until finally they may outnumber the starter organisms. It is not unusual to find numbers of lactobacilli as high as several hundred million or even a billion per gram of cheese that has been ripened for several months. *Lactobacillus casei* and *Lactobacillus plantarum* are the species most often found in normal cheese.

Because of their frequent occurrence and the relationship of their growth to the appearance of normal cheese flavor, the lactobacilli have been assigned an important role in Cheddar ripening. These organisms as well as the starter bacteria release enzymes that can hydrolyze casein. For this reason they are believed to be responsible for part of the proteolytic changes, especially after the first few weeks of ripening. Some cultures of *Lactobacillus casei,* and probably some of *Streptococcus lactis,* also release intracellular lipolytic enzymes that can liberate *n*-butyric, caproic, caprylic, and capric acids from butterfat; hence they are thought to be important in flavor development (53,55).

Many attempts have been made to add lactobacillus cultures to milk for cheese and thus to hasten flavor development. Success in this direction has been variable. Very often the milk so inoculated yields cheese with a harsh or fermented flavor; at other times there is no effect. These and other results suggest that there is considerable variation between strains within a single species insofar as their action in cheese is concerned. It is also probable that excessive numbers even of a desirable strain may cause too much change, and the resulting flavor will thereby be undesirable.

Several factors determine the rate of development of lactobacilli in Cheddar cheese. The numbers and kinds in the milk obviously affect their rate of growth, as does the temperature at which the cheese is held. *Lactobacillus casei* is fairly sensitive to heat, and if not eliminated entirely, it is greatly reduced in numbers by ordinary pasteurization. Therefore, it usually develops slowly, and sometimes not at all, in cheese made from pasteurized milk. This fact probably accounts in part for the slower flavor development in pasteurized milk than in raw milk cheese. Since the lactose is completely utilized by the starter organisms early in the ripening period, there is no readily fermentable sugar for the lactobacilli. A few of them utilize lactate slowly, but they probably depend mostly on protein decomposition products for their carbon and nitrogen requirements. Therefore their growth can not be rapid until some of the protein has been hydrolyzed. Inhibitory substances produced by the starter organisms may cause delayed growth of lactobacilli in cheese. Some strains of *Streptococcus lactis* and *Streptococcus cremoris,* for example, produce a substance that inhibits growth of *Lactobacillus casei* (4).

Other organisms have been reported in Cheddar cheese and may have a desirable effect during ripening. Various micrococci have been found in numbers of ten to fifty million per gram early in the ripening period of cheese made from raw milk, and some workers believe that they can contribute to flavor development (2). These organisms do not reach significant numbers in cheese made from pasteurized milk. Alford and Frazier (3) have accelerated flavor development in pasteurized milk cheese by adding selected strains of micrococci to the milk. Some of these organisms release lipases when they die and autolyze (53).

Enterococci have been found in Cheddar cheese and may have an effect on ripening, though their function is not known. Ordinarily these organisms are overgrown in raw milk cheese, but since they survive ordinary pasteurization, they may reach considerable numbers and be detected in cheese made from pasteurized milk. Of this group, *Streptococcus faecalis* appears most often and in greatest numbers.

It is entirely possible that some of the organisms that develop in Cheddar cheese in relatively small numbers may have an important effect on ripening. Up to now most attention has been paid to the starter organisms and the lactobacilli. The numerical predominance of these organisms has complicated the problem of counting and isolating others, and it is possible that some essential groups have been missed in earlier studies. Development of selective media that will permit easy enumeration and isolation of other organisms may reveal some that have not yet been reported and that may play a significant part in the ripening changes.

The realization that enzymatic action is responsible for the changes associated with ripening has suggested the addition of rich sources of proteolytic and lipolytic enzymes and thus perhaps acceleration of the ripening changes in cheese made from pasteurized milk. Natural materials from many sources have been tried—ground animal organs such as the pancreas and the mammary gland, papaya juice, mulberry juice, pure trypsin, and many others. Ripening changes can easily be accelerated in this way, but the results are rarely if ever as desired. No doubt some of the changes progress too far or in too great proportion to others so that the final product does not have the most desirable characteristics. In this connection it might be mentioned that flavor development in Cheddar cheese made from pasteurized milk can be accelerated by simply grinding the cheese and then reforming it. Presumably this mechanical process breaks up the colonies of ripening organisms and distributes them throughout the mass, thus bringing the bacteria and enzymes in contact with fresh substrate. Exposure of cheese to ultrasonic waves also accelerates ripening, but the mechanism of this action of sound waves has not been explained.

After several months of ripening, small, hard white specks usually appear in Cheddar cheese. These are not considered to be defective, but are indicative of extensive aging. Studies made to identify the specks have shown them to be variable in composition. Some workers have found them to consist of calcium lactate, others have reported them to be collections of crystallized tyrosine, and still others have found them to be mixtures of these. By means of microbiological assay and X-ray diffraction procedures, Harper et al. (30) showed that the white specks from different samples of Cheddar cheese most often contained tyrosine and calcium lactate, but in some of the samples they found cystine, leucine, and probably isoleucine.

### DEFECTS

In the manufacture of Cheddar cheese with its complicated series of chemical, physical, and microbial changes, each of which must proceed at a certain rate and in conjunction with other changes, it is inevitable that the procedure will not always go as is desired and that the product will therefore lack some desirable characteristic. Many of the defects in flavor, body, and texture are traceable to an abnormal composition of the freshly-made curd. The composition and physical characteristics of the curd are determined in large measure by the acidity; hence failure by the cheese maker to control acid production by the starter organisms is responsible for numerous defects in the ripened product.

Excessive acidity (below about pH 5.05 at 3 or 4 days) may cause a short, crumbly body and a sour, often bitter flavor. Normal body "breakdown" and flavor development will not occur in this cheese. However, with too little acid (pH above 5.3 at 3 or 4 days) the body may be corky, pasty, or even sticky, normal flavor does not develop, and the texture is likely to be open because of failure of the curd particles to fuse properly. Furthermore, undesirable bacteria are likely to grow, causing defects ranging in severity from a simple off-flavor to a serious gassiness.

Cheddar cheese is subject to all of the defects described in the section on cheese spoilage. The reader should refer to this section for causes and remedies.

## PROVOLONE AND CACIOCAVALLO SICILIANO

Provolone is an Italian variety whose production in the United States has increased greatly since World War II. It is made from raw or pasteurized milk by a procedure similar to that of Cheddar up to the time of matting the curd. At this point the curd for Provolone is cut into large blocks, which are held in the vat until the desired acidity has developed for the molding operation. Then the curd is cut into strips, immersed in hot water, and kneaded and stretched until it is smooth and free of lumps. The hot curd is molded into the desired shape, chilled, salted in brine, smoked, paraffined, and ripened as for Cheddar. Caciocavallo siciliano is made by a process similar to that for Provolone except that the curd is soaked in hot whey, and the cheese is not smoked. It has a lower fat and moisture content than Provolone (Table 13.1, page 356) and is cured for at least 90 days. In both of these varieties the curd has a stringy appearance, that is, it can be pulled apart in shreds owing to the stretching it receives while being molded into shape. Much of the typical flavor of both varieties results from lipolysis achieved by using rennet paste or rennet plus special lipase mixtures extracted from animal glandular sources.

Little information is available on the microorganisms in these cheeses. Maskell et al. (44) reported that the number of bacteria in Provolone decreased during ripening from one hundred million per gram at 1 month to less than one million at 12 months. They found *Lactobacillus lactis* and *Streptococcus faecalis* predominant in most samples of ripened cheese made from pasteurized milk.

## SWISS CHEESE

As the name implies, Swiss cheese originated in Switzerland. In Europe it is called Emmentaler after the Emmen Valley in the canton of Bern. Commercial production in the United States began in Ohio in the 1860's and has since expanded to other states, notably Wisconsin, New York, Pennsylvania, Wyoming, Utah, and Idaho. Traditionally Swiss cheese is made in discs or wheels resembling millstones in appearance and weighing 175 to 225 pounds each. However, large amounts now are made in square pieces weighing about 90 pounds. Gruyère is a variety closely resembling

Swiss in its manufacture but made in smaller wheels. It undergoes some surface ripening and has a stronger flavor. Swiss and related types are distinguished from other cheeses by the presence of holes or eyes.

Domestic Swiss cheese usually contains 37 to 39 per cent moisture, 27 to 29 per cent fat, 26 to 28 per cent protein, and 1.0 to 1.6 per cent salt.

### MANUFACTURE

Figure 13.8 illustrates the main steps in Swiss cheese manufacture. In the traditional method of making this variety in the United States (58), raw milk of good quality is clarified and standardized to a fat content of 2.8 to 3.5 per cent so that the final product will contain about 45 per cent fat in the dry matter. The milk should have a methylene blue reduction time between 3 and 6 hours, and the number of gas-forming organisms must be low. Attempts to use heated milk for Swiss cheese both in Europe and the United States have met with variable degrees of success.

The milk is placed in a circular copper vat called a kettle and warmed to 31°C. to 35°C. (87.8°F. to 95°F.). Starter is added, as will be described later, and the milk is coagulated (set) with rennet extract. The curd is cut with a device called a harp into particles about ⅛ inch in diameter and heated to a temperature of 49°C. to 54°C. (120.2°F. to 129.2°F.). As soon as the curd is sufficiently firm, the entire mass is collected in a coarse cloth (dipped) and transferred to a circular hoop on a draining table, where it is held until the next morning. During this time pressure is applied, and the cheese is turned occasionally to promote uniform drainage of the whey. The curd particles mat together to form a dense, homogeneous, close-textured mass.

After pressing, the cheese is held for 2 or 3 days in brine containing approximately 23 per cent sodium chloride. The temperature of the brine room should be about 13°C. (55.4°F.), and the relative humidity 80 to 85 per cent. After it is removed from the brine, the cheese is kept at this temperature and humidity while the surface dries somewhat and the salt becomes more evenly distributed. Every 2 or 3 days the cheese is washed and wiped with a cloth that has been dipped in salt water and is again sprinkled with dry salt.

After 7 to 10 days the cheese is removed to a warm room where the temperature is maintained at 20°C. to 23°C. (68°F. to 73.4°F.), and the humidity at 80 to 85 per cent. This permits development of the eye-forming bacteria. When the eyes are large enough, the cheese is moved to the curing cellar and held at about 13°C. (55.4°F.) and 80 to 85 per cent relative humidity. Washing and turning of the cheese is continued throughout the ripening period of 3 to 9 months. At least 6 months and sometimes longer is necessary to develop the fine, full flavor characteristic of well-ripened Swiss. During this time a rind about ¼ inch thick forms on the cheese. As a rule, eyes appear to within about 1 inch of the surface.

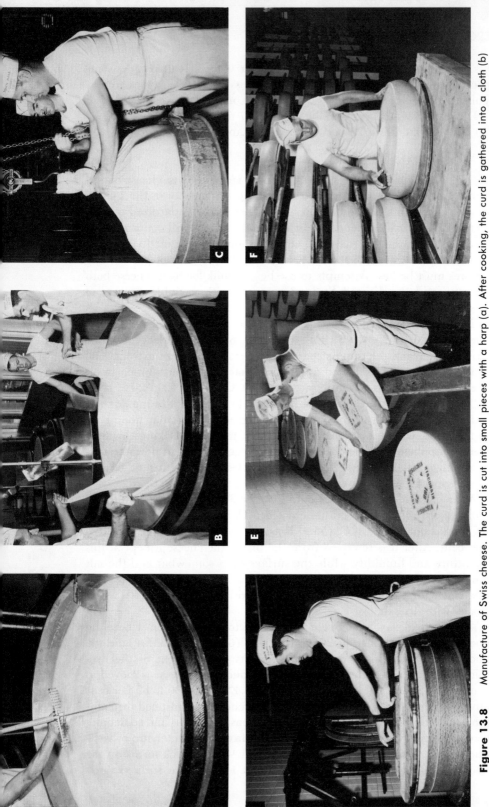

**Figure 13.8** Manufacture of Swiss cheese. The curd is cut into small pieces with a harp (a). After cooking, the curd is gathered into a cloth (b) and transferred to the hoop (c) where it is pressed (d). The next morning the fresh cheese is placed in the salt bath (e). During curing the cheese is cleaned, rubbed with salt, and turned two or three times per week (f). Photos courtesy of Wisconsin Swiss and Limburger Cheese Producers Association.

Several modifications of the traditional method of making Swiss cheese have been introduced to simplify the procedure or to effect desirable changes in the product. For example, some makers press the cheese into large square blocks. After salting, these are wrapped in a plastic film and ripened inside tight-fitting boxes. This procedure reduces moisture loss and the amount of handling necessary to control surface spoilage. A variety called Iowa-type Swiss has been developed, using pasteurized milk with *Streptococcus lactis* as the starter. For this cheese it is necessary to add a culture of propionic acid bacteria. The curd is cut much as for conventional Swiss, but it is heated to only 37.8°C. (100°F.) and is allowed to mat together on the bottom of the vat. After most of the whey is removed and the curd particles have fused, the curd is cut into blocks of about 5 pounds each. These are placed in round metal hoops about 7 inches in diameter and pressed to finish draining. The cheese is salted in brine, coated with wax, and ripened like conventional Swiss.

A patent has been granted for making Swiss cheese without rind and with eye development to the surface (60). According to the patent, whole milk is pasteurized and inoculated with *Streptococcus thermophilus, Lactobacillus bulgaricus* and *Propionibacterium shermanii*. The making procedure is essentially the same as that for conventional Swiss up to the stage of pressing the curd, which is done in rectangular rather than round forms. The block thus produced is cut into the size desired and then is salted in brine. After the surface is dry, the cheese is coated with a flexible wax or is wrapped in an elastic, moisture-proof film and placed in close-fitting individual forms for curing under conditions similar to those used for conventional Swiss. Because of its square or rectangular form and lack of rind, this cheese can be cut into convenient sizes with minimum waste.

### CHANGES DURING MANUFACTURE

*Preparation of Starter.* At one time Swiss cheese makers prepared their own rennet by soaking calves' stomachs in whey from the previous day's cheese. The resulting product called "lab" contained both the coagulating enzyme and acid-forming bacteria which served as the starter. As knowledge of the bacteriology of Swiss cheese has improved, there has been an increasing trend both in the United States and in Europe to use pure culture starters. Practically all of the milk made into Swiss cheese now is inoculated with a culture of *Streptococcus thermophilus* and a lactobacillus. Any of several lactic rods can be used, the most common in this country being *Lactobacillus bulgaricus* and *Lactobacillus lactis*. A rod called *Thermobacterium helveticum* (*Lactobacillus helveticus*) is used commonly in Europe. In addition, some makers add a culture of *Propionibacterium shermanii* or *Propionibacterium petersonii* to function during ripening.

To be used successfully in Swiss cheese, a starter organism must be resistant to heat and must be able to grow at a relatively high temperature. The strains of lactic acid bacteria used in making Swiss are selected for their ability to survive the cooking process without harm and to initiate growth rapidly while the cheese is in the press. Furthermore they are handled in a manner designed to keep them at their maximum state of activity. This is accomplished by careful attention to the acid development in the culture and to the temperature of incubation. Cultures that are too young or too old, as indicated by acid determinations, are not as resistant to heat as others, nor do they grow as actively after cooking is completed. Similarly, cultures grown at their optimum temperatures or slightly above are more active in the cheese than are those incubated at lower temperatures.

It is common practice to cultivate the Swiss cheese starter organisms in milk in association with a film yeast. This strictly aerobic organism grows as a thick, wrinkled film on the surface. There it tends to keep oxygen from being absorbed into the milk, it makes available soluble nitrogenous compounds and accessory growth substances, and it utilizes some of the lactic acid produced by the bacteria. All of these activities are favorable to the maintenance of vitality in the culture. Swiss cheese starter cultures grown in association with a film yeast are more resistant to heat and can grow at higher temperature than can cultures grown alone. Thus they start to grow and produce acid more rapidly when the cheese cools slightly after cooking. The film yeast is inactive in the cheese because of the high temperature and the lack of air.

Mother cultures of *Streptococcus thermophilus* and the lactobacilli ordinarily are carried in sterile milk. The cultures are incubated at 37°C. (98.6°F.) until the milk curdles, then they are cooled to about 15°C. (59°F.). Extreme chilling is harmful to these organisms. Transfers should be made daily or at least 3 times a week. Cultures grown with a film yeast retain their activity longer and may not need to be transferred more often than once or twice a week. Care must be taken to protect the cultures against infection with bacteriophage. Some Swiss cheese makers do not attempt to carry their own mother cultures but prefer to obtain new ones on a weekly or semi-weekly schedule from a culture supply laboratory.

Bulk starter cultures are prepared in pasteurized milk or whey. The amount of mother culture added is adjusted to yield the desired acidity in the bulk starter at the time of its use. To have maximum activity in the cheese, milk cultures of *Streptococcus thermophilus* should have a titratable acidity of 0.70 to 0.75 per cent when used; whey starters 0.30 to 0.33 per cent (20). Lactobacillus cultures should contain 1.0 to 1.1 per cent acid in milk (20) or 0.60 to 0.65 per cent in whey. Cultures with appreciably more or less acidity than these figures will not be sufficiently active in the cheese.

Some cheese makers still use natural whey starters with success. To prepare these, a sample of whey from the kettle is heated to 60°C. to 70°C. (140°F. to 158°F.), then is allowed to cool gradually to the incubation temperature of about 37°C. (98.6°F.). This treatment destroys many of the organisms, leaving alive only the most heat-resistant cells. The acidity at use the next day usually is between 0.55 and 0.65 per cent. Often it is difficult by this procedure to maintain the cocci and rods in the most desirable proportion. Some makers inoculate the pasteurized whey with cocci and rods before incubation.

The amount of culture added to the milk in the kettle can vary considerably, but it is always small in comparison with that used for most other types of cheese. Ordinarily it is in the range of 0.03 to 0.1 per cent of each organism. Cheese makers have learned that it is better to use cultures with maximum activity and to regulate their rate of growth in the cheese by varying the amount of each organism added to the milk.

Cultures of propionibacteria are grown in a suitable medium such as lactose peptone broth at about 30°C. (86°F.). They are ready to use as soon as growth is heavy. They can be held in a refrigerator and used for several weeks before a fresh culture is necessary. Only a few drops of such cultures are used per kettle of milk.

*Changes in the kettle.* The time required for the curd-making operation, that is from setting to dipping, usually is 1.5 to 3 hours. The main factor determining this time is the ripeness of the milk. Milk in which considerable microbial growth has occurred, as shown by a short methylene blue reduction time, usually will permit a shorter making operation because it contains a small amount of preformed acid to hasten firming of the curd. Conversely, milk with a very long methylene blue reduction time will "work" more slowly. Many makers prefer to use milk with a reduction time of 3 or 4 hours so that making will proceed fairly rapidly. Attempts to ripen milk with *Streptococcus thermophilus* have shown no particular benefit unless the methylene blue time was 5 hours or more (21).

Table 13.3 shows typical changes in numbers of starter organisms, acidity, moisture content of the curd, and temperature up to the time of

## Table 13.3    Changes in Swiss cheese in the kettle

| MAKING OPERATION | ELAPSED TIME FROM SETTING (min.) | TEMPERATURE* (°F.) | TEMPERATURE* (°C.) | MOISTURE CONTENT OF CURD* (%) | pH OF MILK OR CURD + WHEY** | PLATE COUNTS/ML OR/G** S. thermophilus | PLATE COUNTS/ML OR/G** L. bulgaricus |
|---|---|---|---|---|---|---|---|
| Starter and rennet added | 0 | 90.5 | 32.5 | 87.8 | 6.57 | 2,700,000 | 360,000 |
| Curd cut | 30 | 89.6 | 32.0 | | | | |
| Foreworking begun | 35 | 89.6 | 32.0 | | | | |
| Cooking begun | 80 | 89.6 | 32.0 | 64.9 | 6.54 | 3,200,000 | 340,000 |
| Cooking finished | 110 | 127.4 | 53.0 | 53.6 | | | |
| Dipping | 140 | 122.9 | 50.5 | 52.6 | 6.48 | 13,000,000 | 240,000 |

*From Sanders et al. (59).
**From Frazier et al. (22).

dipping. Ordinarily *Streptococcus thermophilus* grows a little during this period but the lactobacillus does not multiply. *Streptococcus lactis*-type bacteria from the milk may show a negligible increase in numbers during the first 80 minutes or so while the temperature is favorable. Coliform bacteria do not grow in the kettle unless they are present in abnormally large numbers. Propionibacteria also fail to multiply, and in fact, their numbers may decrease between setting and dipping (22).

### CHANGES IN THE PRESS

The purpose of draining and pressing the curd is to regulate its moisture content and to allow sufficient acid production to cause the curd particles to knit together in a dense, elastic mass. To accomplish this it is essential that the whey drain uniformly from the curd. Whey drainage is affected by the rate of acid formation, which in turn is influenced by the temperature and the activity of the starter organisms.

Figure 13.9 illustrates typical changes in temperature, acidity, and numbers of bacteria while the cheese is in the press. The rate at which the mass of curd cools and the final temperature attained naturally depend on the temperature of the room. Too rapid cooling does not permit sufficient acid development. The pH of the cheese drops fairly rapidly for the first 7 or 8 hours, then continues steadily downward at a slower rate to a

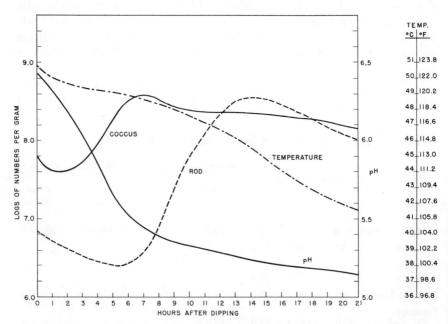

**Figure 13.9**     Typical changes in numbers of starter organisms, pH and temperature of Swiss cheese in the press. Counts and pH values from Frazier et al., (19); temperatures from Burkey et al., (7).

minimum at 21 to 36 hours. To promote proper drainage it is essential that acid formation be neither too fast nor too slow. It is usually accepted that the acidity of the curd should increase about 0.3 to 0.4 pH unit during the first 3 hours in the press. At 21 hours the acidity of the cheese should be about pH 5.1 to 5.2 (7).

At dipping, the temperature of the curd is too high for any of the normal cheese organisms to multiply. As soon as the curd cools to about 49°C. to 50°C. (120.2°F. to 122°F.), however, *Streptococcus thermophilus* begins to grow rapidly and may attain numbers of several hundred million to a billion per gram. During the first 2 or 3 hours the cocci do not multiply, but they increase greatly in size and no doubt are respiring actively. It is to this activity that the initial drop in pH is attributed before there is an actual increase in numbers (19). In the pH range of cheese at dipping (usually 6.3 to 6.4) the buffering action is not great, hence small amounts of acid have a marked effect on the pH.

The rods in the starter often decrease in numbers during the first few hours the cheese is in the press. At some time between the fifth and tenth hours, usually, they begin to grow very rapidly and reach numbers as high as, or higher than, those attained by the cocci. The growth of the rods is responsible for the continued acid production necessary to promote adequate drainage of whey and other changes. The time at which the rods begin to grow depends on the species used, the activity of the individual culture, and the time required for the curd to cool to a temperature at which they can multiply. Active cultures of *Lactobacillus bulgaricus* usually begin to increase rapidly when the temperature falls to 48°C. to 49°C. (118.4°F. to 120.2°F.), whereas cultures of *Lactobacillus lactis* may not grow until the temperature reaches 46°C. to 47°C. (114.8°F. to 116.6°F.). The cheese maker must take these differences into consideration in adjusting his making operations.

Under normal conditions the high temperature of the curd and the rapid activity of the starter organisms effectively suppress growth of other bacteria while the cheese is in the press (19). Numbers of lactic streptococci and coliform bacteria decrease rapidly during the first few hours and usually are not found in significant numbers when pressing is finished. Propionibacteria do not grow during pressing and, in fact, their numbers may even decrease slightly.

### CHANGES DURING RIPENING

*Microbial changes.* Normally the lactic starter organisms reach their maximum numbers while the cheese is in the press. Further growth is halted by the lack of fermentable sugar and by the low temperature of the cheese after it is placed in the salt brine. The numbers of *Streptococcus thermophilus* decrease gradually until by the end of 30 to 50 days the cheese may contain only a few million viable cells of this organism per gram. The lactobacilli from the starter follow a similar course. Usually they die off even more rapidly than do the cocci, and in 15 to 30 days their numbers are reduced to a few million per gram.

Bacteria that produce propionic acid develop rapidly when the cheese is moved to the warm room and usually reach numbers of one hundred million or more per gram by the time the cheese is 2 months old. Throughout the remainder of the ripening period these organisms outnumber all others in the cheese. The best known of this group are the so-called propionic rods of the genus *Propionibacterium*. It has long been accepted that these organisms are responsible for eye formation and much of the typical flavor of Swiss cheese. They ferment lactic acid according to the reaction:

$$3\ CH_3CHOHCOOH \longrightarrow 2\ CH_3CH_2COOH + CH_3COOH + CO_2 + H_2O$$

$\qquad\quad$ *lactic acid* $\qquad\qquad\qquad\qquad$ *propionic acid* $\qquad\;$ *acetic acid*

A group of propionic acid-producing cocci that occur typically in pairs and tetrads also has been found in Swiss cheese (13, 23) and some investigators believe that these so-called "tetracocci" have a special role in eye formation. These organisms have been found regularly in milk for Swiss cheese (13) in greater numbers than the propionic rods, and Frazier and Wing (23) have noted that they often develop more rapidly in the cheese than do the typical propionibacteria. In fact, they have observed that eye formation may be virtually complete before there is abundant growth of the propionic rods. Frazier has found several hundred million propionic cocci per gram of cheese during the early stages of eye formation.

Because the propionibacteria may vary in morphology from typical cocci to diphtheroid rods within a single species, it is likely that most investigators have failed to differentiate between the typical propionibacteria and the cocci that occur in tetrads. Regardless of the specific role of each type, however, there seems to be no doubt that the propionic acid fermentation is responsible for eye and flavor formation in the cheese.

As in Cheddar and other hard cheeses, *Lactobacillus casei* grows during the ripening of Swiss cheese, and some investigators consider it to be an essential ripening organism, though its specific function has not been explained. Its rate of development is fairly slow, but it usually reaches maximum numbers of fifty to one hundred million per gram within a few days after manufacture. Normally this species outnumbers all other lactic acid bacteria throughout the ripening period (12).

*Changes in body.* As ripening progresses, the body of Swiss cheese gradually softens and becomes less tough and elastic. When rubbed between the fingers, the ripened cheese will mash together easily, and when eaten, it will dissolve readily. These changes reflect the solubilizing action of the proteolytic enzymes. About one-third of the protein nitrogen is converted into water-soluble form, approximately 30 to 40 per cent of which can be accounted for in old cheese as amino nitrogen with very little ammonia. Most workers believe that the enzymes responsible for this decomposition are contributed by autolysis of bacteria, the most active of which are the lactobacilli from the starter.

*Flavor development.* The characteristic flavor that distinguishes Swiss from other cheese does not appear until eye formation is well under way and, in fact, the flavor continues to increase long after eye formation is halted. The increase in propionic and acetic acids parallels flavor development, and for this reason many persons believe that these acids and their salts, especially the propionates, are responsible for most of the sweet, nut-like flavor characteristic of Swiss cheese. Analyses of good quality Swiss cheese have demonstrated small amounts of butyric, caproic, caprylic, and capric acids in addition to the lower volatile fatty acids. Acetic and propionic acids arise mainly from lactate fermentation, but the others presumably result, in part at least, from hydrolysis of fat by intracellular lipases liberated on autolysis of the ripening organisms.

Products of protein hydrolysis also must contribute appreciably to the flavor of Swiss cheese. Among the amino acids, glutamic acid, proline, and asparagine have been found most consistently in greatest amounts (37). Virtanen and Kreula (66) attribute much of the characteristic sweetness of well-aged Swiss cheese to proline. This idea is not in accord with the belief that salts of propionic acid are responsible for the sweetness, and thus it accentuates the fact that much is yet to be learned about the actual mechanism of flavor development in Swiss and other types of cheese.

*Changes in acidity.* The pH of Swiss cheese begins to increase soon after pressing is completed and continues to rise throughout ripening. The rate at which the rise occurs varies widely with different cheeses so that it is difficult to predict with accuracy what the pH will be at any given age. Unpublished results obtained by W. C. Frazier from a large number of cheeses show the following range of values:

| AGE OF CHEESE | STAGE OF RIPENING | pH RANGE |
|---|---|---|
| 21 hours | After pressing | 5.00–5.15 |
| 13 days | Into warm room | 5.20–5.25 |
| 30 days | Eye formation begins | 5.30–5.35 |
| 75 days | At grading | 5.45–5.55 |
| 6 months | In curing cellar | 5.50–5.60 |
| 9 months | In curing cellar | 5.60–5.90 |

*Eye formation.* The appearance of the eyes is one of the main criteria on which the quality of Swiss cheese is judged. In the best grade cheese the eyes are round, smooth, and glossy. They are ¾ to 1 inch in diameter and are distributed about 1 to 3 inches apart.

Normal Swiss cheese eyes are essentially accumulations of carbon dioxide produced by the lactate-fermenting organisms. The gas diffuses through the curd and collects at weak points. The "bubbles" thus produced continue to increase in size until the cheese is moved to the cold room to finish ripening. The number of eyes depends on the rate of gas production and the physical characteristics of the curd. If gas forms too rapidly, for example, it cannot diffuse away fast enough, and the result is many small eyes rather than the desired few large ones. A similar effect is obtained if the curd particles do not knit together properly so that the curd has numerous weak spots. A cheese with too many eyes is said to be "over-set." Insufficient gas production results in too few eyes or even none (a "blind" cheese).

The rate of gas formation is dependent on the number of propionic acid bacteria present and on the environment inside the cheese. Many cheese makers depend on natural inoculation to provide these organisms, which are almost always present in small numbers in the milk and on the factory equipment. Within the last 2 or 3 decades, however, it has become common practice to add pure cultures of propionibacteria to the milk in the kettle. Whether added or not, however, the number of propionic acid bacteria should not exceed a few thousand per milliliter of kettle milk.

The rate of development of the propionic acid bacteria in the cheese is markedly affected by the pH and salt concentration. The maximum acidity for growth of these organisms is very near pH 5.0. If too much acid develops in the curd, therefore, eye formation is likely to be inadequate. Too little acid, on the other hand, may permit excessive growth and cause oversetting. The propionic organisms are very sensitive to salt, hence Swiss cheese must be salted lightly if eyes are to form normally. Cheese makers sometimes prevent excessive eye formation by applying additional salt to the cheese in the warm room.

Swiss cheese curd is subjected to considerable strain as the gas accumulates (Figure 13.10). If the curd is not sufficiently elastic the tension caused by eye formation may cause fissures or cracks called "checks" to appear inside the cheese. If these cracks are sizable, the defect is commonly called "glass," a derivation of the descriptive German word *Gläsler*. Appearance of this defect indicates brittleness or lack of elasticity of the curd. Once the eyes are formed, the curd must become firm enough to hold its shape and prevent shrinkage or deformation of the openings. This firming results from reducing the temperature of the cheese after the eyes are formed, from the normal proteolytic changes that convert the cheese to a firm, meaty product, and from a loss of moisture by evaporation. Swiss cheese made in the traditional wheels usually loses about 10 per cent of its moisture during ripening.

Anything that causes weakness or brittleness of the curd will result in defective eye formation. Mastitic milk, for example, or milk with excessive amounts of fat yields cheese with weak or inelastic curd. The milk of some cows inherently forms a weak curd. With milk of normal composition, however, the moisture content and the acidity probably are the most important factors in determining the properties of the curd. Fortunately these are to a considerable extent under the control of the cheese maker. They

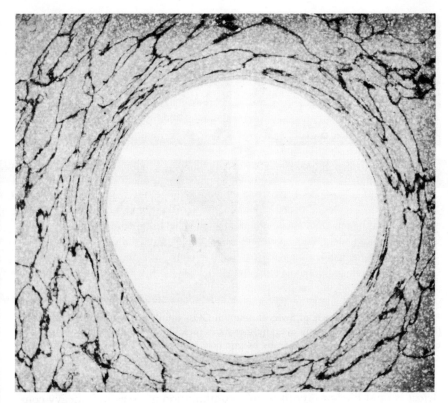

**Figure 13.10**     Section through a normal eye of Swiss cheese. Observe how curd is stretched. Photo courtesy of Drs. J. Kürsteiner and W. Staub, *Merkblätter für den Emmentalerkäser* (41).

can be regulated by proper handling of the starter cultures and by careful attention to the behavior of the curd in the kettle and in the press.

*Defects.* Some of the important defects of body and eye formation of Swiss cheese already have been described. One of the most common body defects is "glass" which results from failure of the curd to stretch when under tension (Figure 13.11a). Defects of the eyes are many. In addition to such faults as too many eyes (Figure 13.11b) or too few, the individual eyes themselves may not have a glossy surface ("dead eyes"), or the surface may be ridged and uneven ("nutshell eyes"). The underlying causes of many of these defects are not understood.

Growth of undesirable microorganisms can give rise to a wide variety of defects of texture and flavor (41). Sometimes, for example, gas-forming organisms grow while the cheese is in the press ("pressler" defect) and produce varying degrees of blowing, ranging from "pinholes" to much larger (Figure 13.11c). The most common cause is *Aerobacter aerogenes,* although early gassing of this type has been caused by *Bacillus polymyxa* (63). This

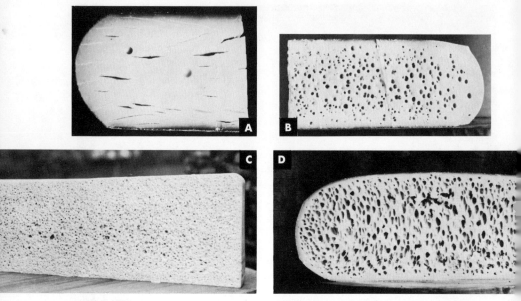

**Figure 13.11**    Defects of Swiss cheese. (a) Glass (gläsler defect) with too few eyes. (b) Overset cheese (too many eyes). (c) Early gas (pressler defect) caused by *Aerobacter aerogenes*. (d) Late gas formation by butyric acid anaerobes. Photos courtesy of Drs. J. Kürsteiner and W. Staub, *Merkblätter für den Emmentalerkäser* (41).

defect is most likely to result from a combination of excessively heavy contamination and an inactive starter culture of *Streptococcus thermophilus*.

Sometimes abnormal gassing develops later during ripening (Figure 13.11d). The gas may appear as pinholes, in which case it is described as a "nissler" defect, or the holes may be much larger and may appear in clusters or "nests." The usual cause of late gassing is lactate-fermenting species of *Clostridium*. Among those most feared by the Swiss cheese makers is the group known as the butyric acid anaerobes (e. g., *Clostridium butyricum*), which produce considerable amounts of butyric acid in addition to large quantities of carbon dioxide and hydrogen. Other clostridia may cause gas and undesirable flavors in Swiss cheese. *Clostridium lentoputrescens,* for example, produces a very bad odor, usually in localized areas, giving rise to the term "stinker" cheese.

Anaerobes, such as those just described, can be controlled in most types of cheese by insuring sufficient acid production, by thorough salting, and by holding the cheese at the lowest practicable temperature. In Swiss cheese, however, salting must be light, and the temperature must be fairly high for a time to permit eye development. Therefore, anaerobes can grow if they are present in sufficient numbers, especially after the pH rises to about 5.3. The only really effective preventative is to keep them out of the milk.

A variety of undesirable flavors and odors may develop in Swiss cheese if foreign microorganisms are allowed to grow. All of the gas formers, for example, produce a mixture of waste products that cause off-flavors known as "unclean," "fermented," "yeasty," "rancid," "putrid," and the like. Small rust-colored spots sometimes appear in Swiss cheese, often, but not always, associated with the eyes. Such spots usually represent colonies of *Propionibacterium rubrum* or other pigmented species of the genus. They can best be prevented by careful attention to sanitation on the farm and in the factory so that the organisms do not get into the milk.

## EDAM AND GOUDA

These varieties originated in Holland, but they are made in considerable quantities in America. In certain characteristics they resemble the semi-soft cheeses, but in others, especially the method of ripening, they are more like the hard cheeses. Both are made from partly skimmed milk and, like Swiss, they contain less fat in the dry matter than do Cheddar and related varieties (Table 13.1, page 356). Their moisture content is slightly less than 45 per cent.

Edam cheese is made with *Streptococcus lactis*-type starter, and the curd is formed, cut, and cooked as was described for Cheddar. When it is sufficiently firm, the curd is dipped into perforated molds and pressed. The cheese is salted on the surface, either with dry salt or in brine. It is cured at 10°C. to 20°C. (50°F. to 68°F.) for a few weeks, then is coated with red paraffin, and is ready for market. Care is taken to prevent slime formation on the surface during ripening. The final product is mild in flavor.

Gouda is made by a process similar to that for Edam. The curd is cut into smaller pieces and cooked to a slightly higher temperature, hence it is a little lower in moisture. It is pressed into discs resembling Swiss in shape but much smaller. These are ripened like Edam, but, because of the slightly lower moisture content, they may be cured longer.

Edam and Gouda are subject to most of the defects described in the section on spoilage of cheese. Sometimes propionic acid bacteria develop and cause small eyes to form. In Edam this is undesirable, but in Gouda slight eye formation is acceptable.

## SEMI-SOFT CHEESES

Varieties intermediate in consistency between hard and soft cheeses may be combined in a group called semi-soft. In general these contain more moisture than the hard cheeses but less than the soft varieties. Most of them are ripened by a combination of enzymes and microorganisms acting within the mass (like the hard varieties) and microbial growth on the surface (like the soft cheeses). Three general types may be recognized within the semi-soft class: (a) varieties that are consumed shortly after manufacture and in which little ripening takes place; (b) varieties ripened primarily by the action of molds; and (c) varieties on which a surface smear or slime is caused to develop.

Monterey cheese represents the first group, being consumed essentially as fresh cheese. This product is made by practically the same process as stirred-curd or granular cheese (page 365) except that the moisture content of Monterey is higher (up to 44 per cent) and the body is thereby softer. High-moisture jack cheese is a similar variety that contains 44 to 50 per cent moisture. Ordinarily both of these cheeses are consumed within 30 days or less; hence they must be made from pasteurized milk.

The mold-ripened cheeses include Roquefort, Stilton, Gorgonzola, Blue, and similar varieties made from whole milk, and Gammelost, a Norwegian cheese made from skimmilk. The smear-ripened cheeses include Limburger, Brick, and many others. With Limburger and related varieties, a heavy surface growth is encouraged to develop the characteristic strong flavor. With others, such as Brick, smear growth may be limited so that the flavor will be mild. All of the mold-ripened and surface-ripened cheeses are surface salted, although part of the salt may be mixed with the curd before pressing.

## BLUE CHEESE

Although molds are undesirable on Cheddar, Swiss, and most other kinds of cheese, they are necessary in Blue cheese and its relatives. In the manufacture of these varieties, spores of the mold are inoculated into the milk or curd, and the cheese is held under conditions that permit good growth and activity of the mold. This requires, among other things, a very open texture so that the mold can obtain air and have space in which to grow. The species employed usually is *Penicillium roqueforti*. Its blue-green spores cause the inside of the cheese to have a mottled or marbled appearance because of which varieties in this group often are referred to as blue-veined or blue-mold cheeses.

The best known of the blue-veined cheeses is Roquefort. This variety has been made for centuries from sheep's milk in the southern part of France and is ripened in natural caves that provide ideal conditions of temperature and relative humidity. The cheese gets its name from the village of Roquefort near which are located some of the best ripening caves. A Roquefort-type cheese is made from cow's milk in the United States and in several European countries. In America the domestic product is called Blue cheese; the imported product is designated as *Bleu*. The English Stilton and the Italian Gorgonzola are mold-ripened varieties usually made from cow's milk by methods similar to those used for Blue cheese. Sometimes Gorgonzola is made from goat's milk.

In addition to its typical mottled appearance when cut, Blue cheese is characterized by a sharp, peppery flavor and a semi-soft consistency. The composition of the domestic product may vary considerably, but for most lots the ripened cheese contains 41 to 43 per cent water, 30 to 32 per cent fat, 21 to 23 per cent nitrogenous compounds (expressed as protein), and 4.0 to 5.0 per cent salt. The high salt concentration (about 10 to 12 per cent salt in the water) is characteristic of Roquefort-type cheeses and is an important factor in controlling the changes during ripening.

MANUFACTURE

No single process is followed by all makers of Blue cheese, but the method described here incorporates the essential features of most. Raw or pasteurized whole milk at about 30°C. (86°F.) is inoculated with 2 to 3 per cent of *Streptococcus lactis*-type starter. Prior to pasteurization the milk may be homogenized or it may be separated, and the cream homogenized and then recombined with the skimmilk. Homogenization increases the area of fat globule surface and thus accelerates lipolysis. Some makers bleach the milk with peroxide (16, 17) to provide a white cheese in which the blue-green color of the mold is prominent.

The milk is ripened until the acidity increases by 0.03 to 0.05 per cent. Rennet is added, and the curd is cut when it becomes firm and "porcelain-like" (usually 60 to 90 minutes). As soon as the curd particles reach the desired firmness the whey is removed, either by dipping the curd into draining cloths or by draining off the whey by the method described for Cheddar cheese. In either process the curd is stirred during draining to prevent its matting together. A common procedure is to add 1.0 to 1.5 per cent salt to the drained curd in the vat. Usually the curd also is inoculated with spores of *Penicillium roqueforti* at this time, although some makers add the spores to the milk before curdling or even mix the spores with the curd while the hoops are being filled. The curd is scooped into round metal hoops about 7 inches in diameter. These are placed on a draining table without pressure (Figure 13.12a) and turned at intervals to facilitate drainage and to promote uniform matting. The temperature should be about 20°C. (68°F.).

On the following day the fresh cheese is removed from the hoops and salted in a cold room. Some makers hold the cheese in brine for 2 or 3 days, then complete the process by rubbing dry salt on the cheese. Others use dry salting alone, the entire process requiring 6 to 10 days.

After the surface has dried for 2 or 3 days the cheese may be dipped in paraffin; then it is punctured with long, slender needles to admit air and favor growth of the mold (Figure 13.12b). The cheese is stored on edge in rooms or caves maintained at 9°C. to 12°C. (48.2°F. to 53.6°F.) and 95 to 98 per cent relative humidity (Figure 13.12c). If the cheese is not paraffined a slimy surface growth develops and must be scraped off occasionally, usually 2 or 3 times during the curing period (Figure 13.13).

**Figure 13.12**     Manufacture and ripening of Blue cheese. (a) Curd on draining table. (b) Piercing fresh cheese to stimulate development of the mold. (c) Blue cheese in the curing room. Photos courtesy of Department of Dairy Husbandry, University of Minnesota.

When the cheese is about 3 months old it is cleaned, wrapped in foil, and stored at 7°C. (44.6°F.) or below until the desired flavor and body characteristics are attained. This may require several months.

The mold spores used to inoculate Blue cheese are obtained by growing *Penicillium roqueforti* on cubes of sterile whole wheat bread. Only cultures of proven suitability should be used for this purpose (42). After

**Figure 13.13**    Removing the smear from Blue cheese. The cheese on the left has the smear intact. The one on the right has been scraped. Photo courtesy of Department of Dairy Husbandry, University of Minnesota.

growth and sporulation are well advanced, the bread is dried and powdered. Usually 2 to 4 g of this powder per 1,000 pounds of milk or 0.1 to 0.2 g per 5-pound cheese is sufficient.

### CHANGES DURING MANUFACTURE

The amount of starter culture used in making Blue cheese is larger than for most other types because it is essential that acid be produced rapidly. This is necessary to suppress growth of undesirable organisms, to insure sufficient firmness of the curd, and to promote drainage of whey before salting. Cheese that does not drain sufficiently will have a sour flavor, its texture will not be sufficiently open, and it will not ripen normally. Most of the moisture is lost while the cheese is on the draining table. For best results the moisture content at the end of this step should be 47 to 48 per cent (27). Salting further reduces the moisture content, usually to 42 to 43 per cent. In addition, the salt firms and hardens the surface of the cheese.

The acidity reaches its maximum about 24 hours after the making process is started. At this time the pH of the fresh curd is 4.5 to 4.7 (9, 61).

### CHANGES DURING RIPENING

At the time of salting, Blue cheese contains several hundred million to a few billion cells of *Streptococcus lactis* per gram. Because of the high acidity and the increasing concentration of sodium chloride as absorption from the surface continues, this organism dies off rapidly so that few viable cells can be found after 2 or 3 weeks. Whether *Streptococcus lactis* contributes appreciably to the ripening changes is not known. Normally no other bacteria grow in significant numbers during the curing period.

Growth of *Penicillium roqueforti* normally becomes evident inside the cheese within 8 to 10 days after puncturing. Gradually the mold grows throughout the spaces between the curd particles and along the puncture holes until it reaches its maximum development within 30 to 90 days (Figure 13.14). Usually the mold grows more rapidly near the center of the cheese where the salt concentration is lower initially.

*Penicillium roqueforti* is mainly responsible for ripening Blue cheese. In cheese made without the mold the characteristic flavor does not develop, and the body fails to soften as it should. Of considerable interest have been the reasons why *Penicillium roqueforti* should predominate in Blue cheese over other species that might get into the curd. Aside from the fact that the desirable mold is added in great numbers to the cheese, this species also is more tolerant of salt and grows better at low concentrations of oxygen than do most others (62). As Blue cheese ripens, its oxygen content decreases rapidly, and the carbon dioxide content rises. These conditions are unfavorable to all molds, but they tend to affect *Penicillium roqueforti* to a lesser extent than other species likely to be present and able to grow at

**Figure 13.14**    Cured Blue cheese showing development of *Penicillium roqueforti*. Photo courtesy of USDA.

the salt concentration found in Blue cheese. It has been suggested that piercing the cheese stimulates growth of this mold by allowing carbon dioxide to escape (26).

Within 2 or 3 weeks after unparaffined Blue cheese is placed in the curing room a whitish, sticky growth of yeasts appears on the surface along with patches of blue-green mold. Gradually these organisms are replaced by a slimy, reddish-orange growth consisting of micrococci and rods, primarily *Bacterium linens* or *Bacterium erythrogenes* (31). It has long been supposed that the slime has no useful function except to indicate satisfactory conditions of temperature and humidity for ripening. In experimental trials, however, Morris et al. (45) found that cheese with slime had slightly higher pH, volatile acid and amino nitrogen values, better body and texture, and a somewhat finer flavor than waxed cheese on which slime did not form. Excessive slime development, however, is deleterious.

The pH of Blue cheese increases rapidly and steadily from its initial minimum of 4.5 to 4.7 at 24 hours to a maximum of 6.0 to 6.25 at 2 to 3 months (10). This increase is more rapid and more pronounced in the outer part of the cheese near the slime layer. Subsequently the pH remains unchanged, or it may go down again slightly, presumably because of liberation of fatty acids by lipolytic enzymes. The initial decrease in acidity probably results from destruction of lactic acid by *Penicillium roqueforti*.

Soon after Blue cheese is made, its volatile acid content begins to increase. In fact, if the raw cream is homogenized, butyric acid often can be detected in the fresh curd, due apparently to the action of milk lipase. As the mold develops it produces lipases that release butyric, caproic, caprylic, and capric as well as higher acids from the fat. It has been shown that the mold lipases are active at the temperature, pH, and salt concentration found in ripening blue cheese (46, 61). Hammer and Bryant (28) believe that the mold metabolizes part of the products of fat hydrolysis during the early part of ripening just as it does lactic acid. As its growth rate decreases, because of lack of oxygen, diffusion of salt, and accumulation of by-products, the volatile acids tend to increase. During this time the typical Blue cheese flavor becomes more intense.

At one time it was believed that the characteristic peppery flavor of Roquefort cheese was attributable entirely to the presence of caproic, caprylic, and capric acids and their readily hydrolyzable salts. However, it is known now that methyl-*n*-amyl ketone (heptanone 2) is an essential component of the flavor. Apparently the mold forms this compound by oxidation of the beta carbon atom and decarboxylation of caprylic acid:

$$CH_3(CH_2)_6 \cdot COOH + O_2 \longrightarrow CH_3(CH_2)_4 \cdot CO \cdot CH_3 + H_2O + CO_2$$

caprylic acid                                 methyl-*n*-amyl ketone

Other ketones have been found in Blue cheese and may be flavor contributants (51). Methyl-*n*-heptyl ketone (nonanone 2) and methyl-*n*-propyl ketone (pentanone 2) apparently can be formed from capric and caproic acids, respectively, by a reaction similar to that described for methyl-*n*-amyl ketone from caprylic acid.

Products of protein hydrolysis probably contribute in some way to the flavor of Blue cheese, but definite information on their contribution is not available.

Attempts have been made to hasten flavor development in Blue cheese by adding animal lipase (steapsin) to speed up fat hydrolysis. Volatile fatty acids appear more rapidly and in greater amounts in cheese made in this way, and typical Roquefort flavor develops sooner than in cheese made with mold alone (8), but the product always has a bitter flavor. Ripening of cheese made from pasteurized milk has been accelerated by inoculating the milk with selected strains of *Candida lipolytica* or by adding extracts of this organism to the milk (50, 52), but these procedures have not been used commercially.

The body of Blue cheese gradually softens as the casein is hydrolyzed. Protein decomposition in this cheese has not been studied as extensively as it has in Cheddar, although it is known that a considerable increase in amino nitrogen occurs (45). This increase is most rapid during the first 6 months, and it continues until the cheese is consumed. Some proteolysis may result from the rennet enzymes, but most of it probably is accomplished by the mold. The proteinase formed by *Penicillium roqueforti* resembles trypsin in its general characteristics (61). It is active from pH 5.3 to 7.0 with its optimum near pH 6.0. It causes extensive degradation of casein, yielding considerable amounts of amino acids and simple peptides in proportion to the more complex polypeptides.

### DEFECTS

Even when Blue cheese is made from raw milk, the vigorous acid fermentation and the high salt concentration combined with a fairly low curing temperature effectively control bacterial spoilage except under unusual conditions. In addition, the volatile fatty acids produced early in ripening, especially if the cream is homogenized, are inhibitory to many bacteria, and they probably help minimize spoilage. Sometimes gas is noticeable in Blue cheese in small amounts, but rarely is it in sufficient quantity to be objectionable. One reason, probably, is the open texture, which permits escape of the gas.

Probably the most common defect of Blue cheese results from improper development of *Penicillium roqueforti*. Excessive growth may cause an undesirable, musty, unclean flavor, and in fact, it may cause loss of typical flavor because the mold is able to destroy the methyl-*n*-amyl ketone after it is formed (28). Insufficient growth of the mold causes defects in color, the body is too firm, and insufficient flavor develops. The mold may not grow enough if the texture of the cheese is too close or if the humidity of the ripening room is so low that the cheese dries out. Sometimes inadequate mold growth results from using an atypical culture. Some milk supplies do not contain enough iron to support good growth and pigmentation of *Penicillium roqueforti* (38).

Surface defects are not uncommon on Blue cheese, and sometimes they cause considerable loss. Black molds, usually species of *Cladosporium*, may grow on the surface and into the puncture holes, causing a musty flavor in the cheese. A red mold called *Sporendonema casei* has been found on Blue cheese (29). Molds of these and other genera are not likely to cause trouble unless they develop in the curing rooms in unusually large numbers. Their control is best accomplished by careful sanitization of the shelves and other surfaces. Waxing the cheese before ripening helps to minimize their development. Excessive slime growth may cause softening of the surface and undesirable flavors in the cheese. Usually this is an indication of infrequent cleaning of the surface and often of excessive humidity in the curing room. A serious softening of the surface has been observed on cheese placed too near a humidifier, where excess moisture could strike the cheese directly. Considerable loss occurs when cheese with heavy slime is washed because the soft edges break off easily.

### CHEESE MADE WITH WHITE MUTANTS OF PENICILLIUM ROQUEFORTI

By ultraviolet irradiation of a pigmented culture of *Penicillium roqueforti*, Knight et al. (38) obtained stable white mutants that were even more actively lipolytic and proteolytic than was the parent strain. Some of these mutants have been used at the University of Minnesota to produce a mold-ripened cheese that is called "nuworld." This cheese displays no prominent mold coloration and has a very smooth and creamy body with good spreading qualities even at refrigerator temperatures. The flavor is relatively mild unless the cheese is ripened for an extended period. Nuworld ripens faster than Blue cheese. It is more readily accepted by consumers who object to the "moldy" appearance of Blue cheese for aesthetic reasons.

## GAMMELOST

For centuries Gammelost has been made in Norway but only in recent years has it been imported into or made in the United States (16). Its description is included here because it represents a cheese that differs widely from most other varieties in that the milk is not curdled with rennet, the curd is heated to boiling during manufacture, and the cheese is not salted.

Two making procedures are in common use in Norway (24). In both of them skimmilk is curdled with a *Streptococcus lactis*-type of starter. In the *Hardanger* method the curd is broken up, heated to about 63°C. (145°F.), and drained. Then it is packed into perforated wooden forms and held for several hours in boiling whey. In the *Sogn* method the curd is broken up, boiled in the whey, drained, cooled, inoculated with spores of *Penicillium roqueforti*, and then packed into forms. After the forms are removed, the surface of the cheese is inoculated with *Mucor* species obtained from older cheeses by rubbing with the hands. The interior of Hardanger cheese is inoculated with *Penicillium roqueforti* or a closely related species by being pierced a few times with a long needle dipped in a culture of the mold. Gammelost is ripened at 10°C. to 12°C. (50°F. to 53.6°F.) and a high relative humidity for about 4 weeks. During this time the *Penicillium* develops throughout the interior, and the *Mucor* covers the surface with a thick, cottony growth that is stroked down at intervals with the hands.

In Norwegian Gammelost the moisture content usually ranges between 46 and 52 per cent, protein 45 to 50 per cent, fat 0.5 to 1.0 per cent, and ash 1.0 to 1.5 per cent (24). Eighty to 90 per cent of the protein nitrogen is converted to water-soluble form, one-third to one-half of which is found as ammonia and amino nitrogen. The pH rises rapidly, varying in the ripe cheese from 6.0 to 7.5, depending on the amount of ammonia formed. The maximum pH is reached in the outer portion of the cheese.

Various types of yeasts and aerobic bacteria grow in Gammelost during ripening, but Funder (24) attributes most of the changes to the molds. In his studies the species found most commonly inside the cheese were *Penicillium roqueforti* and *Penicillium frequentans*. On the surface various species of *Mucor* and *Rhizopus* were found, *Mucor racemosus*, *Mucor mucedo*, and *Rhizopus nigricans* being the most common.

## BRICK CHEESE

Brick is one of the few varieties developed in the United States. It is said to have originated in 1865 in a factory in Wisconsin where "Backstein," a cheese of German origin, was being made. The source of the name is not known with certainty. Brick cheese is made in a rectangular loaf that measures about 3 x 5 x 10 inches; hence, the name may come from its resemblance to an ordinary building brick. It is also possible that the name originated from the fact that a brick commonly is used as a weight during pressing of the curd.

This variety is representative of a large group of related cheeses including Muenster, Tilsiter, Bel Paese, the Trappist types such as Port du Salut and D'Oka, and many others. All of them are ripened with the aid of a surface growth of yeasts and bacteria.

Good quality Brick cheese has a smooth, mellow, elastic body and a fairly close texture. Occasional mechanical openings and a few gas holes are not objectionable, but the cheese should be free of pinholes and cracks. The flavor is described as sweet, mild, clean, and nut-like. There is considerable variation, however, depending on the amount of surface growth that develops. Brick cheese usually contains about 42 per cent moisture,

31 per cent fat, and 21 per cent protein. The final salt content is 2 to 3 per cent.

### MANUFACTURE

Pasteurized whole milk is warmed to about 32°C. (89.6°F.) and inoculated with a starter of lactic streptococci. A combination of *Streptococcus lactis* and *Streptococcus thermophilus* may be used if a cooking temperature much above 37°C. (98.6°F.) is to be employed. The milk is curdled with rennet. The curd is cut, cooked at 37°C. to 45°C. (98.6°F. to 113°F.), and dipped into rectangular forms. Some makers add water to the curd and whey to wash out part of the lactose before dipping. The cheese is turned at intervals while it is draining at room temperature.

On the following morning the cheese is removed from the forms and salted in brine for 1 or 2 days as was described for Swiss. Then it is placed on shelves in a room maintained at about 15°C. (59°F.) and a relative humidity of 90 to 95 per cent. Within 2 or 3 days a surface growth of yeasts (*Mycoderma*) appears, followed a few days later by micrococci and then by *Bacterium linens*. Growth of the bacteria gives to the surface a reddish-orange color. Some makers wash the cheese at intervals with a dilute salt solution to minimize development of the smear, but others allow the smear to develop undisturbed. Figure 13.15 shows smear development on Brick cheese.

When about 2 weeks old, the cheese is moved to a room held at 5°C. to 10°C. (41°F. to 50°F.) for further ripening. If a mild flavor is desired, the surface growth is washed off, and the cheese is dried and coated with wax before the final curing. If a stronger flavor similar to that of Limburger is wanted, the cheese with smear intact is wrapped in parchment and foil to complete the curing. Brick cheese is ready for consumption when 6 to 8 weeks old.

### CHANGES DURING MANUFACTURE

Control of the acidity is essential if Brick cheese is to have the desired body and flavor characteristics. If the acidity is too high the cheese will have a short, crumbly, mealy body, and the flavor will be sour. If insufficient acid develops, however, the cheese will almost invariably develop late gas and undesirable flavors. To obtain the best quality cheese the maker must aim at a final pH between 5.0 and 5.2.

As Brick cheese is usually made, the lactose disappears and the minimum pH is reached within 1 to 3 days. If the curd is made by the conventional process and contains the maximum permissible amount of moisture (44 per cent), there will be enough sugar to yield a final pH of 4.7 to 4.9. Such cheese will not ripen properly. A fairly high moisture content is desirable to increase the yield and to make a soft-bodied cheese. Brick cheese can be made with the maximum permissible amount of moisture

**Figure 13.15**    Smear development on Brick cheese. (The smear has been scraped aside from a small area to provide contrast.) Photo courtesy of Dr. W. V. Price, University of Wisconsin.

without risking excessive acidity if the curd is washed with water before dipping. By adjusting the amount, temperature, and time of applying the water, the residual lactose content can be regulated so as to yield any final acidity desired.

The starter organisms develop rapidly in Brick cheese in the vat and during draining, reaching maximum numbers of a few billion per gram within a few days (25). The changes in numbers depend on the kind of starter used and on the temperature of cooking. If *Streptococcus thermophilus* is in the starter, for example, it will grow rapidly during cooking and for the first few hours of drainage, but it will slow down as the curd cools to the temperature of the room. *Streptococcus lactis,* on the other hand, usually does not grow much in the vat, especially if the cooking temperature is high, but it will develop rapidly after the curd cools down to about 32°C. (89.6°F.) and below. Use of a mixture of these 2 organisms permits acid production throughout the making process.

The pH of Brick cheese drops steadily from the time the starter is added. Within 2 hours after dipping the pH may be down to 5.6 or 5.7 and by the end of 10 hours it is usually 5.1 to 5.3. Ideally it should go no lower than pH 5.1 to 5.2.

### CHANGES DURING RIPENING

The starter organisms die off during ripening; *Streptococcus thermophilus* fairly quickly, *Streptococcus lactis* more slowly. In cheese made from raw milk, rods of *Lactobacillus casei* or similar species develop rapidly and within 2 to 4 weeks may reach several hundred million per gram. These organisms rarely develop in significant numbers in cheese made from pasteurized milk. Various other organisms are found from time to time in large numbers in Brick cheese. *Streptococcus bovis* and *Streptococcus faecalis*, for example, have been found in numbers of one hundred million or more per gram in cheese made from pasteurized milk (18).

By exercising care to avoid contamination from external sources and by using pasteurized milk of excellent quality, Zorn et al. (70) made Brick cheese in which no organisms developed in significant numbers during ripening. The number of starter bacteria decreased from about one billion per gram initially to ten million or less at 2 weeks. A few micrococci and enterococci were found, but their numbers never exceeded a few million per gram. The cheese ripened satisfactorily and was ready for consumption in the usual 6 to 8 weeks. These results suggest that no organisms other than those in the starter are necessary inside the cheese for producing the normal ripening changes.

The acidity of Brick cheese decreases gradually as ripening progresses. If the minimum pH attained is 5.0 to 5.2 at 1 to 3 days, the pH will rise gradually to about 5.25 to 5.3 at 4 weeks, and about 5.35 to 5.45 at 6 to 8 weeks. If the pH falls to 4.7 to 4.8 during manufacture, however, it may never rise appreciably thereafter.

The only known function of the surface organisms on Brick cheese is to contribute to the flavor. The yeasts reduce the acidity at the surface and produce vitamins that doubtless stimulate growth of the bacteria (33, 56). Some workers believe that the micrococci are essential for production of the typical mild Brick cheese flavor and that *Bacterium linens* is responsible for the stronger Limburger-like flavor and aroma. Micrococci that have been isolated include *Micrococcus varians*, *Micrococcus freudenreichii*, and *Micrococcus caseolyticus*. These organisms can produce alcohol and a variety of volatile fatty acids.

Relatively little proteolysis occurs during the ripening of Brick cheese. Langhus et al. (43) showed that 80 to 85 per cent of the nitrogenous compounds still are insoluble in water at the end of the normal ripening period. On the basis of present knowledge it must be assumed that whatever proteolysis does occur results from the action of proteinases from the rennet and from the bacteria that grow within the cheese. Any proteolytic action of the smear organisms is limited to the surface and has no demonstrable effect on the body of the cheese.

### DEFECTS

Probably the most common defect of Brick cheese is excessive acidity. The remedy has already been discussed. Coliform bacteria often grow in the cheese during draining and salting, causing early gas that may vary in intensity from an occasional pinhole to a spongy condition. These organisms can best be controlled by using good quality, pasteurized milk. Late gas formation by clostridia often occurs in cheese in which there is insufficient acid and salt. This defect is most likely to occur if the pH after making does not go below 5.3. Failure of the smear to develop sometimes occurs if the humidity of the curing room is too low. Foreign molds may grow on the surface if the smear is slow in appearing.

## LIMBURGER CHEESE

This variety usually is made in rectangular blocks weighing 1 to 2 pounds each. During ripening it undergoes extensive protein decomposition, the results of which are primarily responsible for the distinctive flavor, aroma, and body of the cured product. Good quality Limburger cheese has a soft, waxy body with no evidence of curdiness at the center. A moderately close texture is desired, although slight mechanical openness and occasional gas holes are not objectionable. The moisture content of the cured product should be approximately 45 to 46 per cent. As it is usually made, Limburger contains 27 to 29 per cent fat, about 20 to 24 per cent protein, and 1.5 to 3.0 per cent salt.

### MANUFACTURE

Only a few years ago Limburger cheese was made exclusively from raw whole milk, but pasteurization now is a common practice, especially during the summer months when the quality of milk is likely to be poorest. Many makers do not add starter to raw milk. Even to pasteurized milk they may add only 0.1 to 0.2 per cent of a culture of *Streptococcus lactis*. Some makers use a mixture of *Streptococcus lactis* and *Streptococcus thermophilus*.

The milk is warmed to about 30°C. (86°F.), starter is added if desired, and rennet is used to form a curd. After cutting, the curd is cooked at about 35°C. (95°F.) and dipped into perforated rectangular forms. As soon as the pieces of curd are firm enough to handle without breaking, they are cut into blocks weighing 1 to 2 pounds each. These are rubbed with dry salt, then transferred to a room maintained at 15°C. to 20°C. (59°F. to 68°F.) and a relative humidity of 90 to 95 per cent. While in this room, the cheese is rubbed daily to close openings on the surface and to distribute the surface ripening organisms. Within a few days a heavy reddish slime develops. When the cheeses are 10 to 15 days old, they are wrapped in parchment and foil and stored at about 10°C. (50°F.), where ripening continues. The surface growth is not removed before wrapping. The cheese is ready for consumption at 6 to 8 weeks.

### CHANGES DURING MANUFACTURE

Acid-forming organisms grow rapidly while the curd is being made and usually reduce the pH about 0.1 to 0.2 unit before dipping. Rapid acid production continues and by the end of 24 hours the pH is 4.8 to 5.0 (68). The amount of whey lost by the curd (and therefore the moisture content of the final cheese) is determined largely by the rate of acid development while the curd is draining. This is affected, in turn, by the number and activity of the acid-producing organisms and by the temperature of the room. If acid is produced too rapidly, the curd becomes too dry and the body of the final cheese will tend to be firm. Inadequate drainage, on the other hand, yields cheese with a wet, soggy body and a sour flavor. Such a cheese will not ripen properly.

### CHANGES DURING RIPENING

Within 2 or 3 days after manufacture of Limburger cheese, a whitish growth consisting of aerobic, salt-tolerant yeasts and often a small amount of *Geotrichum candidum* appears on the surface. A few days later the surface film becomes reddish-orange in color and very sticky to the touch. The growth continues to increase in quantity and assumes the consistency of warm butter. Coincident with the change in color, bacteria can be isolated from the slime in great numbers. The predominant one found is *Bacterium linens,* although various micrococci, non-pigmented rods, and other bacteria sometimes are present (34, 69).

Even though experiments have shown that it is possible to make good Limburger cheese by inoculating the surface with pure cultures of the desired organisms, this procedure is unnecessary in practice. The organisms get on the shelves and are thereby transferred to the surface of fresh cheese. The frequent rubbing of the surface with the hands also helps to transfer the ripening organisms from old cheese to new. As the growth develops, the pH at the surface of the cheese rises rapidly until at the end of 6 or 7 days it may be 5.7 to 6.0 or even higher (35). Attainment of this pH coincides with the appearance of *Bacterium linens* in the smear. Gradually the pH of the cheese beneath the surface also rises until at the end of 2 months it is usually 6.20 to 6.80. At this time the pH at the center of the cheese normally is about 5.40 to 5.70.

The surface growth is responsible for most of the changes that occur during the curing of Limburger cheese. The gradation in pH from a maximum in the smear itself to a minimum at the center suggests that the products of the organisms in the slime, rather than growth of organisms within the cheese, are responsible for neutralization of the acid. Also, the change in body to a soft, smooth, waxy condition proceeds from the surface inward, as can be shown by cutting a cheese that is incompletely cured. In such a cheese there will be a core of unchanged curd in the center.

Not all of the changes caused by the organisms in the surface growth are known. The yeasts destroy lactic acid, thereby raising the pH to a point where *Bacterium linens* can grow. Kelly and Marquardt (35) reported that this species could grow when the pH reaches 5.85. In addition, the yeasts liberate vitamins that are needed by the rod. One of importance is pantothenic acid (56). *Bacterium linens* is believed to be mainly responsible for the typical flavor of Limburger. This organism decomposes casein actively, liberating a large part of the nitrogen as amino acids and ammonia. Limburger cheese contains hydrogen sulfide and indole, but the organisms responsible for their formation are not known. It has been suggested that the fatty acids found in ripe Limburger may result from deamination of amino acids or from oxidation of alcohols produced by the action of yeasts on lactose (1).

### DEFECTS

Limburger cheese is subject to practically the same defects as were described for Brick.

## SOFT RIPENED CHEESES

Cheeses in this group owe their softness to a high moisture content and to extensive protein decomposition. All of them are made in small pieces to permit the enzymes formed at the surface to diffuse throughout the cheese. They ripen quickly and have a keeping time of only a month or two.

Most if not all of the changes in the soft ripened cheese are caused by organisms growing on the surface. These may be combinations of molds, yeasts, and bacteria, as are found on Camembert and certain types of Brie, or yeasts and bacteria as are active on Liederkranz and Romadour. Ripening of the latter group follows essentially the course described for Limburger.

## CAMEMBERT

This is one of the oldest and best known of the soft cheeses. It originated in Camembert, France, shortly before 1800 and now is made in many countries. Its manufacture in the United States began in California in 1880. Camembert is made in discs about 5 inches in diameter and 1 inch thick and weighing approximately ½ pound when fully cured. During ripening the cheese becomes soft and buttery, the change beginning at the outside and proceeding to the center. A crust or rind develops on the surface and lends rigidity to the ripened cheese. The flavor is described as slightly salty, slightly bitter, and slightly rancid, but in a pleasing combination. The odor of ammonia is noticeable in fully ripened cheese. The moisture content of good quality Camembert usually is 48 to 52 per cent; fat, 25 to 27 per cent; protein, 18 to 20 per cent; and salt, about 2.5 to 3.0 per cent. Fat in dry matter approximates 50 to 52 per cent.

### MANUFACTURE

Raw, or preferably pasteurized, milk at about 30°C. (86°F.) is inoculated with a starter of lactic streptococci and held until the acidity reaches 0.20 to 0.23 per cent. Some makers add 1 or 2 per cent of starter and allow a ripening period; others obtain the acidity directly by adding as much as 4 or 5 per cent of starter. A very firm curd is formed with rennet: The curd is dipped, with or without cutting, into round, perforated metal forms placed on special woven reed mats for draining (Figure 13.16a, b). The temperature of the room should be 18°C. to 22°C. (64.4°F. to 71.6°F.), and the relative humidity should be 85 to 90 per cent to prevent excessive evaporation. At higher temperatures drainage may be too rapid, and the curd will become too dry. Also there is better opportunity for gas-forming organisms to grow. If the temperature is too low, however, acid production and drainage will be impeded, and the cheese will be too wet.

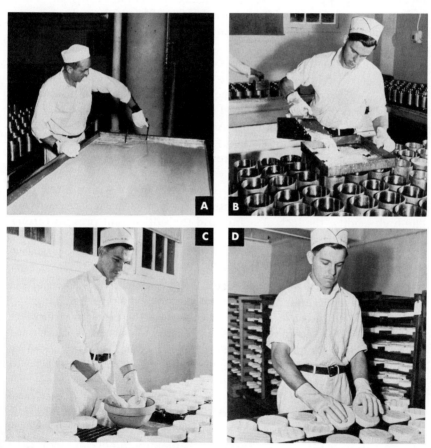

**Figure 13.16** Manufacture of Camembert cheese. (a) Cutting the curd. (b) Dipping the curd into forms for draining. (c) Inoculating the surface of the fresh cheese with spores of *Penicillium camemberti* (the cheeses are dipped into the spore suspension). (d) Turning the cheese in the curing room to promote uniform development of the surface growth. Photos courtesy of Kraft Foods Co.

As soon as the cheese can be handled without breaking, it is removed from the forms and dry salted. The salt removes moisture from the surface and thus makes the outside of the cheese more firm.

For ripening, the cheeses are laid on special lattice-like mats that permit good air circulation. The cheeses are turned at 2- to 4-day intervals to permit uniform growth of organisms on both surfaces (Figure 13.16d). Temperatures used for curing commonly are between 11°C. and 15°C. (51.8°F. and 59°F.). The humidity of the air is 85 to 90 per cent, and ventilation is varied in accordance with the condition of the cheese, that is, whether it needs to lose more moisture or not. The cheeses remain under these conditions until the moisture content is reduced to about 50 per cent and the surface growth has developed sufficiently. In American practice the cheese is wrapped in tinfoil and packaged soon after softening is first noticed; thereafter it is held at about 10°C. (50°F.). Methods of curing and selection of the stage of ripening for wrapping and shipment vary considerably between factories.

## CHANGES DURING MANUFACTURE

The most important requirement of the making process is to insure sufficient drainage of the curd so that the moisture content will be about 58 to 60 per cent at salting. Active acid production is essential for this because the curd is not cooked. The only microorganisms that grow appreciably during manufacture are those from the starter. These reach numbers of a few billion per gram within the first few days, then die off gradually thereafter (14). The pH reaches 4.7 to 4.9 within a few days after making, at which time the lactose supply is exhausted or nearly so. The high acidity, the lack of sugar, and the salt content prevent further growth of the starter organisms.

## CHANGES DURING RIPENING

Two essential steps occur during the ripening of Camembert cheese: (a) microorganisms grow on the surface and cause the changes in body and flavor, and (b) the moisture content of the cheese is reduced to about 50 per cent. According to most authorities, the excess moisture must be eliminated by gradual evaporation during ripening. If it is removed by extensive draining of the fresh curd, microbial growth on the surface will be unsatisfactory.

Under normal conditions of ripening, film yeasts and species of *Geotrichum* appear on the surface of the cheese within 3 or 4 days after it is placed in the curing room. A few days later *Penicillium camemberti* appears and spreads over the surface, reaching its maximum development at 10 to 12 days. Next there appears a reddish growth of pigmented short rods, presumably *Bacterium linens* or related types.

Even though all of these organisms are found on good quality Camembert cheese, there is disagreement on the necessity for, and function of, each group. The yeasts that grow first may ferment any residual lactose at the surface and, along with the *Geotrichum* organisms, reduce the acidity at the surface of the cheese. Some workers believe that these organisms are unnecessary and that *Penicillium camemberti* that follows can cause the necessary ripening changes. Others think the *Geotrichum* organisms are necessary for the initial softening of the cheese and for normal flavor development. Weigmann (67), for example, attributes the "mushroomlike" flavor of Camembert to the *Geotrichum* organisms.

Regardless of the specific action of the film yeasts and *Geotrichum* that develop initially, their growth should not be excessive. They are somewhat restricted by the high initial salt concentration at the surface and by keeping the exterior of the cheese fairly dry through careful regulation of the humidity and movement of the air. Excessive growth of these organisms causes too much softening of the rind and too strong flavors in the cheese. Furthermore, cultivated strains of *Penicillium camemberti* can not easily establish themselves on a surface that is heavily covered with film yeasts (40).

The vegetative growth of *Penicillium camemberti* is white, but it forms grayish-green spores. There is general agreement that this species is essential for the development of normal body and flavor in Camembert. Since it is normally present in great abundance on the cheese, this mold overgrows all others if the ripening conditions are satisfactory. Attempts to accelerate the growth of *Penicillium camemberti* have included studies of its pH and salt tolerance. Kundrat (39) showed that its spores do not germinate well at the pH and salt content of the surface of fresh Camembert cheese. Therefore the initial reduction of the acidity by the film yeasts and *Geotrichum* and the absorption of some of the surface salt by the interior of the cheese seem to be necessary before *Penicillium camemberti* can develop well.

The pigmented bacteria (species of *Bacterium*) cannot grow until the acidity at the surface has been reduced by the action of the yeasts and molds. Most investigators agree that these bacteria contribute significantly to the flavor of the cheese, although their specific action is not known. Excessive development causes a strong flavor. Usually they can be checked successfully by holding the cheese in a cold, dry atmosphere.

To insure the presence of *Penicillium camemberti* some makers inoculate the surface of the cheese with a suspension of spores prepared from a culture of the mold on moistened sterile crackers (Figure 13.16c). Others inoculate the milk itself with the spores. Many depend on chance inoculation in the curing room. Weigmann (67) recommends inoculating the milk occasionally with desirable strains of *Geotrichum, Penicillium camemberti,* and the pigmented bacteria to insure their constant presence in sufficient numbers.

Optimum development of the surface flora depends on the initial moisture content of the curd and on the correct balance of temperature, humidity, and air movement. Cheese that contains much above 60 per cent water at the start of ripening cures too rapidly and becomes too soft or even fluid. Conversely, cheese with too little moisture does not ripen properly. If the temperature of the curing room is too high, the molds grow excessively, and the cheese is strong in flavor. If the temperature is too low, they do not develop sufficiently, and the ripening changes are delayed. With excessive humidity and inadequate air movement not enough water evaporates from the surface, thus allowing excessive growth of film yeasts, species of *Geotrichum, Mucor,* and bacteria, so that *Penicillium camemberti* is inhibited. If the humidity is too low or the air movement is excessive, on the other hand, the surface dries out too much, the normal ripening organisms can not grow, and wild molds, usually green-spored penicillia, will develop. Thus for the best results it is desirable to have a series of ripening rooms adjusted to different temperatures and humidities so that optimum development of the surface organisms and dehydration of the cheese can be accomplished by moving the cheese to the most desirable conditions. This practice is followed in many European factories.

Although the ripening changes in Camembert cheese usually are attributed to the organisms that grow on the surface and the enzymes they produce, bacteria other than those in the starter sometimes develop within the cheese. *Lactobacillus casei* and related species, for example, may reach significant numbers during ripening (14), but it is unlikely that they have much effect on the characteristics of the cheese.

Within about 10 to 14 days after ripening begins, Camembert cheese shows a softening under the rind. Shortly after this the cheese may be wrapped and boxed. Normally it reaches the consumer about 2 or 3 weeks later. By this time the softening has reached the center of the cheese. During this latter part of curing, Camembert develops its fine flavor. If ripening is prolonged excessively, the odor of ammonia becomes more and more noticeable, especially near the rind.

Softening of the cheese is accompanied by a marked increase in solution of proteins. Table 13.4 shows the changes in nitrogen-containing compounds during the normal ripening period. In this study, hydrolysis of the protein was slow until about the tenth day, after which it increased markedly and continued to increase thereafter until, in the fully ripened cheese, 80 per cent of the nitrogen was in water-soluble form.

As the cheese ripens there is a rapid decrease in acidity presumably owing to the formation of alkaline materials and to oxidation of the lactic acid by molds and film yeasts at the surface. Table 13.5 shows typical changes in pH at the surface and at the center of the cheese.

### DEFECTS

Early gas formation during drainage is a common defect in Camembert cheese made from raw milk of poor quality. However, the high initial acidity and salt concentration combined with the short holding time effectively prevent growth of clostridia. Growth of wild molds is a serious problem in the Camembert factory. Among the species reported most commonly are *Penicillium glaucum, Penicillium bruneo-violaceum,* and *Penicillium roqueforti.* These organisms are most likely to develop on cheese that becomes too dry for normal growth of *Penicillium camemberti.* Makers of Camembert must watch the cheese carefully during ripening and remove any contaminated pieces immediately to avoid infection of other cheeses. If contamination becomes serious, the curing room must be emptied and disinfected.

**Table 13.4**   Protein decomposition in Camembert cheese during ripening *

| AGE OF CHEESE | PER CENT OF TOTAL NITROGEN AS | |
|---|---|---|
| (*days*) | *Water-soluble Nitrogen* | *Ammonia* |
| 1 | 11.72 | 0 |
| 3 | 15.02 | 0 |
| 5 | 16.02 | 0 |
| 7 | 18.51 | 0 |
| 10 | 25.98 | 0 |
| 12 | 23.79 | 0 |
| 14 | 56.51 | 0 |
| 18 | 60.69 | 0.35 |
| 19 | 60.00 | 0.75 |
| 20 | 63.79 | 2.07 |
| 21 | 67.55 | 2.27 |
| 28 | 80.08 | 8.05 |

* From Bosworth (5).

**Table 13.5**   Changes in pH of Camembert cheese during ripening *

| AGE OF CHEESE | pH | pH |
|---|---|---|
| (*days*) | *Surface* | *Inside* |
| 0 | 6.36 | 6.36 |
| 1 | 5.02 | 5.03 |
| 3 | 4.97 | 4.89 |
| 5 | 5.10 | 4.92 |
| 7 | 5.25 | 4.80 |
| 9 | 5.61 | 4.85 |
| 11 | 6.13 | 4.89 |
| 13 | 6.84 | 5.04 |
| 18 | 7.61 | 5.45 |
| 21 | 7.73 | 5.99 |

* From Eigel (14).

Defects traceable to abnormal composition and ripening conditions are many. Cheese made with excessive moisture or insufficient salt or cheese held at too high temperature develops a strong flavor and becomes too soft. Oversalting and uneven salting cause defective surface growth. A dry surface caused by too low humidity or too rapid air movement does not permit good development of *Penicillium camemberti,* but a surface that is too wet develops a smear growth similar to that of Limburger.

## PROCESS CHEESE AND RELATED PRODUCTS

The term process cheese is applied to those products that have been heated and packed into sealed containers. The process first was applied to Camembert and other soft cheeses to lengthen their keeping time. Later Swiss cheese was treated in this way for export from Europe. World War I stimulated wide interest in processing cheese to avoid spoilage and to permit distant shipment. The first American patent for processing cheese was issued in 1916. Since that time the process cheese industry in the United States has increased to an extent whereby a very large part of the cheese now is marketed in this form.

Processing cheese has advantages beyond the increased keeping time of the product. By blending cheeses of different ages it is possible to obtain a product of uniform characteristics from one lot to another. Two or more varieties may be combined to make an almost limitless number of blends. Additional substances such as fruits, vegetables, meats, smoke, spices, and the like can be added at the time of mixing to increase further the many possible variations in flavor and consistency. Of primary importance, also, is the fact that any pathogenic microorganisms that may be present are destroyed during heating.

Processing cheese includes four major steps:

(1) *Selecting and blending.* Cheeses with different degrees of flavor development are mixed in a proportion that will yield the desired characteristics in the final product. One or more varieties of cheese may be included. The cheese is comminuted finely and delivered to the cooker.

(2) *Addition of optional ingredients.* To obtain the desired smoothness in the final product, certain chemicals may be added to help dissolve the protein and emulsify the fat. Substances that may be used for this purpose singly or in combination include various phosphates, citrates, and tartrates (17). The total weight of emulsifying salts cannot exceed 3 per cent of the weight of the product. The cheese can be acidified, if desired, with vinegar or with lactic, citric, acetic, or phosphoric acid. Salt, harmless artificial coloring, spices, and fruits, vegetables, or meats may be added. In addition, water, cream, or non-fat milk solids in various forms can be used to adjust the composition of the product to meet legal requirements. It should be emphasized that the optional ingredients listed in this paragraph can

be used only with certain processed products and only if the products are properly labelled.

(3) *Heating the cheese.* The mixture of cheese and other ingredients is heated with agitation until it is a smooth plastic mass. Federal standards (17) require that the heat treatment be no less than 66°C. (150°F.) for at least 30 seconds.

(4) *Filling the containers.* The hot mass of cheese is caused to flow into plastic- or foil-lined cartons of convenient size that then are sealed to exclude air. Some of the hard cheeses are marketed as slices wrapped in transparent plastic films.

Definitions and standards have been established for the many types of heated or processed cheese (17). Three general classes of products are recognized:

(1) *Pasteurized process cheese.* Except for the emulsifying agent, salt, acid, and cream, cheese contributes practically all of the solids in this product. The limits for moisture and fat are near, or identical to, the limits imposed for the corresponding variety of natural cheese (Table 13.1, page 356). The quantity of acid added must be such that the pH is not reduced below 5.3. Omission of the acid and emulsifying agents yields a product called pasteurized blended cheese.

(2) *Pasteurized process cheese food.* This product differs from pasteurized process cheese in that part of its solids are added as cream, milk, skimmilk, cheese whey, or albumin from cheese whey. The moisture content does not exceed 44 per cent, the fat content is not less than 23 per cent, and the pH may not be adjusted lower than 5.0 with added acid.

(3) *Pasteurized process cheese spread.* The moisture content of this product is greater than 44 per cent but not more than 60 per cent. The fat content is at least 20 per cent. The ingredients listed for pasteurized process cheese food may be included in its preparation. One or more of the following may be added in such amounts that the total weight of the substances listed does not exceed 0.8 per cent of the weight of the product: carob bean gum, gum karaya, gum tragacanth, guar gum, gelatin, carboxymethylcellulose, carrageen, oatgum, algin (sodium alginate), and algin derivative (propylene glycol ester of alginic acid). Sweetening agents may be added in a quantity necessary for seasoning. These include sugar (sucrose), dextrose, corn sugar, corn sirup, corn sirup solids, maltose, malt sirup, and hydrolyzed lactose. The pH may be reduced, if desired, to 4.0. If the emulsifying agents are omitted, the product is called pasteurized cheese spread.

Few bacteria other than spore-formers survive the heat treatment given processed cheese mixtures. Of these, the anaerobic species are the ones most likely to grow (32). *Clostridium sporogenes* has been reported as the most common cause of process cheese spoilage, but *Clostridium pasteurianum* and 1 or 2 other species have been implicated in a few outbreaks. All of these organisms produce gas, and the proteolytic species, such as *Clostridium sporogenes,* also cause putrefaction.

Spores of anaerobic bacteria can be found in a large percentage of samples of process cheese products. Even though these products are stored at room temperature, the anaerobes normally can not grow because of the unfavorable pH and salt content. Only if the acidity is too low or if unusually high numbers of spores are present is spoilage likely to result. Excessive numbers of these organisms may be contributed to the processing mixture by defective cheese, skimmilk powder, or occasionally by other ingredients. Processed cheese products containing skimmilk powder, whey powder, pimiento, or other sugar-containing foods are more likely to undergo spoilage by clostridia because the added sugar may permit growth of organisms that otherwise could not develop.

Although molds are killed during processing, they may recontaminate the product during packaging and will grow if oxygen is available. This problem is most serious with packaged sliced process cheese because of the greater surface involved and the greater opportunity for contamination. Mold spoilage can be controlled by thorough sanitation to minimize airborne contamination and by packaging in air-tight containers.

### COLD-PACK CHEESE

The product made by comminuting and blending into a homogeneous mass one or more varieties of cheese without heat is called cold-pack cheese, club cheese, or comminuted cheese. Except for the emulsifying agents, the optional ingredients listed for pasteurized process cheese may be used in the cold-pack product. Moisture and fat requirements for this product are the same as those for the corresponding natural varieties (Table 13.1, page 356). If acid is added, the pH may not be reduced below 4.5. Since no heat is applied during manufacture, all cheeses used in the cold-pack product must be made from pasteurized milk or be held for at least 60 days at a temperature not less than 1.67°C. (35°F.). If dairy products other than cheese are used in the mixture, the product is called cold-pack cheese food.

Cold-pack cheese and cheese food are more perishable than the pasteurized cheese products because they are not heated. They have about the same preservative factors as the corresponding natural cheeses except that they can be more acid. Under normal conditions their preservation depends largely on protecting the surface against contamination with molds and film yeasts and on packaging to exclude air.

## TRANSMISSION OF DISEASES THROUGH CHEESE

Although it has long been known that cheese could serve as a vehicle for disease transmission, little was done by American regulatory authorities to prevent spread of pathogens in this way until 1944. During the next few years several states enacted laws that required that cheese either be made from pasteurized milk or be ripened for at least 60 days. In 1951 the

Federal Security Agency established a similar requirement (17) for all cheese handled in interstate commerce, the minimum holding period being 60 days at not less than 1.67°C. (35°F.).

Food poisoning and typhoid fever account for practically all of the disease outbreaks that have been traced to cheese. Information on the causes of the food poisoning outbreaks often is not available, but doubtless the causal organisms include staphylococci and species of *Salmonella*. These organisms might get into milk from the cow, the milk handler or cheese maker, rodents, or other sources. Especially important are cases of staphylococcal mastitis. Typhoid organisms most likely would be added by a carrier who handled the milk or made the cheese. Regardless of the source, however, none of these organisms survives ordinary pasteurization. Therefore, they could be present in cheese made from properly pasteurized milk only if introduced after the heat treatment. It should be pointed out that staphylococcal enterotoxin, in contrast to the organisms themselves, is fairly stable to heat. If the toxin is formed in the milk before pasteurization, it may cause illness when the cheese is eaten. This eventuality will not occur if the milk is cooled promptly and held below 10°C. (50°F.), which is below the minimum temperature for growth of food poisoning staphylococci.

The 60-day holding period offered as an alternative to pasteurization is based on the assumption that any pathogens present in the fresh cheese will die within this period. Various factors, but primarily the acidity of the cheese, cause the pathogens to die. The rate of death increases with a rise in ripening temperature. Experimental trials have shown that pathogens do indeed die during cheese ripening, although not all may die within the 60-day period. Cultures of *Brucella* inoculated into milk, for example, have been found viable in Cheddar cheese for several months. Even so, there is little doubt that the pasteurization requirement or the alternative holding period will reduce the incidence of disease outbreaks traceable to cheese.

## References

1. Albert, J. O., H. F. Long, and B. W. Hammer, Classification of the organisms important in dairy products, IV: *Bacterium linens, Iowa Agr. Exp. Sta. Research Bull. 328,* 1944.

2. Alford, J. A., and W. C. Frazier, Occurrence of micrococci in Cheddar cheese made from raw and from pasteurized milk, *J. Dairy Sci.,* 33 (1950): 107–114.

3. ———, Effect of micrococci on the development of flavor when added to Cheddar cheese made from pasteurized milk, *J. Dairy Sci.,* 33 (1950): 115–120.

4. Baribo, L. E., and E. M. Foster, The production of a growth inhibitor by lactic streptococci, *J. Dairy Sci.,* 34 (1951): 1136–1144.

5. Bosworth, A. W., Chemical studies of Camembert cheese, *N. Y. Agr. Exp. Sta. (Geneva) Tech. Bull. 5,* 1907.

6. Brown, L. W., and W. V. Price, A study of the relationships between hydrogen ion concentration, titratable acidity, and quality in Cheddar cheese, *J. Dairy Sci.,* 17 (1934): 33–45.

7. Burkey, L. A., G. P. Sanders, and K. J. Matheson, The bacteriology of Swiss cheese, IV: the effect of temperature upon bacterial activity and drainage in the press. *J. Dairy Sci.,* 18 (1935): 719–731.

8. Coulter, S. T., and W. B. Combs, The use of steapsin in the manufacture of Blue cheese, *J. Dairy Sci.,* 22 (1939): 521–525.

9. Coulter, S. T., W. B. Combs, and J. S. George, Influence of acidity variations during manufacture on the quality and rate of ripening of Blue or American Roquefort cheese, *J. Dairy Sci.,* 21 (1938): 239–245.

10. ———, The pH of Blue or American Roquefort cheese, *J. Dairy Sci.,* 21 (1938): 273–274.

11. Davis, P. A., and F. J. Babel, Slime formation on cottage cheese, *J. Dairy Sci.,* 37 (1954): 176–184.

12. Demeter, K. J., A. Janoschek, and E. Günther, Weiteres über die Bakteriologie der Emmentalerkäse-Bereitung und -Reifung, *Milchwissenschaft,* 8 (1953): 420–426.

13. Dorner, W., and M. Thöni, Untersuchungen über kokkenformige Propionsäurebakterien, *Landwirtsch. Jahrb. Schweiz,* 53 (1939): 86–96.

14. Eigel, G., Mikroflora und Struktur des reifenden Camembertkäses, *Milchwissenschaft,* 3 (1948): 46-51.

15. Fagan, H. J., J. B. Stine, and R. V. Hussong, The identification of reducing sugars in Cheddar cheese during the early stages of ripening, *J. Dairy Sci.,* 35 (1952): 779–782.

16. Federal Security Agency, Food and Drug Administration, Cheeses; processed cheeses; cheese foods; cheese spreads; and related foods: definitions and standards of identity, *Federal Register,* 15 (1950): 5656–5690.

17. ———, Definitions and standards for food—title 21, part 19—cheeses; processed cheeses; cheese foods; cheese spreads, and related foods, June, 1951.

18. Foster, E. M., J. C. Garey, and W. C. Frazier, The bacteriology of Brick cheese, III: the bacteria involved in ripening, *J. Dairy Sci.,* 25 (1942): 323–333.

19. Frazier, W. C., L. A. Burkey, A. J. Boyer, G. P. Sanders, and K. J. Matheson, The bacteriology of Swiss cheese, II: bacteriology of the cheese in the press, *J. Dairy Sci.,* 18 (1935): 373–387.

20. Frazier, W. C., W. T. Johnson, Jr., F. R. Evans, and G. A. Ramsdell, The bacteriology of Swiss cheese, III: the relations of acidity of starters and of pH of the interior of Swiss cheese to quality of cheese, *J. Dairy Sci.,* 18 (1935): 503–510.

21. Frazier, W. C., H. F. Long, and W. T. Johnson Jr., The bacteriology of Swiss cheese, V: the use of *Streptococcus thermophilus* in ripening milk for Swiss cheese, *J. Dairy Sci.,* 19 (1936): 535–539.

22. Frazier, W. C., G. P. Sanders, A. J. Boyer, and H. F. Long, The bacteriology of Swiss cheese, I: growth and activity of bacteria during manufacturing processes in the Swiss cheese kettle, *J. Bacteriol.,* 27 (1934): 539–549.

23. Frazier, W. C., and Helen U. Wing, *Bacterium acidi-propionici* and other lactate-fermenting bacteria of Swiss cheese (abstract), *J. Bacteriol.*, 23 (1932): 60–61.

24. Funder, S., *The Chief Molds in Gammelost.* Oslo: A. W. Broggers Boktrykkeri, 1946.

25. Garey, J. C., E. M. Foster, and W. C. Frazier, The bacteriology of Brick cheese, I: growth and activity of starter bacteria during manufacture, *J. Dairy Sci.*, 24 (1941): 1015–1025.

26. Golding, N. W., The gas requirements of molds, I: a preliminary report on the gas requirements of *Penicillium roqueforti* (various strains of blue mold from cheese), *J. Dairy Sci.*, 20 (1937): 319–343.

27. Goss, E. F., V. Nielsen, and M. Mortensen, Iowa Blue cheese, a Roquefort type cheese made from cows' milk, *Iowa Agr. Exp. Sta. Bull. 324*, 1935.

28. Hammer, B. W., and H. W. Bryant, A flavor constituent of Blue cheese (Roquefort type), *Iowa State Coll. J. Sci.*, 11 (1937): 281–285.

29. Hammer, B. W., and J. C. Gilman, Red mold on Blue cheese, *J. Dairy Sci.*, 27 (1944): 413–418.

30. Harper, W. J., A. M. Swanson, and H. H. Sommer, Observations on the chemical composition of white particles in several lots of Cheddar cheese, *J. Dairy Sci.*, 36 (1953): 368–372.

31. Hartley, C. B., and J. J. Jezeski, The microflora of Blue cheese slime, *J. Dairy Sci.*, 37 (1954): 436–445.

32. Hood, E. G., and K. N. Smith, Bacterial spoilage in process cheese, *Sci. Agr.*, 31 (1951): 520–540.

33. Iya, K. K., and W. C. Frazier, The yeast in the surface smear of Brick cheese, *J. Dairy Sci.*, 32 (1949): 475–476.

34. Kelly, C. D., The microbiological flora on the surface of Limburger cheese, *J. Dairy Sci.*, 20 (1937): 239–246.

35. Kelly, C. D., and J. C. Marquardt, The influence of hydrogen ion concentration and salt on the surface flora of Limburger cheese, *J. Dairy Sci.*, 22 (1939): 309–320.

36. Kosikowsky, F. V., The liberation of free amino acids in raw and pasteurized milk Cheddar cheese during ripening, *J. Dairy Sci.*, 34 (1951): 235–241.

37. Kosikowsky, F. V., and A. C. Dahlberg, A quantitative appraisal of the free amino acids in foreign type cheese, *J. Dairy Sci.*, 37 (1954): 167–172.

38. Knight, S. G., W. H. Mohr, and W. C. Frazier, White mutants of *Penicillium roqueforti*, *J. Dairy Sci.*, 33 (1950): 929–933.

39. Kundrat, W., Der Einfluss der Wasserstoffionenkonzentration (cH°) auf den Ertrag verschiedener Schimmelstämme, *Arb. Ber. Süddeut. Vers.—u. Forsch. Milchw. Weihenstephan*, 1 (1950): 147–150 [Cited in *Dairy Sci. Abstr.*, 14 (1952): 618.]

40. ———, Bakterienentwicklung und Reifungsbedingungen beim Camembertkäse, *Deut. Molkerei-Ztg.*, 72 (1951): 1122–1124.

41. Kürsteiner, J., and W. Staub, *Merkblätter für den Emmentalerkäser.* Bern: Schweiz Käse-union AG. und Schweiz Milchwirtschaftlicher Vereines, 1950.

42. Lane, C. B., and B. W. Hammer, The bacteriology of cheese, III: some factors affecting the ripening of Blue (Roquefort-type) cheese, *Iowa Agr. Exp. Sta. Research Bull. 237,* 1938.

43. Langhus, W. L., W. V. Price, H. H. Sommer, and W. C. Frazier, The "smear" of Brick cheese and its relation to flavor development, *J. Dairy Sci.,* 28 (1945): 827–838.

44. Maskell, K. T., R. E. Hargrove, and R. P. Tittsler, A preliminary report on the bacteriology of Provolone and Romano cheese (abstract), *J. Dairy Sci.,* 34 (1951): 476.

45. Morris, H. A., W. B. Combs, and S. T. Coulter, The relation of surface growth to the ripening of Minnesota Blue cheese, *J. Dairy Sci.,* 34 (1951): 209–218.

46. Morris, H. A., and J. J. Jezeski, The action of microorganisms on fats, II: some characteristics of the lipase system of *Penicillium roqueforti, J. Dairy Sci.,* 36 (1953): 1285–1298.

47. Mulder, H., Taste and flavor forming substances in cheese, *Neth. Milk Dairy J.,* 6 (1952): 157–168.

48. Parker, R. B., and P. R. Elliker, Effect of spoilage bacteria on flavor component of cottage cheese, *J. Dairy Sci.,* 35 (1952): 482–483.

49. Parker, R. B., V. N. Smith, and P. R. Elliker, Bacteria associated with a gelatinous or slimy curd defect of cottage cheese, *J. Dairy Sci.,* 34 (1951): 887–893.

50. Parmelee, C. E., and F. E. Nelson, The use of *Candida lipolytica* cultures in the manufacture of Blue cheese from pasteurized homogenized milk, *J. Dairy Sci.,* 32 (1949): 993–1000.

51. Patton, S., The methyl ketones of Blue cheese and their relation to its flavor, *J. Dairy Sci.,* 33 (1950): 680–684.

52. Peters, I. I., and F. E. Nelson, The influence of *Mycotorula lipolytica* lipase upon the ripening of Blue cheese made from pasteurized homogenized milk, *J. Dairy Sci.,* 31 (1948): 611–618.

53. Peterson, M. H., and M. J. Johnson, Delayed hydrolysis of butterfat by certain lactobacilli and micrococci isolated from cheese, *J. Bacteriol.,* 58 (1949): 701–708.

54. Peterson, M. H., M. J. Johnson, and W. V. Price, Lipase activity during making and ripening of Cheddar cheese, *J. Dairy Sci.,* 31 (1948): 39–46.

55. ———, Liberation of fatty acids during making and ripening of Cheddar cheese, *J. Dairy Sci.,* 32 (1949): 862–869.

56. Purko, M., W. O. Nelson, and W. A. Wood, The associative action between certain yeasts and *Bacterium linens, J. Dairy Sci.,* 34 (1951): 699–705.

57. Sanders, G. P., Cheese varieties and descriptions, *USDA Agriculture Handbook No. 54,* 1953.

58. Sanders, G. P., L. A. Burkey, and H. R. Lochry, General procedure for manufacturing Swiss cheese, *USDA Circular 851,* 1950.

59. Sanders, G. P., R. R. Farrar, R. E. Hardell, F. Feutz, and L. A. Burkey, The relationship of moisture in Swiss cheese to quality and yield, *J. Dairy Sci.,* 23 (1940): 905–918.

60. Stine, J. B., Emmenthaler Cheese, U. S. Patent 2,494,636. 1950.

61. Thibodeau, R., and H. Macy, Growth and enzyme activity of *Penicillium roqueforti, Minn. Agr. Exp. Sta. Tech. Bull. 152,* 1942.

62. Thom, C., and J. N. Currie, The dominance of Roquefort mold in cheese, *J. Biol. Chem.,* 15 (1913): 249–258.

63. Tjepkema, R., W. V. Price, and E. M. Foster, An early gas defect in Swiss cheese caused by *Bacillus polymyxa, J. Dairy Sci.,* 36 (1953): 1272–1278.

64. Van Slyke, L. L., A summary of research studies relating to casein and some of their applications, *N. Y. Agr. Exp. Sta. (Geneva) Tech. Bull. 139,* 1928.

65. Van Slyke, L. L., G. A. Smith, and E. B. Hart, Experiments in curing cheese at different temperatures, *N. Y. Agr. Exp. Sta. (Geneva) Bull. 234,* 1903.

66. Virtanen, A. I., and M. S. Kreula, On the significance of amino acids for the taste of Emmentaler cheese, *Meijeritieteellinen Aikakauskirja,* 10(1–2): 13–23. 1948.

67. Weigmann, H., *Handbuch der Praktischen Käserei,* 4th Ed. Berlin: Paul Parey, 1933.

68. Yale, M. W., Factors affecting the quality of Limburger cheese made from pasteurized milk, *N. Y. Agr. Exp. Sta. (Geneva) Tech. Bull. 253,* 1940.

69. ———, The surface flora and the use of pure cultures in the manufacture of Limburger cheese, *N. Y. Agr. Exp. Sta. (Geneva) Tech. Bull. 268,* 1943.

70. Zorn, R. A., F. F. Butzi Jr., and E. M. Foster, The bacteriology of sweet-curd Brick cheese, *J. Dairy Sci.,* 35 (1952): 1067–1075.

# 14

## The microbiology of cream and butter

Butter consists primarily of milkfat, a small amount of milk solids-not-fat (curd), salt (if salted butter), and water. Federal regulations require that butter contain at least 80 per cent butterfat. The approximate composition of commercial salted butter is as follows: 80.5 per cent butterfat, 16.5 per cent water, 2.0 per cent salt, and 1.0 per cent curd. In the case of unsalted butter the percentage of fat, water, or both may be somewhat greater.

Microorganisms are important in butter for several reasons. Cream used in butter making may be affected by growth of bacteria, molds, and yeasts. If this is extensive, the quality of butter made will be impaired. Selected cultures may be used in the manufacture of butter to enhance its flavor and keeping quality. These must be handled properly for best results. Microorganisms have ample opportunity to gain access to butter during its manufacture. A knowledge of microorganisms' sources and methods of control is essential in preventing contamination with bacteria, molds, and yeasts, which often cause undesirable effects. The growth of undesirable organisms in butter is a major cause of its deterioration during storage. An understanding of the factors that favor or discourage growth of bacteria in butter often may be used to advantage in making butter of good keeping quality. Finally, there is the possibility that disease may be spread by butter that has been contaminated with human pathogens.

Butter is made by churning pasteurized sweet or neutralized sour cream of about 30 to 35 per cent butterfat content. The churning process involves vigorous agitation of the cream at a temperature of approximately 10°C. (50°F.) and in a large barrel-type apparatus, the churn, made of wood or metal (Figure 14.1). Agitation or churning is accomplished by revolving the churn. During churning the butterfat globules coalesce until finally a definite and rather exhaustive separation of the fat in granular form occurs. The buttermilk fraction that remains is drained off, and the granules usually are rinsed with water to remove excess buttermilk. Considerable butter, however, is made without washing the granules. In this

**414**

**Figure 14.1**    A metal-type churn. Courtesy of General Dairy Equipment, Inc., Minneapolis, Minnesota.

event the buttermilk is drained thoroughly, and that which remains is incorporated into the butter during the working process.

Salting may take place at this time by merely sprinkling the salt over the granules, or by distributing it in a trench made in the butter after the granules have been gathered into a fairly homogeneous mass. After salt has been added the butter is "worked." The purpose of working is to bring the butter granules into a compact homogeneous mass and to distribute the water and salt uniformly throughout the butter. Working usually is done in the churn as it is revolved. In roller-type churns the butter passes between rollers, which effect a kneading action on the butter mass. In rollerless churns internal shelves lift the butter upward as the churn revolves. As the butter nears the top, it is dropped to the bottom of the churn with considerable force, and working is accomplished by means of these repeated impacts.

After sufficient working the butter is removed from the churn, packed in boxes or tubs, and placed under refrigeration. Sooner or later most butter is packaged in ¼-, ½-, or 1-pound portions by a process called "printing" (Figure 14.2). This is generally done by forcing the butter through a power-operated machine that forms the butter into sizes desired for retail packages. The printed butter may be wrapped by hand or by mechanical means.

Considerable technology, including microbiological considerations, is

**Figure 14.2**    The printing operation in a large butter manufacturing plant. Courtesy of Land O'Lakes Creameries, Inc.

involved in connection with all of the various steps in the butter making process. This will be discussed in some detail later.

Recently equipment has been developed for the manufacture of butter by a more continuous operation than that employed in the conventional procedure (30). Major factors for the interest in this type of butter making procedure are the possibilities of (a) saving of labor, (b) greater control over the manufacturing operation, (c) greater uniformity of body and texture, and salt and moisture distribution, and (d) immediate packaging. The third and fourth reasons are of primary interest from a microbiological standpoint, because the uniformity of body and texture and the uniformity of salt and moisture distribution are extremely important in the manufacture of butter having characteristics unfavorable for microbial activity. In one procedure of continuous butter making as developed by an American equipment manufacturer (see flow diagram in Figure 14.3), cream is partially destabilized by agitation. This is followed successively by (a) separation, which yields a product containing approximately 80 per cent fat, (b) pasteurization and adjustment of pH, color, water, and salt content, (c) chilling and working in a machine called a "texturator," and (d) packaging as the butter leaves the machine. Several such installations have been made in the United States, and procedures based upon the contin-

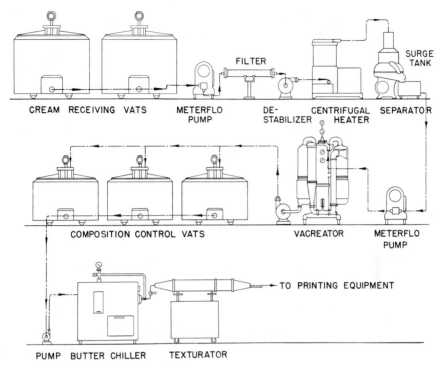

CREAM  RECEIVING  VATS    METERFLO    DE-    CENTRIFUGAL  SEPARATOR
                         PUMP        STABILIZER    HEATER

FILTER

SURGE
TANK

COMPOSITION CONTROL VATS    VACREATOR    METERFLO
                                        PUMP

TO PRINTING EQUIPMENT

PUMP  BUTTER CHILLER    TEXTURATOR

**Figure 14.3**    Continuous butter making flow diagram. Courtesy of Cherry-Burrell Corporation.

uous operation principle have been in use for some time in Germany, Switzerland, and Australia. However, most of the butter still is made by the conventional procedure described previously.

### TYPES OF BUTTER MADE

Much of the butter made in the United States is made from neutralized sour cream, although a large amount is made from sweet cream. In addition a small amount of butter is made from whey cream (prepared by separation of milk fat remaining in whey after the manufacture of cheese made with whole milk). Butter in retail market channels may or may not contain salt, artificial color, or butter culture. Certain markets prefer unsalted butter. Butter culture almost always is used in making unsalted butter. In the United States the use of culture in the manufacture of salted butter has declined greatly. This is not true in several other countries, for example, Denmark, where this is almost a universally used practice.

The following terms describe butter found on the market today:

a. Sweet cream salted butter, made from sweet cream with no culture added.

b. Neutralized sour cream butter, made from sour cream neutralized by the addition of alkalies or alkaline salts; salt but no culture added.

c. Ripened cream salted butter, made from sweet or neutralized sour cream with culture added.

d. Unsalted butter, often called "sweet butter." Made from sweet cream with culture added. Considerable quantities of unsalted butter without culture are made and stored for later use as a source of butterfat for ice cream mixes and other products. Such butter is called "sweet butter."

e. Whey butter, made from cream separated from cheese whey; salt added.

## PROCUREMENT OF CREAM AND MILK

Cream for butter making may be procured as farm-separated sweet or sour cream, or as whole milk that is separated at the plant. In the large butter producing areas most creameries have one or more trucks that are used for gathering cream and milk from farms in their surrounding area.

Considerable cream is procured through cream stations. These are cream gathering places located in outlying towns, where cream brought in by producers is weighed, tested, graded, and prepared for shipment by rail or truck to large central plants often located long distances away. Creameries that manufacture butter from cream obtained through cream stations are called "centralizers." Many farmers ship cream directly to a centralizer. They are commonly referred to as "direct shippers."

In the large butter producing areas a trend toward the establishment of large diversified manufacturing plants has taken place in recent years. Many of these have resulted from the consolidation of several small neighboring creameries that were engaged in the manufacture of only butter. The advent of these larger and more diversified plants has resulted in a shift to the procurement of a large proportion of the raw product in the form of whole milk, rather than farm-separated cream, this change being necessary to permit the manufacture of a variety of products.

## GRADING MILK AND CREAM

The quality of butter made will depend, to a great extent, upon the quality of the cream used in its manufacture. Off-flavors present in cream may be carried over into the finished butter, although some can be removed partially or even completely during processing. Defects of butter that are due to off-flavors present in cream can be controlled through judgment in the selection of cream; consequently cream is graded as it is received at the plants. Many states have regulations to define the grades of cream that may be purchased for butter making. Cream is graded largely on the basis of the quality of butter that might be expected from its use. Generally, the highest quality butter can be made only from good flavored sweet cream. Some acid development may not be harmful if other objectionable fermentations have not occurred concurrently. Acceptable butter, but of lower quality, can be made from cream that has been greatly affected by microbial activity and that possesses a wide variety of off-flavors. This is due to the fact that many objectionable flavors are volatile and may be removed during the pasteurizing heat treatments to which the cream may be subjected. Technological advances in processing equipment and methods, i. e., vacuum treatment of hot cream, have contributed greatly in this regard.

Full advantage of grading cream can be obtained only if creams of different grades are segregated at the plant. If this is not done, a relatively small amount of off-flavored cream when mixed with cream of excellent quality may result in lowering the quality of the butter made.

### ROUTINE METHODS OF GRADING

Generally, the methods used in grading cream are simple and capable of being performed at the receiving platform. Organoleptic examination is the most commonly applied test. By this procedure cream may be graded on the basis of its flavor (taste and odor) into grades commonly designated as Sweet, Number One, Number Two, and Undergrade.

Other terms may be used but, in general, most state regulations permit 3 acceptable grades of cream having the following or similar characteristics. Sweet cream usually is described as possessing a clean flavor and as having a titratable acidity not exceeding 0.2 per cent calculated as lactic acid. Off-flavors such as definite feed flavors and other abnormal flavors should be absent. Experienced judges usually are capable of accurate selection of such cream organoleptically and without the use of any other test. Cream having definite feed flavors and other off-flavors in moderate degree and possessing a titratable acidity greater than 0.2 per cent but not exceeding 0.5 or 0.6 per cent usually is placed in a second grade, often designated as Number One. If cream possesses marked off-flavors, possibly being due to extensive proteolysis and lipolysis, or if it has an acidity in excess of 0.5 or 0.6 per cent, it is usually placed in a third grade, frequently designated as Number Two. This usually is the lowest acceptable grade. Cream that is badly decomposed and that possesses flavors difficult or impossible to remove during processing is rejected as Undergrade cream and is returned to the producer. In some states a harmless dye is added to rejected cream to prevent any possibility of its being sold elsewhere.

Although segregation of sweet from sour cream is usually done organoleptically, borderline cases are frequently checked by the usual titration procedure. In this connection a "rapid acid test" often is applied. This test consists of adding, by means of a dipper, a standard amount of

NaOH solution of known concentration to a prescribed amount of cream containing a few drops of phenolphthalein indicator solution. The absence or development of a color change indicates whether or not the acidity is above or below a certain level. The test is useful in rapidly segregating cream shipments into various grades according to the amount of acid present.

The methylene blue test, which is used mostly in grading milk, may also be used in grading cream. For grading cream, it has been recommended that a triple strength solution of methylene blue be used (36). The standard concentration used in grading milk is incapable of imparting sufficient color to cream to make accurate reading possible.

The sediment test commonly is used in grading both milk and cream. This consists of passing the product through a small lintine disc. The discs or sediment test pads containing the retained sediment are then compared with standard discs containing a known quantity of extraneous matter. The test pads are graded accordingly. Some regulations require that acceptable milk or cream regardless of grade must not contain more than a stated amount of sediment. This is known as the single sediment test standard. Others specify the amount of sediment permissible for each grade. The results of the sediment test may or may not bear any relationship to the bacterial content of cream or milk. The test provides an indication only of the care taken to prevent the entrance of extraneous materials that are large enough to be retained by the test pads. Bacteria may or may not be associated with such materials.

The grading standards for milk procured for butter making and for other manufacturing purposes are much higher than those for cream. Standards that are in effect in the state of Minnesota and that are comparable to those of several other states require that the poorest grade of acceptable milk must not have off-flavors of more than a moderate degree of intensity nor a methylene blue reduction time of less than 1 hour nor a direct microscopic clump count of more than 3,000,000 per milliliter. On the other hand the highest grade of cream, even though graded as sweet cream, may contain bacteria greatly in excess of the numbers permitted for the lowest acceptable grade of milk.

### SPECIAL METHODS APPLIED TO CREAM

Any of the ordinary microbiological methods for the examination of milk may be applied to cream (see Chapter 5). However, total plate and microscopic counts and various selective culture methods such as proteolytic and lipolytic bacterial counts, and yeast and mold counts are rarely applied to raw cream for butter making. These are more frequently applied to samples of pasteurized cream taken at various stages of processing and handling in order to evaluate the efficiency of pasteurization and the sanitary care used in post-pasteurization operations.

In some areas where farm separated cream is the major source of cream for butter making, special methods have been introduced to detect and subsequently to eliminate decomposed or otherwise unfit cream. Tests for the presence of molds and for the concentration of water insoluble acids (WIA) and butyric acid (BA) are used for this purpose. Enforcement agencies frequently apply these tests to butter for the purpose of obtaining information on the quality of raw product used in its manufacture.

*Tests for molds.* Methods which have been commonly used are (a) a microscopic method (66) called the "mold mycelia count," (b) a macroscopic method (66) known as the "methylene blue borax" (MBB) test, and (c) a modification of the MBB test (48, 49) called the "visual mold test." The macroscopic procedures have had greatest application to cream. A small amount of cream is mixed with a reagent containing methylene blue and alkaline salts. The mixture is stirred while it is being heated. This causes the fragments of mold mycelium that may be present to gather into a mass or clot. The mixture is filtered, and the mold mycelium retained is measured visually. Further details of these procedures may be found in the references cited above.

The merits of the visual mold tests for evaluating the quality of cream depend upon the assumption that, when conditions have been such as to permit the development of molds, it is likely that bacteria and yeasts, being capable of more rapid growth, have grown extensively and have caused undesirable change to occur in the cream. Some relationship exists between the visual mold test and other methods of grading. Nelson et al. (44) found that organoleptic grade and visual mold score were related to some degree, but numerous exceptions to the general relationship were encountered. Agreement between the acidity of cream and the mold content was best when the acidity was low, and it was generally unsatisfactory when the acidity was high. In general, visual mold tests may be used advantageously in grading cream produced in areas where the quality of cream received is poor. As cream quality improves, it is better to apply more discriminating tests.

*Tests for water-insoluble acids (WIA) and butyric acid (BA).* In 1947 Hillig (21) proposed a method for the determination of water-insoluble acids in cream and butter in order to establish the quality of the raw cream used in the manufacture of a particular lot of butter. Later the determination of butyric acid was applied for the same purpose. When low grade cream is churned, high WIA and BA values may be obtained on the butter. Normal milk lipase and microbial lipases contribute to high WIA values. Milk lipase probably is not a highly important factor when considerable development of acidity occurs, for the enzyme is not active at an acid reaction. Similarly, the activity of several lipases produced by bacteria commonly found in milk and cream is retarded by acid conditions (41, 42). On the other hand, certain microbial lipases, such as those of

*Geotrichum candidum* and *Candida lipolytica,* may cause high WIA values in the presence of considerable acid (50, 51).

Cream held for long periods under good refrigeration may show high WIA values. This may be due to favorable conditions for the activity of normal milk lipase and bacterial lipases, for at low temperature the probability of inhibition of organisms that rapidly produce acid is increased, while the development of psychrophilic organisms, many of which are lipolytic, may be favored (41, 42).

When lipolytic bacteria such as *Pseudomonas fragi, Pseudomonas fluorescens,* and *Achromobacterium lipolyticum* (often responsible for flavor defects of butter) have grown extensively in butter, high WIA and BA values may be obtained (29). The cream used in the manufacture of such butter, however, may have been of very high quality. Therefore, it can not always be assumed that high WIA and BA values obtained on butter are due to the use of unfit cream.

## FACTORS INFLUENCING THE QUALITY OF CREAM FOR BUTTER MAKING AND THEIR CONTROL

The sources of microorganisms in raw milk, their control, and the various factors that are important in producing high quality milk have been discussed at length in Chapter 6. These are fully applicable to the production of high quality cream for butter making. There are, however, influences surrounding the production of cream for butter making that often present certain problems relative to quality that usually are not encountered in the production of milk for market milk or for manufacturing purposes. Before considering these influences, some discussion of the general microbial quality of cream as commonly encountered may be helpful in gaining an understanding of the problems involved.

The distribution of the types of microorganisms present in farm-separated cream is extremely variable, though generally the lactic acid streptococci predominate. Table 14.1 illustrates the distribution of

**Table 14.1**      Mold, yeast, and bacterial counts of raw cream (45 samples obtained during one year)*

| DISTRIBUTION OF MOLD AND YEAST COUNTS | | | DISTRIBUTION OF BACTERIAL COUNTS | |
|---|---|---|---|---|
| Ranges (per ml) | Mold counts (per cent) | Yeast counts (per cent) | Ranges (per ml) | Bacterial counts (per cent) |
| 0 | 0.0 | 0.0 | | |
| 1– 9 | 6.7 | 0.0 | Less than 100,000 | 0.0 |
| 10–99 | 48.9 | 4.4 | 100,000–9,999,999 | 23.7 |
| 100–999 | 37.8 | 46.7 | 10,000,000 or more | 77.3 |
| 1,000 or more | 6.6 | 48.9 | | |

* Macy et al. (37).

bacteria, mold, and yeast counts of farm-separated cream as received in a typical creamery. These data are based upon samples of sweet cream used in 45 churnings over a period of a year. Even though graded as sweet, 77.3 per cent of the samples had bacterial counts of 10,000,000 or more per milliliter.

Bacterial counts of sour cream frequently reach several hundred million per milliliter. Total plate counts on cream a few days old should be interpreted carefully as the bacteria may be in a declining population phase at that time; hence, such counts may not be an accurate indication of the number of organisms that may have been present at one time. It should not be concluded, however, that inferior butter from the standpoint of flavor and keeping quality necessarily would result from the use of sour cream. It has been pointed out previously (Chapter 3) that an acid fermentation exerts a preserving effect that inhibits many undesirable organisms, particularly of the proteolytic and lipolytic types. Consequently cream having high acidities when received at the plant may be free from other undesirable flavors. Such a situation illustrates the importance of the types of microorganisms present, rather than total number, in relation to the presence or development of off-flavors.

Sweet or sour cream may contain a variety of off-flavors. These may be of microbial or of non-microbial origin. Cheesy, putrid, stale, old cream, unclean, bitter, and rancid flavors are frequently encountered. High acidity also may be associated with these flavors. The presence of these defects indicates that extensive decomposition of the milk constituents, particularly of the protein and fat, has taken place, owing to the action of naturally occurring enzymes and a variety of microorganisms including molds. The latter are frequently found in cream that has been held for a long period on the farm. These defects are particularly objectionable because they may easily be carried over into the finished butter and may seriously impair its flavor.

A malty flavor defect may occur in cream, owing to the predominant growth of *Streptococcus lactis* var. *maltigenes*. This flavor is more common in cream that has a slightly or moderately developed acidity, but that has not undergone any extensive protein or fat decomposition. The unfortunate practice followed in some butter plants of dumping incoming cream into the pasteurizing vat and holding it without cooling until enough cream is received to begin pasteurizing is a very hazardous procedure from the standpoint of the development of the malty defect. The practice may result in the development of the flavor before pasteurization begins. Pasteurization will destroy the bacteria responsible for the defect, but it will not completely remove the malty flavor once it has been formed.

Attempts should be made to grade out milk and cream that show objectionable odors or tastes. Patrons should be cautioned to take better care of milking utensils and to cool milk or cream properly during holding on the farm. Furthermore, cream should be kept cool while it is being held in the butter plant prior to pasteurization for butter making.

Some of the defects mentioned above, as well as others, may occur in butter owing to the growth of various microorganisms during storage. They will be discussed in a later section of this chapter.

Lactose-fermenting yeasts are especially troublesome in cream that may be held for relatively long periods on the farm. They may cause losses because of off-flavors produced and the production of gas, which, if extensive, may force cream from the cans. Many yeasts grow in the presence of considerable acid and consequently are able to grow well after growth of bacteria has been retarded or stopped by the concentration of acid.

Non-lactose-fermenting yeasts frequently are found in cream and butter. Counts of these organisms may run into the hundreds of thousands, or even into the millions, per milliliter of cream during the summer when conditions are most favorable for their growth. Although some of these yeasts cause no detectable change in the cream or butter in which they develop, other strains may cause defects such as yeasty, rancid, unclean, bitter, cheesy, and putrid. In some cases the defect intensity is enhanced by simultaneous growth of the yeast with *Streptococcus lactis*. Since these organisms have no unusual heat resistance, their presence in pasteurized cream or in butter may be looked upon as an indication of post-pasteurization contamination or of inefficient pasteurization.

The mold content of farm-separated cream may be excessive, and a variety of species may be present. The most common species encountered is *Geotrichum candidum* (see Chapter 2). Excessive mold growth usually is found in sour cream that has been held on the farm for several days without adequate refrigeration. The molds, being aerobic, often are evident as a film or mat on the surface of the cream. Mold growth usually is accompanied by extensive growth of bacteria and yeasts. The bacteria and yeasts grow throughout the cream and may cause serious deterioration long before mold growth has become extensive. Consequently, off-flavors present in moldy cream are due more frequently to bacteria and yeasts rather than to molds. Various factors influence the amount of mold that may be present in cream. Among these are method of separation, amount of cream in the container, fat content of the cream, age of the cream, and temperature of storage (5, 12). The latter two factors are of primary importance. The problem of mold in cream is regional: sourthern areas having hot, humid weather, where farms are small and dairying is often a sideline enterprise, appear to encounter more difficulty than northern sections having cooler weather, where dairying is more extensive.

Defects of non-microbial origin frequently are due to feeds consumed by the cows. Many of these are removed during processing, but certain weed flavors such as those of French weed, wild onion, and garlic are difficult if not impossible to remove completely. In addition, flavors absorbed from fly sprays, disinfectants, gasoline, and kerosene occasionally are encountered.

## FACILITIES FOR CARE OF CREAM ON THE FARM

A large amount of butter is made from cream that is separated on the farm. Much of this cream comes from areas where dairying is not the major farm enterprise. The amount of milk produced on each farm is small, and the frequency with which cream is received from farms may vary greatly, with intervals as long as one week being common. This may be contrasted with daily or every-other-day pick-up of milk. For the cream producer specifically, no significant regulations pertain to housing of cattle, water supplies, type and care of utensils, and the presence of a milk house or of cooling equipment. As a result, many farms do not have facilities that make it convenient to keep milking equipment in proper sanitary condition and that are otherwise helpful in producing a high quality product. In the interest of improving cream quality, it is necessary, therefore, that more than the usual amount of effort be directed toward educating the producers with respect to cleanliness in milking methods and in the care of utensils, proper cooling, more frequent delivery of cream, and full utilization of the limited equipment and facilities commonly found on the farm.

## CARE OF EQUIPMENT

Proper cleaning and sanitizing of all equipment used in handling milk on the farm has been emphasized in Chapter 6. Cream producers frequently have an additional piece of equipment, the separator, which usually is not found on farms from which whole milk is shipped. The effect of separation on the bacterial count and content of milk has been discussed in Chapter 4. The separator frequently does not receive proper sanitary care, and therefore it may be a significant source of contamination. The separator must be washed after each use. Materials that are removed from the milk collect in the outer spaces of the separator bowl and between the discs. If these materials are not removed, microbial growth will occur. In the warm months of the year such growth may be very rapid, and extensive decomposition of the extraneous material may result. Use of an unclean separator may contribute large numbers of microorganisms and objectionable flavors to the cream. Storage of such cream for even a short time without adequate refrigeration will result in further deterioration.

All parts of the separator that contact the milk should be dismantled and washed thoroughly with the aid of a brush and one of the common cleaning compounds available for washing dairy equipment. Following washing, the parts should be rinsed thoroughly with clean water and left to dry in a protected place. Just before use the parts should be sanitized and reassembled. Various methods of washing the separator in place or completely assembled, often referred to as the "flush methods," have been suggested. These methods, if carefully and consistently performed, will clean the separator effectively; however, experience has shown that the use of such simplified procedures in the cleaning of separators usually leads to short cuts and to additional attempts at simplification, with the result that effective cleaning and sanitizing are not accomplished.

### COOLING

Cream should be cooled promptly after separation. The necessity for this and the type and efficiency of cooling equipment have been discussed in Chapter 6. The lack of good cooling facilities presents a serious problem to many cream producers. In the warm summer months it is impossible to cool cream adequately unless mechanical refrigeration or an ample supply of cold water is available. Mechanical coolers are preferable, but adequate cooling can be accomplished by immersing cans of cream in a tank supplied with well water, at a temperature not exceeding 10°C. (50°F.), which is continually circulated through the tank. If this method is used, the water should enter near the bottom of the tank and pass out through an overflow located at a point safely below the top of the cans. When the cream has been cooled to a temperature approximating that of the water, the water may be shut off; however, it should be turned on again at intervals frequent enough to keep the cream cold. The practice of filling the tank only once, i. e., of not replacing the original water with a fresh, cold supply, should be avoided. In many areas well water may be somewhat above 10°C. (50°F.), especially in the summertime. In such instances cream must be delivered promptly, or a mechanical cooler must be used to prevent its deterioration.

Warm cream should not be added to previously cooled cream, for the temperature will rise and thus provide suitable temperatures for rapid growth of microorganisms. Furthermore, the shipment of warmed cream may promote churning, which leads to excessive fat losses.

### OTHER FACTORS

Ideally, cream should be picked up at the farm daily. Under present conditions this often is not practicable, but delivery at intervals of not less than 2 or 3 times a week should be encouraged. Some states have regulations requiring that cream not be held on the farm longer than 4 days. These have served to reduce the age of cream received in certain areas, but much remains to be desired in this regard. The longer cream is held on the farm the greater is the danger that it will undergo fermentations detrimental to its quality. Many of the defects previously mentioned are due to holding cream too long before delivery.

Care should be taken in the selection of containers for shipping cream. It is largely the responsibility of plant management to assist in obtaining and using proper milk or cream cans for this purpose. Badly rusted and dented cans with open seams and ill-fitting covers should be discarded and replaced with new ones. Such cans are difficult if not impossible to keep in proper sanitary condition. The cans should be clean when they are returned to the producer, and the producer should take the additional precaution of sanitizing them before adding the cream.

Trucks that are used to haul cream from farms to plants should be insulated, or at least covered, to protect the cream against the warming effects of summer weather and against freezing in the winter. It is fruitless to care for cream properly on the farm and then to subject it to quality-lowering abuse during transit to the plant.

When cream is received at the plant, it should be dumped promptly and pasteurized and processed the same day as received. Where this is not possible, it should be cooled promptly, or pasteurized, and then cooled and held at low temperatures until it can be processed. Allowing the cream in the cans to stand overnight without adequate refrigeration is an undesirable practice and only increases the problem of maintaining cream quality.

## EFFECT OF PROCESSING AND SUBSEQUENT HANDLING ON THE MICROFLORA OF BUTTER

The microflora of butter may be influenced greatly by various processes, equipment, and materials used in its manufacture. The relationship of these factors to the microbiology of butter is discussed in this section.

### NEUTRALIZATION

Normally, neutralization of sour cream takes place before cream is pasteurized. It would not be expected that bacteria, yeasts, or molds would be present to any appreciable extent in commercial neutralizers. Only if it is of poor quality will water used as a solvent constitute a source of bacteria. Such water should not be used in any food plant. However, neutralization changes the pH of the cream to levels of near neutrality at which the heat used in pasteurization is less lethal than it is for sour cream.

Through its effect on the pH of butter, the neutralization of cream may affect the growth of microorganisms in butter during storage. The effect of acidity, however, will considered later in the section on the use of butter cultures.

### PASTEURIZATION

The fundamental aspects of the destruction of microorganisms by heat have been discussed at length in Chapter 4. The same principles are operative in the pasteurization of cream for butter making.

In this processing perhaps less emphasis has been given to pasteurization safeguards, particularly with respect to assurance of obtaining the desired period of exposure at a specified temperature, than has been given to such safeguards in the pasteurization of market milk. If a certain heat treatment is desired, for example 71.1°C. (160°F.) for 30 minutes, the following checks should be used in making certain that every particle of cream is held at 71.1°C. (160°F.) continuously for 30 minutes (or for any other desired temperature-time combination).

(a) If all of the cream is in the pasteurizing vat and is raised to 71.1°C. (160°F.) in the vat, and cooling is begun in the vat simultaneously with, or before, the opening of the outlet valve, the temperature recording chart should show 30 minutes at 71.1°C. (160°F.)

(b) If cream is preheated to 71.1°C. (160°F.) before it is pumped into the pasteurizing vat, the recording chart should show 30 minutes at 71.1°C. (160°F.), plus the time of filling from the level of the temperature recorder bulb.

(c) If cooling is begun in the pasteurizing vat after the opening of the outlet valve, or is done entirely outside the pasteurizing vat (over a surface cooler, for example), the recorder chart should show 30 minutes at 71.1°C. (160°F.), plus the time of emptying to the level of the recorder bulb.

(d) Recording temperature charts should be examined carefully for any discrepancies that might indicate possible under-holding or under-heating of the cream. If such are disclosed, steps should be taken immediately to prevent their reoccurrence. Such things as dumping of a can or two of late-arriving cream into the vat after the holding period has begun or cutting the holding period somewhat because of a desire on the part of some employee to complete the day's work more quickly occasionally occur. These will result in inadequate heat treatment of the cream. Organisms may survive and cause defects in the finished butter. Employees should be thoroughly instructed about the importance of being certain that pasteurization is properly done.

The pasteurization of cream for butter making usually results in the destruction of a high percentage of the bacteria present, as shown in Table 14.2. Frequently, this destruction reaches greater than 99.9 per cent. Two reasons largely account for this. First, the heat treatment used is considerably above that employed for fluid milk. Most cream intended for butter is pasteurized at not less than 71.1°C. (160°F.) with a holding time of 30 minutes. This should be the minimum heat treatment for cream for butter making. In practice, however, higher heat treatments commonly are applied. All but the most highly resistant vegetative forms of bacteria and those that may exist in the spore state at the time of pasteurization are destroyed. Proper pasteurization will destroy those bacteria commonly associated with the development of bacterial defects of butter, and essentially all yeasts and molds are killed. Years ago, when pasteurization was first applied in butter making, lower heat treatments were used. As a consequence, bacterial destruction was not as great, and frequently a few molds and yeasts would survive.

**Table 14.2** Changes in bacterial, yeast, and mold counts during the manufacture of butter (numbers per milliliter)*

| CHURNING NO. | COUNT | RAW CREAM | PASTEURIZED CREAM | CREAM IN CHURN | BUTTERMILK | UNSALTED BUTTER | SALTED BUTTER |
|---|---|---|---|---|---|---|---|
| 413 | Bacteria | 20,000,000 | 74,000 | 3,080,000 | 4,400,000 | 630,000 | 32,000 |
|  | Yeast | 10,000 | 160 | 50 | 60 | 400 | 460 |
|  | Mold | 32,000 | 0 | 4,000 | 4,000 | 4,000 | 4,000 |
| 415 | Bacteria | 10,700,000 | 620,000 | 1,430,000 | 9,600,000 | 640,000 | 101,000 |
|  | Yeast | 850 | 0 | 10 | 220 | 480 | 820 |
|  | Mold | 350 | 0 | 0 | 100 | 70 | 40 |
| 441 | Bacteria | 26,000,000 | 24,900 | 159,000 | 131,000 | 9,000 | 6,400 |
|  | Yeast | 300 | 0 | 0 | 4 | 27 | 13 |
|  | Mold | 280 | 0 | 0 | 3 | 2 | 0 |
| 511 | Bacteria | 5,000,000 | 4,700 | 3,810 | 6,400 | 380 | 860 |
|  | Yeast | 300 | 0 | 0 | 10 | 6 | 2 |
|  | Mold | 35 | 0 | 0 | 80 | 12 | 3 |
| 27 | Bacteria | 28,500,000 | 890 | 1,160 | 5,200 | 300 | 250 |
|  | Yeast | 500 | 0 | 0 | 0 | 0 | 0 |
|  | Mold | 740 | 0 | 0 | 0 | 0 | 0 |
| 29 | Bacteria | 13,300,000 | 3,300 | 2,410 | 720 | 3,130 | 7,200 |
|  | Yeast | 1,000 | 0 | 0 | 0 | 6 | 15 |
|  | Mold | 10 | 0 | 0 | 0 | 0 | 0 |

*From data of Macy et al. (37).

A second reason for the high bacterial destruction frequently observed is the predominance of acid producers, primarily the lactic streptococci, that are present particularly in sour cream. These types are relatively sensitive to heat.

Organisms remaining in pasteurized cream eventually may be found in the butter. This may result in serious consequences if organisms capable of causing defects are allowed to survive through improper pasteurization.

EFFECT OF EQUIPMENT

The equipment used to pump, transport, hold, and churn cream, may or may not affect the microflora of butter. If such equipment is in satisfactory sanitary condition, the amount of contamination likely to occur will be insignificant. On the other hand, the possibility for contamination is great, and any laxness in the cleaning and sanitizing procedures will inevitably be reflected in the microflora of the cream and butter. The data in Table 14.2 for churnings 413, 415, and 441, which show counts of cream immediately after pasteurization and also counts after the cream had reached the churn, indicate the extent of contamination that may occur from equipment. The importance of pipelines, valves, vats, pumps, and various other types of equipment common to all dairy products processing plants, as sources of microorganisms, has been treated at length in Chapters 6 and 7. Their importance is fully as great in connection with the manufacture of butter.

The importance of the churn as a source of microorganisms, particularly molds and yeasts, needs emphasis. Most churns are still made of wood, although in recent years metal churns have become fairly numerous. The typical wooden churn as found in most creameries, however, is the most highly contaminated and most difficult to sanitize of any piece of dairy equipment. Macy et al. (38) in a study to locate outstanding areas of contamination or foci of infection, especially concerning molds, dismantled and dissected 2 churns that had been in use for several years. Of 230 samples taken from 2 single churns, 192 contained molds. Several of these samples represented areas in joints between stays at depths of 0.75 inch to 1 inch from the inner surface of the churn. This work demonstrated the ability of molds to penetrate deep into the porous wood and into the crevices and openings that form when a churn is allowed to remain idle and to dry out. Wood is very difficult to sterilize at best. Experiments by Morrison et al. (40) showed that about 1.5 hours were required to heat the wood in a churn at a depth of 0.5 inch to 82.2°C. (180°F.) when the surface of the wood was exposed to water at 96.7°C. to 97.2°C. (206°F. to 207°F.); at a depth of 0.875 inch and at 1.375 inches the temperatures reached 73.9°C. (165°F.) and 60°C. (140°F.), respectively. Thus, it would seem, the microorganisms on the inner surfaces of the churn can be destroyed with certainty only by using extensive heat treatments. It is important that a churn be treated daily to prevent microbial growth, especially growth and sporulation of molds that might be embedded in the wood; otherwise microorganisms may grow out to the surface, contaminate the butter during churning, and later develop in the butter.

A churn cleaning and sanitizing procedure, recommended by the Minnesota Agricultural Experiment Station and proven to be adequate under normal conditions, is as follows:

(1) Rinse by revolving the churn for 10 minutes when ⅓ full of water at 43.3°C. (110°F.).

(2) Drain.

(3) Wash with water at 60°C. (140°F.) to which a washing compound containing a wetting and sequestering agent has been added. The churn should be half full and should be revolved for 15 to 20 minutes.

(4) Drain.

(5) Rinse with water at not less than 87.8°C. (190°F.). The churn should be half full and should be revolved for 15 minutes.

(6) Allow the churn to drain for 5 minutes through the doors at the bottom.

(7) Turn the churn so that the doors are at the top and open. After 15 minutes turn the churn again so that the doors are down. This will allow water that has accumulated to drain away and that which remains will be distributed over the inner surface of the churn, thus enhancing drying.

(8) Turn the churn so that doors are at the top. Place screens over the doors. (The above steps should be repeated daily, whether or not the churn has been used. In instances where the churn has not been employed, the addition of washing powder to the water may be omitted.)

(9) Just prior to churning cream, rinse the churn with a solution containing 200 parts per million of available chlorine.

## USE OF BUTTER CULTURES

Perhaps the greatest competitive advantage possessed by butter over other fat-type spreads is its flavor. Attempts to improve the flavor of butter have resulted in the development of special cultures of bacterial species selected for their ability to form desirable flavor compounds. The earliest attempts at the use of such cultures (starters) in the manufacture of butter was the addition of "natural" cultures to cream prior to churning. These cultures were simply portions of sour milk or cream, or buttermilk from a churning of such cream, that had a desirable flavor. Later on pure cultures were introduced. The first were *Streptococcus lactis* or related types; then mixed cultures that contained *Streptococcus lactis, Leuconostoc citrovorum,* and *Leuconostoc dextranicum* were introduced. In recent years, strains of *Streptococcus diacetilactis* have been introduced and have been used either singly or in mixtures with *Streptococcus lactis*. At the present time, the mixed types of cultures are used almost exclusively in the manufacture of starter butter.

The addition of butter cultures to cream materially increases the bacterial count, as many of the culture organisms are carried over into the butter. Occasionally, starters may become contaminated. Continued propagation of a contaminated culture may result in the starter's becoming an important source of undesirable bacteria, as well as of yeasts and molds. When this occurs, the cause can be attributed to lack of proper care either in handling the mother cultures or in the preparation of the bulk starter. The propagation and care of cultures, the various flavor compounds produced, and the general mechanism of their formation have been discussed in Chapter 11.

*Method of using butter cultures.* In general, butter cultures are used in three ways: (a) culture is added to the cream, and the cream is held at 10°C. (50°F.) or below for several hours or overnight and then churned, or the culture is added and the cream is ripened at 21.1°C. (70°F.) for several hours or overnight and then churned; (b) culture is added to the cream at the time of churning; and (c) culture is added at the time the butter granules are formed and then is worked into the butter. When cream is ripened, the flavor imparted to the butter will be dependent largely upon the amount of flavor formed by growth of the culture organisms during the ripening period. On the other hand, when ripening does not take place, the amount of flavor imparted to the butter will depend largely upon the amount of flavor compounds present in the culture at the time of its addition to the cream or to the butter granules.

*Advantages of using butter culture.* In addition to the improvement of flavor of butter made through the use of butter culture, several other advantages are obtained. Certain rather common off-flavors of butter such as feed, oxidized, neutralizer, cooked, and so forth may be masked somewhat by the flavors contributed through use of culture. The development of bacterial defects such as cheesy, putrid, and surface taint may be retarded considerably. This occurs primarily because many of the active proteolytic and lipolytic bacteria are inhibited, owing in large measure to the lowering of the pH by the lactic acid formed by the culture.

The effect of butter culture in retarding or inhibiting the development of bacterial species capable of causing defects is dependent upon the species involved. In experimental studies, *Pseudomonas putrefaciens* was effectively inhibited by the addition of 5 or 10 per cent of starter prior to churning (8, 34). Likewise, ripening to churning acidities not less than 0.35 per cent effectively inhibited *Pseudomonas fluorescens* (57). On the other hand *Pseudomonas fragi*, the organism most commonly associated with the rancid defect of bacterial origin, is only slightly retarded. There is evidence that the inhibiting effects of butter culture may be due to metabolic products other than lactic acid (15). It has been shown that lipolytic organisms such as *Achromobacter lipolyticum, Alcaligenes lipolyticus,* and *Pseudomonas fluorescens* were inhibited when added to cream; yet, when lactic acid was added, even in sufficient quantity to result in a titratable acidity of 1 per cent, all of the cultures grew. High acidity alone is not completely effective in preventing the growth of undesirable organisms in butter as shown by the data in Table 14.3. These data were obtained in a study (69) of a comparison of the keeping quality of sweet-cream, salted butter made in the normal manner (pH 6.5 to 6.9) with butter made by the addition of 50 per cent edible lactic acid to the butter granules at the rate of 1.25 ounces per 100 pounds of butter (pH 5.0 to 5.8). Samples from each churning were subjected to keeping quality tests as indicated in the Table. Some improvement in keeping quality at 36.6°C. (98°F.) and at 21.1°C (70°F.) may have been obtained, but little if any improvement was obtained at 12.8°C. (55°F.) or 7.2°C. (45°F.).

Although high serum acidity in butter may affect the growth of many microorganisms adversely, it cannot be relied upon to prevent all types of deterioration due to microorganisms. Acid-tolerant bacteria may be present quite frequently in butter, and molds and yeasts generally are not inhibited to any appreciable extent over the range of pH encountered in butter made with culture. On the other hand, the inhibiting effect of acid in combination with other factors such as salt and thorough working, which also tend to inhibit growth, generally can be depended upon to increase the storage life of butter.

*Disadvantages of using butter cultures.* Several factors have tended to discourage the use of butter cultures (14). If cultures are to be employed successfully, extreme care must be used in their propagation from day to

**Table 14.3**  Effect on the keeping quality of butter of the adjustment of pH through the direct addition of lactic acid *

| KEEPING QUALITY INCUBATION TEST | NUMBER AND PER CENT OF 41 CHURNINGS OF CONTROL BUTTER (pH 6.5–6.9) SHOWING "SURFACE TAINT" DEFECT | | NUMBER AND PER CENT OF 44 CHURNINGS OF ADJUSTED BUTTER (pH 5.0–5.8) SHOWING "SURFACE TAINT" DEFECT | |
|---|---|---|---|---|
| | *Number* | *Per cent* | *Number* | *Per cent* |
| 98°F.—2 days | 4 | 9.76 | 2 | 4.6 |
| 98°F.—3 days | 11 | 26.80 | 7 | 15.9 |
| 70°F.—1 week | 1 | 2.44 | 1 | 2.3 |
| 70°F.—2 weeks | 4 | 9.76 | 2 | 4.6 |
| 55°F.—4 weeks | 0 | 0.00 | 0 | 0.0 |
| 55°F.—6 weeks | 3 | 7.33 | 2 | 4.6 |
| 55°F.—8 weeks | 4 | 9.76 | 2 | 4.6 |
| 45°F.—4 weeks | 0 | 0.00 | 0 | 0.0 |
| 45°F.—8 weeks | 1 | 2.44 | 1 | 2.3 |

* From data of Zakarisen et al. (69).

day. Proper equipment must be made available, and a prescribed routine for handling and transferring the cultures must be followed. Consequently many operators of butter plants feel that the meticulous care, the amount of labor, and the equipment costs are too great to justify the advantages gained through the use of the cultures. Generally the price differential between butter made with and without culture does not provide sufficient incentive to encourage manufacturers to use culture. In salted butter, chemical deterioration may be accelerated by the presence of acid. Thus, the acid present in butter made from cream that has been ripened to a full aroma and flavor is detrimental to the keeping quality of salted butter. Oily and fishy flavors also may develop.

*Survival of culture organisms in butter.* Generally there is a tendency for a gradual decrease in the numbers of butter culture organisms in salted butter during storage. This decrease occurs quite regularly when the salt and moisture are well dispersed throughout the butter. When this is not the case, there may be many areas within the butter where the environment is favorable and the culture organisms may grow. On the other hand bacterial counts commonly increase in unsalted butter stored at temperatures that will permit the growth of bacteria. This is accompanied by an increase in serum acidity and a decrease in pH, indicating that the changes occurring are the direct result of considerable growth of the butter culture organisms.

*Changes in flavor compounds during the manufacture and storage of butter.* During the churning process, the biacetyl content of cream increases (52). This increase is to be expected, since the agitation occurring during the churning process should favor the oxidative processes leading to the formation of biacetyl. However, butter will contain much less biacetyl and acetylmethylcarbinol, since a high percentage of these compounds is lost in the buttermilk. Studies by Prill and Hammer (52) showed that an average of only 8.8 per cent of the biacetyl and 4.5 per cent of the acetylmethylcarbinol present in the cream plus culture prior to churning were retained in the butter; also, considerable quantities were lost in the wash water. In salted and unsalted butter, biacetyl and acetylmethylcarbinol are found in greater concentrations in the serum than in the fat; however, a smaller percentage of the total acetylmethylcarbinol (26.2 to 46.8 per cent) than of the biacetyl (44.4 to 75.0 per cent) is contained in the fat (24).

Changes in the concentration of biacetyl and acetylmethylcarbinol may be expected to occur during the storage of butter. Butter culture organisms are inhibited by salt. The culture organisms may not grow in butter having salt and moisture uniformly distributed by thorough working; therefore, no increases in these flavor compounds would be expected. In poorly worked butter some growth may be expected in areas where salt concentration permits. In such butter pH may be a controlling factor, since the pH of salted butter frequently is too high to permit the formation of biacetyl. In unsalted butter the conditions are much more favorable for growth of the culture organisms, and increases in biacetyl and acetyl-methylcarbinol commonly occur during storage (19).

An extensive review of the action of butter cultures in butter has been prepared by Babel and Hammer (1). This review should be referred to for further information.

*Use of starter distillate.* The volatile compounds present in butter cultures may be collected by distillation of cultures that are prepared under conditions favorable to maximum production of the flavor compounds (55). These distillates, commonly known as "starter distillates," are available commercially and may be added directly to the butter granules at the time of working. The use of starter distillate has several advantages: (a) flavor intensity can be varied; (b) a highly flavored butter may be produced without the danger of impairing keeping quality (such a danger exists when butter culture is used in the manufacture of salted butter, owing to the combination of salt and high acidity that may be present); (c) the use of starter distillate is more economical than the use of butter culture; and (d) difficulties such as those occasioned by starter failure and poor methods of handling cultures are eliminated. The primary disadvantages are: (a) the flavor of butter may lack the fine delicate flavor that is characteristic of butter made with a good butter culture, and thus it may tend to have a somewhat coarse or sharp aromatic flavor; and (b) any enhancement of keeping quality in unsalted and lightly salted butter due to the use of butter cultures is lost.

### EFFECT OF CHURNING

During the churning of butter, a number of factors exert influences that may cause quantitative changes in the microflora of cream, buttermilk, and butter. The agitation of cream during churning undoubtedly results in the breaking up of bacterial clumps, thus affecting the bacterial count, but not the content, unless organisms are contributed by the equipment. Contamination arising from the churn may be a factor. Observations from experimental work, as well as from practice, have shown that, generally, most of the bacteria in the cream are retained in the buttermilk fraction; consequently the bacterial count of buttermilk is higher than that of the cream or the butter. Table 14.2, page 429, shows the quantitative changes in bacterial, mold, and yeast counts that occurred at various points in the manufacture of several lots of butter. The effect of the churn as a source of contamination is particularly evident from the data shown for several of the churnings. Also, the large number of bacteria lost with the buttermilk is quite apparent. In properly pasteurized cream, viable yeasts and molds are rarely found. Their presence in butter therefore must be attributed to contamination from equipment, particularly the churn. The mold and yeast counts of butter and of buttermilk follow the same general relationships as those observed for bacterial counts. This is shown in Table 14.4.

**Table 14.4**     Relation between counts of butter and of butter-milk from the same churning (45 churnings)*

| COUNTS | COMPARED WITH COUNTS OF UNSALTED BUTTER, BUTTERMILK COUNTS WERE: | | | COMPARED WITH COUNTS OF SALTED BUTTER, BUTTERMILK COUNTS WERE: | | |
|---|---|---|---|---|---|---|
| | *Higher* (per cent) | *Lower* (per cent) | *Same* (per cent) | *Higher* (per cent) | *Lower* (per cent) | *Same* (per cent) |
| Mold | 66.7 | 11.1 | 22.2 | 64.4 | 8.9 | 26.6 |
| Yeast | 64.4 | 26.7 | 8.9 | 55.6 | 37.8 | 6.6 |
| Bacteria | 86.7 | 13.3 | 0.0 | 84.4 | 15.6 | 0.0 |

* From data of Macy et al. (37).

The retention of total mold filaments, viable or dead, by butter during the churning process has been of some interest in connection with the interpretation of mold mycelia counts and visual mold tests on butter (see section on tests for molds). It has been shown (10, 11) that most of the total mold mycelia are retained in the butter, the retention usually being greater than 50 per cent; however, most of the tiny fragments pass into the buttermilk, while most of the long filaments are retained in the butter.

### EFFECT OF WORKING AND PRINTING

The working of butter causes little quantitative change in microflora. However, the microflora are affected. The physical structure of butter that is created or established by the working process greatly influences the microenvironment and, hence, the activity of the microflora. The importance of working, therefore, lies in its effect upon the growth of bacteria in butter, rather than in the effect on numbers.

The total volume of water droplets and the percentage of droplets that are free of bacteria are dependent largely upon the number of bacteria in the pasteurized cream, the contaminants added during processing, and the degree of water dispersion in the butter. The degree of water dispersion is affected by working, the addition of salt, and reworking as occurs in the mechanical printing of butter. The ability of bacteria to grow in butter likewise is affected by these factors.

Boysen (3) has shown that the number of water droplets in butter is very large, ranging from about ten to eighteen billions per gram. A large percentage of the moisture droplets must be sterile, for, even in the case of highly contaminated butter, the number of bacteria would be far less than the number of water droplets. On the basis of an average moisture distribution as found in German butter and by assuming various bacterial counts of the buttermilk, Rahn and Boysen (54) calculated the percentage of sterile water in butter that is contaminated to different levels. The results were as follows:

BACTERIAL COUNT OF BUTTERMILK:

| | 1 billion | 100 million | 10 million | 1 million | 100 thousand | 10 thousand | 1 thousand |
|---|---|---|---|---|---|---|---|
| Per cent of total moisture sterile | 45.2 | 57.4 | 62.5 | 71.0 | 88.0 | 99.0 | 99.99 |

When butter is properly washed, water is present predominantly in the form of minute droplets dispersed in the fat. Hammer and Hussong (18) found that, when the serum of unsalted butter was separated from the fat, the development of bacteria was much more rapid at either 7°C. or 21°C. (44.6°F. or 69.9°F.) than when the product was in the normal physical condition. This would indicate that the availability of nutrients for growth of bacteria is limited in butter having its moisture finely dispersed. Examination of micro portions of butter (32) has shown the irregular distribution of bacteria throughout butter, thus indicating that growth is limited to certain areas where droplets are large or where limiting factors such as pH or salt concentration are not inhibitory.

The effect of moisture dispersion in butter on the growth of bacteria has been studied by varying the extent of working during the making of butter. For example, Long and Hammer (33) have shown that organisms are more active in under-worked butter than in thoroughly worked butter. This is indicated by comparative rates of appearances of defects and of changes in serum acidity, fat acidity, and numbers of organisms. Figure 14.4 is representative of results obtained after storage of unsalted butters

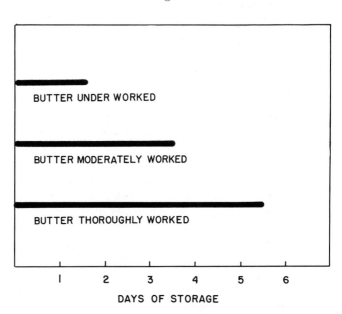

**Figure 14.4** Days required for production of a rancid defect in butter by *Achromobacterium lipolyticum*. Taken from data of Long and Hammer (32).

BUTTER UNDER WORKED

BUTTER MODERATELY WORKED

BUTTER THOROUGHLY WORKED

1    2    3    4    5    6

DAYS OF STORAGE

made from several lots of cream, each inoculated with a defect-producing organism.

Moisture dispersion also may be influenced by the treatment butter receives subsequent to manufacture. Occasionally the moisture content may be too high and may necessitate reworking to eliminate some of the water. The mechanical printing of butter often is comparable to reworking. Reworking tends to alter the physical structure of butter and thus may affect moisture dispersion and growth of organisms. Frequently there is a striking loss of water during printing. Moisture droplets are aggregated and forced from the butter; however, the moisture that drains away is not the only moisture that is aggregated. Relatively large droplets are formed in the mass of butter. The effect is more noticeable with butter worked insufficiently at the time of manufacture. The effect of reworking during printing may explain the development of defects in printed butter while unprinted butter from the same churning left in boxes or tubs has remained unchanged. It should be emphasized, however, that the sanitary condition of the printer may be a factor in such instances.

Several theoretical considerations (34) relative to the effect of reworking butter are as follows: (a) if little bacterial growth has occurred in the butter and there is no tendency to aggregate moisture droplets during reworking, there should be a finer dispersion of the moisture and a decreased food supply for the organisms, the effect being essentially the same as working at the time of manufacturing; (b) if little growth has occurred, but owing to certain temperature relationships and other factors there is a tendency for moisture droplets to unite during reworking, the bacterial cells in the larger droplets should have more food available; (c) with considerable bacterial growth in the butter and no tendency for collection of the moisture droplets during reworking, organisms should be distributed among more droplets so that bacterial activity could be increased; (4) with considerable growth and a tendency for aggregation of moisture into large droplets during reworking, extensive bacterial development should occur owing to distribution of the increased number of bacteria in areas favorable for growth.

Each of the above possibilities singly or in various combinations undoubtedly occurs in practice. Evidence of this was obtained by Long and Hammer (34), who showed the following: (a) reworking butter generally resulted in more rapid deterioration, particularly in butter that had been stored for a period of time before being reworked; (b) reworking resulted in a more rapid change in pH in the serum of butter made from cream inoculated with butter culture; (c) reworking resulted in increased fat acidities of butter made from cream inoculated with lipolytic bacteria. Their results also indicated that reworking influenced the growth of yeasts in butter in much the same way as it influenced the growth of bacteria.

Further evidence of the detrimental effect of reworking butter was shown by Hiscox and House (23), who studied the effect of blending (reworking) butter from different sources. Table 14.5 shows the effect of the blending process on the growth of bacteria during subsequent storage. The flora of both types of butter had apparently reached a stable phase prior to blending, and there was no obvious bacterial growth in either of the bulk samples during 28 days at room temperature. The reworked and blended butters on the other hand showed definite growth, and there was considerable increase in count when these samples were held at 4.4°C. (40°F.) for 28 days.

The microenvironment in butter may be made more unfavorable by a uniform distribution of salt. This will result in many of the water droplets having a salt concentration that is inhibitory to many microorganisms. Generally, salted butter will show marked decreases in total bacterial, yeast, and mold counts during storage, and the tendency for growth to be checked increases with salt content. As would be expected, the presence of salt in butter tends to retard the development of defects caused by specific organisms. Generally, this effect increases with an increased salt content, although many exceptions have been observed. Certain of these may be due to the growth of salt-tolerant organisms. More frequently, however, the explanation may be based upon the lack of uniformity of salt distribution. In butter containing 16 per cent moisture and 2.5 per cent salt the percentage of salt in the brine would be 15.625 per cent if all the salt were distributed uniformly. Results obtained by analyzing micro portions of butter (25) have shown that the distribution of salt, as well as of moisture, varies considerably. Thus it is extremely unlikely that the brine dispersed as droplets throughout butter would be uniform in salt content. This explains to a considerable extent the occurrence of microbial deteri-

**Table 14.5**  Effect of reworking and blending of butter on bacterial growth *

| Sample: | Bacterial counts after periods indicated | | | | |
|---|---|---|---|---|---|
| | Days held at room temperature | | | | Days held at 40°F. |
| | 0 | 3 | 14 | 28 | 28 |
| *Overseas sweet cream butter:* | | | | | |
| A. Bulk | 26,000 | 33,500 | 57,000 | 10,300 | 22,200 |
| AA. Reworked | 27,000 | 635,000 | 6,250,000 | 1,950,000 | 235,000 |
| *Continental ripened cream butter:* | | | | | |
| B. Bulk | 1,000 | 900 | 790 | 630 | ——— |
| BB. Reworked | 1,000 | 8,000 | 790,000 | 1,310,000 | 238,000 |
| AB. Blend of A and B | 25,500 | 23,300 | 3,050,000 | 2,555,000 | 720,000 |

* From data of Hiscox and House (23).

oration even in highly salted butter. In this connection, it should be mentioned that the water of butter originates principally from 2 sources: the buttermilk included in the butter granules during churning; and the wash water remaining after washing and later included during working. It might be expected that a substantial proportion of the moisture droplets originating from the buttermilk remains free of salt, while those originating from the wash water contain most of the salt. This is indicated by the results of Hoecker and Hammer (25), who found that, when certain organisms causing defects in butter were added to the wash water, no defects were produced in the butter in which salt was either well distributed or poorly distributed. However, when organisms were added to the cream, defects often appeared, especially in the butter in which salt was poorly distributed. This is shown by the data in Table 14.6. Furthermore, these data show the effect of poor working (poor moisture distribution), which resulted in defects occurring in all samples of poorly worked unsalted butter. Defects also developed in some thoroughly worked butter (good moisture dispersion), but in each case the defect was produced earlier in butter that was poorly worked.

Salt distribution and moisture distribution in butter are very closely related, for each is affected greatly by the working process. Although proper pasteurization and good sanitation will largely prevent presence of harmful micoorganisms, the safety factor attained by having the moisture well dispersed and the salt distributed as uniformly as possible throughout

**Table 14.6**     Effect of salt distribution on development of defects in butter (Pseudomonas putrefaciens added to cream or wash water)*

| CHURNING NO. | ORGANISM ADDED TO | DAYS REQUIRED FOR PRODUCTION OF DEFECT IN BUTTER HELD AT 15.5°C. (59.9°F.) | | | |
|---|---|---|---|---|---|
| | | Salted Butter | | Unsalted Butter | |
| | | salt well distributed | salt poorly distributed | thoroughly worked | poorly worked |
| 1 | Cream | —[a] | 5 | — | 2 |
| 1A | Wash water | — | — | 5 | 2 |
| 2 | Cream | — | 3 | 9 | 2 |
| 2A | Wash water | — | — | 5 | 2 |
| 3 | Cream | — | — | — | 5 |
| 3A | Wash water | — | — | — | 5 |
| 4 | Cream | — | — | 5 | 2 |
| 4A | Wash water | — | — | 5 | 2 |
| 5 | Cream | — | — | 3 | 2 |
| 5A | Wash water | — | — | 3 | 2 |
| 6 | Cream | — | 3 | 4 | 2 |
| 6A | Wash water | — | — | — | 2 |

* From data of Hoecker and Hammer (25).
[a] Indicates no defect development during storage period.

the moisture droplets will afford a significant measure of protection in the event of inadvertent infection.

### TEMPERATURE OF STORAGE

Normally as butter is removed from the churn its consistency is not sufficiently firm to allow satisfactory printing. Usually overnight storage at approximately 5°C. (41°F.) will result in butter acquiring the necessary firmness for printing. Frequently, a week to 10 days elapses between the manufacture and the printing of butter. This delay occurs because the printing operation often takes place in a central plant. Time is required for accumulation of sufficient butter at the place of manufacture to warrant shipment, and transit may require several days. Likewise, in the case of butter that is placed in cold storage (usually in tubs or boxes), several days may elapse before the butter reaches the cold storage house, and further delays occur subsequent to removal from storage, prior to printing. During these periods, as well as during those required in retail sales channels, the temperature remains well above 0°C. (32°F.).

Many micoorganisms causing defects in butter tolerate relatively low temperatures and can grow at temperatures slightly above the freezing point; the rate of growth increases markedly with increasing temperature (see discussion of psychrophilic bacteria, Chapter 7). Low storage temperature therefore constitutes one of the important factors in the control of growth of microorganisms in butter. For the most part little growth occurs in butter held below 0°C. (32°F.); none would be expected at −17.8°C. (0°F.), the temperature commonly used for holding butter during long periods of storage; and as temperatures are increased above 0°C. (32°F.), growth conditions become increasingly favorable.

Slight increases in bacterial counts of salted butter stored as low as −11.1°C. (12°F.) have been reported (31). The depression of the freezing point due to the presence of salt, together with the presence of organisms with a sufficient degree of salt tolerance, probably accounted for the observed increases in counts. Grimes and Hennerty (17) observed that total counts of salted butter increased during storage at −9.4°C. (15°F.). These total counts included both bacteria and yeasts, but the increases were due to the growth of yeasts rather than bacteria.

Bacterial counts may be expected to decrease somewhat in butter stored at approximately −17.8°C. (0°F.). Such decreases have been observed to occur to a greater extent in salted than in unsalted butter. The effect of any bacterial destruction that might occur during cold storage, however, is negligible. Sufficient microorganisms can survive to cause extensive damage to the butter after it is removed from storage. This is indicated by results of experimental work, as well as by observations in practice. For example, Turgasen (61) reported that samples of printed butter developed a cheesy defect when held at 21.1°C. (70°F.), after being held previously for 6 months at −28.9°C. (−20°F.).

## MISCELLANEOUS FACTORS

The water used in washing and standardizing butter may contain undesirable types of bacteria that may cause defects in butter during storage. This is discussed in a later section on defects.

Butter color, if protected from contamination, rarely contributes significantly to the microflora of cream or butter; however, color solutions if mishandled may become significant sources of bacteria, yeasts, and molds (28).

Once the butter is churned, there is apt to be ample opportunity for contamination during the packaging processes. Generally, the quantitative change in microflora is slight; however, the types of bacteria and molds that may be present on unclean surfaces of equipment such as ladles, tampers, boxes, conveyer belts, the printing machine, tables, parchment liners, and wrappers, or in the atmosphere may contaminate the surface layers of butter and cause excessive losses if conditions become favorable for their growth during storage.

The use of various chemical preservatives in butter is prohibited by law. At one time however their use was extensive, and sodium benzoate and benzoic acid were commonly used (47). The use of preservatives to enhance the keeping quality of butter has not been studied very extensively. Aversion to the idea of adulterating butter and other dairy products, and the lack of availability of suitable compounds have largely discouraged work of this nature.

Carbonation of cream for butter making and the storage of butter in an atmosphere of carbon dioxide have been shown to exert little influence upon the growth of bacteria in butter (53, 56). Storage of butter in an atmosphere of carbon dioxide and in sealed containers does, however, prevent the growth of molds. Similar results are obtained when nitrogen gas is used (46).

## BUTTER DEFECTS

Defects of butter may be of microbial or non-microbial origin. In general, defects of microbial origin have the following characteristics that distinguish them from those due to other causes:

(a) The defect is not present in fresh butter but develops during storage. Notable exceptions to this are the off-flavors present in cream (see discussion on cream defects) that are carried over into the butter; however, these usually do not increase in intensity during storage of the butter. Microorganisms must grow in butter in order to develop a defect, unless extremely large numbers of them are present initially, in which case change may occur owing to massive amounts of microbial enzymes present.

(b) The defect often can be reproduced by inoculating sterile milk or butter made from sterile cream with a portion of the defective product.

Failures may occur, however, in attempts to reproduce defects. Many factors, in addition to mere presence of causative organisms, determine whether or not changes will occur. These have been set forth in previous discussions in this chapter and in the discussion on associative growth of microorganisms in Chapter 2. Further consideration of this will follow in the discussion of specific defects.

### SURFACE TAINT, PUTRID, CHEESY

Perhaps the most commonly occurring bacterial defect of butter is a flavor suggesting the decomposition of protein. An excellent review of this defect has been prepared by Wagenaar (62).

In Australia, the defect usually is known as "decomposed odor" or "rabbito," in New Zealand "foetid" is the term used, and in Denmark and the United States "putrid" is a common designation. The term "surface taint" is widely used in Canada and the United States; also, "cheesy" is commonly used to describe the defect in the United States. This latter term undoubtedly includes the typical surface taint defect as well as a wide variety of other proteolytic defects probably caused by several species of bacteria singly or in synergistic association. Although the defect initially involves the surface layers of butter, the characteristic odor and taste may develop very quickly throughout the mass of butter.

This defect became an important problem to the butter industry with the advent of pasteurization of cream for butter making. Laboratory experiments and observations in the field have shown that typical surface taint occurs most frequently in butter made from pasteurized high quality cream that requires little or no neutralization. Apparently the heat treatment renders at least one milk constituent more susceptible to the activity of the organism responsible for the defect.

The causative organism primarily is *Pseudomonas putrefaciens,* which was first described in 1931 by Derby and Hammer (8) but which was designated at that time as *Achromobacter putrefaciens.* Long and Hammer (35) later gave the organism its present name. Other species of bacteria are reported to be capable of causing the typical surface taint defect; however, with one exception, such reports are inconclusive. Wolochow et al. (67) described a yellow-pigmented organism capable of causing surface taint, although the odor was less intense than that caused by *Pseudomonas putrefaciens.* The name *Flavobacterium maloloris* was suggested. The fact that only 5 cultures among 5,000 random isolations were found to be *Flavobacterium maloloris* would indicate that this species is much less important in causing outbreaks. From the work of Herried et al. (20) it appears that many of the off-flavors of butter characterized by a cheesy or putrid odor and taste are produced as a result of the associative activity of 2 or more species.

Rapid development of the defect in butter takes place at temperatures within 4.4°C. to 7.2°C. (40°F. to 45°F.). In commercial butter held at such temperatures the defect may become apparent within a week to 10 days. When skimmilk is inoculated with *Pseudomonas putrefaciens* or *Flavobacterium maloloris* a typical putrid odor is produced. It is very likely that surface taint of butter and the odor produced in heated milk by these organisms are identical (68). In attempts to identify the specific compound responsible for the odor, Dunkley et al. (9) found that acid mixtures obtained by steam distillation of acidified skimmilk cultures of *Pseudomonas putrefaciens* contained formic, acetic, butyric, and isovaleric acids. It was concluded that the substance causing the typical odor produced by this organism was closely related chemically to isovaleric acid.

The control of the surface taint and allied defects of butter requires close attention to a number of plant practices. The characteristics of the most important causative organisms are sufficiently well known to establish operating procedures that will greatly reduce the possibility of the defect's occurring. Proper pasteurization of every particle of cream is the first essential. The organisms are easily destroyed by heat; thus, pasteurization is effective in eliminating the organisms from the cream. Malpractices in the pasteurizing procedure must be avoided.

A satisfactory water supply is essential in the control of surface taint, for it has been shown repeatedly that water supplies may contain the causative organisms. The suitability of a water supply often can be determined by inoculating samples of pasteurized cream with the water in question and by observing the inoculated cream for presence of the off-flavor after a few days of storage at 4.4°C. to 7.2°C. (40°F. to 45°F.). Suitable uninoculated controls also should be prepared and stored. Laboratory churnings of inoculated cream held for 24 hours at 15.5°C. (60°F.) with observation of the butter after storage for a few days in the refrigerator may be helpful. Water supplies found to be unsatisfactory may be made suitable for use by chlorination. The organisms involved are relatively sensitive to low concentrations of chlorine. Because waters vary in their chlorine demand (adsorbing capacity), concentrations somewhat above those ordinarily needed should be used. A concentration of 5 to 10 ppm of available chlorine added to water followed by holding for 15 minutes usually will be an effective procedure.

Strict attention must be given to the sanitary condition of all surfaces that may come in contact with the pasteurized cream or butter. These include pumps, pipes, coolers, storage vats, liners and wrappers, the printing machines, butter boxes or tubs, and above all the churn.

*Pseudomonas putrefaciens* is relatively salt sensitive; consequently, 2 per cent of salt uniformly distributed in the butter will assist greatly in controlling the defect.

The use of starter in the manufacture of butter may assist in retarding the development of surface taint. Biacetyl has been shown to have a marked effect in delaying or reducing the development of surface taint (68). The suppressing effect does not appear to be related to inhibition of the growth of *Pseudomonas putrefaciens* by biacetyl or lactic acid, for growth occurs at concentrations of biacetyl normally found in starter butter and in which the development of the defect has been delayed; moreover, the defect may be produced over a wide range of pH or concentration of lactic acid (7). Other work (13) has shown that a definite decrease in the concentration of biacetyl accompanies the growth of *Pseudomonas putrefaciens* during storage of butter. The explanation of the mechanism of the delaying effect thought to be due to biacetyl is not clear and must await further work.

There is no rapid and simple procedure for determining whether any particular churning of suspected butter actually contains *Pseudomonas putrefaciens*. The quantitative estimation and isolation of this organism are problems that have been worked on for many years by investigators in many countries. *Pseudomonas putrefaciens* loses viability rather quickly during storage; hence, part of the difficulty encountered in recovering the organism may be due to the small number of viable cells in an infected sample. Also, ordinary distilled water, often used as dilution water in plating procedures, is very toxic to the organism. Although it is difficult to culture *Pseudomonas putrefaciens* from butter, once the organism has been isolated and grown on laboratory media it will initiate growth readily on transfer to fresh media. Wagenaar and Jezeski (63) have recommended a procedure for the isolation of *Pseudomonas putrefaciens* from butter that resulted in isolation of the organism from better than 40 per cent of a series of samples examined by them. These same samples were examined by conventional plating techniques and by the litmus milk enrichment method (35). Less than 20 per cent of the samples yielded *Pseudomonas putrefaciens* by the litmus milk enrichment method, and no isolations were obtained by conventional plating techniques.

### RANCIDITY AND FRUITINESS

Rancidity is a common defect of butter and other dairy products. The defect results from the hydrolysis of butterfat with the liberation of fatty acids. Butyric acid is the principal acid that contributes to the flavor of a typically rancid product.

Butterfat is hydrolyzed by the enzyme lipase. Lipase may originate in milk itself, for all milk, when secreted, will contain lipase. Numerous bacteria and molds and an occasional yeast possess it; consequently, rancidity in butter and other dairy products may be caused by the activity of the lipase normally present in milk or by the activity of this enzyme secreted by various microorganisms.

The lipase of milk is easily destroyed by the mild heat treatment of pasteurization. Therefore proper pasteurization of milk will effectively control the occurrence of rancidity that may be caused by the lipase of milk. In this regard care must be taken to prevent activity of the milk lipase prior to pasteurization of milk or cream, for if rancidity has developed prior to pasteurization the off-flavor may be carried over into finished products.

Rancidity may not always be recognized by the typical pungent odor of butyric acid, but may be masked or modified by flavors contributed by other break-down products of the butterfat and protein. A fruity odor often may occur owing to the early phases of the activity of these lipolytic bacteria. Apparently the two most common organisms responsible for the occurrence of rancidity and fruitiness are *Pseudomonas fragi* and *Pseudomonas fluorescens*. Both of these species are proteolytic as well as lipolytic; therefore, flavors due to protein decomposition often are associated with the rancid or fruity defect.

Studies by Hussong et al. (26) and Morrison and Hammer (39) have shown that *Pseudomonas fragi* may be isolated frequently from soil, water, raw milk supplies, and a variety of dairy products. The organism is not difficult to culture if plates are incubated below 30°C. (86°F.). When grown in milk, cream, butter, and cottage cheese, an ester-like odor suggestive of the flavor of the May apple is noticeable but later is replaced by the more intense fruity or rancid odors.

*Pseudomonas fluorescens* is representative of a variety of fluorescent bacteria capable of causing rancid and fruity defects in butter and other products (16). Such organisms are widely distributed, and their presence in dairy products, as in the case of *Pseudomonas fragi*, may be explained by their frequent occurrence in water, feeds, and soil from which they gain access to utensils and equipment used in the production and processing of the products.

The organisms responsible for the rancid and fruity defects are easily killed by pasteurization, and they are sensitive to low concentrations of chlorine. Strict attention to the sanitary condition of equipment and the use of a suitable water supply are important factors in the control of these organisms.

Certain molds may cause rancidity of butter, but these organisms are more important in causing surface discolorations and will be discussed later.

MALTY DEFECT

Occasionally rather extensive outbreaks of a malty flavor in butter may occur. The organism primarily responsible is *Streptococcus lactis* var. *maltigenes*. This species may be isolated from raw milk and cream quite readily. It is easily destroyed by pasteurization; however, if the organism has been allowed to grow extensively in cream before pasteurization, the taste and odor present in such cream may be carried over into the butter. Also, through faulty sanitation of equipment the organism may contaminate the pasteurized cream and the off-flavor may develop in the butter during storage.

The elimination of cream having this defect at the time it is received, and prompt cooling of cream after it arrives at the plant are important in the control of this defect.

### SKUNK-LIKE ODOR

This rather unusual butter defect was described by Claydon and Hammer (6), and the organism responsible for the defect was designated *Pseudomonas mephitica*. The defect was observed in several samples of commercial unsalted butter. The use of a 4 per cent casein medium may be helpful in isolating the organism, as colonies may be small on ordinary media and difficult to distinguish from colonies of other bacteria on the plates. The organism grows optimally at 21°C. (69.8°F.). It is easily destroyed by pasteurization.

### BACTERIAL DISCOLORATION OF BUTTER

Occasionally a black discoloration of butter by a black pigment-producing bacterium may be observed (see Figure 14.5). White (64, 65) reported several outbreaks of this defect in butter from several Canadian creameries. He isolated and described the organism and gave it the name *Pseudomonas nigrifaciens*. A similar defect was reported by Hiscox (22), and the organism responsible for the discoloration closely resembled *Pseudomonas nigrifaciens* as later described by White.

Optimum conditions for pigmentation on culture media appear to be incubation at 4°C. (39.2°F.) with 1.5 to 2.5 per cent of salt in the medium. Temperatures above 25°C. (77°F.) and media free of salt or with concentrations above 5 per cent inhibit pigment formation by *Pseudomonas nigrifaciens*. The organism is easily destroyed by pasteurization. This indicates that contamination of cream or butter occurs at some point after

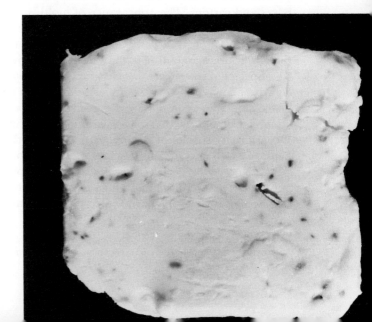

**Figure 14.5** A portion of a tub of butter showing black discoloration due to *Pseudomonas nigrifaciens*. Courtesy of Department of Dairy Husbandry, University of Minnesota.

pasteurization. Attempts to isolate *Pseudomonas nigrifaciens* from water and soil samples have not been successful. This is surprising in view of the fact that species of *Pseudomonas* are common soil and water bacteria. However, isolations have been made by swab technique from floors, drains, and butter printing and wrapping tables.

As in the case of many other butter defects, meticulous plant sanitation with thorough cleaning and sanitizing of all equipment, especially that used in post-pasteurization operations, is essential for the control of this defect. Salting at the rate of at least 1.5 to 2.0 per cent also will assist in controlling the defect, providing the salt is uniformly distributed. Extraneous moisture caused by the use of excessively wet wrappers or wet surfaces of butter boxes may lower the salt concentration at the surface of the butter sufficiently to permit pigment formation by the organism if present. The use of dry parchment and the elimination of excess water on the surface of butter are important precautions to be considered in the control of this defect.

### SURFACE DISCOLORATION OF BUTTER DUE TO MOLDS AND YEASTS

The major defect produced in butter due to the growth of molds is surface discoloration. At one time, moldiness throughout the body of butter was quite prevalent. With the advent of pasteurization and increased emphasis upon proper sanitation of plant equipment, butter became less apt to be as heavily seeded with mold spores and mycelial fragments than it formerly was. However, surface molding still is a major problem and is frequently manifested by discolored areas, usually in shades of black, brown, or green. These appear on the surface, usually at the butter-parchment paper interface. In badly molded butter, mold may be found growing on the outer surfaces of the wrappers and the inner surfaces of the boxes and cartons. The appearance of mold is more frequent on unsalted butter, and it occurs most commonly during the late spring, summer, and early fall months. Generally, moldy butter occurs as an isolated case, although at times an outbreak may assume the proportions of an epidemic.

Species of the genera *Cladosporium*, *Hormodendrum*,* *Alternaria*, *Aspergillus*, *Mucor*, and *Rhizopus* often are associated with dark, and at times almost black, smudgy-appearing areas. Species of *Penicillium* may be isolated frequently from areas that have various shades of green and blue-green. Occasionally species of *Aspergillus* may cause this type of discoloration. Figure 14.6 shows different stages of mold discolorations on butter surfaces.

*Geotrichum candidum* (*Oospora lactis*, see Chapter 2) commonly is found in butter. This organism may cause discolored areas that appear as various shades of orange and yellow. Other types appear colorless and often may

---

*Members of this genus are frequently mentioned in the literature as having been isolated from defective butter. It is now considered synonymous with *Cladosporium* (59).

go unnoticed unless off-flavors they may have produced draw attention to them.

Occasionally "black yeasts," often designated as species of *Torula* or *Monilia,* may be isolated from discolored butter surfaces. Some species of these genera also produce a reddish pigment and are responsible for pink discolorations sometimes observed on defective butter.

Although much progress has been made in reducing the likelihood of mold infection due to faulty methods of processing and manufacturing butter, sufficient attention often is not given to the prevention of air-borne contamination of butter surfaces. Such contamination may occur at various stages of manufacture, probably the most important of which is the packing and printing of butter. High humidity in the churn room and lack of proper ventilation may allow molds to grow on the walls and ceilings. Such growth also may occur in coolers where butter is stored. Existing conditions in creameries often are such that windy weather, together with carelessness in the prevention of excessive air currents within the plant, may carry mold conidia to exposed butter surfaces. Care should be taken to reduce the time that butter surfaces may be left exposed to the atmosphere, and excessive air currents due to open windows and doors in the vicinity of the printing and packaging operations should be avoided. Adequate ventilation to prevent the condensation of moisture on walls and ceilings should be provided.

One approach to the control of air-borne contamination is the treatment of parchment paper used in wrapping butter. The parchment itself, if improperly stored and handled, may be an important source of contamination. Treatment of the parchment in boiling water will effectively destroy the molds and harmful bacteria that may be present, but it will not necessarily insure freedom from surface discoloration caused by mold contamination of the surfaces prior to wrapping. Certain chemicals have been employed or recommended as agents that might be used to treat parchment paper, in the hope that retention of these agents by the paper in contact with the butter would serve to inhibit and possibly to prevent growth of mold. As a general rule federal and state food inspection officials have been critical of the use of such substances because of possible violation of food adulteration laws.

**Figure 14.6**     Prints of butter showing different stages of molding. Courtesy of Department of Dairy Husbandry, University of Minnesota.

Boiling parchment wrappers and liners in a saturated solution of sodium chloride will afford considerable protection against surface molding of salted butter. Such treatment can not be used with unsalted butter. A method that has met with some success in treating parchment paper for wrapping unsalted butter is immersion of the parchment in a 10 per cent solution of calcium propionate at a temperature of 82.2°C. (180°F.) (45). This product is known by the trade name "Mycoban." A 5 per cent solution acidified to pH 5.5 with lactic acid is fully as effective and has the additional advantage of retarding the development of certain surface off-flavors that might otherwise develop. Calcium propionate is not germicidal in the concentrations recommended, but it does serve to delay the appearance of mold for several weeks, depending upon the temperature and humidity conditions under which the butter may be stored. Parchment paper may be impregnated with calcium propionate at the time of its manufacture. Impregnated paper must be used in dry wrapping, for immersing such paper in water before wrapping will leach the propionate from the paper, and consequently there will be a loss in effectiveness.

Sorbic acid also has been suggested for use in treating butter wrappers. However, use of this compound for inhibiting mold growth on the surface of butter has not been studied sufficiently to permit proper evaluation of its effectiveness.

Some operators have obtained beneficial results in the control of mold growth by installing ultraviolet lamps over conveyors carrying butter to printers and wrapping machines. However, elimination of the primary source of contamination is the more effective long-range control procedure.

In general, the control of mold growth in or on butter requires strict attention to proper sanitation of plant equipment and to the control of air-borne infection. Specifically the important points in this regard are: (a) adequate pasteurization of cream; (b) proper sanitization of pipelines and pumps that carry the pasteurized cream; (c) proper sanitation of churn and printing equipment (see previous discussion of the churn as a source of microorganisms); (d) prevention of air-borne contamination by avoiding excessive air currents within the plant; (e) adequate ventilation; (f) the use of hot water or hot salt brine for treatment of tubs and parchment wrappers and liners used in packaging salted butter, or use of "Mycoban" in the case of unsalted butter; and (g) cleanliness in the habits of personnel handling the butter.

## ANALYSIS OF BUTTER FOR SPECIAL PURPOSES

Certain microbiological methods or other tests are applied to butter for various purposes. One of these, the test for water-insoluble acids and butyric acid, was discussed previously in the section on cream grading.

Other procedures, their application, and the interpretations of results obtained are discussed below.

### MOLD AND YEAST COUNTS

The determination of yeasts and molds in butter by the agar plate method (see Chapter 5) normally is included among the routine laboratory analyses of butter. High mold and yeast counts usually mean faulty methods in the plant or elsewhere, especially in connection with inadequate sanitation of the churn. Inefficient pasteurization, low salt content in the butter, improper conditions of storage, or a combination of any of these may be responsible for high counts.

The evidence available indicates that there is a tendency for butter with low mold and yeast counts to possess better keeping quality than butter with high counts. The relationship, however, is associative rather than direct. One cannot predict with any great measure of certainty the keeping quality of a single lot of butter on the basis of a mold and yeast count. For example, *Geotrichum candidum* commonly found on mold and yeast plates is not particularly detrimental to the keeping quality of butter, although occasionally surface discolorations and off-flavors may develop as a result of its growth. Its presence, however, will indicate some faulty condition that may lead to difficulty. Molds that may cause serious defects may be missed entirely, for it may require very few spores or mycelial fragments to cause an eventual serious defect.

The mold and yeast count presents very helpful information to a creamery operator or butter buyer. Counts should be below 10 per gram, for such counts indicate that considerable attention is being given to proper sanitation of equipment.

### KEEPING QUALITY TESTS

Considerable time is involved in the movement of butter through commercial marketing channels. Several weeks or months may be required. The keeping quality of the butter during this period is of great importance.

Many attempts have been made to apply various objective tests to butter with the idea of being able to predict the keeping quality of the product from the results of the tests. Total bacterial counts have found little application, for they bear little relationship to keeping quality.

For many years the industry has used a keeping quality test that consists of placing a small sample of butter in a glass jar and observing for off-flavors after several days of storage. Two storage conditions are quite commonly used and are the bases for the 2 tests designated as the 48-hour and the 7-day keeping quality tests. The incubation temperatures for these tests are 37°C. (98°F.) and 21.1°C. (70°F.), respectively. The wide use of these tests or slight modifications of them would indicate that they give a fairly reliable index of keeping quality. Experimental work (27, 43) provides confirmation of this.

At times the keeping quality test will indicate poor keeping quality, yet the butter will pass through marketing channels without undergoing significant deterioration. Likewise an off-flavor may not appear in the stored sample, yet the lot of butter it represents may deteriorate badly. Several factors may account quite logically for these discrepancies. There is no question that the body of butter, as established by the workmanship applied incident to its manufacture, is an important factor in keeping quality. In the 48-hour test the high incubation temperature often causes considerable oiling off of the fat and consequent alteration of butter structure. The restraining influences relative to bacterial growth may no longer be operative; hence, deterioration may occur rapidly. Furthermore, the high temperature of storage used for both tests may encourage the growth of defect-producing bacteria, which may not grow at the lower temperatures of storage prevalent in commercial distribution channels. On the other hand 37°C. (98°F.) may be too high for the growth of certain types capable of causing defects in butter stored at normal storage temperatures.

The printing operation, which often alters considerably the physical structure of butter, may influence the results of the tests; therefore, in the case of butter to be printed, prints of butter should be used in the keeping quality test rather than samples taken from the unprinted butter. In this connection, sporadic outbreaks of poor keeping quality of certain lots of butter showing satisfactory keeping quality tests have been traced to contamination of such butter at the printer owing to the printing of a badly contaminated preceding lot.

### THE COLIFORM TEST APPLIED TO BUTTER

The presence of coliform bacteria in butter often is interpreted in the same manner as is their presence in pasteurized fluid milk (see Chapters 5 and 7). Singh (58) has shown that such an interpretation may be somewhat erroneous.

The finding of considerable numbers of coliform bacteria in a sample of butter probably would indicate gross contamination in most instances, but there are circumstances when considerable proliferation of these organisms may occur even in salted butter. In unsalted butter coliform bacteria may grow readily at temperatures in the vicinity of 8.9°C. (48°F.), and certain strains may grow at lower temperatures.

The finding of few or no coliform bacteria in butter, as frequently may be the case among commercial samples, may only mean that the bacteria have died because of the toxic effect of the salt present and possibly because of the low temperature and length of storage. The coliforms vary in their sensitivity to salt. Some strains are fairly tolerant, others are quite sensitive. Apparently sensitivity is greater among strains of *Escherichia coli* than among strains of *Aerobacter aerogenes*.

The primary area of usefulness of the coliform count would seem to be in the examination of line run samples to detect sources of post-pasteurization contamination. As a test to be used on commercial butter samples of miscellaneous histories, the coliform test seems to have little applicability as an index of contamination or of keeping quality because of the many opportunities for erroneous interpretation, owing to the unpredictable multiplication and death behavior of this group of bacteria in butter.

### PROTEOLYTIC AND LIPOLYTIC COUNTS

The enumeration of proteolytic and lipolytic bacteria in butter (see Chapter 5) may be helpful in drawing attention to unsatisfactory manufacturing and handling procedures. Figure 14.7 shows the appearance of proteolytic colonies on a milk medium.

Species of several groups of bacteria that may be isolated from butter may actively hydrolyze butterfat, or the glyceride tributyrin, and casein. Among these is a large group of gram-negative rods, as is shown by the work of Stark and Scheib (60), who found that 84 per cent of 188 cultures of gram-negative rods isolated from butter digested milk, 89 per cent hydrolyzed butterfat, and all of them hydrolyzed tributyrin. Ninety-seven per cent of those that digested milk also hydrolyzed butterfat. Most of the frequently occurring bacterial defects of butter are caused by gram-negative non-spore-forming rods. Some of these defects are well characterized, and the specific organisms responsible for them are known.

**Figure 14.7**    The appearance of surface and sub-surface colonies of a proteolytic bacterium growing on a milk medium. Courtesy of Department of Dairy Husbandry, University of Minnesota.

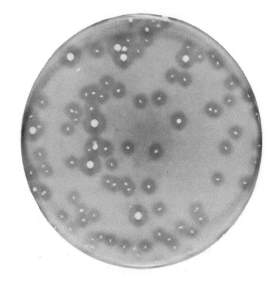

Several of the common spore-formers that may be present in butter are actively proteolytic or lipolytic, as are some of the micrococci; however, they rarely cause deterioration during storage.

It should be kept in mind that perhaps the most important defect-producing organism of all, *Pseudomonas putrefaciens,* rarely is detected by ordinary plating methods; however, the presence of other proteolytic or lipolytic bacteria, particularly gram-negative types, would indicate the potential presence of this organism.

Sensitivity to heat and frequent occurrence in water and on improperly sanitized equipment are characteristic of many of the proteolytic or lipolytic gram-negative bacteria found in butter. Therefore, their presence in appreciable numbers is good evidence of faulty processing.

## SPREAD OF DISEASE THROUGH BUTTER

Essentially all commercial butter is made from pasteurized cream; therefore pathogens likely to be present in raw milk or cream would be destroyed. There is always the possibility, however, that pasteurization may be done improperly, or that contamination of cream may occur after pasteurization, or that butter may be contaminated at the time of printing and packaging. Furthermore, butter that is made on the farm for home use frequently is made from raw cream. Occasionally some of this home-made butter may be purchased and consumed by persons other than members of the farm family.

Ample evidence exists to show that certain pathogenic bacteria are capable of remaining viable in butter for periods of time ranging from a few days to several months, depending upon the type of organism and upon other factors (2, 4). Consequently, butter made from raw cream or from cream contaminated after pasteurization would be dangerous from a health standpoint.

Actually very few recorded outbreaks of disease have been traced to butter. The unfavorable microenvironment in butter having salt and moisture well distributed and the long periods of storage that frequently occur may be factors that tend to reduce the likelihood of disease transmission through butter. Furthermore, it is difficult to trace outbreaks of disease that may be caused by butter owing to the wide distribution of the product and the fact that a particular lot or churning of butter frequently loses its identity when it is assembled with lots or churnings from other sources, and when it is printed and packaged for distribution.

Recognition of the fact that various diseases may be spread through the use of contaminated butter should serve to re-emphasize the importance of proper pasteurization of cream and of using sanitary methods during all post-pasteurization processes. In the case of butter made on the farm, the availability of small inexpensive home pasteurizing units makes home pasteurization of milk and cream convenient, and use of these units will provide safe milk and cream for any purpose.

## References

1. Babel, F. J., and B. W. Hammer, Action of butter cultures in butter, *J. Dairy Sci.*, 27 (1944): 79–141.

2. Berry, A. E., Viability of pathogenic organisms in butter, *J. Prev. Med.*, 1 (1927): 429–442.

3. Boysen, H., Die Wasserverteilung in der Butter, *Milchw. Forsch.*, 4 (1927): 221–248.

4. Bryan, C. S., and P. S. Bryan, The viability of certain udder infection bacteria in butter made from raw cream, *J. Milk and Food Technol.*, 7 (1944): 65–67.

5. Claydon, T. J., Some factors affecting the mold content of cream and the mycelial count of butter, *Ark. Agr. Exp. Sta. Bull. 432*, 1943.

6. Claydon, T. J., and B. W. Hammer, A skunk-like odor of bacterial origin in butter, *J. Bacteriol.*, 37 (1939): 251–258.

7. ———, Bacteriology of butter, VIII: relationship of *Achromobacter putrefaciens* to the putrid defect of butter, *Iowa Agr. Exp. Sta. Research Bull. 267*, 1939.

8. Derby, H. A., and B. W. Hammer, Bacteriology of butter, IV: bacteriological studies on surface taint butter, *Iowa Agr. Exp. Sta. Research Bull. 145*, 1931.

9. Dunkley, W. L., G. Hunter, H. R. Thornton, and E. G. Hood, Studies on surface taint butter, II: an odourous compound in skimmilk cultures of *Pseudomonas putrefaciens*, *Scientific Agr.*, 22 (1942): 347–355.

10. Elliker, P. R., A new quantitative method for estimation of total combined length of mold fragments in butter, *J. Dairy Sci.*, 27 (1944): 369–375.

11. ———, Retention of mold fragments by butter, buttermilk, and wash water during manufacture of butter, *J. Dairy Sci.*, 27 (1944): 563–569.

12. Elliker, P. R., and W. H. Brown, Factors affecting mold content and quality of cream, *Purdue University Agr. Exp. Sta. Bull. 465*, 1942.

13. Elliker, P. R., and B. E. Horrall, Effect of growth of *Pseudomonas putrefaciens* on diacetyl and flavor of butter, *J. Dairy Sci.*, 26 (1943): 943–949.

14. Fabricius, N. E., The manufacture and use of butter culture, *Dairy Industries*, 5 (1940): 159–160.

15. Fouts, E. L., Effect of lactic acid on the hydrolysis of fat in cream by pure cultures of lipolytic microorganisms, *J. Dairy Sci.*, 23 (1940): 303–306.

16. Garrison, E. R., and B. W. Hammer, Fluorescent bacteria in dairy products, *Iowa State Coll. J. Sci.*, 16 (1942): 363–377.

17. Grimes, M., and A. J. Hennerty, A study of the quantitative changes in the microbiological flora of sweet cream salted butter of good keeping quality when held at 15°F. for a period of two to eight months, *J. Dairy Research*, 5 (1934): 137–143.

18. Hammer, B. W., and R. V. Hussong, Bacteriology of butter, I: influence of the distribution of the non-fatty constituents on the changes in bacterial content during holding, *Iowa Agr. Exp. Sta. Research Bull. 134,* 1930.

19. Hedrick, T. I., and B. W. Hammer, Diacetyl and acetylmethylcarbinol production in the manufacture of unsalted butter, *Iowa Agr. Exp. Sta. Research Bull. 301,* 1942.

20. Herried, E. O., H. Macy, and W. B. Combs, The microbiology of cheese-like flavors in unsalted butter, *Minn. Agr. Exp. Sta. Tech. Bull. 97,* 1934.

21. Hillig, F., Determination of water-insoluble fatty acids in cream and butter, *J. Assoc. Offic. Agr. Chemists,* 30 (1947): 575–582.

22. Hiscox, E. R., A pigment-producing organism (*Pseudomonas sp.*) isolated from discoloured butter, *J. Dairy Research,* 7 (1936): 238–243.

23. Hiscox, E. R., and A. G. House, Bacteriological aspects of the reworking and blending of stored butter, *J. Dairy Research,* 18 (1951): 291–295.

24. Hoecker, W. H., and B. W. Hammer, Distribution of diacetyl and acetylmethyl-carbinol between fat and water, with special reference to butter, *J. Dairy Sci.* (1942): 175–185.

25. ———, Bacteriology of butter, IX: salt distribution in butter and its effect on bacterial growth, *Iowa Agr. Exp. Sta. Research Bull. 339,* 1945.

26. Hussong, R. V., H. F. Long, and B. W. Hammer, Classification of the organisms important in dairy products, II: *Pseudomonas fragi, Iowa Agr. Exp. Sta. Research Bull. 225,* 1937.

27. Jacobson, D. H., A holding test made at room temperature as an indication of the keeping quality of butter in storage, *S. D. Agr. Exp. Sta. Bull. 308,* 1937.

28. Jamieson, M. C., and H. K. Chen, Microorganisms in butter color, *Can. Dairy and Ice Cream J.,* 22 (1943): 25–27.

29. Kester, L. T., F. E. Nelson, and I. I. Peters, Production of water-insoluble acids and butyric acid in butter by defect-producing bacteria, *J. Dairy Sci.,* 36 (1953): 794–798.

30. King, N., The present status of continuous buttermaking in practice, *Dairy Industries,* 18 (1953): 783–784, 789.

31. Loftus-Hills, G., L. R. Scharp, and T. S. Bellair, The study of factors influencing the keeping quality of some Victorian salted butters in cold storage, *J. Dairy Research,* 5 (1934): 124–136.

32. Long, H. F., and B. W. Hammer, Examination of butter with the Burri smear culture technic, *Iowa State Coll. J. Sci.,* 12 (1938): 441–450.

33. ———, Bacteriology of butter, VI: effect of moisture dispersion in butter on the growth of bacteria, *Iowa Agr. Exp. Sta. Research Bull. 246,* 1938.

34. ———, Bacteriology of butter, VII: the effect of reworking butter on the growth of bacteria, *Iowa Agr. Exp. Sta. Research Bull. 263,* 1939.

35. ———, Classification of the organisms important in dairy products, III: *Pesudomonas putrefaciens, Iowa Agr. Exp. Sta. Research Bull. 285,* 1941.

36. Macy, H., Experiments with the methylene blue reduction test for the grading of sweet cream, *Minn. Agr. Exp. Sta. Bull. 310,* 1934.

37. Macy, H., S. T. Coulter, and W. B. Combs, Observations on the quantitative changes in the microflora during the manufacture and storage of butter, *Minn. Agr. Exp. Sta. Tech. Bull. 82,* 1932.

38. Macy, H., W. B. Combs, and H. B. Morrison, Jr., The churn as a source of molds in butter, *J.Dairy Sci.,* 14 (1931): 398–403.

39. Morrison, H. B., and B. W. Hammer, Distribution of *Pseudomonas fragi, J. Dairy Sci.,* 24 (1941): 9–18.

40. Morrison, H. B., Jr., H. Macy, and W. B. Combs, Preliminary studies of churn sanitation, *J. Dairy Sci.,* 14 (1931): 404–415.

41. Nashif, S. A., and F. E. Nelson, The lipase of *Pseudomonas fragi,* II: factors affecting lipase production, *J. Dairy Sci.,* 36 (1953): 471–480.

42. ————, The extracellular lipases of some gram-negative non-sporeforming rod-shaped bacteria, *J. Dairy Sci.,* 36 (1953): 698–706.

43. Naylor, H. B., and E. S. Guthrie, The incubation test as an indication of the keeping quality of butter, *Cornell Agr. Exp. Sta. Bull. 739,* 1940.

44. Nelson, F. E., W. H. Martin, R. W. Morrison, and W. J. Caulfield, An evaluation of the visual mold test for cream, *J. Dairy Sci.,* 26 (1943): 375–384.

45. Olson, J. C., Jr., and H. Macy, Propionic acid, sodium propionate and calcium propionate as inhibitors of mold growth, I: observations on the use of propionate-treated parchment in inhibiting mold growth on the surface of butter, *J. Dairy Sci.,* 28 (1945): 701–710.

46. Olson, J. C., Jr., and H. J. Fournelle, Unpublished data, *Minn. Agr. Exp. Sta.,* 1949.

47. Orla-Jensen, S., *Dairy Bacteriology,* pp. 120–121. Philadelphia: Blakiston, 1921.

48. Parsons, C. H., Testing cream for mold mycelia, *Am. Butter Review,* 2 (1940): 382–384.

49. ————, A visual mold test for cream, *Natl. Butter and Cheese J.,* 32 (1941): (3), 12, 13, 56–59.

50. Peters, I. I., and F. E. Nelson, Factors influencing the production of lipase by *Mycotorula lipolytica, J. Bacteriol.,* 55 (1948): 581–591.

51. Purko, M., W. O. Nelson, and W. A. Wood, The liberation of water-insoluble acids in cream by *Geotrichum candidum, J. Dairy Sci.,* 35 (1952): 298–304.

52. Prill, E. A., and B. W. Hammer, Changes in the diacetyl and the acetylmethyl-carbinol contents during the manufacture of butter, *J. Dairy Sci.,* 22 (1939): 79–88.

53. Prucha, M. J., J. M. Brannon, and H. A. Ruehe, Carbonation of butter, *J. Dairy Sci.,* 8 (1925): 318–329.

54. Rahn, O., and H. H. Boysen, Distribution and growth of bacteria in butter, *J. Dairy Sci.,* 11 (1928): 446–470.

55. Ruehe, H. A., Controlling flavor in butter, *The Creamery J.,* 49 (1938): (6) 5, 28.

56. Sherwood, F. F., and F. G. Martin, Influence of carbon dioxide upon the quality and keeping properties of butter and ice cream, *Iowa Agr. Exp. Sta. Research Bull. 95,* 1926.

57. Shutt, D. B., Contaminated water as a source of surface flavor in pasteurized creamery butter, *Scientific Agr.,* 9 (1929): 316–320.

58. Singh, Raj Nath, Coliform organisms as an index of butter quality. Ph.D. thesis, Iowa State College, 1948.

59. Skinner, C. E., C. W. Emmons, and H. M. Tsuchiya, *Henrici's Molds, Yeasts and Actinomycetes,* 2nd Ed., p. 111. New York: Wiley, 1947.

60. Stark, C. N., and B. J. Scheib, A study of fat splitting and casein digesting bacteria isolated from butter, *J. Dairy Sci.,* 19 (1936): 191–213.

61. Turgasen, V. L., Troubleshooting for flavor defects—observations in practice. Mimeographed report for 31st annual meeting, American Butter Institute, 1939.

62. Wagenaar, R. O., The bacteriology of surface-taint butter: a review, *J. Dairy Sci.,* 35 (1952): 403–423.

63. Wagenaar, R. O., and J. J. Jezeski, The influence of type of diluent on the growth and survival of *Pseudomonas putrefaciens, J. Dairy Sci.,* 35 (1952): 738–754.

64. White, A. H., A bacterial discoloration of print butter, *Scientific Agr.,* 20 (1940): 638–645.

65. ———, Observations on bacterial discoloration of butter, *Can. Dairy and Ice Cream J.,* 21 (1942): (7) 19–21, 44, 46.

66. Wildman, J. D., Development of methods for the estimation of mold in cream and butter, *J. Assoc. Off. Agr. Chemists,* 20 (1937): 93–100.

67. Wolochow, H., H. R. Thornton, and E. G. Hood, Studies on surface taint butter, VI: other bacterial species as causal agents, *Flavobacterium maloloris (n. sp.), Scientific Agr.,* 22 (1942): 637–644.

68. ———, The cause and control of surface taint butter: part I, cause, *Can. Dairy and Ice Cream J.,* 21 (1942): (10) 21–26.

69. Zakariasen, B. M., L. Eckberg, and R. W. Mykleby, A study of methods for evaluating the keeping quality of sweet cream butter, *J. Dairy Sci.,* 35 (1952): 484.

# 15

# *Dairy plant waste disposal and utilization of by-products*

## DAIRY PLANT WASTE DISPOSAL

The conversion of raw materials into finished products always results in a certain amount of waste. The wastes may result from unintentional losses during processing, or they may represent valueless portions of the original material. To complicate their disposal, industrial wastes usually are dispersed in water so that burning or a similar inexpensive method of disposal is impracticable. Therefore, the natural tendency is to discharge the liquid into the nearest stream or lake and to let drainage and dilution take care of it. Because few industrial wastes contain pathogenic microorganisms, there was little concerted public reaction to stream pollution by industries until about 1930. Gradually the problem worsened as industrial plants increased in number and size and as streams became loaded with wastes to the point where their aesthetic and recreational values were threatened or destroyed. As a result, the public, through various state and federal officials, has demanded that industrial pollution of streams be stopped.

The dairy industry is one of many industries concerned with treatment and proper disposal of wastes. Canners, brewers, meat packers, coal miners, beet sugar processors, and oil refiners—to name only a few—are equally involved, and each industry has its own problems. Waste treatment plants are expensive to build and to operate, and many industrial concerns find their installation a severe economic burden. Nevertheless, the trend is established, and it seems clear that all industries must make plans to dispose of their wastes in such a way that pollution of water will be avoided.

To understand the recent intensification of the dairy waste disposal problem, it is necessary to consider the changes that have occurred in the

**459**

dairy industry over the years. Several decades ago, before adequate refrigeration and transportation facilities were available, dairy processing was largely a home industry. Much of the milk was separated on the farms, and the cream was shipped to creameries or churned into butter in the home. The skimmilk and buttermilk thus produced on the farm were fed to animals, hence there was little waste to be handled. Disposal of buttermilk at creameries was accomplished in various ways with little thought about stream pollution. Some of the milk was converted to cheese, but the factories by necessity were located near the producing farms, and the wastes were never in large quantity because most of the whey was returned to the farms for animal feeding. Relatively little milk was converted to concentrated products such as milk powder, condensed milk, and ice cream.

More recently, improved sanitation on dairy farms and wider use of mechanical refrigeration have made it possible to collect milk over considerable areas and to haul it to large central processing plants. This practice has resulted in greater concentrations of waste in certain places, frequently in small towns, where sewage treatment facilities may be inadequate to handle the increased load thus introduced. World War II stimulated the demand for concentrated and dry milk products, which, because of the expensive equipment required, can be produced most efficiently in large establishments. Cheese factories and butter making plants have tended to centralize. Even the bulk of the by-products that are used for animal feeding are concentrated or dried in relatively large plants. These trends toward centralization and utilization of more of the milk constituents than formerly were saved have resulted not in more waste but in greater concentrations in certain areas, thus accentuating the problem of proper disposal of the waste.

An additional complicating factor is seasonal production. Because there is a much greater flow of milk during the late spring and early summer, it is necessary to provide facilities for handling the wastes at the time of the "flush" period of production. This means that treatment facilities must be larger than would be necessary during other times of the year.

The large dairy processor is not the only one who has waste disposal problems. There are still hundreds of "cross roads" cheese factories and other small plants in the country, many of which discharge their wastes into the nearest drainage ditch or brook. They are causing no more nuisance than they ever did. But with the intensified campaigns to stop stream pollution, operators of these small plants are coming to the attention of regulatory authorities, and some of them are being required to provide treatment facilities for their wastes.

Many dairy plants that are not located on streams and some of those that have been forced to stop discharging their wastes to streams have been able to share the use of municipal sewage treatment facilities. Under this arrangement the dairy plant usually pays part of the operating costs of the treatment plant and sometimes part of the construction costs as well.

Problems arise even under this system, however. Fluctuations in the rate of discharge make dairy plant wastes difficult to handle, especially in treatment works of limited capacity. Disruption of the normal process of sewage decomposition can occur if a sudden load of dairy waste appears at the treatment plant, as might occur if spoiled products are dumped into the sewer. For these and other reasons, municipal waste disposal authorities often impose limits on the total volume and strength of wastes that can be discharged by a plant within a given period of time.

### EFFECT OF ADDING DAIRY WASTES TO A BODY OF WATER

To understand why it is undesirable to discharge large amounts of dairy wastes into a stream or other body of water, it is necessary to consider the effects of these wastes on the stream. Dairy wastes consist of a dilute solution or suspension of decomposable organic matter. The main constituents are lactose and proteins, with smaller quantities of fat and other organic materials plus the mineral constituents of milk. A variety of microorganisms is in the waste and in the water of the stream. Under normal conditions, aerobic organisms absorb the soluble organic matter and oxidize most of it to obtain energy. Insoluble materials first are hydrolyzed by the appropriate extracellular enzymes, and the soluble products are absorbed and oxidized by the microorganisms. The following reactions illustrate the aerobic decomposition of lactose:

$$C_{12}H_{22}O_{11} + H_2O \xrightarrow{\text{Lactase}} 2\ C_6H_{12}O_6\ \text{(glucose + galactose)}$$
$$2\ C_6H_{12}O_6 + 12\ O_2 \longrightarrow 12\ CO_2 + 12\ H_2O$$

Thus, 12 molecules of oxygen are required for the complete oxidation of each molecule of lactose. Similar reactions can be written for any of the amino acids resulting from protein hydrolysis. The final products of their oxidation are carbon dioxide, water, ammonia, sulphate, and phosphate. The ammonia then is oxidized to nitrate by autotrophic nitrifying bacteria. In this way all of the organic materials are converted to completely oxidized inorganic compounds that can be utilized by green plants as food.

The limiting factor in the complete oxidation of organic materials is free oxygen. The amount of oxygen available for this purpose is limited to that dissolved in the water, and this depends on temperature, turbulence, and other factors. A fair estimate of the amount in most streams is 7 to 8 ppm. Assuming a concentration of 7.5 ppm, all of the oxygen in 1,600 gallons of water is required to oxidize the organic solids of only 1 pint of whole milk.

The effect of insufficient oxygen on fish and other aquatic life is well known. When the dissolved oxygen (D.O.) in the water drops below 5 ppm, many species of fish do not thrive and reproduce, and if the D.O. becomes less than 3 ppm, game fish must migrate or die. Thus an overloaded stream or lake has no recreational value for fishermen. But the harm of pollution does not stop with destruction of the animal life in the water. When its oxygen content is depleted the water becomes anaerobic, and then the type of decomposition is entirely different from that described above. Anaerobic and facultative microorganisms ferment and putrefy the organic materials, yielding incompletely oxidized compounds that still have an oxygen demand. Lactose is fermented to acids, and these may reduce the pH of the water to the point where casein is precipitated. The precipitate settles to the bottom as sludge, and it putrefies. Many of the products of anaerobic decomposition of proteins have unpleasant odors, and these are deleterious to the value of the stream. The following reactions illustrate some of the changes that can result from anaerobic decomposition of lactose and proteins:

$$C_{12}H_{22}O_{11} + H_2O \xrightarrow{Lactase} 2\ C_6H_{12}O_6\ (glucose + galactose)$$

$$2\ C_6H_{12}O_6 \xrightarrow{\text{Anaerobic decomposition}} 4\ C_3H_6O_3\ (lactic\ acid)$$

$$Protein + X\ H_2O \xrightarrow{\text{Extracellular hydrolytic enzymes}} Amino\ acids$$

$$Amino\ acids \xrightarrow{\text{Anaerobic decomposition}} Fatty\ acids,\ ammonia,\ carbon\ dioxide,\ methane,\ hydrogen,\ amines,\ indol,\ skatol,\ mercaptans,\ hydrogen\ sulfide,\ and\ so\ forth.$$

Thus it is apparent that dairy wastes can not be added to a stream without harm if they use up too much of the oxygen in the water. Very small amounts of organic waste actually may be beneficial because the final products of oxidation (carbon dioxide, nitrates, sulphates, and phosphates) serve as food for aquatic plants, and these in turn are eaten by the animals. If the strength of the waste is too great, however, the water is ruined for most purposes. Much of the animal life disappears, farm animals will not drink the water, and, if conditions are bad enough, the odors from the stream may discourage living near it. Furthermore, the water may not be suitable for industrial or municipal water supply.

To determine how much organic material can be added safely to a stream it is necessary to know not only the amount of oxygen in the water but also the strength and volume of the waste itself. The strength of organic sewage commonly is measured in terms of biochemical oxygen demand or B.O.D. This figure is a measure of the amount of oxygen required to oxidize the organic materials in the waste. It is determined by diluting a measured quantity of the waste with water that is saturated with oxygen and by incubating the mixture at 20°C. (68°F.). A control consisting of the dilution water alone is incubated at the same time, and after incubation the residual oxygen in both the control and the test sample is measured by titration. The difference represents the oxygen-consuming capacity of the waste and, after appropriate calculations, is expressed as parts of oxygen per million parts of waste. About 20 days are required for oxidation of all the organic material in a dairy waste at 20°C. (68°F.). Because it is inconvenient to incubate for so long, the B.O.D. usually is determined at 5 days, at which time about 65 per cent of the organic matter is oxidized. The resulting 5-day B.O.D. is satisfactory for comparison of different samples and for evaluating the efficacy of treatment processes.

Another method of measuring the strength of an organic waste involves determination of the chemical oxygen demand or C.O.D. (9). This test is made by heating a measured amount of the waste with a known quantity of dichromate, then determining the residual dichromate by titration. Not all of the organic matter is oxidized in this test, but the method is useful for comparing strengths of different waste or water samples. The procedure yields results in only a few hours, and it is especially useful with materials that are toxic or otherwise unsuitable for the B.O.D. test.

Since the B.O.D. represents parts of oxygen per million parts of waste, it is possible to calculate the strength of the waste in terms of pounds of B.O.D. as follows:

$$\frac{\text{ppm 5-day B.O.D.} \times \text{gallons of waste} \times 8.34}{1,000,000} = \text{pounds B.O.D.}$$

With this figure one can convert the oxygen demand of a dairy plant waste into terms of population equivalent (P.E.) on the assumption that the domestic sewage of one person is equivalent to ⅙ pound of B.O.D. per day. Thus, if the waste of a dairy plant amounts to 100 pounds B.O.D. per day, the P.E. = 600. In other words, the wastes of the plant are equivalent in strength to those of 600 people.

### PREVENTING WASTE AT THE DAIRY PLANT

The foregoing statements show that a stream or other body of water can dispose of a fairly definite amount of organic matter, this being determined by the quantity of oxygen dissolved in the water, the amount of water in the stream, the extent of mixing of the waste with the water, and other factors. Similarly, any sewage treatment plant has a definite capacity, and if this is exceeded there will be an incompletely decomposed effluent. If the disposal capacity of the method used by a dairy plant is limited, the operator of the plant either must reduce the oxygen demand of the waste, or he must build additional disposal facilities. Reduction in strength of the waste can best be accomplished by keeping organic materials out of the sewer. Further reduction can be effected, if necessary, by some kind of treatment as will be discussed later.

The B.O.D. of the sewage from any dairy plant naturally depends on the care with which the operators avoid waste. Some loss of product inevitably occurs, but careless operations greatly increase the strength of the waste and thereby complicate the problem of disposal. Table 15.1 shows examples of the strength and volume of sewage from a variety of dairy plants. Note that the wastes from a cheese factory handling 100,000 pounds of milk per day would be equivalent in B.O.D. to the domestic sewage of a town with 1,800 inhabitants. It should be emphasized that the values in Table 15.1 represent averages. Much higher or lower figures can be obtained at individual plants, the extent of variation depending on the efforts made by the plant operators to avoid waste.

The total amount of milk solids lost to the sewer each year is tremendous when examined in the aggregate. A study made by the Wisconsin State Board of Health showed that about 2 per cent of the milk produced in the state was lost during handling and processing at dairy plants. Based on a total estimated production for the year of fifteen billion pounds, this loss amounts to three hundred million pounds of milk. Others have estimated that the wastes from dairy plants practicing good housekeeping may contain 1 per cent milk. Using the volume figures in Table 15.1, 1 per cent milk in the waste would mean that a receiving station loses 1.5 per cent of the milk it takes in (1 per cent of 180 gallons × 8.34 pounds per gallon × 100 ÷ 1,000 = 1.5 per cent). Even higher losses are indicated for general dairies and bottling plants. Average losses in various dairy plant operations with reasonably modern equipment and careful operation are shown in Table 15.2. Even if loss reduction cannot be justified entirely on the basis of additional products recovered, many plants have found that increased care in avoiding waste will more than pay for itself by the resulting simplification of the disposal problem.

Before a dairy plant operator begins an intensive waste-saving campaign in his plant he should, if at all possible, make provision for measuring

## Table 15.1    Average volume and strength of milk plant wastes *

| TYPE OF PLANT | PER 1,000 POUNDS OF MILK RECEIVED | | |
|---|---|---|---|
| | 5-day B.O.D. (ppm) | Volume (gallons) | B.O.D. population equivalent |
| Receiving station | 500 | 180 | 4.5 |
| Milk bottling plant | 600 | 240 | 7.2 |
| Cheese factory | 2,000 | 180 | 18.0 |
| Creamery | 1,000 | 100 | 5.0 |
| Condensery† | 800 | 150 | 6.0 |
| Dry milk plant | 800 | 150 | 6.0 |
| General dairy | 600 | 300 | 9.0 |

* The data in this table were adapted from Wisniewski (12).

† Exclusive of vacuum pan water. Usually this water has no more than 50 ppm B.O.D. and amounts to 1,000 to 1,500 gallons per 1,000 pounds of milk received.

**Table 15.2**     Average process losses from various milk plant operations *

| PROCESS | POUNDS OF B.O.D. IN WASTE PER 10,000 POUNDS OF MILK OR MILK EQUIVALENT HANDLED |
|---|---|
| 1. Receiving and cooling milk | 4 |
| 2. Tank truck delivery to and from plant, including washing tank truck | 1 |
| 3. Storage of fluid product in tanks | 1 |
| 4. Milk pasteurization, cooling, and bottling | |
|    a. In glass | 8 |
|    b. In paper | 6 |
| 5. Whole milk | |
|    a. Evaporating | |
|       (1) Floor waste | 2 |
|       (2) Entrainment loss | 1 |
|    b. Spray drying | 1 |
| 6. Canning and sterilizing evaporated milk | 2 |
| 7. Cream | |
|    a. Separating | 2 |
|    b. Pasteurization, cooling, and can filling | 2 |
| 8. Separated milk | |
|    a. Pasteurization, cooling, and can filling | 2 |
|    b. Condensing | |
|       (1) Plain | |
|          (a) Floor waste | 3 |
|          (b) Entrainment loss | 0.5 |
|       (2) Sweetened | |
|          (a) Including barreling floor waste | 6 |
|          (b) Entrainment loss | 0.5 |
|       (3) Superheated | 12 |
|    c. Drying | |
|       (1) Spray process | 1 |
|       (2) Roll process | 16 |
| 9. Whey | |
|    a. Condensing | |
|       (1) Sweet | |
|          (a) Floor waste | 8 |
|          (b) Entrainment loss and volatile | 2 |
|       (2) Acid | |
|          (a) Floor waste | 8 |
|          (b) Entrainment loss and volatile | 4 |
|    b. Drying (Spray process) | 5 |
| 10. Buttermilk condensing | |
|    a. Floor waste | 8 |
|    b. Entrainment loss and volatile | 4 |

* The data in this table were adapted from the report of the Task Committee on Dairy Waste Disposal (8).

**Table 15.2**     (Continued)

| Process | Pounds of B.O.D. in waste per 10,000 pounds of milk or milk equivalent handled |
|---|---|
| 11. Cottage cheese or casein manufacture | 16 |
| 12. American cheese making | |
|     a. Unwashed curd | 10 |
|     b. Washed curd | 16 |
| 13. Ice cream | |
|     a. Mix making (vat or pan) | 4 |
|     b. Freezing | 0.5 |
| 14. Cultured buttermilk making | 5 |
| 15. Butter churning and washing | 2 |

the volume and strength of the sewage effluent. Without this information it is difficult to demonstrate progress in the campaign. The volume of the waste can be measured by installing a weir box in the sewer line (8). A sampling device, preferably automatic, should be installed, and the samples thus collected should be analyzed for their B.O.D. Analyses ought to be made for several days before the campaign is started and then at frequent intervals thereafter. Employees should be informed about the importance of avoiding product losses to the sewer. Frequent posting of volume and B.O.D. determinations in the plant will keep the employees informed of progress and will stimulate an effort to improve.

Whether or not the volume and strength of the wastes are known, each operation in the plant should be examined critically with a view to reducing product losses (8). One of the most important single sources of waste is drip from milk cans after emptying. Losses at this point vary considerably, depending on the rate of emptying, but a loss of 1 per cent of the milk is not unusual. Waste to the sewer can be reduced by the installation of drip-saver pans and by pre-rinsing the cans into the drip collector with 3 to 4 ounces of water applied as a jet into each can before it enters the can washer. In this way it is possible to keep the milk loss to the sewer in receiving room operations below 0.35 per cent. Vats, pipelines, pasteurizers, and other equipment also should be rinsed with small amounts of water prior to actual washing. The pre-rinse waters contain most of the residual milk solids, and these, along with the milk collected in the drip-saver pans, should not be discharged to the sewer. They can be used as animal feed directly or after concentrating or drying.

Leakage, overflow, and spillage are important causes of product loss. Leakage can be kept to a minimum by proper maintenance of equipment. An occasional small leak can be accommodated during operations by catching the milk in a pail and disposing of the product as animal feed. Overflowing of vats and tanks is minimized by proper supervision or by installation of liquid level controls or signal devices. Special non-overflow type whey removal tanks installed on cheese vats will avoid loss of whey to the sewer. Spills usually result from carelessness and can be minimized by employee education and supervision. Foam from open type separators is an important source of waste but is prevented by installing air-tight machines. Freezing-on of product at milk coolers and ice cream freezers results in losses that are prevented by proper operation of the equipment. Entrainment losses in vacuum pan operation are avoided by installation of equipment with efficient entrainment separators. Floor sweepings from milk or whey powder storage rooms should never be wasted to the sewer, but should be disposed of as animal feed or in some other way. Similarly, spoiled products must not be discharged to the sewer.

Satisfactory disposal of by-products is a difficult problem for some plants, hence many of them discharge excess whey, skimmilk, and buttermilk to the sewer. Provision must be made to dispose of these products in some other way. Preferably they should be concentrated or dried and used as human food. If they are not produced in sufficient volume to justify the installation of drying equipment, they may be hauled to other plants that are equipped for this purpose. If this is not practicable, they may be sold or given to farmers for animal feeding. If none of these outlets is available, it may be necessary to haul the by-products to available land to dispose of them. The part of this chapter that deals with fermentation of dairy by-products suggests uses for some of them.

### TREATMENT OF DAIRY WASTES

If careful housekeeping does not reduce the quantity of organic sewage to a point where it can be discharged into a stream or an existing municipal disposal plant, it becomes necessary to construct some kind of treatment facility at the dairy plant. The capacity and kind of equipment depend on several factors, including the volume and B.O.D. of the waste and the amount of B.O.D. reduction required. It should be mentioned that a reduction of 75 per cent is relatively easy to achieve, but to increase this to 95 per cent may double the cost.

For any type of sewage disposal method other than discharge to a stream (where maximum dilution is desired) the wastes of a dairy plant should be segregated according to their different characteristics. Because it may contain pathogenic microorganisms, sanitary sewage should be discharged directly to a sanitary sewer or, if none is available, to a suitable treatment system such as a septic tank-dry well combination. Cooling water has little B.O.D. and usually can be discharged directly to a stream or storm sewer. Material with extremely high acidity, such as spent Babcock test acid, should be disposed of on waste land unless for some reason it is desirable in the sewage to correct an otherwise unfavorable hydrogen ion concentration. The remaining plant wastes containing most of the organic matter thus are kept in as small volume as possible, reducing the size and cost of the necessary treatment equipment.

As was mentioned earlier in this chapter, the extreme fluctuations in the rate of discharge of dairy wastes complicates their treatment. Under normal conditions practically all of the waste of a dairy plant is discharged during the usual 8- to 12-hour working day. This results in a relatively high concentration of wastes in the stream or treatment plant at certain hours with little at other times. To remedy this the dairy plant operator may install a flow-equalizing and aeration tank as the first step in treatment. This tank should have sufficient capacity to hold the organic sewage output for the entire day and should be equipped with controls that discharge the waste over the entire 24-hour period, thus reducing the B.O.D. load on the stream or treatment plant by one-third to one-half what it would be if all the wastes were discharged during the working day. The waste should be aerated during holding to keep it from souring. This process also accomplishes considerable reduction of the B.O.D. By aerating the wastes in this way and discharging them evenly throughout the day and night, many plants have found it possible to reduce the "shock" load on the stream or municipal disposal plant to a point where no other treatment is necessary.

Several satisfactory methods are available to a dairy plant that must install its own disposal system. Some plants are located in areas where it is possible to collect the wastes in lagoons or oxidation ponds in which the organic matter undergoes partial decomposition. The residual can be discharged gradually to a stream, especially at times of high water. A few plants are located in areas where the wastes can be disposed of by irrigation of fields, woods, or waste land. The great majority of plants, however, must construct and operate some kind of biological disposal system (9). A type commonly used today is the trickling filter, although activated sludge systems, septic tank-dry well combinations, combined chemical and biological systems, and others have been used successfully. Unfortunately all of these installations are expensive to build, some are costly to operate, and all require a certain amount of supervision. The choice of system depends on the geographical and topographical location of the plant, the characteristics of the waste, the degree of treatment required, and the method of ultimate disposal of the effluent. This choice should be made only with the aid of a competent engineer who is familiar with the disposal of dairy plant wastes.

## REGULATORY AGENCIES IN POLLUTION CONTROL

Several branches of the Federal Government are concerned with control of stream pollution, but the one most directly involved is the United States Public Health Service. This agency administers the application of Public Law 845, which gives to the Federal Government certain controls over the pollution of interstate waters. Among its many functions the Public Health Service conducts stream surveys, acts in cooperation with various state agencies, and often takes the lead in organizing pollution abatement campaigns in interstate watersheds.

Direct control of stream pollution usually is administered by state governments. Most states have anti-pollution laws that are enforced by a Committee on Water Pollution, a Sanitary Water Board, or a similar group established for the purpose. The method of operation of the control authorities varies with different states, but in effect the authorities are empowered to control pollution of streams. In doing this the state agencies first make surveys of certain streams to determine whether they are receiving excessive amounts of domestic or industrial waste. This involves a complete study of the stream itself, its volume, reaeration capacity, rate of flow, and other characteristics, as well as the origin of organic materials going into it. If the study shows that the stream can not handle the wastes without harm, the state agency may, after public hearings, order the offending communities or industrial plants to make provision to stop the pollution. A period of time is allowed for preparation and presentation of plans for adequate waste treatment facilities, which, after approval, then are built.

The wastes of a dairy plant may be discharged into a stream for years without apparent harm. Understandably, the operator of such a plant may be puzzled at the fact that, without changing his operating procedures, he is required to install waste treatment equipment. It must be remembered, however, that any stream can accommodate only a given amount of organic matter without becoming overloaded. The capacity of a stream may be sufficient to handle the wastes of one or a few plants, but as more plants are built, the cumulative effect of all the wastes is enough to exceed the capacity of the stream. The only alternative of the regulatory authorities, then, is to require treatment of all wastes that drain into the stream.

One problem in the past has been to determine the degree of treatment that was necessary. Orders to industrial plants often stated that the waste must be no greater than a certain volume and that the B.O.D. must be reduced by an arbitrary amount, say 95 per cent. This approach is not very realistic because one group of plants might reduce the B.O.D. load by only 50 per cent and then be able to add the wastes to a stream without harm, while other plants on a different stream might effect 95 per cent reduction and still overload the stream. The present trend is to judge the extent of treatment required by the characteristics of the stream itself. Thus for some streams only a relatively slight B.O.D. reduction might be necessary, although for others it might be essential to reduce the B.O.D. very much more to avoid overloading. The initial survey of the stream and its waste-handling capacity is used to determine the degree of treatment required.

Several industries have organizations that help solve the waste disposal problems of the industry as a whole. Examples of these are the Dairy Industry Sub-Committee on Waste Disposal and the National Canners Association. Whereas these and similar organizations are not regulatory bodies, they have done a great deal to help solve the waste disposal problems of their respective industries by conducting and financing research on waste disposal methods, by conducting campaigns designed to educate workers in the importance of waste prevention, and by cooperating with state regulatory bodies in formulating standards and regulations regarding waste control practices.

## THE USE OF WHEY IN INDUSTRIAL FERMENTATIONS

The foregoing discussion emphasized the problems encountered in effecting satisfactory disposal of dairy wastes. Certain components of milk that remain after the manufacture of various dairy products constitute a problem that involves not only waste disposal, but the loss of milk constituents having nutritional value. When cream is separated from milk for uses in ice cream, butter, and other products, the residual skimmilk finds many uses in cultured milks, cottage cheese, ice cream mix, bakery products, skimmilk, Cheddar cheese, and so forth. Casein can be removed from the skimmilk for use in making paper-coating, glue, paints, various casein fibers, plastics, and other industrial products (11).

There is, however, a large volume of whey for which profitable uses have not been found and which must be disposed of as waste. The manufacture of cured cheese results in the availability of more whey than the present outlets in animal feeds can utilize. Casein and cottage cheese manufacture provide further sources of this product. Perhaps the greatest hindrance to whey utilization is the high percentage of water present. In order to preserve whey solids by condensation or drying, the cost of removing the water becomes excessive in comparison with the market value of the resulting products. In addition, the whey frequently has to be collected and transported. This is necessary so that a sufficient volume can be provided to enable plants to process the whey economically. These factors must be considered in locating a whey utilization plant, in order to have a financially sound investment.

The development of new uses for whey would do much for the dairy industry in reducing waste disposal costs, in stabilizing the prices paid to producers for milk, and in preventing the loss of many valuable milk nutrients. These possibilities offer some of the most interesting challenges to the dairy scientist. Since this book is concerned with the microbiological aspects of the dairy industry, certain industrial methods concerned primarily with fermentation processes will be given. Furthermore, since the utilization of non-fat milk in cultured milk products has been discussed previously, processes concerned only with whey utilization will be presented.

Although whey contains about 93 per cent water, the following typical composition of cheese whey indicates the presence of valuable nutrients:

|                        |               |
| ---------------------- | ------------- |
| lactose                | 4.90 per cent |
| nitrogenous compounds  | 0.90 per cent |

| | |
|---|---|
| ash | 0.60 per cent |
| fat | 0.30 per cent |
| lactic acid | 0.20 per cent |
| water | 93.00 per cent |

The fat is separated from the whey and churned as whey cream or added to cream to be churned for butter; it can also be used in certain processed foods. Of the ash constituents, the calcium and phosphorus have valuable nutritional qualities. The nitrogenous compounds consist primarily of lactoglobulin, lactalbumin, proteoses or peptones, amino acids, ammonia, creatinine, creatine, uric acid, and urea. Lactose, though having certain unique nutritional values, is the main constituent that is used for conversion to desired end-products in industrial fermentations. The lactic acid present is formed by starter cultures used in making the cheese and provides a limited preservative action in the whey. The large amount of water is the chief problem in whey utilization, for in most fermentation processes the water increases the cost of distillation, concentration, or recovery of the finished product (6, 10).

Since lactose is the carbohydrate to be fermented, the availability of a microorganism capable of effecting the desired fermentation may impose a limitation on the suitability of whey as a substrate. The microorganism used must be able to utilize lactose. Molasses, in the crude form, is a cheap source of carbohydrate, which is readily fermentable by many microorganisms. It is used as a source of carbohydrate in many industrial fermentations and could be used in the place of whey. In whey, however, the nutrients that are present in addition to the lactose usually are sufficient to supply the nitrogen, vitamins, and other growth requirements of the selected culture. Also, after converting the lactose to the desired product, the nitrogen, mineral, and vitamin content of the residue have nutritive values that allow its use in animal feed.

## LACTIC ACID PRODUCTION FROM WHEY

The culture best suited for this fermentation is *Lactobacillus bulgaricus*. It is homofermentative, and it is able to convert over 90 per cent of lactose to DL-lactic acid. This culture grows rapidly, particularly at 45°C. to 50°C. (113°F. to 122°F.), and can ferment all the lactose in whey to lactic acid in about 40 hours. The use of the high temperature is not only favorable to the more rapid growth of the culture, but also is effective in controlling the development of many contaminants that could grow at lower temperatures and reduce the yield of lactic acid. The growth of many cultures of *Lactobacillus bulgaricus* is enhanced by the associative growth of a film-forming yeast (a species of *Candida*). Stock cultures of these microorganisms are usually carried as mixtures of the two types. There are large differences in the suitability of various strains for this fermentation, and one that has the ability to give the highest yield of product in the shortest time should be selected. Strains of *Lactobacillus bulgaricus* can be selected to accomplish this without associative growth of the film-forming yeast.

Stock cultures can be carried conveniently and satisfactorily in sterilized milk containing 5 per cent tomato juice or 0.5 per cent tryptone, using incubation at 45°C. (113°F.) for 24 hours and then refrigeration between transfers. These cultures should be transferred weekly or semimonthly. Lyophilization of the culture is desirable for long periods of storage. In building up the volume of culture to be used in the main fermentation vat, the culture is first grown in skimmilk pasteurized at 82.2°C. (180°F.) for 30 minutes until the starter culture is prepared, and then is grown in whey pasteurized at 82.2°C. (180°F.) for 30 minutes. The use of milk as the medium for the cultures up to the whey starter is desirable as the culture grows better in milk and often becomes attenuated if carried for many transfers in whey alone. Transfers in milk are usually made with 1–2 per cent inoculum, and the whey starter is made in a volume of 5–10 per cent of the volume of the main vat to be fermented; the larger the volume of the starter used, the less will be the time required for the fermentation process. An incubation temperature of 45°C. to 50°C. (113°F. to 122°F.) for 16–24 hours normally is used for the milk cultures and whey starter.

The whey used for the main fermentation is adjusted to 45°C. to 50°C. (113°F. to 122°F.), and the starter culture is added. As the culture grows, the lactic acid produced will soon retard its growth or cause cessation of growth. For this reason the whey is neutralized intermittently or continuously to keep the reaction at pH 5–6. This relatively low pH will favor the conversion of lactose to lactic acid and also discourage the growth of contaminants. The neutralizer generally used is lime $(Ca (OH)_2)$, added as a water slurry, which reacts with the lactic acid to form calcium lactate. The use of this neutralizer is desirable since the resultant calcium lactate is adaptable to later purification procedures. When the lactose becomes completely fermented further addition of neutralizer is not required, and the whey will show a negative test for reducing sugar; when this occurs the fermentation is completed.

The first step involved in recovering the calcium lactate is to adjust the fermented whey to pH 7. The whey is then boiled to coagulate the whey proteins (globulin and albumin); the precipitate is filtered off and used as protein supplement in animal feed. The filtrate containing the calcium lactate is concentrated under vacuum, the calcium lactate allowed to crystallize, and the crystals recovered. Depending upon the quality of lactates or lactic acid desired, vegetable carbon adsorptions, washing of the lactate crystals, and other treatments are used to increase purity of the final product. From the calcium lactate, either lactic acid or metallic lactates can be formed.

There are a number of commercial uses for lactic acid and its salts. These are utilized as acidulants in pickles, soft drinks, and sherbets; in production of acrylate plastics, which are employed for resistant metal coatings; in lactates for pharmaceutical uses; and in the tanning of leather.

A flow diagram of a commercial process for the production of lactic acid from whey is given in Figure 15.1.

## ALCOHOLIC FERMENTATION OF WHEY AND YEAST DELACTOSED WHEY

Various lactose-fermenting yeasts can convert lactose to ethyl alcohol and carbon dioxide (7). Alcohol has been produced from whey comparatively infrequently, owing primarily to the relatively high costs of transporting and processing of the whey. This fermentation has, however, been used in producing a delactosed whey for use as an animal feed supplement (2). The product has been found to have excellent nutritional qualities owing to the concentration of whey proteins (albumin and globulin), minerals, and vitamins; furthermore, vitamins contained in the yeast cells contribute to its nutritional value. The conversion of the lactose into volatile compounds allows high concentration of the remaining nutrients by condensing or drying. The removal of lactose from whey

**Figure 15.1**    A flow diagram of the process for manufacturing calcium lactate from whey. Courtesy Sheffield Chemical Company, Inc., Norwich, N.Y.

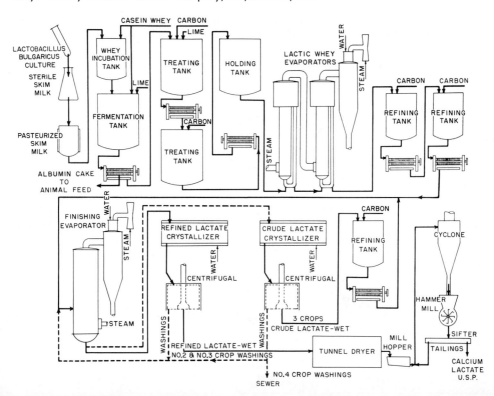

eliminates about 70 per cent of the original solids in the whey and permits advantageous uses of the other whey nutrients; also its conversion into other compounds that have immediate use is desirable. In such a fermentation process the alcohol can be considered as a by-product in the preparation of the delactosed whey.

Of the various yeasts that are able to ferment lactose to alcohol, *Saccharomyces fragilis* and *Candida pseudotropicalis* (*Torula cremoris*) have usually been found to have a faster fermentation rate and to produce the highest yields of alcohol. These yeasts require a temperature of 30°C. to 34°C. (86°F. to 93.2°F). Their optimum pH is 4.8–5.2; at this low pH the growth of many bacteria is minimized, although lactic acid and acetic acid bacteria can grow, thus lowering the efficiency of alcohol production. By providing agitation with moderate aeration, the rate of lactose fermentation can be accelerated without appreciable loss of ethyl alcohol.

A diagram of a yeast fermentation of whey is given in Figure 15.2. The yeast used for the fermentation process can be carried as stock cultures on slants of whey agar. After incubation at 30°C. (86°F.) for 2 days, the slants should be refrigerated between transfers. The culture to be used for fermenting the main batch of whey is built up through a series of transfers in pasteurized or sterile whey. Each batch of whey for a given starter culture is inoculated with 10 per cent of the previous whey culture.

The whey used for the starter and main batch is "ripened" in order to develop a titratable acidity of about 0.5 per cent (as lactic acid), which

**Figure 15.2** A flow diagram for the production of delactosed whey and ethyl alcohol from whey. Courtesy Consolidated Products Co., Danville, Illinois.

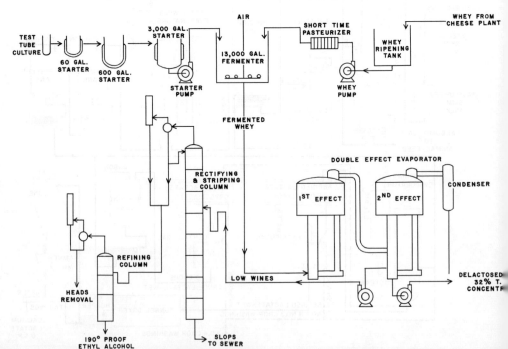

is favorable to the yeast and unfavorable to contaminants. As cheese whey is normally the type available for such processes, usually sufficient lactic acid streptococci and lactobacilli are present to develop the desired acidity without having to add any inoculum at this point. After the "ripening" process the whey is given a high-temperature short-time pasteurization. This is desirable in order to destroy the lactic-acid-producing bacteria and to prevent further conversion of the lactose to lactic acid. Whey cooled to approximately 30°C. (86°F.) is then piped to the fermenter and inoculated with 10 per cent of the yeast starter.

The inoculated whey is aerated with filtered, cool air, and the lactose will be completely fermented in 14–20 hours. The activity of the starter, quality of the whey, temperature, and similar factors will determine the exact time required to ferment the lactose. A qualitative test for reducing sugar may be performed on the fermentation mash, and this will show when the lactose has been exhausted. The yield of alcohol from the lactose might be greater if no aeration were used during the fermentation, for aeration does promote some evaporation of the alcohol. On the other hand, aeration does accelerate the rate of fermentation and effects an economy in time required to ferment each batch of whey. Frequently the yeast fails to ferment all of the lactose without some aeration. Furthermore, the yeast crop is smaller when aeration is not provided. The main contaminants that should be eliminated in the fermentation are lactic acid and acetic-acid-producing organisms, which reduce the yield of alcohol and which may result in a delactosed whey that has greater than the desired acidity.

The fermented whey is condensed to about 32 per cent total solids (which can be dried), and the condensate containing 4–6 per cent alcohol (low wines) from the evaporator is collected. The low wines are then treated in a rectifying and stripping column and finally in a refining column to produce 95 per cent (190 proof) alcohol. Included among the many industrial uses of ethyl alcohol is that of a starting material for vinegar production, and this use has been made of alcohol obtained in the making of delactosed whey. The delactosed whey is used as a protein and vitamin supplement for animal feeds.

## SYNTHESIS OF VITAMINS

Many microorganisms synthesize water-soluble B vitamins during their growth; certain ones produce large amounts that are liberated into the medium in which the culture is growing. The reason for such cultures' producing vitamins greatly in excess of their own needs for growth has not been explained. This phenomenon, however, has been used as the basis of industrial processes for increasing the vitamin content of whey that can be used in human or animal feed supplements (3, 4). An organism that has this ability and that grows readily in whey is *Clostridium acetobutylicum* (Weizmann's bacillus).

This organism requires anaerobic conditions for growth, and this necessitates certain precautions in its culturing. In carrying small cultures anaerobic conditions are provided, but in larger batches anaerobiosis normally is obtained after sterilization of the whey. *Clostridium acetobutylicum* grows best at about 38°C. (100.4°F.) and in a slightly acid medium. During its growth acetone, butanol, ethanol, carbon dioxide, and hydrogen are produced in appreciable quantities. Certain metals have been found to have marked effects on the synthesis of vitamins, especially riboflavin, which is synthesized to an extent greater than any other. The iron content is particularly critical; a concentration of greater than 5 ppm reduces the riboflavin synthesis markedly. Thus, the type of vat used for the fermentation, and the equipment previously used in handling the whey are very important to the success of this fermentation.

Stock cultures are preferably carried in the spore state, eliminating the necessity for frequent transfers. After allowing the culture to sporulate in a suitable medium, the spores can then be mixed with a sterile, sandy soil and air-dried. Such cultures remain viable for years. Active cultures can be obtained by inoculating the soil-spore mixture into sterile medium. Before incubation the inoculated medium is placed in a bath of boiling water for a minute to heat-shock the spores; this results in a more vigorous culture. The culture is then built to a sufficient volume so that it can be added at a rate of 5 per cent of the volume of whey to be fermented.

The whey is sterilized in pressure vats at a temperature of 121°C. (250°F.) for 15 to 20 minutes. After cooling and tempering at 38°C. (100.4°F.) the inoculum is added. Care must be taken to maintain anaerobic conditions in the whey, and the vats are constructed so as to prevent contamination by bacteria and bacteriophage. The temperature is maintained at 38°C. (100.4°F.) during the fermentation process, which usually is completed in 48 hours or less. The carbon dioxide and hydrogen are allowed to escape through vents in the fermentation vat. The ethyl alcohol, acetone, and butanol are recovered from the condensate during the condensing of the whey. These solvents can then be obtained singly from the condensate by fractional distillation. The condensed whey product can be dried and standardized to a given composition by blending with regular dried whey.

A flow diagram of a process used in the commercial production of riboflavin, ethanol, acetone, and butanol from whey is shown in Figure 15.3.

The foregoing are examples of industrial uses of whey in which microbiological fermentations of whey have been used advantageously. Other processes have been proposed and patented, viz., preparation of an alcoholic and carbonated whey beverage, food yeast, and yeast products (1, 5, 11). The extent to which these processes and others that may be proposed will be used commercially will depend largely upon the development of economic factors that might favor the use of whey over other raw materials as a starting fermentable product.

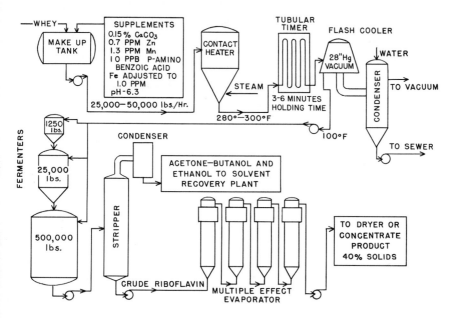

**Figure 15.3**    A flow diagram of the production of riboflavin, ethanol, acetone, and butanol from whey. Courtesy of Western Condensing Co., Appleton, Wisconsin.

## *References*

1. Meade, R. E., and J. M. Stringham, Process of making whey food products. U. S. Patent 2,465,905. 1949.

2. Myers, R. P., and S. M. Weisberg, Treatment of milk products. U. S. Patent 2,128,845. 1938.

3. Pollard, H. L., N. E. Rodgers, and R. E. Meade, Method of enhancing the yield of vitamins in fermentations. U. S. Patent 2,449,140. 1948.

4. ———, Method for improving the yield of riboflavin in fermentation processes. U. S. Patent 2,449,142. 1948.

5. Porges, N., J. B. Pepinsky, and L. Jasewicz, Feed yeast from dairy by-products, *J. Dairy Sci.,* 34 (1951): 615–621.

6. Riggs, L. K., The utilization of whey, *J. Milk and Food Tech.,* 10 (1947): 105–108.

7. Rogosa, M., H. H. Browne, and E. O. Whittier, Ethyl alcohol from whey, *J. Dairy Sci.,* 30 (1947): 263–269.

8. Task committee on dairy waste disposal, Waste prevention in the dairy industry, *Milk Dealer,* 39 (February, 1950): 49; (March, 1950): 51; (April, 1950): 47.

9. *An Industrial Waste Guide to the Milk Processing Industry.* Washington, D. C.: United States Department of Health, Education, and Welfare, 1953.

10. Webb, B. H., and E. O. Whittier, The utilization of whey: a review, *J. Dairy Sci.*, 31 (1948): 139–164.

11. Whittier, E. O., and B. H. Webb, *By-Products from Milk*. New York: Reinhold, 1950.

12. Wisniewski, T. F., Waste disposal, *Nat. Butter Cheese J.*, 38 (1947): 40.

# INDEX

**479**